Springer Series in
Electronics and Photonics 28

Edited by D. H. Auston

Springer Series in Electronics and Photonics

Editors: D.H. Auston   W. Engl   T. Sugano

Managing Editor: H.K.V. Lotsch

This series was originally published under the title
Springer Series in Electrophysics
and has been renamed starting with Volume 22.

Volumes 1–20 are listed on the back inside cover

To Paola, Luisa and Marta
my wife and my children

Preface

The introduction of molecular beam epitaxy (MBE) in the 1960s paved the way during the subsequent two decades to the realization of a large class of semiconductor heterostructures where the composition and doping can be modulated over a length scale comparable to or smaller than the electron de Broglie wavelength. In this regime, layer thicknesses range from a few hundred angstroms down to a monolayer (~ 2.5 Å). The resulting quantum size and tunnelling effects along the growth direction form the basis of quantum wells and superlattices. These are the building blocks of many modern quantum devices.

In addition, with the aid of appropriate techniques such as modulation doping in heterostructures, electrons in a degenerate Fermi gas at cryogenic temperatures can propagate coherently over macroscopic distances (~ 1 μm). Interference and waveguide phenomena can thus be observed, with possible potential for devices such as quantum interference transistors.

More recently, remarkable advances in electron beam and X-ray lithography and in other semiconductor processing techniques have made possible the definition of minimum feature sizes $\lesssim 1000$ Å, thus extending the domain of quantum effects to the lateral directions (i.e., the growth plane) as well. These breakthroughs have made possible the fabrication of structures such as quantum wires, dots and boxes.

The ability to create man-made materials and heterostructures by engineering the wavefunctions and the band structure over a length scale previously inaccessible to technology (band-gap or band-structure engineering) has led to a new class of electron semiconductor devices. Their operation and performance is controlled by quantum effects. These structures represent not only exciting tools for the investigation of new quantum phenomena in artificially structured materials ("do-it-yourself quantum mechanics," in the words of L. Esaki) but often also offer exciting opportunities for electronic applications. For example, functional devices based on resonant tunnelling through quantum wells promise to greatly reduce circuit complexity in a variety of digital and analog applications.

The purpose of this volume is to provide an in-depth and up-to-date discussion of recent (in general after 1980) important advances in the rapidly expanding area of semiconductor quantum electron devices. Although many books have addressed the physics and applications of Zener tunnelling in semiconductors and of tunnel diodes, no such volume exists covering in a comprehensive fashion the important advances made in the field of quantum electron devices during the past two decades.

The present volume is an attempt in this direction. It focuses on quantum electron semiconductor devices whose operation (e.g. the $I-V$ characteristic) and performance *directly* depend on the wave nature of the electron. These include structures based on the quantum size effect, tunnelling and quantum interference phenomena. Electron devices where quantum effects play an important but not central role, such as selectively doped FETs, have already been adequately discussed. Quantum optoelectronic devices (lasers, detectors, modulators, SEEDs, etc.) are not covered by our volume; in-depth reviews of this topic can be found in the literature. Similarly, band discontinuities, which play a fundamental role in the physics and design of quantum semiconductor devices, have been extensively covered elsewhere.

Each chapter is written by one of the internationally recognized experts or groups in this field. In the choice of topics and authors, I have tried to emphasize the synergistic and interdisciplinary character of this field, at the frontiers between physics, device technology and crystal growth. The content of the book should therefore represent an up-to-date description of quantum phenomena in exploratory electron devices and their applications. It may be of particular interest also to researchers and graduate students in the field of microelectronics. Undergraduate courses in wave mechanics and in the physics of semiconductors are prerequisites for this book.

The author is grateful to AT&T Bell Laboratories not only for the permission to publish this book, but also for having provided the intellectual excitement, the stimulating research atmosphere and the "critical mass" of colleagues essential for a successful and productive work at the frontiers of such a rapidly expanding field. During the preparation of this volume I have enjoyed collaborations and discussions with many colleagues and friends; in particular F. Beltram, A. Y. Cho, A. C. Gossard, A. L. Hutchinson, R. A. Kiehl, D. V. Lang, B. F. Levine, S. Luryi, R. J. Malik, D. A. B. Miller, R. C. Miller, K. Mohammed, S. Sen, and J. Shah.

Finally, I would like to thank Professor D. Auston, Series Editor of the Springer Séries in Electronics and Photonics, for encouraging me to undertake this project, Dr. H. Lotsch for his cooperation in the editing procedure and the colleagues who have contributed to this volume.

Murray Hill,
October, 1989   *Federico Capasso*

Contents

Contributors

Beltram, Fabio
AT&T Bell Laboratories, Room 6E-312, 600 Mountain Avenue,
Murray Hill, NJ 07974, USA

Brown, Elliott R.
Lincoln Laboratory, MIT, Lexington, MA 02173, USA

Capasso, Federico
AT&T Bell Laboratories, Room 7A-209, 600 Mountain Avenue,
Murray Hill, NJ 07974, USA

Cho, Alfred Y.
AT&T Bell Laboratories, Room 6H-422, 600 Mountain Avenue,
Murray Hill, NJ 07974, USA

Craighead, Harold G.
National Nanofabrication Facility, Cornell University, Ithaca, NY 14853, USA

Datta, Supriyo
School of Electrical Engineering, Purdue University, West Lafayette,
IN 47907, USA

Eaves, Laurence
Physics Department, University of Nottingham, University Park,
Nottingham, NG7 2RD, United Kingdom

Ferry, David K.
Arizona State University, Center for Solid State Electronics Research,
Tempe, AZ 85287, USA

Fischetti, M. V.
IBM Research Division, Thomas J. Watson Research Center,
Yorktown Heights, NY 10598, USA

Heiblum, Mordehai
IBM Research Division, Thomas J. Watson Research Center,
Yorktown Heights, NY 10598, USA

Goodue, W. D.
Lincoln Laboratory, MIT, Lexington, MA 02173, USA

Imamura, K.
   Fujitsu Limited, 10-1, Morinosato-Wakamiya, Atsugi 243-01, Japan

Inata, T.
   Fujitsu Limited, 10-1, Morinosato-Wakamiya, Atsugi 243-01, Japan

Le, Han A.
   Lincoln Laboratory, MIT, Lexington, MA 02173, USA

Madhukar, A.
   University of Southern California, Los Angeles, CA 90007, USA

Mori, T.
   Fujitsu Limited, 10-1, Morinosato-Wakamiya, Atsugi 243-01, Japan

Muto, S.
   Fujitsu Limited, 10-1, Morinosato-Wakamiya, Atsugi 243-01, Japan

Ohnishi, H.
   Fujitsu Limited, 10-1, Morinosato-Wakamiya, Atsugi 243-01, Japan

Petroff, Pierre M.
   Materials Department, University of California,
   Santa Barbara, CA 93106, USA

Sen, Susanta
   Department of Electronic Science, University of Calcutta, 92 A.P.C. Road,
   Calcutta 700009, India (Work performed at AT&T Bell Laboratories)

Sheard, Fred W.
   Physics Department, University of Nottingham, University Park,
   Nottingham, NG7 2RD, United Kingdom

Skocpol, William J.
   Physics Department Boston University, 590 Commonwealth Avenue,
   Boston, MA 02215, USA (Work performed at AT&T Bell Laboratories)

Sollner, T.C.L. Gerhard
   Lincoln Laboratory, MIT, Lexington, MA 02173, USA

Toombs, Geoffrey A.
   Physics Department, University of Nottingham, University Park,
   Nottingham, NG7 2RD, United Kingdom

Yokoyama N.
   Fujitsu Limited, 10-1, Morinosato-Wakamiya, Atsugi 243-01, Japan

1. Introduction

F. Capasso

1.1 A Perspective on the Evolution of Quantum Semiconductor Devices

Quantum mechanics started to have a substantial impact on solid-state electronics shortly after the invention of the transistor in the late forties [1.1, 2]. It had already been providing the theoretical background on which our modern understanding of solids, in particular semiconductors, is based, i.e. band structure theory.

Fermi statistics [1.3], and such nowadays widely used concepts as Fermi energies and quasi-Fermi levels, played a key role in the understanding of the process of doping and of the equilibrium and nonequilibrium properties of devices such as *pn* junction diodes, bipolar transistors and semiconductor lasers [1.4].

In the mid-fifties it became apparent that very heavily doped *pn* junctions did not behave as "regular" diodes, satisfying Shockley's equation. *Leo Esaki*, then at Sony, first correctly interpreted these anomalies (a peak in the current-voltage ($I–V$) characteristic) as due to Zener tunnelling of electrons from the n to the p region, across the band gap [1.5]. The tunnel diode represents the first example of a semiconductor device whose $I–V$ characteristic and operation is directly controlled by quantum tunnelling effects.

Shortly after its invention, the tunnel diode was hailed as a revolutionary component for electronics in light of its potentially extremely high switching speed. As time went by, however, its limitations became apparent. The threshold logic applications envisioned for this device place very stringent requirements on the reproducibility of the $I–V$ characteristic. The latter is difficult to achieve in light of the high doping levels required and the sensitivity of the $I–V$ to these levels. Furthermore, the lack of success in incorporating the Esaki tunnelling concept into a transistor (i.e. a device with input/output isolation and gain, essential for modern logic circuits) also contributed to the relative early demise of the tunnel diode as a component for large scale electronic circuits. This device is still used nowadays for a limited number of applications such as high speed sampling. Nevertheless the impact of the tunnel diode on the physics of semiconductors and solid-state electronics in general was large, leading to important developments such as tunnelling spectroscopy [1.6] and to increased understanding of tunnelling phenomena in solids. This impact was recognized by the awarding of the 1974 Nobel prize in physics to *Leo Esaki* (in conjunction with *Giaever* and *Josephson*).

The advent of the semiconductor laser in the early sixties [1.7] and the gradual emerging of heterojunctions [1.8], set the stage for an expanded role of quantum physics in solid-state electronics. In addition, the prediction of a new quantum phenomenon, electroabsorption (or photon-assisted tunnelling across the band-gap) by *Franz* and *Keldysh* [1.9] in 1958 not only led to the development of a new powerful spectroscopic technique for semiconductors (electroreflectance) [1.10], but also opened up new opportunities for devices such as modulators and detectors.

The discussion of quantum-size effects in semiconductor devices dates back to *Schrieffer*. In 1957 he postulated that electrons confined in the potential well of an inversion layer in a silicon MOS structure would not behave classically if the carrier wavelength is comparable to the distance between the Si–SiO$_2$ interface and the classical turning point [1.11]. A set of discrete energy levels E_n then arises from the quantization of the carrier motion in the direction perpendicular to the interface. When one includes the free electron motion along the interface, the energy levels take the form of two-dimensional subbands

$$E = E_n + \frac{\hbar^2}{2m_e^*}(k_x^2 + k_y^2),$$

where k_x and k_y are the components of the wave vector in the plane of the channel and m_e^* the electron effective mass. Each E_n is the bottom of a subband. Although *Schrieffer* felt that broadening due to interface scattering would probably smear out these energy levels [1.11], many groups started the search for these quantum effects. The magnetoconductance measurements of *Fowler* et al. in 1966 provided the first direct demonstration of the lifting of the valley degeneracy by the quantum size effect in Si inversion layers and of the two-dimensional nature of the electrons [1.12]. The physics of parallel transport in such systems, with particular emphasis on magnetotransport, has been reviewed in depth by *Ando* et al. [1.13].

The invention of molecular beam epitaxy (MBE) by *Arthur* and *Cho* in the sixties [1.14] paved the way for unprecedented progress in the area of hetero-junction structures and quantum devices in the next two decades. This epitaxial growth technique allowed the realization of multilayered heterojunctions with atomically abrupt interfaces and nowadays, with its latest advance, electron beam assisted MBE applied to III–V alloys [1.15], precisely controlled compositional and doping profiles over distances as short as a few tens of angstroms.

The investigation of the novel physical phenomena made possible by MBE grown structures has proceeded in parallel with their exploitation in novel devices. As a result a new approach to designing heterojunction semiconductor devices, bandgap or band-structure engineering, has gradually emerged in recent years [1.16]. The starting point of band gap engineering is the realization of the extremely large number of combinations made possible by the variety of lattice matched and strained layer [1.17] heterojunctions. This allows one to design a large variety of new energy band diagrams. For example, through the use of bandgap grading, band discontinuities and doping profiles, one can obtain, starting from a basic energy band diagram, practically arbitrary and continuous variations of this diagram [1.16]. Thus the transport and optical properties of a semiconductor structure can be tailored to a specific device application. Applied to quantum devices this approach, as the readers will see, makes it possible to artificially tailor and externally control the wavefunction of carriers (wavefunction engineering) [1.18], i.e. what *Leo Esaki* jokingly calls "do it yourself quantum mechanics" [1.19].

The early achievements of MBE include quantum wells, which are key building blocks of band-gap engineered structures. These potential energy wells are formed by sandwiching an ultrathin lower gap layer (of thickness comparable to a smaller than the carrier thermal de Broglie wavelength, which is $\simeq 250\,\text{Å}$ for electrons in GaAs at room temperature) between two wider gap semiconductors. Following *Esaki's* and *Tsu's* 1970 seminal theoretical paper [1.20] on multi-quantum well superlattices, the existence of discrete energy levels in such wells was demonstrated by resonant tunnelling [1.21], superlattice transport experiments [1.22] and optical absorption measurements [1.23] in 1974. These results clearly demonstrated the potential of MBE for quantum devices. The resonant tunnelling diode [1.21] and the quantum well laser [1.24] are in fact the first examples of an electronic and optical device whose principle of operation is based on the quantum-size effect. In the resonant tunnelling double barrier diode the enhanced electron transmission at energies corresponding to the bottom of the discrete subbands of the quantum well leads to negative differential conductance. On the other hand, in the quantum well laser the emission wavelength can be artificially controlled by changing the well thickness and the threshold current density is reduced by the two-dimensional nature of the density of states. These lasers, arranged in suitable arrays, have nowadays important applications in the field of optical recording.

When many quantum wells are grown on top of one another and the barriers are made so thin that tunnelling between coupled wells becomes important, a superlattice with minibands and minigaps in the band structure is formed. In the context of heterojunctions and alternatively *n*- and *p*-type doped layers this concept dates back to the previously cited paper of *Esaki* and *Tsu* [1.20]. The idea of an artificial superimposed periodicity, capable of opening up minigaps in the Brillonin zone of a solid, was originally proposed in 1962 by *Keldysh* in the context of an ultrasonic wave [1.25]. The formation of minibands in a superlattice, as a result of coupling between quantum wells, was directly documented by the optical experiments of *Dingle* [1.26]. *Esaki* and *Tsu*, in addition to calculating the miniband spectrum of the superlattice, predicted negative differential resistance arising from electrons moving into the negative mass region of the first minizone and, in the case of negligible scattering, Bloch oscillations, i.e. the oscillatory motion at the Bloch frequency of electrons in real- and *k*-space. Although the observation of such transport effects proved elusive,

Esaki's and *Tsu's* paper greatly stimulated research in superlattices and artificially structured materials in general.

The first superlattices were synthesized in 1970 by *Blakeslee* and *Alliotta* using chemical vapor deposition and consisted of $GaAs_{0.5}P_{0.5}$/GaAs strain-layer structures with 200 Å period [1.27]. In 1971 *A. Y. Cho* reported the first growth of superlattices by MBE [1.28]. In 1976 *Gossard* et al. achieved superlattices with alternate-atomic-layer composition modulation [1.29].

Although the advent of MBE allowed the demonstration of new quantum phenomena and device structures, the overall material quality (e.g. interface state density, background doping, etc.) was not high enough to have significant impact on quantum devices and solid-state electronics in general for quite a number of years. For example the early resonant tunnelling diodes exhibited small negative differential resistance effects even at low temperature [1.21], despite the fact that theory predicted high peak-to-valley ratios.

The steady progress of MBE material quality in the seventies led to important physics and device advances near the end of the decade. For example the reduction in interface states densities in the AlGaAs/GaAs system and the achievement of low background doping in GaAs, made possible the demonstration of selective (or modulation) doping and high electron mobilities parallel to the heterointerfaces by *Dingle* et al. in 1978 [1.30]. This work paved the way to the conception and a realization of the selectively doped heterojunction transistor (SDHT, also called modulation doped FET or MODFET) in 1980 [1.31]. The concept of selective doping has been fruitful not only for devices but also for physics studies. The demonstration of the two-dimensional nature of the electron gas at a selectively doped AlGaAs/GaAs interface [1.32] was followed soon after by a flurry of experimental and theoretical investigations. Continuing magneto-transport studies in the Si/SiO_2 system and in selectively doped AlGaAs/GaAs heterojunctions, culminated in the discovery of two striking quantum phenomena in two-dimensional systems in a high magnetic field: the integer and fractional quantum Hall effects [1.33, 34]. For the discovery of the integer quantum Hall effect *K. Von Klitzing* was awarded the 1985 Nobel prize in physics. The quantization of the Hall resistance with a precision of one part in 10^7 [1.33], will lead to a new resistance standard on 1 January, 1990. The fractional quantization of the Hall resistance instead, has revealed the existence of a new quantum fluid of correlated spin polarized electrons [1.35]. These discoveries demonstrate that semiconductor devices can be excellent tools for the study of fundamental physical phenomena.

The late seventies and the subsequent decade have also witnessed the rapid development of a new epitaxial growth technique, first conceived and demonstrated in 1968 by *Ruhrwein* and *Manasevit*, metal organic chemical vapor deposition (MOCVD) [1.36]. MOCVD has proven to be capable of growing extremely high quality abrupt interfaces in the AlGaAs/GaAs system as well as devices which exploit these properties, such as quantum well lasers and SDHTs [1.37].

The eighties have been characterized by unprecedented progress in quantum microstructures. Continuing advances in MBE, breakthroughs in nanolithography which have added new degrees of freedom in the design of quantum structures, and the discovery and first demonstrations of new quantum phenomena and devices, have brought about a beautiful synergy between material science, physics and device technology.

The observation of the quantum confined Stark effect [1.38] in AlGaAs/GaAs multiquantum wells has led to new bistable optical switching devices (the so-called SEED devices) which may have important applications in optical logic and computing [1.39]. These devices exploit excitonic effects at room temperature, which are an important manifestation of the two-dimensional nature of the states in quantum wells [1.23].

On the electron device side, the impressive resonant tunnelling experiments at terahertz frequencies of *Sollner* and coworkers [1.40] in 1983 stimulated renewed interest in negative differential resistance devices. The tremendous improvement in MBE material quality is best demonstrated by the recent achievement of peak-to-valley ratios of 30:1 at 300 K in a strained layer resonant tunnelling diode [1.41]. Resonant tunnelling oscillators with frequencies in excess of 200 GHz have recently been reported by *Brown* et al. [1.42].

As early as 1963 *Davis* and *Hosack*, and *Ioganson* suggested that the well in a unipolar resonant tunnelling double barrier could act as the control electrode of a transistor [1.43].

In 1984 *Capasso* and *Kiehl* proposed the first resonant tunnelling bipolar transistor and pointed out the interesting circuit applications of such devices [1.44]. Resonant tunnelling transistors allow the implementation of a large class of circuits (e.g. analog-to-digital converters, parity checkers, frequency multipliers, etc.) with greatly reduced complexity (i.e. less transistor per function compared to a circuit using conventional transistors). The inherent functionality of these and other quantum electron devices has led a group at Texas Instruments to project an intriguing scenario for the future of electronics [1.45, 46]. The progress of integrated circuits has so far been marked by increased levels of miniaturization to the point that nowadays certain VLSI chips contain an average of eight million components. Due to interconnection limitations, this scaling strategy will probably approach practical limits at a minimum lateral dimension of patterned geometries of ~ 0.25 μm [1.46]. After reaching the limits of conventional scaling some time in the next fifty years, electronics will have to find new paths for its evolution in order to survive as an industry [1.45]. New devices and circuit architectures will be devised. Resonant tunnelling transistors and quantum coupled devices may provide a way out, in light of their functionality and the possibility of direct device interconnections via tunnelling [1.46]. It has also been pointed out that the inherent multistate nature of a resonant tunnelling transistor could lead to new computer architectures using multiple valued logic [1.44].

Shortly after the initial proposal, *Yokohama* et al. reported the low temperature (77 K) operation of a resonant tunnelling hot electron unipolar transistor [1.47] and demonstrated the exclusive NOR logic function with only one device, as opposed to eight conventional transistors. Room temperature operation of a resonant tunnelling bipolar transistor, with a double barrier in the base, was demonstrated in 1986 by *Capasso* and coworkers [1.48].

The emergence of AlInAs/GaInAs as a heterojunction ideally suited for resonant tunnelling devices, due to the small electron effective mass in the barrier (AlInAs) and the relatively large (direct gap) conduction band discontinuity, has further increased the pace of progress in this area, with many groups currently involved in resonant tunnelling transistor research. The recent demonstration in this material system of multiple peaks in the $I-V$ characteristic by sequential quenching of resonant tunnelling through a series of vertically stacked double barriers [1.49] has led to the implementation of the first resonant tunnelling transistor with multiple negative transconductance regions in the transfer characteristic and to the demonstration of circuits with greatly reduced complexity and multilevel logic [1.50].

The physics of resonant tunnelling diodes has also attracted a lot of interest. Such structures represent a considerable challenge for the theorist since a realistic theory must take into account many interrelated effects. These include space charge in the well (typical densities are in the range of 10^{11} to 10^{12} electrons per unit area) and in the contact regions; scattering, which can produce breaking of phase coherence and transition to a sequential picture [1.51]; and hot electron effects (typical electric fields approach 10^5 V/cm at resonance). This implies the need of a fully quantum mechanical and self-consistent calculation in the presence of scattering and coupling to the reservoirs (contacts), a formidable task indeed! New phenomena in these structures such as intrinsic bistability [1.52] and as yet unanswered questions such as tunnelling times, are the focus of current investigations and controversies. MBE grown tunnelling structures with single barriers have also revealed intriguing oscillatory phenomena in the conductance [1.53].

Another tunnelling device, the tunnelling hot electron amplifier (THETA), has shed considerable light in recent years on the physics of transport on very short spatial and times scales [1.54]. This device consists of a hot electron transistor with electrons injected in an ultrathin base via a tunnelling emitter. The basic design resembles the tunnel hot electron transistor with metal base proposed by *C. A. Mead* in 1960 [1.55]. In 1985, *Heiblum*, using a THETA device [1.56] and a Bell Labs/Bellcore team [1.57], using a planar doped barrier transistor, demonstrated ballistic electron transport in GaAs by means of hot electron spectroscopy. Spectacular quantum interference phenomena have been observed in the base of THETA devices [1.58].

Superlattice devices utilizing perpendicular transport hold promise particularly for optoelectronic applications. A new infrared detector with spectral response in the 8 to 12 μm atmospheric window has been recently demonstrated by *Levine* et al. [1.59]. In this structure, made of AlGaAs/GaAs n-type doped quantum wells, absorption takes place between the ground state of the well and a resonant state or a miniband in the continuum. These devices have background limited detectivity comparable to that of HgCdTe detectors and are promising for many applications such as medical imaging, earth resource mapping and military ones. The potential advantage compared to HgCdTe/CdTe based detectors is the superior material quality of AlGaAs/GaAs and the possibility of monolithic integration with the read-out electronics.

Intriguing possibilities may also exist for superlattice infrared lasers or amplifying type devices utilizing sequential resonant tunnelling to achieve population inversion between excited states of quantum wells, as originally proposed by *Kazarinov* and *Suris* in 1971 [1.60]

Doping superlattices, i.e. alternated $n-p$ or nip ultrathin layers, also proposed in 1970 [1.20], offer an interesting range of opportunities for optoelectronic research. These include detectors, modulators, tunable light sources and non-linear optical devices [1.61]. N-i-p-i superlattices with alternate monolayer doped n and p regions have recently been reported [1.62]. Such delta doping techniques are nowadays starting to be used in selectively doped FETs and in a variety of exploratory devices.

Measurements and theory of heterojunction band-discontinuities, essential for the understanding and design of many quantum devices, have also made tremendous progress in recent years. These important developments have been reviewed in a comprehensive fashion elsewhere [1.63].

Novel opportunities for quantum devices have been opened up by the remarkable advances made by nanolithography for submicron structures in recent years. Electron beam lithography has made possible the realization of quasi-one-dimensional quantum structures. For example quasi-one-dimensional MOSFETs in silicon have revealed the universal conductance fluctuations due to random quantum interference predicted by *Altshuler* and *Lee* and *Stone* [1.64]. The understanding of the physics of noise, transport phenomena and basic processes such as doping in these lower dimensionality structures will be the subject of intensive research in future years. The recent observation of the quantized ballistic resistance (without magnetic field) of a two-dimensional electron gas confined to a short and narrow channel (i.e. a quantum wire) has generated considerable excitement [1.65].

Quantum boxes and wires have been fabricated by *Cibert* et al. using a combination of e-beam lithography and impurity induced disordering [1.66]. Quantum boxes should exhibit very large optical nonlinearities in light of their large polarizability ($\alpha \sim L^3$, where L is the size of the box).

Quantum interference semiconductor devices have recently started to attract the attention of several investigators. A very interesting idea is the possibility of achieving transistor action by adjusting, via an applied voltage, the relative phase of ballistic electrons propagating in two parallel channels [1.67]. Quantum interference phenomena in mesoscopic physics, such as the Ahronov Bohm [1.68] effect, have of course been subject of considerable investigation in metallic structures such as rings [1.69] and are also well-known in the context of Josephson devices. The observation of related phenomena in semiconductor heterostructures [1.70] is contributing to bringing together these neighboring fields of investigation [1.71].

It is our opinion that quantum microstructures will eventually have a profound and lasting impact on electronics and optoelectronics as functional devices. In a remarkable and pioneering paper [1.72] entitled "From Physics to Function", *J. A. Morton*, more than twenty years ago, introduced the concept of functional device. The key characteristic of such devices is that "nowhere within [the structure] can we identify the separate elements of an equivalent circuit" and, Morton continued, "they promise to reduce greatly the number of elements and process steps per function when their capabilities are properly matched to an old or new system function". Morton provided a few examples of functional devices, among which the tunnel diode, but there is no question that he was ahead of his time. As we have seen from this historical survey, such a vision, strongly relying on dramatic progress in growth techniques, material science and semiconductor physics, is only now gradually starting to show its promise. The invention of functional devices (in the sense of Morton) based on quantum confinement, however, occurred later in the eighties. In the optoelectronics area an excellent example is the SEED optical switching device, while among the electron devices resonant tunnelling transistors are emerging as some of the most interesting and potentially useful functional devices.

It is interesting to note that Morton's vision inspired in a conspicuous way Japanese research on functional devices, as documented in the book by *Kikuchi* [1.73]. To stimulate and promote funding of research in this area an "Association for Functional Devices" was founded. The investigation of functional devices, with medium-to-long-term goals, is currently aggressively pursued in all major Japanese electronic industries and research centers. Efforts are also picking up in the U.S. and in Europe.

No doubt the strong synergy between technology, physics and crystal growth in this exciting area of investigation promises more unexpected advances and breakthroughs in the year to come. It is indeed befitting to conclude this historical survey with a quote from Morton's paper [1.73]: "Electronics may be approaching a plateau. To ensure a renewed growth a new philosophy of engineering is needed. In such a philosophy, systems engineering and the physical sciences will provide complementary and lasting disciplines for our future innovators".

1.2 Outline of the Book

Chapters 2 and 3, on MBE (*Madhukar*) and nanolithography (*Craighead*) respectively, in addition to reporting on recent advances in these areas, serve as important background and introductory material for most of the subsequent chapters.

The fourth chapter by *Ferry* discusses the theory of tunnelling through single and double barriers, the concept of tunnelling time, along with its many definitions and controversial aspects and the Wigner function approach to quantum transport through these structures. This material represents important theoretical background for Chaps. 5–8. The physics of superlattice transport effects such as negative differential resistance, Bloch oscillators and sequential resonant tunnelling is also covered and its theoretical foundations clarified. The theory of surface superlattices is also given along with recent implementations of these structures by electron-beam lithography and preliminary transport experiments.

Eaves and coworkers in Chap. 5 examine some important physical properties of single and double barrier tunnelling structures. Particular emphasis is placed on the use of magnetic fields in studying not only the tunnelling process itself, but also the way electrons relax their energy and momentum. The physical origin of LO phonon oscillations in the I–V of single barriers is clarified in a definitive way both experimentally and theoretically. Tunnelling phenomena in single barriers, associated with skipping orbits in magnetic fields are also discussed. New phenomena in double barriers such as the direct evidence of sequential tunnelling due to intersubband scattering and the unambiguous observation of intrinsic electronic bistability are examined.

Chapters 6–8 cover the important and rapidly developing area of resonant tunnelling devices. *Sollner* and coworkers (Chap. 6) emphasize microwave and millimeter wave diodes; oscillators, self-oscillating mixers and resistive multipliers are also discussed.

In Chap. 7, *Capasso* and his collaborators discuss the physics of new resonant tunnelling two terminal devices, such as parabolic wells and stacked double barriers, and resonant tunnelling transistors. The latter include a variety of field-effect and bipolar structures. Analog and digital circuits utilizing these devices are examined in detail. A new hot electron spectroscopic technique based on resonant tunnelling and several superlattice tunnelling devices are also discussed.

Chapter 8 by *Yokoyama* and his colleagues provides an in-depth discussion of the physics, device and circuit performance of resonant tunnelling hot electron transistors.

Chapter 9 by *Heiblum* and *Fischetti* deals with the physics of tunnelling hot electron transistors. Hot electron spectroscopy, ballistic transport, direct intervalley transfer and quantum interference effects are among the topics covered.

In Chap. 10, one of the most speculative and intriguing of this volume, *Datta* explores new transistors where the current is modulated by controlling the quantum mechanical interference between channels connecting source and drain. He also discusses the possibility of quantum circuits relying on interference effects to implement resistor networks that can be programmed by a remote gate through non-local quantum effects.

The final two chapters of the book deal with recent advances in the physics of one and zero dimensional structures (wires and boxes). Petroff (Chap. 11) examines the fabrication and optical properties of quantum boxes and wires in AlGaAs/GaAs heterostructures.

Finally in Chap. 12, *Skocpol* provides an in depth discussion of quantum transport phenomena in narrow, quasi-one-dimensional MOSFETs. A careful analysis of the hierarchy of relevant length scales which determine the various quantum regimes is given. Tunnelling and hopping through localized states, diffusion which preserves quantum phase information, weak localization, universal conductance fluctuations and trapping of single electrons are among the many phenomena discussed. The purpose of this last chapter is also to provide a link with the neighboring field of the physics of mesoscopic systems.

References

1.1 J. Bardeen, W. H. Brattain: Phys. Rev. **74**, 230 (1948)
1.2 W. Shockley: Bell Syst. Tech. J. **28**, 435 (1949)
1.3 E. Fermi: Rend. Lincei 3, 146 (1926); Z. Physik **36**, 902 (1926)
1.4 For a comprehensive discussion, as well as early references, see S. M. Sze: *Physics of Semiconductor Devices*, (Wiley, New York 1981), 2nd ed.
1.5 L. Esaki: Phys. Rev. **109**, 603 (1958)
1.6 R. N. Hall, J. H. Racette, H. Ehrenreich: Phys. Rev. Lett. **4**, 456 (1960)
1.7 R. N. Hall, G. E. Genner, J. D. Kingsley, T. J. Soltys, R. O. Carlson: Phys. Rev. Lett. **9**, 366 (1962);
     M. I. Nathan, W. B. Dumke, G. Burns, F. J. Dill, Jr., G. J. Lasher: Appl. Phys. Lett. **1**, 62 (1962);
     T. M. Quist, R. H. Rediker, R. J. Keyes, W. E. Krag, B. Lax, A. L. McWhorther, H. J. Zeigler: Appl. Phys. Lett. **1**, 92 (1962)
1.8 R. L. Anderson: Solid State Electron. **5**, 341 (1962)
1.9 W. Franz, Z. Naturforsch. **a13**, 484 (1958);
     L. V. Keldysh, Zh. Eksp & Teor. Fiz. **34**, 1138 (1958)
1.10 B. O. Seraphin, Proc. 7th Int. Conf. on the Physics of Semiconductors, Paris (Dunod, Paris), p. 165 (1965);
     For a review of modulation spectroscopy see D. E. Aspnes in *Handbook of Semiconductors*, Volume 2, Chapter 4A, M. Balkanski ed. (North-Holland, Amsterdam 1980)
1.11 J. R. Schrieffer: In *Semiconductor Surface Physics*, R. H. Kingston ed. (University of Pennsylvania Press, Philadelphia, p. 55
1.12 A. B. Fowler, F. F. Fang, W. Howard, P. J. Stiles: Phys. Rev. Lett. **16**, 901 (1966)
1.13 T. Ando, A. B. Fowler, F. Stern: Rev. Mod. Phys. **54**, 437 (1982)
1.14 For a review of the early developments in MBE see A. Y. Cho, J. R. Arthur: Progr. Solid State Chem. **10**, 157 (1975)
1.15 R. J. Malik, J. Vac. Sci. Technol. **B5**, 722 (1987)
1.16 The term band-gap engineering was first introduced in F. Capasso: J. Vac. Sci. Technol. **B1**, 457 (1983). For a recent review of band-gap engineering the reader is referred to F. Capasso in *Semiconductors and Semimetals*, Volume 24, R. K. Willardson, A. C. Beer eds. (Academic, New York 1987), p. 319
1.17 For a review on strained layer superlattices see G. C. Osbourn, P. L. Gourley, I. J. Fritz, R. M. Biefeld, L. R. Dawson, T. E. Zipperian: In *Semiconductors and Semimetals*, Volume 24, R. K. Willardson and A. C. Beer eds (Academic, New York 1987), p. 459
1.18 H. Sakaki: Proc. Int. Symp. Foundation of Quantum Mechanics, Phys. Soc. J., p. 94 (1984)
1.19 L. Esaki: IEEE J. Quantum Electron. **QE-22**, 1611 (1986)
1.20 L. Esaki, R. Tsu: IBM J. Res. Develop. **14**, 61 (1970)
1.21 L. L. Chang, L. Esaki, R. Tsu: Appl. Phys. Lett. **24**, 593 (1974)
1.22 L. Esaki, L. L. Chang, Phys. Rev. Lett. **33**, 495 (1974)

1.23 R. Dingle, W. Wiegmann, C. H. Henry: Phys. Rev. Lett. **33**, 827 (1974)

1.24 J. P. van der Ziel, R. Dingle, R. C. Miller, W. Wiegmann, W. A. Nordland, Jr.: Appl. Phys. Lett. **26**, 463 (1975)

1.25 L. V. Keldysh: Fiz. Tverd. Tela (Leningrad), **4**, 2265 (1962) [Transl. Sov. Phys.-Solid State **4**, 1658 (1962)]

1.26 R. Dingle, A. C. Gossard, W. Wiegmann: Phys. Rev. Lett. **34**, 1327 (1975)

1.27 A. E. Blakeslee, C. F. Alliotta: IBM J. Res. Develop. **14**, 686 (1970)

1.28 A. Y. Cho: Appl. Phys. Lett. **19**, 467 (1971)

1.29 A. C. Gossard, P. M. Petroff, W. Wiegmann, R. Dingle, A. Savage: Appl. Phys. Lett. **29**, 323 (1976)

1.30 R. Dingle, H. L. Stormer, A C. Gossard, W. Wiegmann: Appl. Phys. Lett. **33**, 665 (1978)

1.31 R. Dingle, A. C. Gossard, H. L. Stormer: U.S. Patent 4194935 (1980);
T. Mimura, S. Hiyamizu, T. Fuji, K. Nambu: Jpn. J. Appl. Phys. **19**, L125 (1980);
D. Delagebeaudeuf, P. Delescluse, P. Etienne, M. Laviron, J. Chaplart, N. T. Linh: Electron. Lett. **16**, 667 (1980)

1.32 H. Stormer, R. Dingle, A. C. Gossard, W. Wiegmann, M. D. Sturge: Solid State Commun. **29**, 705 (1979)

1.33 K. Von Klitzing, G. Dorda, M. Pepper: Phys. Rev. Lett. **45**, 494 (1980)

1.34 D. C. Tsui, H. L. Stormer, A. C. Gossard: Phys. Rev. Lett. **48**, 1559 (1982)

1.35 R. B. Laughlin: Phys. Rev. Lett. **50**, 1395 (1983)

1.36 R. E. Ruhrwein: U.S. Patent 3364084 (1968); H. M. Manasevit, Appl. Phys. Lett. **12**, 156 (1968)

1.37 For an extensive survey on MOCVD see J. Crystal Growth **77** (1986)

1.38 D. A. B. Miller, D. S. Chemla, T. C. Damen, A. C. Gossard, W. Wiegmann, T. H. Wood, C. A. Burrus: Phys. Rev. Lett. **53**, 2173 (1984)

1.39 D. A. B. Miller, D. S. Chemla, T. C. Damen, A. C. Gossard, W. Wiegmann, T. H. Wood, C. A. Burrus: Appl. Phys. Lett. **45**, 13 (1984)

1.40 T. C. L. G. Sollner, W. D. Goodhue, P. E. Tannenwald, C. D. Parker, D. O. Peck: Appl. Phys. Lett. **43**, 588 (1983)

1.41 T. P. E. Broekaert, W. Lee, C. G. Fonstad: Appl. Phys. Lett. **53**, 1545 (1988)

1.42 E. Brown, W. D. Goodhue, T. C. L. G. Sollner: J. Appl. Phys. **64**, 1519 (1988)

1.43 R. H. Davis, H. H. Hosack: J. Appl. Phys. **34**, 864 (1963);
L. V. Ioganson: Zh. Eksp. Teor. Fiz. **45**, 207 (1963) [English Transl. Sov. Phys. JETP **18**, 46 (1964)]

1.44 F. Capasso, R. A. Kiehl: J. Appl. Phys. **58**, 1366 (1985)

1.45 G. H. Heilmeier: Proc. of the 1984 International Electron Devices Meeting, IEDM, p. 2

1.46 R. T. Bate, G. A. Frazier, W. R. Frensley, J. K. Lee, M. A. Reed: Proc. SPIE **792**, 26 (1987)

1.47 N. Yokoyama, K. Imamura, S. Muto, S. Hiyamizu, H. Nishi: Jpn. J. Appl. Phys. **24**, L853 (1985)

1.48 F. Capasso, S. Sen, A. C. Gossard, A. L. Hutchinson, J. H. English: IEEE Electron. Dev. Lett. **EDL-7**, 573 (1986)

1.49 A. A. Lakhani, R. C. Potter: Appl. Phys. Lett. **52**, 1604 (1988);
S. Sen, F. Capasso, D. Sivco, A. Y. Cho: IEEE Electron. Dev. Lett. **9**, 402 (1988)

1.50 F. Capasso, S. Sen, A. Y. Cho, D. L. Sivco: Appl. Phys. Lett. **53**, 1056 (1988);
S. Sen, F. Capasso, A. Y. Cho, D. L. Sivco, IEEE Electron. Dev. Lett. **9**, 533 (1988)

1.51 A. D. Stone, P. A. Lee: Phys. Rev. Lett. **54**, 1196 (1985)

1.52 V. J. Goldman, D. C. Tsui, J. E. Cunningham: Phys. Rev. Lett. **58**, 1256 (1987)

1.53 T. W. Hickmott, P. M. Solomon, F. F. Fang, R. Fischer, H. Morkoc: Phys. Rev. Lett. **52**, 2053 (1984)

1.54 M. Heiblum: Solid State Electron. **24**, 343 (1981)

1.55 C. A. Mead: Proc. IRE **48**, 359 (1960)

1.56 M. Heiblum, M. I. Nathan, D. C. Thomas, C. M. Knoedler: Phys. Rev. Lett. **55**, 2200 (1985)

1.57 A. F. J. Levi, J. R. Hayes, P. M. Platzman, W. Wiegmann: Phys. Rev. Lett. **55**, 2071 (1985)

1.58 M. Heiblum, M. V. Fischetti, W. P. Dumke, D. J. Frank, J. M. Anderson, C. M. Knoedler, L. Osterling: Phys. Rev. Lett. **58**, 816 (1987)

1.59 B. F. Levine, C. G. Bethea, G. Hasnain, J. Walker, R. J. Malik: Appl. Phys. Lett. **53**, 296 (1988)

1.60 R. Kazarinov, B. A. Suris: Fiz. Tekh. Poluprov. **5**, 797 (1971) [English Transl. in Sov. Phys. Semicond. **5**, 707 (1971)]

1.61 For a recent review on doping superlattices see G. H. Dohler: IEEE J. Quantum Electron. **QE-22**, 1682 (1986)

1.62 E. F. Schubert, J. E. Cunningham, W. T. Tsang: Phys. Rev. **B36**, 1348 (1987)

1.63 *Heterojunction Band-Discontinuities: Physics and Device Applications*, F. Capasso, G. Margaritondo eds. (North Holland, Amsterdam 1987)

1.64 B. L. Altshuler: Pis'ma Zh. Eksp. Teor. Fiz. **41**, 530 (1985) [English Transl. JETP Lett. **41**, 648 (1985)];
      P. A. Lee, A. D. Stone: Phys. Rev. Lett. **55**, 1622 (1985)

1.65 B. J. van Wees, H. van Houten, C. W. Beenakker, J. G. Williamson, L. P. Kouwenhoven, D. van der Marel, C. T. Foxon: Phys. Rev. Lett. **60**, 848 (1988)
      D. A. Wharam, T. J. Thornton, R. Newbury, M. Pepper, H. Ahmed, J. E. F. Frost, D. G. Hasko, D. C. Peacock, D. A. Ritchie, G. A. C. Jones: J. Phys. C: Solid State Phys. **21**, L209 (1988)

1.66 J. Cibert, P. M. Petroff, G. J. Dolan, S. J. Pearton, A. C. Gossard, J. H. English: Appl. Phys. Lett. **49**, 1275 (1986)

1.67 S. Datta, M. R. Mellock, S. Bandyopadhyay, M. S. Lundstrom: Appl. Phys. Lett. **48**, 487 (1987)

1.68 Y. Aharonov, D. Bohm: Phys. Rev. **115**, 485 (1959)

1.69 S. Washburn, H. Schmid, D. Kern, R. A. Webb: Phys. Rev. Lett. **59**, 791 (1987) and references therein

1.70 S. Datta, M. R. Melloch, S. Bandyopadhyay, R. Noren, M. Vaziri, M. Miller, R. Reifenberger: Phys. Rev. Lett. **55**, 2344 (1985)

1.71 See, for example, the Proceedings of the International Conference on Electronic Materials, June 13–15, 1988, Tokyo, to be published by MRS

1.72 J. A. Morton: IEEE Spectrum, Sept. 1965, p. 62

1.73 M. Kikuchi: *Japanese Electronics* (Simul Press, Tokyo, 1983)

1.74 *Semiconductors and Semimetals*, R. K. Willardson, A. C. Beer eds., Volume 24, R. Dingle ed. (Academic, San Diego 1987)

2. The Nature of Molecular Beam Epitaxy and Consequences for Quantum Microstructures

A. Madhukar

With 28 Figures

While the early half of the present century saw a scientific revolution in the form of development of quantum mechanics, it is undoubtedly the latter half which would be remembered for its ability to begin to fruitfully conceive and realize devices based upon these quantum mechanical principles. In particular, since the discovery of the solid state transistor action which lead to the demise of the bulky, though operationally quantum mechanically based vacuum tubes, the self-created race for more efficient use of the silicon based transistor and for inventing novel solid state devices capable of performing increasingly more complex functions with greater speed and reduced operational cost has progressively intensified. The former has led to the development of silicon based large scale integration (LSI) and very large scale integration (VLSI) of discreet devices on single chips. The latter has led to generation of new device concepts as well as consideration of new semiconducting materials belonging to the III–V and II–VI category. The most recent in this thrust has been the introduction of the notion of compositionally and doping modulated structures [2.1] which exploit the notion of dimensional confinement of elementary or composite particles in the solid on a length scale (L_D) comparable to their de Broglie wave length (λ_{dB}). This volume is largely devoted to the variety of new and novel device concepts that are being generated at an incredibly rapid pace – a pace which at the moment, in most cases, outstrips the reliable technological realization of the desired material structures and their subsequent processing into device structures [2.2, 3]. Nevertheless, it is such concieved devices and their potential use which is, and is likely to remain, the driving thrust towards development of material and structure growth techniques and device fabrication processes. In turn, progress on this side will undoubtedly also stir conceptualization of even more sophisticated and novel devices.

This particular chapter is devoted to examining the present status of one particular approach to realization of material structures of incredibly small dimensions in the growth direction–the so-called technique of molecular beam epitaxy (MBE). Several informative articles on the experimental aspects of the technique of MBE, as well as the variety of materials–semiconductors, dielectrics, and metals, including magnetic materials – grown in modulated form, have appeared in recent years [2.4]. As such, emphasis here is laid on recent developments in gaining a deeper understanding of the atomistic processes controlling the growth of such material structures and consequently their structural and chemical nature [2.5]. In turn, this controls most of the properties upon which the performance of the proposed device rests. The significance of this inter-relationship has begun to be appreciated only recently through advances brought about by systematic investigations of the atomistic kinetics and mechanism of growth via a combined effort comprising of (i) computer simulations of MBE growth [2.5], (ii) measurements of the static and dynamic (i.e. during growth) surface morphology via reflection-high-energy-electron-diffraction (RHEED) intensity dynamics [2.6–12], (iii) comparison of the predicted and observed behavior [2.13–16], (iv) fabrication of structures under such conditions [2.17–20], and finally, (v) measurements of their optical [2.17–21], electrical [2.22] and structural characteristics [2.23] and reconciliation with the atomistic nature indicated by (i) through (iii). A major realization that has emerged from such studies is the presence of at least two types of additional length scales whose origin lies in the atomistic kinetics of the growth process itself [2.15, 18, 19, 24, 25]. These length scales define the degree of structural and chemical perfection of the interfacial regions between two materials in the growth direction (hereafter called the vertical direction) and in the atomic planes perpendicular to the growth direction (hereafter called the lateral plane). It is thus the intent of this chapter to provide a clear picture of the origin of these length scales, their significance in relation to the already noted vertical dimensional confinement (L_D) and de Broglie wave length (λ_{dB}) scales, and implications for the variety of device concepts and structures discussed in other chapters of this volume. I should, at the outset, like to thank Dr. Federico Capasso, the Editor of this volume, for providing the opportunity for the first comprehensive presentation of this point of view.

The chapter is organized as follows. A brief recapitulation of the fundamental concept of dimensional confinement through creation of quantum wells is given in Sect. 2.1 along with an equally brief presentation of some illustrative examples of the types of generic device concepts which, in one way or another, seek to exploit the fundamental quantum mechanical consequences of carrier confinement for transport and/or optical properties. The illustrative examples provide an appreciation of precisely what degree of unprecedented control of the atomic and chemical perfection of materials and structures is demanded by such concepts. In Sect. 2.2 we then begin with a brief description of the basic elements of the conceptual basis and some practical considerations of the MBE technique, emphasizing the useful role played by recent RHEED intensity studies of static and dynamic (i.e. growing) surfaces. This is followed in Sect. 2.3 by a discussion of the role and consequences of surface kinetic processes for the structural and chemical nature of surfaces and interfaces revealed by computer simulations and comparison with RHEED studies. The true nature of the confining potential experienced by the charge or energy carrying particles is thus exposed and the significance, during growth, of the differing lateral and vertical effective migration length scales of different species constituting the materials, particularly in alloys, is made transparent. In Sect. 2.4 we present some results of photoluminescence (PL) studies on GaAs/Al$_x$Ga$_{1-x}$As(100) single square quantum well structures grown systematically under RHEED determined identical growth conditions with the express purpose of checking the view of the confining potentials indicated by the computer simulation and RHEED studies. The behavior of the PL line width as a function of the intended width of the quantum well (d_W) has been found in these studies to be essentially d_W^{-1} significantly different from the d_W^{-3} behavior implied by the long held view of fluctuations in well width which has guided interpretation of material, structure and many device properties since the inception of the field. We end with Sect. 2.5 which provides some thoughts on the significance of the findings for the $GaAs/Al_xGa_{1-x}As$ to other material systems, particularly systems involving lattice mismatch induced strain effects in the growth kinetics, and its implications for some of the device concepts noted in Sect. 2.1, but discussed in detail by other colleagues in various chapters of this volume.

2.1 Dimensional Confinement and Device Concepts

The notion of dimensional confinement of charge carriers near the interface between two appropriate materials and their usage for device operation has been with us for a long time, the best known example being the Si/SiO_2 based heterostructure transistor [2.26]. One exploits the discontinuity between the conduction and valence band energies of Si and SiO_2, combined with the bending of the Si bands achieved via appropriate doping and biasing, to create a "triangular" potential at the interface, as shown schematically in Fig. 2.1a, case A. Such a potential well gives rise to confinement of the carriers in the direction normal to the interface. When its size becomes comparable to the carrier de Broglie wave length, new quantized energy states for motion in the normal direction arise [2.26]. In more recent times, the same notion has been realized in lattice matched and mismatched combinations of epitaxical heterostructures of compound semiconductors belonging to the III–V, II–VI and group IV columns of the periodic table. A particular notion introduced is the controlled placement of dopants in the larger band gap semiconductor (hereafter called the barrier layer) so as to achieve spatial separation between the ionized dopants and the charge carriers in the well created at the interface [2.27, 28] (see Fig. 2.1a, case B). This leads to reduction of the ionized impurity scattering of the carriers in the well. In high quality MBE grown $GaAs/Al_{0.3}Ga_{0.7}As(100)$ heterojunctions low temperature (L. He) electron mobilities near 5×10^6 cm^2/V s have been achieved under suitable conditions using this notion called modulation doping. Such a heterojunction has been exploited for transistor action and is known under various names, the most common perhaps being high electron mobility transistor (HEMT) [2.28].

Different types of confining potentials have been realized due to advancements in growth techniques. These techniques are molecular beam eptiaxy (MBE), metal-organic chemical vapour deposition (MO-CVD) [2.29], gas source MBE (GS-MBE) [2.30], and variations on these basic approaches such as

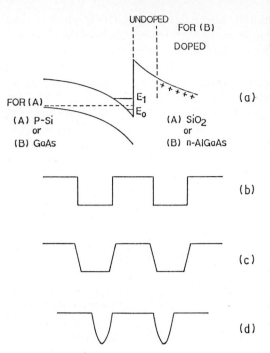

Fig. 2.1a–d. Schematic drawing of the type of confining potential shapes. (a) heterojunction (b) square well (c) trapezoidal well (d) parabolic well

atomic layer epitaxy (ALE) [2.31]. While all these techniques rely upon deposition of the desired materials from gas phase upon suitable single crystal substrates, even the older growth technique of liquid phase epitaxy (LPE) involving growth at liquid-solid interface has seen considerable progress towards realization of single and multiple interface quantum well structures [2.32].

The simplest and most commonly employed configuration beyond the single interface HJ structure is the single or multiple square quantum well shown schematically in Fig. 2.1b realized via growth of alternating thin films of at least two different materials. The degree of confinement, as well as the degree of communication between confined electronic states, can be controlled via the width and depth of the confining potential (denoted by d_W and ΔE, respectively) and the width of the barrier layer (d_B). Indeed, if a sufficiently large number of such quantum wells are grown with d_W, ΔE and d_B such as to allow a reasonable level of communication between wells, then new types of *bulk*, *three* dimensional solids with *highly anisotropic* band structures can be generated [2.33] and have been termed superlattices (SL) [2.1]. In fact, the earliest introduction [2.1] of the notion of compositionally modulated structures was motivated by the possibility of exploiting the modification of the band structure in the "stacking" direction (arising from the superlattice periodicity and the accompanying Brillovin zone folding effects [2.33]) for non-linear transport properties such as negative differential resistance [2.1]. Although the square well configuration in the form of single, multiple or superlattice structure remains the most commonly studied, techniques such as MBE permit realization of other functional forms of the potential through compositional grading of the barrier and well layers. Trapezoidal wells (Fig. 2.1c) and parabolic wells (Fig. 2.1d) in the $GaAs/Al_xGa_{1-x}As$ system have been realized [2.34, 35]. Yet other forms are possible and will undoubtedly be realized.

The fundamental notion behind any such potential shape is, of course, the creation of new electronic quantum states and the exploitation of (i) the nature of energy and momentum distribution and (ii) the spatial nature of the associated wave functions, for creating new and novel electronic transport and optical properties which may be exploited for new and novel device concepts. The effort in recent years has therefore been directed towards greater control in realizing near atomic level structural and chemical perfection of the interfaces, particularly in multi-interface quantum well structures involving ultra-thin ($< 100 \text{ Å}$) layers of materials. The need for this unprecedented degree of control and perfection of not only the interfaces but also sharpness of doping profile is readily appreciated by recognizing the desired objectives for the performance level of the electronic, optical and lattice properties which form the basis for the anticipated device structures and device performance specifications. To cite but one illustrative example, an imperfection of order of one atomic layer in the definition of the width of a square quantum well of GaAs of intended width of 20 atomic layers (i.e. $20\, a_0/2 = 56.6 \text{ Å}$, where a_0 is the lattice constant of bulk GaAs) sandwiched between the larger band gap $Al_{0.3}Ga_{0.7}As(100)$ layers gives rise to an uncertainty in the energy levels of the resulting quasi-two dimensionally confined electron levels of order ± 6 meV [2.17]. While for some purposes such an uncertainty may be acceptable, for many anticipated applications it is not. Similarly, the scattering of charge and energy carriers caused by such imperfections can be detrimental to the full potential offered by their transport and optical properties, parallel or perpendicular to the interfaces.

For completeness it should be noted that separate from the quasi-two-dimensionally (2D) confined electronic states discussed so far, states with wave functions localized at the interfaces can also arise, both from extrinsic effects such as impurities and structural defects [2.36] and intrinsic interfacial chemical bonding effects [2.33], depending upon the nature of the materials involved, the growth conditions and technique employed. However, for many III–V based systems of considerable device potential, interface state densities $< 10^{11}/\text{cm}^2$ can now be fairly routinely achieved. Although we shall not have occasion in this chapter to consider the consequences of compositional modulation for the vibronic states of the resulting system, it is, nevertheless, worth noting that in principle quasi 2D confined as well as interface like phonon modes are possible in such structures [2.37, 38] and could play an important role in influencing the room temperature transport and optical properties of the charge and energy carriers.

Two additional features of compositionally modulated structures and the resulting confining potentials hoped for are worth noting. First of these is the issue of the difference between a SL structure with ultrashort (a few atomic layers) periodicity and a random alloy of the same equivalent composition [2.33]. While the band gap of the latter is fixed by the chosen composition, it can be varied to a degree for the former by appropriately controlling the number of atomic layers, N and M, for the two components, A and B, of the repeated structure $A_N B_M$ in such a way that $N/(N + M)$ remains a constant value. Second, and an even more fascinating, aspect relates to the nature of confining potentials in compositionally modulated structures made of lattice mismatched layers of thickness below the critical thickness for generation of misfit dislocations (for individual layers as well as the entire composite structure). In such systems, the presence of the misfit induced tensile and/or compressive strain can be fruitfully exploited for *independent* adjustment of the SL band gap and the lattice constant [2.39]. Such superlattices, called strained layer superlattices (SLS), thus offer an additional degree of freedom for realization of confining potentials not necessarily available in the highly lattice matched systems.

While the purpose of the preceding brief recapitulation was to capture the underlying motivation for the rapid growth of interest in modulated structures, the main purpose of this chapter is to discuss a particular growth technique, namely MBE, for realization of this variety of confining potentials. In the process, however, the single most important feature that would emerge, and which transcends the particular growth technique, is a deeper appreciation for the true atomistic nature of the confining potentials actually realized due to the inherent nature of the growth kinetics and mechanism(s), as opposed to the simple idealized pictures of Fig. 2.1 which serve to motivate the subject. In particular, it will be seen that the basic features of an idealized confining potential, say the width (d_W) and depth (ΔE) *in the case of the square well, are in fact a function of spatial coordinate in both, the lateral (i.e. in the plane of the layers) and vertical (i.e. in the growth) directions.* While much emphasis has been laid on the latter, as exemplified in the prevalent notion of fluctuations in the well width, the recent work [2.17–21, 24, 25] in the author's group has begun to reveal the significance of the former. Consider, for instance, the interfaces between GaAs/Al$_x$Ga$_{1-x}$As(100) even *assuming structurally ideal* behavior as shown schematically in Fig. 2.2a. In such a situation, while the global average composition of the barrier layers may be the intended value, say x_0 ($x_0 \neq 0, 1$), on a local lateral length scale departures from x_0 can and will occur, controlled by the kinetics of growth. The local length scale of significance depends upon the particular particle probing and being influenced by the interfaces. On such a length, variations in the local average Al composition will thus be perceived as fluctuations in the depth of the confining potential which, if the length scale is larger than needed to define the notion of a band, may be viewed then as fluctuations in the band edge discontinuity. A real interface will involve steps as well, thus giving rise to both, notion of structural fluctuations and confining potential depth fluctuations. Thus, $d_W(R_{||}, Z)$ and $\Delta E(R_{||}, Z)$ is the case and it is the characteristic length scales of the fluctuations in these features of the potential in the lateral and vertical directions in relationship to, (i) the size of the particle responsible for the device, and (ii) the size of the device, which is of

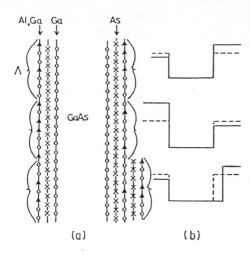

Al,Ga Ga   As

GaAs

(a)   (b)

Fig. 2.2a, b. Schematic illustration of structurally ideal GaAs/Al$_x$Ga$_{1-x}$As(100) interfaces but yet having fluctuations in the depth of the confining potential

fundamental significance to micro and nano structure devices performing to the expectations based upon idealized potentials. This should bring into clear view the recognition that there are five generic types of length scales of fundamental significance to the nature of modulated structures and the contemplated new and novel micro and nano structure devices based upon them. To summarize, these are;

1) the average vertical size of the active device region,
2) the average lateral size of the active device region,
3) the effective migration length(s) of the growth rate controlling species, particularly in alloys,
4) the size of the particle involved in carrying of information,
5) the vertical and lateral length scales of fluctuations in the atomistic nature of the confining potentials.

We now briefly discuss a few generic examples of device concepts and the significance of the true nature of the interfaces (i.e. the confining potentials) to these concepts. Let us first consider electronic devices relying upon the transport properties of the charge carriers. An example of a device involving lateral transport has already been noted in the form of HEMT. Indeed, it has been argued that, even when many practical aspects of growth of such heterojunctions have been brought under control, there is no escape from the intrinsic fluctuations in the crystal potential at and near the interfacial region arising from the growth kinetics controlled fluctuations in the distribution of the atoms belonging to the well and barrier layer materials [2.40, 41]. For the GaAs/Al$_x$Ga$_{1-x}$As HJ involving an alloy as the barrier layer, such fluctuations in the interfacial crystal potential, combined with the alloy disorder scattering experienced by the particles due to the penetration of their wave function into the barrier, is shown to be the ultimate mobility limiting factor. The upper limit on the low temperature mobility is then set by the ability to achieve as uniform a chemical distribution on as large a length scale in the lateral and vertical directions as ingeneous control of growth kinetics would permit. Low temperature mobilities exceeding 10^7 cm^2/V s have been predicted [2.40].

Turning to devices exploiting transport of carriers across interfaces (vertical transport), let us start with consideration of the heterojunction bipolar transistor (HJBT) [2.42]. Since the confining potential barrier for electrons and holes (ΔE_c and ΔE_v, respectively) can be controlled via manipulation of the band gaps, $E_{gW}(Z)$ and $E_{gB}(Z)$, of the well and barrier layers through grading of the composition and doping schemes in the growth direction (Z direction), it has given rise to the band gap engineering approach pioneered by *Capasso* [2.3]. Thus for the HJBT, high injection efficiency without sacrificing high speed/high frequency operation has been proposed through creation of appropriately graded and doped emitter and base regions [2.3]. Another example of device concepts based upon vertical transport which is drawing considerable attention and effort is manifest in the double or multiple barrier resonant tunnelling diode/transistor [2.2]. Negative differential resistance in such structures can be realized due to increased probability of transfer of charge from the emitter into the well or, in multiple well structures, from ground state of one well to the excited state(s) of an adjacent well when such states are brought into resonance through application of an electric field [2.43,44]. The ability, however, to achieve sharp resonant peak structures and high peak to valley ratio in the current (I)-voltage (V) characteristics is dependent upon the perfection of the confining potentials in both, vertical and *lateral* directions. Fluctuations in the confining potential, hitherto viewed in terms of fluctuations in the well width, (δd_W), affect the I–V characteristics not only through fluctuations in the energy of the confined levels within a well and between wells, but also tend to destroy phase coherence of electrons reflected from the two barriers. The same will be true if there were fluctuations in the depth of the confining potential $(\delta \Delta E_{c,v})$. The presence, indeed dominance, of $\delta \Delta E_{c,v}$ has in fact been very recently shown to be the case in most high quality MBE grown structures [2.17–21, 24, 25]. The loss of phase coherence tends to destroy a resonant enhancement of the transmission coefficient which would otherwise accompany negative differential resistance. Of course, the application of the electric field in itself modifies the confining well potential even if it were otherwise ideal so that such resonant enhancement of the transmission coefficient in multiple quantum wells is not possible for identical wells [2.45]. Non identical (either in intended width or depth or both) adjacent wells are necessary. We shall, in later sections, see that the degree of $\delta d_W(\boldsymbol{R}_{||})$ and $\delta \Delta E_{c,v}(\boldsymbol{R}_{||})$ fluctuations not only depends upon the growth kinetics, but is also dependent upon the thickness to which a given layer is grown. Thus, different degrees and length scales of fluctuations can arise in the two different adjacent wells, further adversely influencing the desired achievement of resonant enhancement of the transmission coefficient. Control and judicious exploitation of the growth kinetics and an atomistic understanding of the growth process is thus of value in setting and achieving one's objectives. One such approach is via the notion of *growth interruption* [2.9, 46] which can improve lateral uniformity and shall be discussed in some detail in the following. Of course, even in the absence of phase coherence from one well to another adjacent well in a multi-well structure, tunnelling can still occur through an incoherent, sequential, process in which the particle loses phase "memory" of its earlier state. The criterion for realization of coherent resonant tunnelling is essentially that the collisional broadening of the carriers be smaller than the intrinsic resonance width. As has been pointed out [2.2], collisional broadening is defined by the total scattering rate of the carrier and thus includes both inelastic and elastic scattering processes. The latter include scattering due to the fluctuations $\delta d_w(\boldsymbol{R}_{||})$ and $\delta \Delta E_c(\boldsymbol{R}_{||})$. The tunnelling state life time in a well can lead to space charge effects and thus also depend upon the injection current. To the best of this author's knowledge, this aspect has not yet been examined.

In superlattices, negative differential resistance (NDR) was sought through zone folding effects [2.1], as we noted earlier. However, another type of NDR can result from fluctuations in the confinement crystal potential of a nature such that the potential change across the superlattice period becomes comparable to the width of the SL band in the growth direction [2.47]. In such a situation, the conduction mechanism of the electrons in the SL direction will change from coherent band motion to phonon-assisted variable range hopping within Anderson localized states (at low temperatures), or, at higher temperatures, to an activated conduction mechanism involving promotion of electrons near the Fermi energy below the mobility edge to states at and above the mobility edge [2.47]. A point to be appreciated is that while emphasis is laid here on vertical transport, its character should not be viewed as being a strictly one dimensional problem as the simple idealized pictorial representations and models often tend to portray. If the motion in the vertical direction were a truly one dimensional transport problem, then according to the theory of disorder [2.48], all states are Anderson localized no matter how weak the disorder and transport across the superlattice can never be via coherent band motion if the superlattice thickness is larger than the localization length at the Fermi energy. Indeed, it is therefore the very presence of the three-dimensional, though highly anisotropic (i.e. quasi one-dimensional), character that leads to the requirement of the fluctuations in confinement energy due to $\delta d_w(\boldsymbol{R}_{||})$ and $\delta \Delta E_{c,v}(\boldsymbol{R}_{||})$ exceeding some critical value (i.e. departure from an ideal one dimensional motion problem) for the localization effects to set in and manifest themselves through a change in the nature of the mechanism of carrier transport at very low temperatures [2.49]. An aspect that, to the best of this author's knowledge, has not been addressed in considering the vertical transport behavior in superlattices with band widths of order of the relevant phonon frequencies (for example, the $2k_F$ acoustic phonon or optic phonons in the SL direction) is the role of the electron–phonon coupling in influencing transport at room temperature. Such a situation has been investigated over a decade ago in the literature of transport in quasi one-dimensional conductors [2.50] but workers in the area of semiconductor superlattices seem generally unfamiliar with this literature. It has been shown in that context that under such conditions, phonons act as a time-dependent random potential and can significantly alter the transport characteristics [2.50, 51]. It is thus possible that the room temperature vertical transport characteristics of devices based upon narrow band superlattices as well as tunnelling characteristics of the double and multiquantum well structures are significantly influenced by phonon induced time dependent disorder, quite apart from the static disorder inherent in the structural and chemical nature of the interfaces resulting from the growth kinetics.

Devices involving optical characteristics, in addition to or in place of the transport characteristics, are also, of course, of considerable interest for application to such areas as optical communication, optical storage and optical computing. The need for a variety of sources (lasers), amplifiers, wave guides, detectors, spatial light modulators, etc, in various areas of these technologies is widely recognized and some of these aspects would likely be covered in some of the chapters of this volume. Attention has focussed on quantum well structures of appropriate materials as possible candidates for many such devices due to the range of flexibility available in tailoring their electronic and optical properties. Thus, avalanche photodiodes (APD's), sawtooth rectifiers, including the special case under appropriate bias to produce a staircase like potential giving rise to the proposed staircase solid state photomultipliers and APD's, repeated velocity overshoot devices, etc., involving quantum well structures have been proposed and, in some cases, experimental investigations begun [2.3]. Similarly, double heterostructure lasers (DHL) are now a reality although the need and search for such lasers for different applications and with increasingly stringent demand on performance specification continues. The very thin active layers in such lasers does demand a certain degree of atomistic control of the structural and chemical perfection of the interfaces, including their lateral uniformity. Some of the difficulties associated with the desired reduction of the threshold current density have been suggested [2.3] to be overcome by finely controlled compositional grading of appropriate layers and utilizing the resulting built-in quasi electric fields generated by $dE_g(Z)/dz$, as a means of channelling the electrons into the quantum well region. Once again, however, the lateral uniformity of the injection barrier can be of significance in controlling the characteristics of the laser. As a yet another example of quantum well structure based device, but one which relies on purely optical property and a "neutral", energy carrying, composite particle, i.e. the exciton, let us consider the self electro-optic device (SEED) proposed as an optical gate [2.52]. The characteristics of the interfacial confining potential on the size scale of the exciton, both in the absence of an applied transverse (i.e. across the interface) electric field and in its presence leading to the quantum confined Stark effect (QCSE) which forms the basis for the device, are of paramount significance in controlling the band pass and transmission characteristics of the device.

One could provide other examples, or even discuss in greater detail the examples cited here, but it is hoped that the brief discussion provided in this section has been sufficiently adequate to bring out a central feature of the majority of micro and nanostructure devices being examined and proposed in a wide variety of context – that the atomistic nature of the interfacial confining potential on a vertical length scale of a few atomic layers and lateral length scale of the size of the particle carrying the desired information is of sufficient significance to the physical properties upon which device operation rests so as to demand a greater attention and deeper understanding than has been given and achieved in the past. Since this qualitative and quantitative atomistic nature of the interfacial confining potential is intimately tied to the growth kinetics and mechanism, a point to be demonstrated in the rest of this chapter, it brings the physics and chemistry of the growth process, and of new materials and structures, to the very core of successful development of new and novel devices.

2.2 Molecular Beam Epitaxy

2.2.1 Conceptual Picture

Molecular beam epitaxy is an ultra high vacuum growth technique which relies upon kinetic processes of adsorption, desorption, migration and reaction associated with thermal energy atomic and molecular beams impinging randomly upon a suitable substrate held at an appropriate temperature. The beam source to substrate distance is less than the mean free path of the impinging particles, unlike other vapour phase techniques such as MO-CVD. Since the majority of experimental studies [2.4] have been carried out for growth of III–V compounds, the discussion in the following will be advanced through the specific example of the prototypical system GaAs grown on GaAs(100) surface. It is, however, emphasized that the concepts and kinetic processes involved remain true for other lattice matched III–V binary and ternary systems, as well as II–VI systems. The chronological occurrence of the above noted generic kinetic processes leading to epitaxial growth under appropriate growth conditions can be appreciated by referring to the following conceptual picture [2.5, 53];

Random   Impingement
$\downarrow$
Weak   Adsorption (for molecular species)
$\downarrow$
Surface   Migration
$\downarrow \longrightarrow$ Desorption
Formation of Intermediate Activated Complex
(for molecular species)
$\downarrow$
Chemisorption/Dissociative Reaction (for molecular species)
$\downarrow$
Surface   Migration
$\downarrow \longrightarrow$ Desorption
Incorporation (Epitaxical)

This conceptual representation delineates the generic kinetic processes an atom or molecule may undergo from the time of impingement. It should be helpful in guiding the discussion on the computer simulations of the MBE growth process to be presented in Sect. 2.3. An important feature to be noted is the presence of kinetic steps involving intermediate activated complex(es) for molecular species and the final kinetic step of their dissociative chemisorption reaction. The group V vapour species in III–V MBE growth is generally in a diatomic or tetratomic molecular form, whereas the group III species is in atomic form. Having chosen the material system for the substrate and the film(s) to be grown, the user controlled growth parameters in MBE are

a) the substrate temperature (T_s)
b) the group III flux (F_{III})
c) the group V pressure (P_V).

The choice of the substrate temperature essentially defines the rates of the various kinetic processes since local thermodynamic equilibrium [2.53] is expected to be reached on a time scale faster than almost any kinetic rate process. Of greater relevance is thus the time duration of operation of a given kinetic process. This time can be controlled, to some extent, by the particular choice of the group III and group V fluxes. Note that existence of local thermodynamic equilibrium does not imply that the kinetic rates are necessarily given by an Arrhenius form.

2.2.2 Reflection High Energy Electron Diffraction

A unique feature of MBE growth is that, being a UHV growth technique, it permits use of certain in-situ surface analytical techniques in conjunction with the growth process. Thus, real time information concerning the nature of the static surface (i.e. in the absence of growth) as well as the dynamic growth front is, in principle, accessible. A surface sensitive technique which is compatible with the geometric considerations in the design of MBE growth chambers, and is invariably included, is reflection high-energy electron diffraction (RHEED) with the electron beam incident near grazing incidence [2.4]. A schematic view of the MBE growth chamber is shown in Fig. 2.3. For our purposes it is sufficient to note that use of RHEED in examining the nature of the starting static surface (upon which growth is to be performed) reveals a diffraction pattern which not only provides direct information on the symmetry of the surface unit cell in relation to the bulk crystal symmetries, but the pattern itself consists of either spots or streaks. The observation of a spotty pattern is attributed to the presence of sufficiently 3-dimensional islands on the surface so as to give rise to an effectively electron transmission diffraction pattern. By contrast, the presence of streaks has been generally taken to manifest the absence of such 3D like islands, thus suggesting a smoother surface morphology.

Most of the MBE growth of III–V compounds has been carried out on (100) surfaces of suitable substrates. The thin film to be grown may or may not be

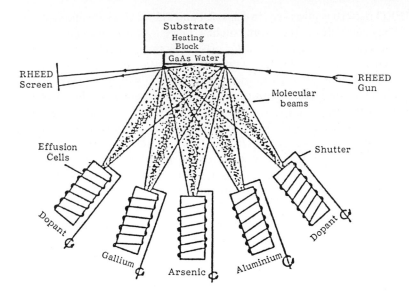

Fig. 2.3. Schematic diagram of III–V MBE growth chamber

reasonably well lattice matched to the chosen substrate. The most extensively studied system is the $GaAs/Al_xGa_{1-x}As(100)$ system which has a very small lattice mismatch, $\Delta a/a_s$, of $\leq 10^{-3}$. Here $\Delta a = [a(\text{overlayer}) - a_s(\text{substrate})]$, where a represents the lattice constant of the corresponding bulk material. However, systems involving high lattice mismatch, such as $GaAs/In_xGa_{1-x}As$ with $\Delta a/a_s$ as high as 7% for $x = 1$ have also been grown with reasonable success [2.46, 54, 55].

For the (100) surfaces of III–V semiconductors, which may ideally terminate with the last atomic plane consisting either solely of group V or group III atoms, the realistic situation is that both types of (100) atomic planes are exposed at the surface. The number of such atomic planes exposed (the surface profile), the overall relative degree of their exposure (the surface stoichiometry), and the details of the atomic arrangement of the exposed atoms is dependent upon the substrate temperature (T_s), the group V pressure, the nature and degree of contaminants present in the UHV ambient, and even possibly on the ex-situ substrate cleaning procedures and the quality of the material. Maintaining surface stoichiometry at growth temperatures requires the presence of group V overpressure to compensate for its preferential evaporation. For a surface arsenic coverage of greater than about 60%, the surface is referred to as As-stabilized [2.56]. The surface is reconstructed and usual MBE growth is carried out in the (2×4) As-stabilized surface conditions.

An aspect of significance to high quality MBE growth which has begun to be appreciated only recently [2.6, 7] is the significance of the *static* surface profile and stoichiometry even within the range of T_s and P_{As_4} in which an As-stabilized

(2 × 4) RHEED pattern is observed. In Figs. 2.4 and 2.5 we show the intensity of the RHEED specular beam (I_0) from such a GaAs surface, measured as a function of temperature at various fixed P_{As_4} (Fig. 2.4, panel a) and as a function of P_{As_4} at a fixed T_s (Fig. 2.5). The data were taken with the incident beam along the 2-fold direction and at an angle of incidence, $\theta = 0.7°$ which corresponds to the "out-of-phase" diffraction condition $qd_{As-As} = \pi$ where q is the electron momentum transfer normal to the surface and $d_{As-As} = a_0/2$, a_0 being the bulk GaAs lattice constant (5.86 Å). Note the significant variation in I_0, thus suggesting an optimum range of (T_s, P_{As_4}) for which the smoothest starting surface can be achieved if a higher intensity of the RHEED specular beam be thought of as being directly related to greater surface structural smoothness. Within a kinematical view of the electron diffraction process this would be definitely true, but the well known strong interaction of electrons with solids introduces multiple and dynamical scattering processes and beam penetration effects which can cause departures from such an expectation [2.5]. Usage of shallowest angle of incidence, as in Figs 2.4 and 2.5, tends to minimize such effects, although the dependence of I_0 on diffraction conditions is also a well known fact, as illustrated in Fig. 2.6. Thus, the measurement under the same (T_s, P_{As_4}) conditions can give widely varying intensities as a function of the angle of incidence with maxima and minima which do not necessarily coincide with the Bragg and out-of-phase diffraction conditions [2.8].

Of pragmatic significance, however, is the reproducibility of I_0 and P_{As_4} as determined by the usual temperature and pressure measuring instruments such as thermocouples, infrared pyrometers and ion gauges. Such instruments in

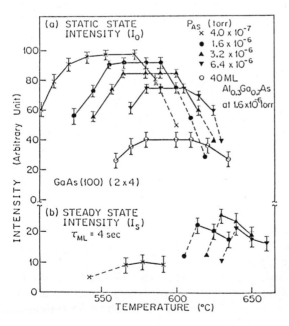

Fig. 2.4. Substrate temperature dependence of the measured static (panel a) and steady state (panel b) RHEED specular beam intensity for GaAs(100), As-stabilized (2 × 4) surfaces. Open circles in panel a are for a $Al_{0.3}Ga_{0.7}As(100)$ surface

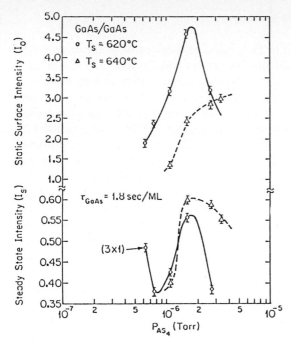

Fig. 2.5. Dependence of I_0 of GaAs(100) I_s of GaAs(100) and AlAs(100) on the As$_4$ pressure in the As-stabilized (2 × 4) regime. Note that maxima in the intensities occur at different As$_4$ pressures

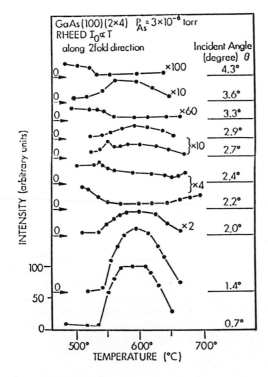

Fig. 2.6. Incident angle dependence of GaAs(100) I_0 as a function of T_s at a fixed As$_4$ pressure of 3×10^{-6} Torr

MBE machines are well known to the crystal growers to be notoriously fickle, even though these aspects of MBE growth are not widely publicized and users of grown materials and structures are either unaware or tend to ignore. Since I_0 is an intrinsic property of the surface, reproducing it prior to every growth is one step in the right direction of achieving the same growth conditions when comparison between different quantum well structures is demanded or used for examining the nature of some physical process. Hardly any attention, however, has been paid to so central an issue. Measuring I_0 alone, however, also does not relieve the burden of uncertainties in determination of T_s and P_{As_4}. Other intrinsic properties of the surface need to be exploited and we shall discuss them shortly. First, however, it is also to be noted that I_0 exhibits a certain irreversibility, as shown in Fig. 2.7, panel a. Note that while I_0 is reversible on the low T_s side of the cap-like behavior, on the high T_s side it is not. *Chen* et al. [2.6, 7], who first reported this behavior, have interpreted it in terms of the surface desorption and migration kinetics at the static surface.

It is now widely known that upon initiation of growth, the intensities of the RHEED pattern exhibit a damped oscillatory behavior [2.57–59]. Figure 2.8 shows illustrative examples of the specular beam dynamics during homoepitaxy of GaAs(100) on As-stabilized (2 × 4) surfaces measured by *Chen* et al. [2.60]. Shown is behavior as a function of both, change in growth condition and

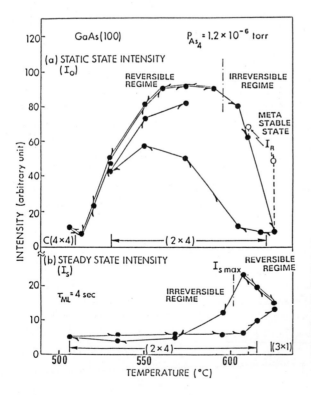

Fig. 2.7. Influence of substrate temperature cycling on I_0 and I_s of GaAs(100) in the As-stabilized (2 × 4) surface regime. Note the presence of reversible and irreversible regions. I_R denotes the recovered intensity after growth interruption and represents metastable surfaces

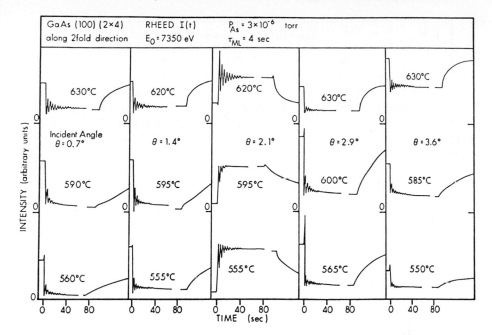

Fig. 2.8. Illustrative examples of the RHEED specular beam dynamics during homoepitaxy of GaAs(100) in the As-stabilized (2 × 4) surface regime. Each column corresponds to a fixed diffraction measurement condition but three different growth temperatures. The As_4 pressure and growth rate are kept constant

diffraction measurement condition. The pragmatic use of the oscillations lies in the fact that the period of oscillations corresponds to the incorporation of one monolayer's worth of material. Under the usual MBE growth conditions, the group III incorporation rate is generally unity so that the period also corresponds to delivery of a monolayer's worth of a growth rate controlling species – namely the group III [2.5]. This permits accurate real-time calibration of the group III flux and hence the growth rate and the thickness of the material grown, typically to better than 0.1 monolayer (ML). During the course of growth of an alloy such as $Al_xGa_{1-x}As$ [2.9, 11] or $In_xGa_{1-x}As$ [2.59], the change in the measured oscillation period from that of the binary component(s), as seen in Fig. 2.9, also permits a very accurate (typically to about 0.2%) real-time determination, and thus control, of the alloy composition – a matter of significance for the barrier height of the confining potential.

While much attention has focussed on the RHEED oscillation period due to its pragmatic value noted above, the behavior of the specular beam intensity when the oscillations have damped out (at least on the detection scale) also provides information of considerable pragmatic value as well as of significance to examining the nature of surface kinetic processes during growth. *Lee* et al. [2.12] and *Chen* et al. [2.6, 7] have examined the behavior of this steady state intensity

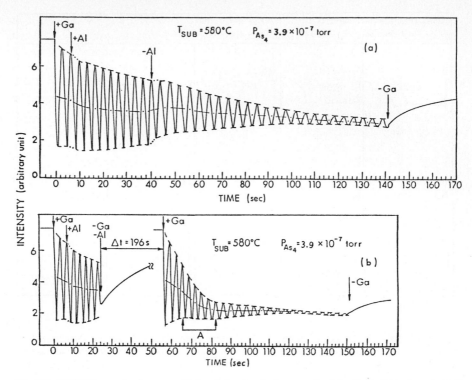

Fig. 2.9. RHEED specular beam oscillation behavior during growth of the GaAs/Al$_{0.3}$Ga$_{0.7}$As(100) system. The change in oscillation period permits an accurate, real-time, determination of the alloy composition

(I_s), examples of which are shown in panel b of Figs. 2.4 and 2.5. Note the presence of a maximum in I_s as a function of T_s for a given fixed choice of P_{As_4} and growth rate or as a function of P_{As_4} for a given T_s and growth rate. Thus a maximum of I_s^{max} exists for an optimum combination of (T_s, P_{As_4}) at a given growth rate. An irreversibility in I_s is also present as seen in panel b of Fig. 2.7. However, unlike I_0, the irreversible behavior of I_s is found at the low temperature side whereas at the high temperature side of the I_s^{max} it is reversible. The I_s behavior is another intrinsic feature of the dynamic growth front whose reproducibility, along with that of I_0, prior to every growth is yet another tool for achieving reproducible growth conditions. This is a practise routinely followed in the author's group and the quantum well structures to be discussed later in this chapter have all been grown under such RHEED determined identical growth conditions so as to allow a meaningful comparison between them. Indeed, the behavior of Al$_x$Ga$_{1-x}$As(100) alloys has been similarly investigated and employed in the growth of quantum well structures [2.7, 61]. An illustrative example of the I_0 behavior of Al$_{0.3}$Ga$_{0.7}$As(100) surface is shown in Fig. 2.4. *Cho* et al. [2.61] have carried out such systematic studies, comparing them with the behavior of

GaAs. A point to be noted is that a combination of (T_s, P_{As_4}) which may be optimum for a given growth rate of GaAs, is not necessarily optimum for growth of $Al_xGa_{1-x}As(100)$ [2.11, 12]. Thus, separate from the first important issue of reproducibility of growth conditions, RHEED intensity behavior can be, and has been [2.11, 12], employed also for determination of somewhat optimized growth conditions for individual layers and for combination of layers. Indeed, the quantum well structures discussed later in this chapter have been grown under such optimized conditions of growth kinetics which is in part a reason for their high quality. An example of a uniquely optimized condition for GaAs and AlAs, in spite of their vastly differing surface kinetics, was reported by *Yen* et al. [2.11] and is shown in Fig. 2.10. Note that the maxima of I_0 of GaAs and I_s of both GaAs and AlAs occur at the same P_{As_4} for the chosen T_s and growth rate.

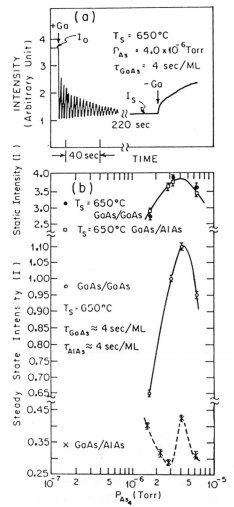

Fig. 2.10. Shows the behavior of I_0 of GaAs and AlAs as a function of P_{As_4}. Note that at the chosen T_s and growth rate, maximum in all three occurs at the same P_{As_4} in spite of the vastly different surface kinetics of GaAs and AlAs. This is not the case at other T_s or growth rate, thus identifying the given combination to be somewhat unique

One final point regarding reproducibility of growth conditions employing RHEED needs to be noted before we proceed with other matters. This has to do with a calibration of the group V pressure, independent of the ion gauge. It has been demonstrated that RHEED oscillations occur when a group III rich surface is exposed to the group V molecular beam. *Lewis* et al. [2.62] have thus shown that since under such conditions, though not employed in usual MBE growth, the growth rate is controlled by the incorporation rate of the group V molecules, the oscillation period can be used to calibrate the group V pressure. The JPL group of *Grunthaner* [2.62] and the author's group have thus exploited this feature for a reliable calibration of the As_4 pressure in the growth of $In_xGa_{1-x}As$ and $Al_xGa_{1-x}As$ quantum well and superlattice structures. In summary then, the combined measurement of I_0, I_s and As_4 controlled RHEED oscillations is a powerful and reliable pragmatic way of ensuring identical growth conditions from day to day and from one MBE machine to another. We now turn to the use of RHEED intensity behavior in examining the underlying surface kinetic processes controlling the nature of growth and the interfaces formed.

2.2.3 Formation of Interfaces and Growth Interruption

The customary practise in MBE growth of structures involving interfaces has been dynamic shuttering of the flux of the growth rate controlling group III species for achieving a change in the layer material. An example of this situation is seen in Fig. 2.9, panel a, for the growth of the GaAs/AlGaAs system achieved by opening and closing only the Al flux shutter while the Ga flux shutter is kept continuously open. The resulting consequence is that the interfaces formed are upon the instantaneous dynamic growth front profile of the preceding layer determined by its growth kinetics. Such a dynamic growth front profile is, under most growth conditions, structurally not as smooth as the corresponding static surface. In addition, the dynamic growth front morphology generally gets progressively worse as the growth continues until it reaches the steady state. Consequently, the nature of interfaces formed also depends upon the thickness of the preceding layer. These aspects are well illustrated by two examples – Fig. 2.9 and Fig. 2.11. In Fig. 2.9, one notes that the specular beam intensity of GaAs at the moment of opening of the Al flux is lower than the starting static surface intensity of GaAs. The interface thus formed upon deposition of $Al_xGa_{1-x}As$ on such a GaAs growth front (called the normal dynamic (ND) interface) is not as good as it can be if $Al_xGa_{1-x}As$ were deposited on the static GaAs surface. The same is true for deposition of GaAs on $Al_xGa_{1-x}As$ (the so-called inverted interface) and, in fact, the intrinsically slower surface migration kinetics of Al generally makes the $Al_xGa_{1-x}As$ growth front even worse than GaAs. The crucial significance of the difference in the surface kinetics of Ga and Al is even better recognized in the behavior seen in curves a and c of Fig. 2.11 representing growth of $(GaAs)_2/(AlAs)_2$ and $(GaAs)_6/(AlAs)_6$ superlattices under the uniquely optimized conditions shown in Fig. 2.10. In spite of such uniquely optimized growth conditions, a clear degradation of each subsequent interface is evident, the rate of degradation being more rapid for the larger thickness layers. This is

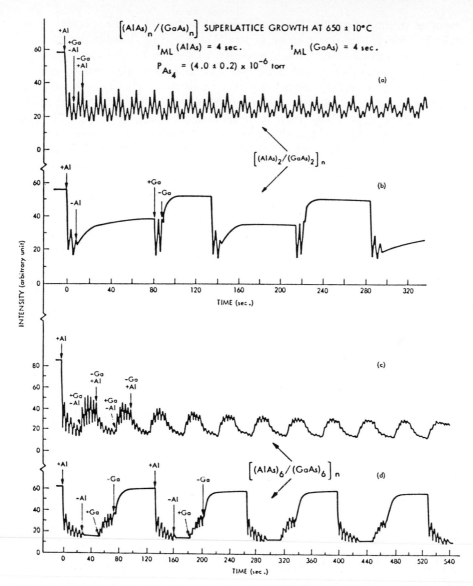

Fig. 2.11. RHEED specular beam intensity along the 2-fold direction of the As-stabilized (2×4) surface and at $0.7°$ angle of incidence for an 8 keV electron beam during growth of GaAs/AlAs superlattices under the uniquely optimized growth conditions indicated in Fig. 2.8. Curves a and c: conventional continuous growth; curves b and d: interrupted growth

primarily a consequence of the adverse effect of the very first inverted dynamic (ID) interface being perpetuated to each subsequent ND and ID interfaces within the customary practise of MBE growth.

A way out of such adverse effect of "freezing-in" dynamic growth fronts at interfaces is to merely *interrupt the growth* and allow the surface kinetic processes to somewhat "heal" the instantaneous growth front profile towards a generally smoother structural profile. This is manifested in the rise of the specular beam intensity upon growth interruption, generally recovering to a value very close to the original starting static surface intensity, as seen in Fig. 2.8, in panel b of Fig. 2.9, and in curves b and d of Fig. 2.11. Indeed, under certain growth conditions, the recovered intensity reaches a value even higher than the original starting static surface intensity, even though such a surface does not generally last in such a state longer than 5 to 15 minutes. *Chen* et al. [2.6, 7], who discovered this behavior, have thus called such surfaces metastable, and an example of this for GaAs is shown in Fig. 2.7, denoted by I_R. This phenomenon is reported by *Chen* et al. [2.6, 7] to occur at growth temperatures slightly higher than the congruent temperature of the bulk material and is dependent upon the growth rate and As_4 pressure. Two important aspects of *growth interruption* however are also to be noted, lest one might carry the impression that it is a panacea for all ills. The first of these is the fact that during interruption one makes the surface susceptible to incorporation of background impurities even in the UHV environment of MBE, particularly for surfaces involving highly reactive elements such as Al. Thus the time of growth interruption needs to be optimized against the rates of the surface kinetic process through appropriate choice of growth temperature and group V pressure, as well as the growth rate and the thickness to which the layer has been grown. The last aspect is of significance since the starting condition of the surface for its recovery under the rates operational at the chosen temperature and pressure is naturally going to determine the time taken for recovery and thus the degree of impurity incorporation. That impurities are incorporated is manifest in the oscillation damping behavior of GaAs grown on the interrupted AlGaAs surface seen in Fig. 2.9, panel b. This point is further discussed in [2.9]. The second point relates to the issue of thickness grown just touched upon, but needs to be separately stated and emphasized. Curves b and d of Fig. 2.11 rather dramatically demonstrate that even under uniquely optimized growth conditions, a difference in the morphology of a dynamic growth front at the end of different thicknesses (2 versus 6 monolayers in the present example) can be sufficiently critical for a material with slow surface migration and high reactivity characteristics, such as AlAs, to make the difference in recovery versus virtually no recovery on any reasonably acceptable time scale. Nevertheless, the fast migration and lower reaction kinetics of Ga in both cases is able to recover the surface and heal the adverse effect of AlAs even for the 6 ML superlattice. Thus, often growth interruption only at the end of growth of the layer with faster migration kinetics (generally correlated with lower congruent temperature) is required and needed to prevent degradation in the quality of each subsequent quantum well formed in a multiple quantum well or superlattice structure.

The notion of growth interruption was first employed [2.46] for the growth of the highly lattice mismatched GaAs/InAs MQW structures of relevance to optical communication technology in the 1.5 μm range. It led to the first successful growth of this system with low defect density [2.46]. Subsequently, the notion was applied to the growth of the GaAs/Al$_x$Ga$_{1-x}$As system [2.9, 63, 64].

Since 1985 it has become sufficiently popular and has been extensively studied for the GaAs/Al$_x$Ga$_{1-x}$As system by several groups [2.65–68]. We shall take up an examination of its consequences for the nature of the interfaces in Sect. 2.4. In the next section we take up some aspects of the kinetics of MBE growth and its consequences, with a particular view towards also examining the *premise of this section – namely a direct relationship between* RHEED *specular beam intensity and the degree of surface smoothness.*

2.3 The Surface Kinetic Processes and Computer Simulations of Growth

In this section we discuss some illustrative results of computer simulations of MBE growth based upon the conceptual picture discussed in Sect. 2.2.1. The results of such simulations have provided an understanding of the significance of growth kinetics in controlling the atomistic nature of the growth mechanism, but perhaps of greater concern in the present context, of the atomic nature of the resulting interfaces and the confining potential.

2.3.1 The CDRI Model

The first kinetic process to be examined is that of adsorption of the atomic group III and molecular group V species upon impingement and the associated notion of sticking coefficient [2.53]. Henceforth we shall advance the discussion in terms of the homoepitaxy of GaAs(100) under As-stabilized surface conditions. It has been shown [2.69–71] that the adsorption of the impinging atomic Ga is directly into a chemisorbed state, binding either with the As or Ga atoms on the surface. By contrast, the impinging As$_2$ or As$_4$ molecules are believed to first adsorb into a weakly bonded state and retain their molecular nature [2.69–71]. Such a state has been referred to as a physisorbed state and the species denoted by As$_2^*$ (or As$_4^*$). The sticking coefficient of the Ga atoms is found to be essentially unity upto about 600°C in the presence of reasonable As$_2$ or As$_4$ flux. By contrast, at substrate temperatures > 200°C, and for As$_2$ or As$_4$ flux of practical interest, the sticking coefficients of As$_2$ or As$_4$ (for binding in the molecular physisorbed state) are essentially zero in the absence of available Ga at the surface. In the presence of available Ga atoms, the sticking coefficient of both As$_2$ and As$_4$ (to go into the As$_2^*$ or As$_4^*$ states) is Ga flux dependent and, according to [2.70, 71], can reach a maximum value of near unity for the former, but does not exceed 0.5 for the latter.

The conversion of As$_2^*$ (or As$_4^*$) into chemisorbed As via surface reactions is indicated by kinetic studies to require two adjacent vacant As sites [2.69–71]. There are, however, many types of Ga atom configurations which would be consistent with such a finding and each such configuration presents a particular reaction path with its own reaction rate constant. *Thomsen* et al. [2.14] have incorporated a variety of Ga configuration in their computer simulations. Some of the configurations involving the smallest number of intraplanar, surface nearest neighbor Ga atoms are shown in Fig. 2.12 (upper two panels). In addition, configurations involving Ga atoms in two different (100) planes, such as would occur at steps, can also provide sites for As_2^* dissociative reaction. A few such configuration are shown in the bottom panel of Fig. 2.12.

To appreciate the relevance of the intra and inter planar Ga configurations and their associated rate constants, $K_i(T)$, for the dissociative chemisorption reaction of As_2^*, two equally important kinetic aspects of growth must be clearly recognized. The first is the steady state population of As_2^* at the surface which depends upon the chosen As_2 (or As_4) vapour flux, the Ga vapour flux and the substrate temperature through the As_2 (or As_4) adsorption and As_2^* desorption kinetics. Let us denote such a steady state population by $N_{As_2}^*(T_s, P_{As_4}, F_{Ga})$. The second is the time dependent probability, $P_i(t)$, of occurrence of the ith Ga atom intra or interplanar configuration. Under the usual GaAs growth conditions the sticking coefficient of Ga is unity. The probabilities P_i are thus a function of time through both, the arrival rate of Ga (the Ga flux, F_{Ga}) and the surface migration rates, $h_\alpha(T)$, for the Ga atoms in the αth chemical bonding state. The hopping

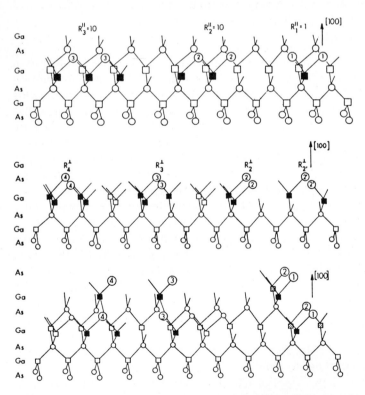

Fig. 2.12. Shows some illustrative examples of intraplanar (*upper two panels*) and inter-planar (*bottom panel*) Ga configurations at which dissociative reaction of molecularly adsorbed As_2^* species can occur at different rates

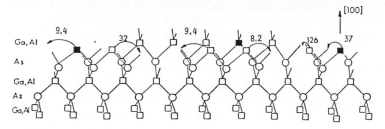

Fig. 2.13. Shows illustrative examples of a few intra-planar hopping configurations. Open and solid squares denote Ga and Al atoms, respectively

rates are taken to be of the Arrhenius form and the activation energy made dependent upon the bonding configuration, α, from which the jump is made. A few illustrative examples are shown in Fig. 2.13. Let us denote the probabilities by $P_i(t, \{h_\alpha(T)\}, F_{Ga})$. Then, the quantity of interest to the growth of the GaAs solid phase being the *incorporation rate* of Ga and As from the vapour, it is readily realized that for the latter it is achieved through the collective role of each of the different Ga configurations at rates given by the product

$$N^*_{As_2}(T, P_{As_4}, F_{Ga}) K_i(T) P_i(t, \{h_\alpha(T)\}, F_{Ga}). \tag{2.1}$$

Several important features of the growth process are revealed by expression (2.1). First, it is seen that the relative significance of the various Ga atom configurations changes with time during the growth of a given layer due to the time dependent change in the P_i's. Second, an explicit As_2 or As_4 vapour pressure dependence is seen to enter [2.13] through $N^*_{As_2}$. Third, an implicit dependence on the local environment dependent Ga hopping rates (both intra and interlayer), $\{h_\alpha(T)\}$, is seen to be present. Equally important, to the extent that the time evolution of P_i depends, at least in the initial states of growth of a given Ga layer, on the hopping rates $h_\alpha(t)$ where α represents the chemical bonding states for the Ga atoms, and to the extent that a change in the bonding state of a given Ga is affected by expression (2.1) defining the incorporation of the As atoms, the life time of the Ga atoms in the ith configuration is itself influenced by $K_i(T)$ and $N^*_{As_2}$. Since it is always the product of a kinetic rate and the time that it is operative that is of physical significance, it is also recognized that the "effective" migration ability [2.14, 15] of the Ga atoms is itself dependent upon the reaction rate constants $K_i(T)$ as well as the As_2(or As_4) vapour pressure through the steady state population, $N^*_{As_2}$. Thus a significant arsenic pressure dependence [2.13–15] of the growth process and surface morphology can be expected under many growth conditions (i.e. choice of T_s and F_{Ga}).

The relevant time scale for the operation of a given kinetic process, such as the surface migration rates $h_\alpha(T)$, is seen to be the lifetime τ_α which is dependent upon the Ga flux, the reaction rate constant $K_\alpha(T)$ and, of course, $N^*_{As_2}$. Thus we may recognize τ_α to be a function of these three quantities by writing it as τ_α

$(P_{As_4}, K_\alpha(T), F_{Ga})$. Assuming the average surface residence time of the Ga atoms to be longer than τ_α (for otherwise growth of the solid would be most unlikely), the effective distance, l_α, moved by the Ga atom in state α is of order $(h_\alpha(T)\,\tau_\alpha)^{1/2}$, in units of the nearest surface neighbor distance [2.5]. The overall range sampled by the atom prior to its incorporation is then some appropriate average of l_α over all α. Let us denote it by $l_{eff} \sim \langle \Sigma_\alpha (h_\alpha(T)\tau_\alpha(P_{As_4}, K_\alpha(T), F_{Ga}))^{1/2} \rangle$. One sees that the effective migration length is a function of the three user controlled growth parameters – T_s, P_{As_4} and F_{Ga}. Thus, for a given choice of these parameters, l_{eff} may or may not be greater than W_0, the average terrace width of the starting substrate. For growth conditions such that $l_{eff} < W_0$, the growth initiation process would involve predominantly addition of material on the terraces. The atomistic mechanism of growth initiation, however, need not be the conventional nucleation and growth mechanism, as shown by *Ghaisas* and *Madhukar* [2.72–74]. Note that within the simulation model, choice of an $(N \times N)$ substrate with no steps in it is equivalent to restricting the simulations to growth on the terraces of a real substrate, i.e. $l_{eff} < W_0$. Periodic boundary conditions on the $(N \times N)$ substrate are employed to avoid edge effects and the convergence of the results tested against the size N.

The expression (2.1) representing the incorporation rate of arsenic also reveals the significant role that the As_2^* reaction rate constants $K_i(T)$ can play in governing the atomistic nature of the MBE *growth mechanisms*. The possibility that the reaction rate constants $K_i(T)$ may become the rate limiting step for arsenic incorporation under certain growth conditions is self evident. There is no analogue of this behavior in the historical atomistic models and computer simulations [2.5]. Thus even though the *time averaged* growth rate of GaAs may be controlled by the arrival rate of the Ga under a sufficient population of As_2^*, the *time dependent* growth rate can be controlled by the reactive incorporation kinetics of the As_2 molecules. *Ghaisas* and *Madhukar* [2.72, 73] have thus termed such a generic growth process a *configuration dependent reactive incorporation* (CDRI) process. At one extreme of the CDRI process is the time dependent growth rate behavior controlled by the As_2^* dissociative incorporation rates. *Ghaisas* and *Madhukar* [2.72, 73] have shown this to be a possibility and called such growth mechanism the reaction limited incorporation (RLI) growth mechanism. On the opposite extreme is also the possibility that the incorporation kinetics of the arsenic is limited by the Ga configuration probabilities, P_i, and not either by $N_{As_2}^*$ or the reaction rate constants, $K_i(T)$. Growth conditions giving rise to such a situation have also been examined by *Ghaisas* and *Madhukar* [2.72, 73] and it has been referred to as the Configuration Limited Reactive Incorporation (CLRI) growth mechanism.

2.3.2 Growth Front Morphology

The structural behavior of the dynamic growth front can be investigated via an examination of two basic properties – the terrace width distribution and the step height distribution – as a function of time. The average terrace width at the growth front is of particular significance in relation to the effective migration length (l_{eff}) of the group III atoms since it is l_{eff} in relation to the average terrace width of the starting surface, $\langle W_0 \rangle$, for real surfaces which defines the operational notion of growth on a "perfect surface" as one for which $l_{eff} \ll \langle W_0 \rangle$. As noted above, this is the case in computer simulations. Consequently, growth initiation on terraces is being addressed, rather than growth initiation via propagation of existing steps on the starting substrate – a process operational if $l_{eff} > \langle W_0 \rangle$. However, once growth is initiated via any of the mechanisms embodied by the CDRI model, the average terrace width will become a time dependent quantity as islands (2D or 3D) begin to form on the terraces. In particular, $\langle W(t) \rangle$ may, depending upon the growth condition controlled surface kinetics and thickness grown, become comparable to or less than l_{eff}, from whence the surface profile would exhibit a steady state behavior. It is thus also of interest to calculate an l_{eff} during growth. We now present some illustrative results for $\langle W(t) \rangle$, l_{eff}, and surface roughness.

In Fig. 2.14 are presented results obtained by *Ghaisas* and *Madhukar* [2.74] on a (50 × 50) substrate at a growth temperature of 575°C, growth rate of 1.1 ML/sec. and in the RLI growth mechanism regime operational at the lower As_4 pressure regime nowadays employed. Curve a shows the behavior of l_{eff} for each Ga layer during its formation. The point to appreciate is that neither is there a single "surface diffusion length" nor is it a time independent value, as has become so customary to implicitly, if not explicitly, assume in thinking about issues relating to crystal growth. Rather, the effective migration length itself shows a periodic variation during the growth of a given atomic layer and is a consequence of the fact that atoms arriving at the earlier stages of growth of the layer can execute larger number of jumps since the probability of forming clusters is lower compared to the effect of increasing coverage felt by the atoms arriving at a later stage. This is so even though the intrinsic jump rates may remain the same throughout the growth of the layer. The damping in the maxima of the l_{eff} with continued addition of the layers is a consequence of the decreasing nature of the maximum average terrace width which defines the average area upon which intralayer migration of the Ga atoms in the next layer can occur. The time dependence of the average terrace width (i.e. averaged over all exposed layers constituting the growth front profile) along one of the principal directions of the surface unit cell is shown in curve b. Note the initial rapid drop caused by incorporation of Ga upon commencement of growth, followed by a damped oscillatory behavior. The maxima and minima are nearly coincident with the time of integral and half-integral Ga monolayer delivery (τ_{MLD}), respectively. Given that for the growth conditions chosen the Ga sticking coefficient is unity, τ_{MLD} is equivalent to the time of growth of a monolayer as well. The damping of the maxima in the average terrace width (measured in units of the surface nearest neighbor distance) is an indication of the kinetic roughening of the growth front profile with continued growth. This kinetically controlled roughening is a consequence of the starting condition that $l_{eff} \ll \langle W_0 \rangle$ and the relationship between the time dependent nature of l_{eff} and $\langle W(t) \rangle$ during growth. As seen in

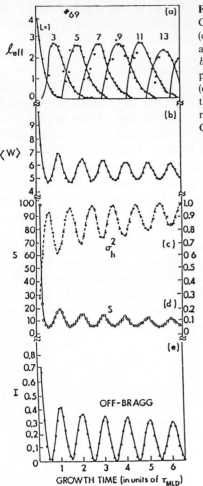

Fig. 2.14. Illustrative example of the dynamics of the Ga effective migration length in each atomic plane (curve *a*), the average terrace width at the growth front along a principal direction of the surface unit cell (curve *b*), the mean square fluctuation in the surface step profile (curve *c*), the surface smoothness parameter (curve *d*), and the RHEED specular beam intensity at the first out-of-phase diffraction condition (curve *e*), revealed by Monte Carlo computer simulations of GaAs(100) homoepitaxy

curves a and b, the value of $l_{\rm eff}$ remains less than $\langle W \rangle$ over the layer thickness simulated, the oscillatory nature of both thus being consistent with each other and with the growth process. Although CPU time considerations have not permitted simulation of larger thicknesses, it is clear that with continued growth a situation is reached where the damped $\langle W \rangle$ will become less than $l_{\rm eff}$ and the oscillatory nature of both $\langle W \rangle$ and $l_{\rm eff}$ will essentially vanish at that point.

The roughening of the growth front suggested by the behavior of $\langle W \rangle$ can, of course, be directly confirmed by examining the step density distribution as a function of time. A measure of the degree of surface roughness is the mean square fluctuation in the height to which the solid has grown in a given local region of the substrate, as opposed to the height it would have if the growth were indeed by absolutely ideal layer-by-layer addition of material. Thus, one may define the quantity,

$$\sigma_h^2(t) = \frac{1}{M} \sum_{i,j} (h_{ij}(t) - \langle h(t) \rangle)^2 \tag{2.2}$$

in which $h_{ij}(t)$ is the height to which the solid has grown at site (i, j), $\langle h(t) \rangle$ is the average thickness over the substrate and M is the total number of sites. Since $h_{ij}(t)$ are a direct output of the computer simulations, $\sigma_h^2(t)$ can be readily calculated. Figure 2.14, curve c, shows the behavior of $\sigma_h^2(t)$ corresponding to the behavior of $\langle W \rangle$ and l_{eff} shown in curves a and b. Once again, a time dependent oscillatory behavior is seen with a steady and gradual rise in the average value of $\sigma_h^2(t)$ which will saturate under steady state conditions reached when $\langle W(t) \rangle$ becomes less than l_{eff}. Note that the maxima in $\sigma_h^2(t)$ occur near half integral monolayer depositions while the minima coincide fairly well with integral monolayer depositions. This is a consequence of the higher degree of steps present at half integral depositions compared to near the completion of a given monolayer.

An overall measure of the degree of smoothness of the surface which combines information in the lateral and vertical directions can be defined in terms of the average terrace widths, $\langle W_i(t) \rangle$ and $\langle W_j(t) \rangle$, in the two principal directions of the surface unit cell and $\sigma_h^2(t)$ as follows:

$$S(t) = \frac{\langle W_i(t) \rangle \langle W_j(t) \rangle}{\sigma_h^2(t)}. \tag{2.3}$$

Thus for an ideal atomically flat surface, $\langle W_{i,j}(t) \rangle = \infty$ and $\sigma_h^2(t) = 0$ so that $S = \infty$ whereas for a truly rough and degraded surface $S \to 0$. The behavior of this smoothness parameter is shown as curve d in Fig. 2.14. One can clearly observe a damped oscillatory behavior of the surface smoothness during growth, with the maxima and minima coinciding with the growth of integral and half-integral monolayers.

The dynamics of the RHEED intensity corresponding to the simulated growth front profile can be obtained provided a reliable theory of electron diffraction were available. Unfortunately, such a theory is not available at the present time. *Ghaisas* and *Madhukar* [2.72, 73] have therefore employed the kinematical theory in the meantime to obtain a first glimpse of the qualitative behavior as a function of growth parameters. Within the kinematical theory and assuming diffraction only from the exposed surface layers, the behavior of the RHEED specular beam intensity dynamics at the first out-of-phase ($qd_{As-As} = \pi$) diffraction conditions for the surface morphology depicted in Fig. 2.14 is shown in curve e of Fig. 2.14. The behavior of the out-of-phase (for short referred to as off-Bragg) RHEED intensity in Fig. 2.14 is seen to conform to the expectation based upon the time dependent nature of the growth front morphology predicted by the computer simulations. One notes that the period of oscillation coincides exactly with the monolayer growth time, the same as the behavior of the average terrace width, the mean square fluctuations in the growth front height and the surface smoothness parameter. One also notes that the maxima and minima coincide with those of the smoothness parameter, thus establishing an important notion of considerable pragmatic value – that the intensity of the specular beam at a given diffraction condition is related to the degree of smoothness of the surface. Finally, the RHEED intensity also shows damping which is a direct manifestation of the increasing roughness of the growth front seen already in the behavior of $\langle W(t)\rangle$, $\sigma_h^2(t)$ and $S(t)$ in Fig. 2.14.

2.3.3 The CDRI Model and the Nature of GaAs/Al$_x$Ga$_{1-x}$As (100) Interfaces

In the preceding subsection we emphasized the consequences of the surface kinetic processes for the dynamics of the morphology of the growth front. It should be clear from this and the behavior of the RHEED intensity dynamics that upon formation of an interface, whether on dynamic or static surfaces, a certain degree of mixing of the two materials is inevitable. A feature of particular significance to the notion of an interface is thus the degree of vertical *and lateral* intermixing near the interfacial planes. For interfaces between two binary materials, such as GaAs/AlAs, if the average terrace widths of the essentially Ga and Al like regions at the intended interface are larger than a length scale on which the notion of bands is meaningful (generally believed to be of order 50 A), then a well defined value of the band edge discontinuity at a well defined spatial area exists. Consequently, a well defined interface can be said to exist in the system, even though its spatial position may fluctuate due to the presence of steps frozen in at the interfaces. Figure 2.15a shows this schematically, although

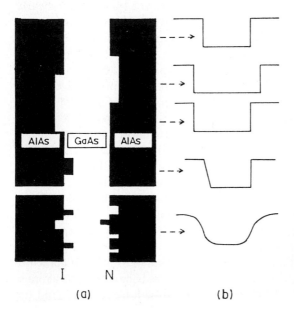

I   N

(a)   (b)

Fig. 2.15. Shows a schematic representation of the nature of GaAs/AlAs interfaces (panel *a*) and the nature of confining potential (panel *b*) experienced by a particle of size less than the average terrace width (upper three illustrations) and larger than the average terrace width (lower two illustrations)

Thomsen et al. [2.14] have found such behavior in Monte Carlo computer simulations. In a particular experiment, the size of the probe particle in relation to the average terrace width will then decide the nature of the interface perceived in that particular experiment. For instance, in the commonly employed photo-luminescence experiments on quantum wells, it is the size of the free exciton (R_{exc}) which sets this length scale [2.17–19, 24, 25]. If $R_{exc} \gg \langle W \rangle$, then the particle experiences an interface which appears compositionally averaged in the lateral and growth directions and consequently the nature of the quantum wells appears graded over a monolayer or two, as schematically indicated in the lower two illustrations of Fig. 2.15b. If on the other hand, $R_{exc} \ll \langle W \rangle$, then the particle locally experiences a well of well defined width and depth but the width fluctuates from one region of the sample to another in discrete units of ± 1, ± 2, etc. monolayers. This is schematically shown in the upper three illustrations of Fig. 2.15b. The main inference then is that the notion of a well defined interface, and consequently of fluctuations in the width of the well in *binary/binary* single or multiple quantum well structures between well lattice matched systems, has a good chance of being meaningful in high quality structures.

By contrast, in compositionally modulated structures involving a ternary alloy as a component, such as the most commonly studied lattice matched $GaAs/Al_xGa_{1-x}As(100)$, $x \neq 0$ and $In_{0.52}Ga_{0.48}As/InP$ systems, the very notion of a structurally and chemically well defined interface on length scales of interest is called into question. This aspect, not particularly well appreciated, has been revealed in the CDRI model based computer simulations of the $GaAs/Al_xGa_{1-x}As(100)$ system carried out by *Thomsen* et al. [2.15]. This is the last topic we cover before closing our discussion of the nature of interfaces and their dependence on the growth kinetics.

In Fig. 2.16 is shown the behavior of the Al composition in each of the atomic planes of a $Al_{0.33}Ga_{0.67}As/GaAs/Al_{0.33}Ga_{0.67}As(100)$ single quantum well with each material layer 4 ML thick [2.32]. The simulation growth conditions are such that growth is in the RLI growth mechanism regime (i.e. low arsenic pressure regime of the As-stabilized surface). Note the presence of 3 to 5% Al in the interfacial atomic planes 9 and 15 which ideally should have no Al in it. In addition, note the variation in the overall Al composition from the intended $x = 0.33$ in the other atomic planes as well. These are consequences of the difference in Ga and Al effective intra- and inter-planar migration kinetics and the resulting structural and chemical nature of the $Al_{0.33}Ga_{0.67}As$ and GaAs growth fronts at the time of formation of the inverted dynamic (ID) and normal dynamic (ND) interfaces defining the quantum well. In Fig. 2.17 is shown the dynamics of the structural smoothness parameter (panel a) and the corresponding RHEED specular beam behavior at the first off-Bragg condition. Once again, the role of the relative effective migration lengths of Ga and Al is clearly seen in the structural characteristics. What is not revealed in these results is the nature of the Al lateral distribution, a feature of utmost significance to the nature of the confining potential well (i.e. interfaces) perceived by charge (electrons and holes) and energy (excitons) carriers. We discuss this aspect next.

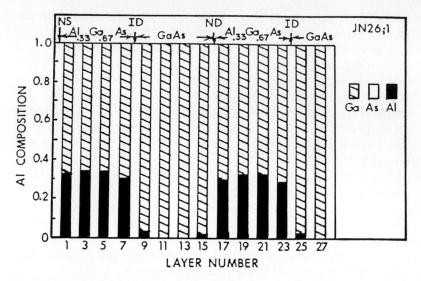

Fig. 2.16. Computer simulation results for the Al concentration in each cation plane of a GaAs/Al$_{0.33}$Ga$_{0.67}$As(100) quantum well structure with each material layer 4 ML thick

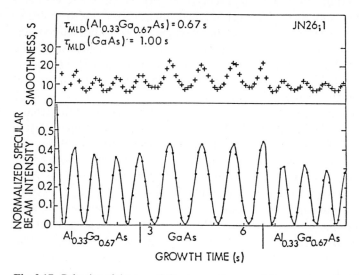

Fig. 2.17. Behavior of the growth front smoothness and the corresponding RHEED specular beam intensity at the first out-of-phase condition obtained from computer simulations of the GaAs/Al$_{0.33}$Ga$_{0.67}$As quantum well of Fig. 2.16

In Fig. 2.18 we show a plot of the *local* Al concentration on layer 7 defining the first ID interface, calculated on various length scales indicated as $(m \times m)$ at points along a given direction within the atomic plane. The area $(m \times m)$ is measured in units of the (100) plane nearest neighbor distance. One observes sizeable fluctuations away from the global average composition of 27% seen in

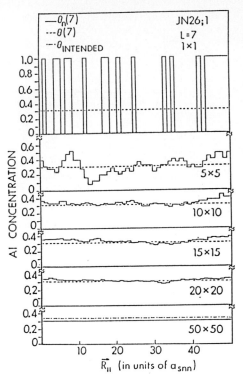

Fig. 2.18. Shows the local Al concentration along a given direction in layer 7 of the GaAs/Al$_{0.33}$Ga$_{0.67}$As quantum well of Fig. 2.16, calculated on various lateral length scales denoted by $(m \times m)$ and measured in unit of the surface nearest neighbor distance, a_{snn}

the bottom most panel corresponding to the (50 × 50) substrate size itself. The dash-dot line in this panel indicates the overall intended average composition of 33% which could not be realized due to mixing of the Al atoms with layer 9. Naturally, the fluctuations in the local average Al composition in the lateral directions decrease with increasing size of the area over which it is averaged. In Fig. 2.19 is shown the behavior of the Al concentration in a (10 × 10) area for each of the cation atomic planes as a function of lateral position. Recall that layers 9 and 15 would ideally contain no Al atoms. A vertical cut of Fig. 2.19 would indicate the nature of the quantum well along the growth direction at that spatial point (within a 10 × 10 area). This is shown for four different spatial regions in the four panels of Fig. 2.20. The solid lines represent the actual Al concentration and consequently the true nature of the quantum well on the chosen length scale. The broken lines are merely to indicate the hoped for ideal quantum well. One recognizes that significant fluctuations in the local Al composition can, and do, occur, thus creating a spatially fluctuating nature of the quantum well. The degree of fluctutions percieved is tied to both, the underlying growth kinetics and the length scale on which the proble particle employed probes the nature of the interface.

An immediate consequence of the behavior seen in Fig. 2.20 is the recognition that the fluctuations in Al concentration on the scale of the probe particle size

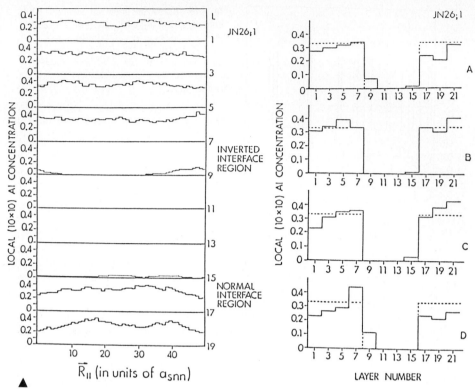

Fig. 2.19. Shows the local Al concentration along a given direction on a fixed lateral length scale of (10×10) for each of the cation planes of the $GaAs/Al_{0.33}Ga_{0.67}As$ quantum well of Fig. 2.16

Fig. 2.20. Shows the behavior of the local Al concentration on (10×10) lateral length scale for a cut across the $GaAs/Al_{0.33}Ga_{0.67}As$ quantum well of Fig. 2.16 at four different spatial locations. The dashed line is hoped for ideal local Al concentration distribution which would lead to an ideal square well potential

imply that, in experiments such as the photoluminescence studies, the exciton always experiences fluctuations in the band edge discontinuity (i.e. the potential depth). The notion of fluctuations in the well width so commonly employed in interpretation of a wide range of properties, including photoluminescence, is in fact a questionable one since no notion of a precise spatial location of band edge discontinuity can be unambiguously defined. If $R_{exc} > \langle W \rangle$, where $\langle W \rangle$ represents a terrace of AlGaAs then the exciton averages both laterally and vertically the Al concentration fluctuations and thus sees graded interfaces. If, on the other hand, $R_{exc} < \langle W \rangle$, then the exciton sees a well defined local width but nevertheless a fluctuating depth of the potential along the terrace. The luminescence line width should thus be dominated by band edge discontinuity fluctuations and the shorter ranged alloy disorder type of scattering. The photoluminescence (PL) and PL excitation spectra studies carried out by *Voillot* et al. on $GaAs/Al_xGa_{1-x}As$ single quantum wells grown under identical growth conditions but with varying intended well thickness (d_W) provide evidence for the essential correctness of this view [2.17–19]. We discuss these in the next section.

A final point worth commenting upon is the behavior of "clustering" in the AlGaAs alloy layers arising from the difference in the Ga and Al kinetics. Note that we are now examining the nature of Al and Ga spatial distribution in the alloy atomic planes and not the behavior at the interfacial planes for which even in the case of the binary-binary combination, GaAs/AlAs, the intermixing of Ga and Al can lead to an alloying effect at the interfacial planes. In Fig. 2.21 is shown a plot of an intraplanar cluster parameter ($C_1^{\parallel}$) calculated for GaAs/Al$_{0.33}$Ga$_{0.67}$As growth. Shown also is the behavior of the parameter, $C_{Ran}^{\parallel}$, for a totally random alloy. The values of $C_1^{\parallel}$ in the alloy layers are noticeably less than $C_{Ran}^{\parallel}$, indicating a tendency for Al atoms to be preferentially located near Ga atoms and vice versa. This tends to suggest a tendency towards "ordering". The underlying reason for this tendency is rooted in the nature of As$_2^{*}$ reaction kinetics at the mixed Ga and Al configurations, as well as the dependence of the Ga hopping rates on the local bonding configuration – a feature which is clearly revealed by the plot of the quantity C_1^{J} in Fig. 2.21. This quantity represents $C_1^{\parallel}$ calculated only along the direction of the cation dangling orbitals, called J here. Since, as discussed in Sect. 2.3.1 the As$_2^{*}$ reaction rates are scaled according to the number of Ga–As and Al–As bonds formed upon As$_2^{*}$ reaction, incorporation of arsenic along linear Ga–Al configurations (i.e. along J direction) occurs at a preferred rate than for configurations in which the Ga and Al are in parallel rows. This asymmetry in the effective kinetics induced by the inherent asymetry in surface bond structure is thus responsible for a tendency towards "ordering" of Ga and Al in the bulk of the alloy. This can lead to even long range ordering under appropriate kinetic conditions and is a testimony to the potential significance of surface bonding and structure induced kinetics of growth.

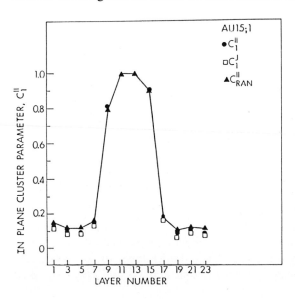

Fig. 2.21. In plane cluster para-meter calculated within the nearest neighbor approximation along the mutually perpendicular I and J (i.e. the direction of cation orbitals) directions for each layer of the GaAs/Al$_{0.33}$Ga$_{0.67}$As quantum well of Fig. 2.16

2.4 Quantum Wells: Growth and Photoluminescence

In the preceding sections we have provided evidence for reasonably expecting a positive correlation between the degree of surface smoothness and the magnitude of the RHEED specular beam intensity. This is so for both static surfaces and dynamic growth fronts, although in either case the chosen diffraction condition dependent dynamical scattering effects must be guarded against. Use of the shallowest angle of incidence is one aspect which is helpful in this regard. The computer simulations provide the connection between the chosen growth condition dependent growth kinetics and the resulting morphology of the static and dynamic surfaces. As such, they also establish connection between, and provide useful insight into, the growth condition dependent growth kinetics and the RHEED specular beam behavior of static and dynamic surfaces. In this section we thus employ such measured behavior of I_0 and I_s as a guideline to the choice of growth conditions for growth of $GaAs/Al_xGa_{1-x}As(100)$ single quantum wells with the intent of post-growth examination of the nature of the interfaces formed and their possible correlation with the RHEED intensity behavior. The experimental technique employed will be primarily photo-luminescence (PL) and PL excitation (PLE) spectroscopy. To the extent that PL and PLE are the most commonly applied techniques for evaluating the quality of quantum well structures through the measured line widths of free-exciton recombination luminescence, our focus here on the possible correlation between the RHEED intensity and PL behavior has the potential of making RHEED into a pragmatic tool for ascertaining optimized growth conditions for realization of high quality structures. As will be seen in the following, an unquestioned belief, either in favor or against such a positive correlation, based upon limited data and superficial examination can, and does, miss the essential nature, and indeed simplicity, of the phenomena involved.

We begin by exploiting the measured behavior of the static and steady state specular beam intensity of GaAs(100), As-stabilized (2×4) surface, shown in Fig. 2.22. We choose as illustrative examples, four SQW samples grown at the four points marked A, B, C and D in Fig. 2.22 and identified by the sample number. Points A and C represent the state of the growing GaAs surface in steady state and are relevant to the formation of the so-called normal interfaces (i.e. deposition of $Al_xGa_{1-x}As$ on GaAs) under the customary practise of growth without interruption. By contrast, points B and D represent the static GaAs surface and are relevant to the formation of normal interfaces under the more recently introduced notion of growth interruption.

All samples were grown on Cr-doped semi-insulating GaAs(100) substrates chemically cleaned via standard procedures and the resulting native oxide removed in the growth chamber under a suitable As_4 pressure at a temperature of $\sim 590°C$ as measured by a substrate thermocouple as well as an independently calibrated infra-red pyrometer. A GaAs buffer layer of $\sim 1000 Å$ was grown in each case and annealed to obtain well defined and clean streaked

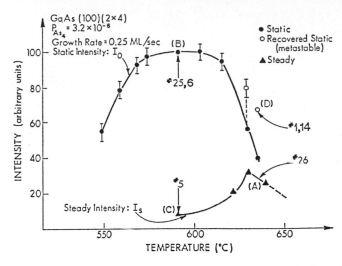

Fig. 2.22. The static (I_0) and steady state (I_s) RHEED specular beam intensity measured for As-stabilized (2×4) surface of GaAs(100) as a function of temperature. Points (A) through (D) correspond to growth conditions employed for growth of single quantum wells. Note that point (D) represents the smoother, though metastable, GaAs surface (see also Fig. 2.9)

RHEED patterns prior to growth of the single quantum well structure. Most importantly, a unique feature followed prior to growth of the SQW for each of these samples is the determination of the I_0 and I_s behavior of the GaAs buffer layer surface in each case to ensure that the RHEED behavior, and thus the growth conditions, are indeed what they were intended to be. Indeed, this has been a distinguishing feature of *all* quantum well structures grown by the USC group over past two years which enables a meaningful comparison of one sample to another without the usual, though unstated, uncertainties resulting from the unreliable nature of temperature and pressure measurement instruments common in commercial MBE systems.

In Figs. 2.23 and 2.24 is shown the specular beam dynamics during the growth of samples 14 and 6, and samples 26 and 5, respectively. The former pair consists of 21 monolayer (ML) thick GaAs well whereas the latter pair consists of 20 ML thick GaAs well sandwiched, in both cases, between 40 ML of $Al_{0.3}Ga_{0.7}As$ barrier layers. The growth rate is 0.25 ML/s for GaAs and 0.375 ML/s for $Al_{0.3}Ga_{0.7}As$. The beam equivalent pressure of As_4 as measured by an ion gauge near the substrate position is $2.5 \pm 0.5 \times 10^{-6}$ Torr.

The low temperature photoluminescence spectra of interrupted growth samples (#14 and #6) is shown in Fig. 2.25 and that for the conventional continuous growth samples (#26 and #5) is shown in Fig. 2.26. Several points relating to the nature of the interfaces and the types of correlations between the observed RHEED intensity and PL behavior emerge from a comparison of these four samples. For brevity we note these pointwise;

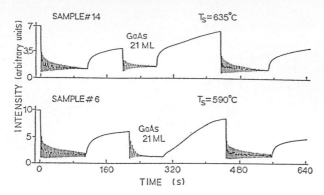

Fig. 2.23. Measured RHEED specular beam dynamics during growth of GaAs/Al$_{0.33}$Ga$_{0.67}$As(100) single quantum wells at points (*B*) and (*D*) of Fig. 2.22. Note the lower starting intensity for the higher temperature growth

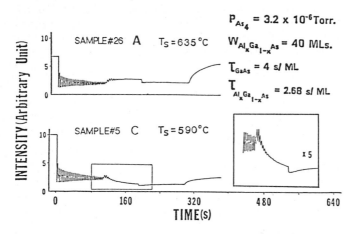

Fig. 2.24. Measured RHEED specular beam dynamics during growth GaAs/Al$_{0.33}$Ga$_{0.67}$ As single quantum wells at points (*A*) and (*C*) of Fig. 2.22. Note that the starting GaAs surface intensity, I_0, is the same as the corresponding cases in Fig. 2.23

1) The appearance of more than one emission line in the interrupted growth samples (Fig. 2.25) in contrast to the single line emission behavior of continuous growth samples (Fig. 2.26) is a consequence of the average terrace width, $\langle W \rangle$ at the interfaces being larger than and less than the exciton radius, R_{exc}, in the two cases respectively. For $R_{exc} < \langle W \rangle$, the exciton experiences locally well defined well widths although the well width fluctuates from one region to another in the sample. The energy positions of the fine structure emission lines correspond well to that calculated for a ± 1 ML change in well width for wells of width 20 ML. The identification of the peaks in Fig. 2.26 is as follows; 1.597 eV $-$ 21 ML, 1.601 eV $-$ 20 ML, 1.606 eV $-$ 19 ML. For $R_{exc} > \langle W \rangle$, the exciton sees an

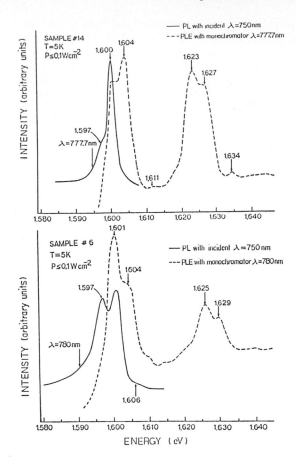

Fig. 2.25. Shows the 5 K photoluminescence (PL) spectra (*solid curves*) taken with excitation wavelength 750 nm and PL excitation spectra (*broken curves*) for samples 14 and 6 grown with growth interruption (see Fig. 2.23) at growth conditions identified by points (*D*) and (*B*) of Fig. 2.22, respectively. The delivered thickness of GaAs is 21 ML and of the $Al_{0.33}Ga_{0.67}As$ barrier layers, 40 ML and of the $Al_{0.33}Ga_{0.67}As$ barrier layers, 40 ML. The detection energies for the two PL excitation spectra are indicated by λ on the corresponding PL curves.

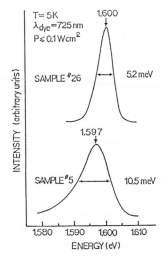

Fig. 2.26. Shows the 5 K photoluminescence spectra taken with excitation wavelength 725 nm for single quantum wells 26 and 5 grown without growth interruption (see Fig. 2.24) at growth conditions identified by points (*A*) and (*C*), respectively, of Fig. 2.22

averaged well width which is equivalent to interfaces graded over one monolayer at least, leading to the single line emission seen in Fig. 2.26 and a slight shift in the emission peak energy. The relative behavior of R_{exc} and $\langle W \rangle$ is, of course, consistent with the significantly larger terrace widths indicated by the RHEED intensity recovery behavior of the interrupted growth samples (Fig. 2.23) compared to the continuous growth samples (Fig. 2.24).

2) The narrower line width of ~ 5 meV (Fig. 2.26) of the higher temperature continuous growth sample compared to the ~ 8 meV line width of the lower temperature continuous growth sample is consistent with their corresponding RHEED specular beam intensity (Fig. 2.23) which shows that while the inverted interface region may appear comparable in the two cases, the normal interface is degraded in the latter case. This is clearly seen in the inset of Fig. 2.23. However, the RHEED specular beam intensity at best manifests the structural smoothness of the growth front but is not sensitive to the chemical nature of the interfaces resulting from the intrinsic differences in the Ga and Al surface migration kinetics. The PL behavior, on the other hand, is sensitive to the chemical nature as well. The difference in the line widths of the high and low temperature continuous growth samples thus also arises in part from the greater inter-mixing effect at lower temperature due to the slower Al migration. This aspect is made clearer by comparing the high and low temperature interrupted growth samples, as discussed in point 3 below.

3) The PL emission of the lower temperature interrupted growth sample (Fig. 2.25) is seen to give comparable intensity for the 21 ML and 20 ML well width regions, unlike the higher temperature growth which has a dominance of the 20 ML region. Even the line widths of the individual fine structure emission lines is wider (~ 3 meV) for the low temperature growth than the ~ 2 meV line width of the predominant 20 ML peak in the high temperature growth sample. At first sight this appears contrary to the higher RHEED specular beam intensity at the lower growth temperature seen in Fig. 2.23. However, as noted in point 2 above, higher RHEED specular beam intensity at best represents higher structural smoothness but is not sensitive to the chemical nature of the atom type in a local distribution of atoms. Thus in spite of the apparent greater smoothness of morphology, there is greater local Al clustering effect due to its reduced surface mobility at lower temperatures. This is an effect revealed well by the computer simulations. The dotted curves in Fig. 2.25 represent the PL excitation spectra of the two samples taken with detection set at the wavelength indicated by λ against the PL spectra. Though one observes the commonly observed Stokes shift (about 4 meV) to higher energy compared to the PL spectra, the line widths of the heavy hole excitons are essentially the same as found in the PL spectra. The two predominant higher energy peaks correspond to the $n = 1$ electron to light hole free exciton recombination in the 21 ML and 20 ML regions of the wells.

Though several more points could be discussed, the preceding three points, it is hoped, have been sufficient to draw attention to the fact that (a) while RHEED intensity dynamics is of immense value in guiding the choice of growth conditions and their reproducibility, one cannot overlook the fact that it is not sensitive to the atomistic chemical nature of interfaces and (b) the inherent differences in the surface kinetics of two species, such as Ga and Al, plays a crucial role in controlling the nature of the interfacial crystal potential and consequently properties of the quantum confined carriers and devices based upon them. We have already seen the significance of this aspect suggested by the computer simulations. Let us therefore end this section by examining one last feature of the PL and PLE behavior which further sheds light on the essential correctness, or lack thereof, of the growth kinetics controlled atomistic nature of the interfaces.

In Fig. 2.27 is shown a plot of the low temperature PL line width of GaAs/Al$_{0.3}$Ga$_{0.7}$As(100) single quantum wells as a function of the well width, d_W. All the wells were grown with conventional continuous growth and under *identical*, RHEED intensity determined, growth conditions corresponding to point A of Fig. 2.23. The kinetics of the growth are as nearly the same as can practically and realistically be hoped for. One notes a nearly d_W^{-1} dependence of the line width. This is contradictory to the notion of fluctuations in the well width controlling the PL line width introduced by *Weisbuch* et al. [2.75] and so unquestioningly and generally employed. Fluctuations in the well width would give rise to a near d_W^{-3} dependence – a dependence which had never been checked through systematic examination until *Voillot* et al. [2.18] reported the data shown in Fig. 2.27. We note that PL line widths measured at higher temperature (20 K) as well as the linewidths obtained from PLE exhibit the same d_W^{-1} like behavior.

The question naturally arises as to the physical scattering mechanism(s) responsible for the nearly d_W^{-1} behavior of the PL linewidths. Based upon the nature of the interface confining potential suggested by the computer simulation results shown in Fig. 2.20, *Ogale* et al. [2.24, 25, 76] have calculated the PL linewidth due to fluctuations in the band edge discontinuity and the shorter ranged alloy disorder scattering at and near the interface experienced by the exciton due

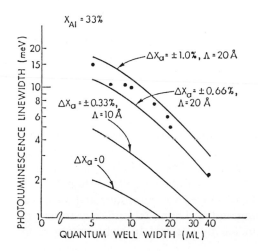

Fig. 2.27. Shows the 5 K PL linewidth (*solid circles*) of single quantum wells of varying well width grown without interruption under identical growth conditions corresponding to point (*A*) of the RHEED specular beam intensity behavior shown in Fig. 2.22. Note the nearly d_W^{-1} dependence. The crosses show the PL behavior at 20 K. Solid curves correspond to the theory based on band edge discontinuity fluctuations and alloy disorder scattering. Broken curve represents contribution of alloy disorder scattering alone

to penetration of the wave function into the alloy barrier layers. While the details of the calculations can be found in [2.25], we only note that the lateral fluctuations in the local Al concentration on the size of the exciton diameter is modelled as a Gaussian given by

$$\langle X_{Al}(R) X_{Al}(R') \rangle = \Delta X_a^2 \exp(-|R - R'|^2 / \Lambda^2),$$ (2.4)

in which ΔX_a is the amplitude of fluctuation and Λ the correlation length. The short ranged alloy disorder scattering is considered within the well known Mott model employing the electronegativity difference of Ga and Al as the strength of the alloy disorder potential [2.25]. The solid lines shown in Fig. 2.27 correspond to the calculated PL linewidth for the values of ΔX_a and Λ shown. The broken line corresponds to the presence only of the alloy disorder scattering. A nearly d_W^{-1} dependence of the PL linewidths is found, consistent with the observed behavior. Even the absolute values of the observed PL linewidths are bracketed by a choice of reasonable values of local Al concentration fluctuation ($\pm 1\%$) and correlation length (~ 30 Å). It can thus be reasonably concluded that, in high quality structures involving an alloy layer, band edge discontinuity fluctuations and short ranged alloy disorder scattering are the predominant physical mechanisms controlling the behaviour of the carriers rather than the prevalent notion of fluctuations in the well width. It is also to be emphasized that the degree of this lateral nonuniformity (i.e. band edge discontinuity fluctuation) is intimately tied to the underlying differences in the kinetics of the species involved in the two materials.

2.5 Concluding Remarks

The central inference of the preceding section – namely the significance of the *growth kinetics controlled lateral compositional uniformity* of interfacial atomic planes – though extracted from systematic studies of the most popular GaAs/Al$_x$Ga$_{1-x}$As(100) quantum well system, should nevertheless be immediately recognized to be of far reaching significance to all other systems involving an alloy layer as one component in the compositionally modulated structure. Such effects can be particularly significant in lattice mismatched systems such as GaAs/In$_x$Ga$_{1-x}$As and Si/Ge$_x$Si$_{1-x}$. While much attention has historically and in recent times been focussed on the role of lattice mismatch induced strain in controlling properties relating to the growth direction (e.g. critical thickness for generation of misfit dislocations), it is this author's view that the surface kinetics influence, and are influenced by, the local, time dependent strain effects in both the lateral and vertical directions during growth. Indeed, the RHEED intensity behavior of GaAs/In$_x$Ga$_{1-x}$As(100) system exhibits [2.59] certain features which are quite distinct from the GaAs/Al$_x$Ga$_{1-x}$As(100) system and have been suggested [2.59] to be indicative of strain induced bimodal surface terrace width distribution, presumably arising from locally Ga and In rich regions at the growth front. A time dependent oscillatory variation in the surface lattice constant during growth of InAs on GaAs(100) has been reported by *Lee* [2.12]. A more detailed analysis by *Grunthaner* et al. [2.77] has revealed a dependence of this oscillatory surface lattice constant on the kinetics of growth. While much remains to be systematically investigated, it is nevertheless sufficiently clear that the strain dependent surface kinetic processes play a crucial role in establishing the atomistic nature of the confining potentials in such systems.

Finally, the nature of interfaces formed in homopolar-heteropolar combinations [2.5] such as Si/GaAs, being referred to these days as hetero-epitaxy (an unfortunate terminology since *all* compositionally modulated structures represent hetero-epitaxy), is no exception to the consideration noted above even though the consequences, qualitatively and quantitatively, would be different. Little, if any, information comparable to the well studied GaAs/ $Al_xGa_{1-x}As(100)$ system is however available as the this writing to allow any well substantiated comments. One can only hope that in spite of the temptation of the technological importance of this system – indeed, perhaps because of it – some systematic studies of the growth kinetics would be forthcoming in the near future.

In conclusion, it is hoped that this chapter has provided a reasonable insight into the nature of the MBE growth process, the inter-relationship of the growth kinetics and the lateral and vertical length scales of chemical and structural perfection of interfaces in ultra-thin quantum well structures, and their consequences for the variety of micro and nano structure devices anticipated for future technological applications. For the quantum wire and quantum box structures [2.78] the features revealed in this chapter will be of even greater significance. It is also hoped that the brief description of the pragmatic usage of RHEED, exposed and emphasized here, will find greater acceptance and that the notion of growth interruption would be found to be of benefit in many cases requiring considerable lateral uniformity of interfaces.

2.6 Recent Advances

Some significant advances have occurred in the two years that have elapsed since this chapter was written in early 1987. We therefore provide a very brief update here of a few developments of particular relevance to the contents of this volume.

On the side of the parallel transport, $GaAs/Al_xGa_{1-x}As(100)$ inverted HEMT structures with LN_2 mobilities within 20% of the high quality normal HEMT structures have now been realized [2.79–81]. This success is directly attributable to the use of RHEED intensity static and dynamic behavior discussed in Sects. 2.2 and 2.3, coupled with exploitation of the faster Ga migration kinetics and growth interruption to enhance $Al_xGa_{1-x}As$ growth front smoothness while employing quite low (500°–550°C) growth temperatures during Si doping to reduce the Si outdiffusion. Indeed, recently in the author's laboratory LN_2 dark mobilities of $\sim 180\,000\ cm^2/V\ s$ in GaAs/

$Al_{0.25}Ga_{0.75}As(100)$ inverted HEMTs at the remarkably low carrier concentrations of $(3-4) \times 10^{10}$ cm^{-2} have been achieved [2.82]. While such carrier concentrations are of no particular device significance, they are a testimony to the degree of atomic level perfection that is possible through a proper understanding and control of growth kinetics.

The computer simulations of MBE growth have been generalized to incorporate the role of strain in lattice mismatched systems such as $In_xGa_{1-x}As$ on GaAs(100). The influence of strain on the growth front morphology and chemical distribution (vertical and lateral), and consequently on the nature of the interfaces responsible for the confining potential has been examined [2.83–85]. Equally significant, the first kinetic model of misfit strain induced defect generation and the time-dependent evolution of such defects has been proposed [2.84–86] and its consequences examined via computer simulations [2.84–86]. The model emphasizes the time-dependent cluster distribution controlled by the growth kinetics and reveals the critical significance of the effective migration length of the cations controlling the average cluster size at the time cluster coalescence sets in. Of pragmatic value to laterally confined quantum devices is thus the prediction [2.84, 85] that highly strained layers can be grown with low defect densities provided the growth is carried out on "finite substrates" of dimensions smaller than the growth-condition-controlled effective migration length. Such substrates can be prepared by pre-growth ex situ or in situ lateral patterning or possibly even through control of growth on substrates patterned ex situ on significantly larger length scales. Work on the experimental investigation of this possibility is underway in the author's laboratory. We conclude, in the meantime, with an illustrative example of growth of the lattice-matched GaAs/$Al_xGa_{1-x}As$ system on patterned GaAs(100) substrates to create laterally confined quantum structures.

Most quantum devices relying on more-than-one-dimensional confinement are presently realized via post-growth lateral patterning using electron beam lithography, X-ray lithography, or focused ion beams to creat impurity-induced disordering. By contrast, the creation of such two-dimensionally and three-dimensionally confined structures via growth on patterned substrates is an attractive alternative, particularly if it can be achieved in situ, without requiring ex situ pre- or post-growth patterning (lithography or direct-write) on the scale of the device dimensions. Following the initial studies [2.87, 88] of *Cho* and coworkers over a decade ago, in recent years laser structures on optically patterned (on the scale of $\geq 5\ \mu$m) GaAs (100) surfaces have been grown via MBE [2.89] and MOCVD [2.90]. This is not yet the regime of lateral quantum confinement of electronic states. However, starting from substrates with ex situ patterning on the scale of $\geq 2\ \mu$m, researchers in this author's laboratory have been able to exploit the thermodynamics and kinetics of growth on the different crystallographic planes involved to realize, in situ, laterally confined structures on the scale of ~ 2000 Å. An illustrative example [2.91] of a wire structure realized in this way is shown in the TEM micrograph of Fig. 2.28. The inset (SEM micrograph) shows the top (100) terrace and the (111) side wall region of a V-

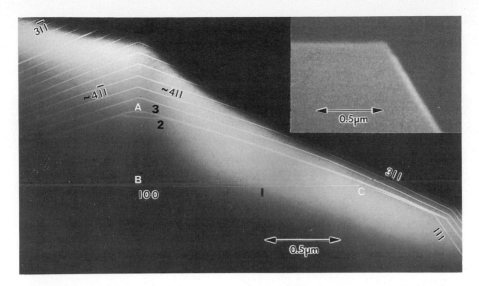

Fig. 2.28. TEM micrograph of GaAs/Al$_x$Ga$_{1-x}$As layers grown on GaAs(100) substrate with V-shaped grooves defined via ex situ optical lithography. Shown are the top (100) terrace region, the (111) side wall, and the (311) facet arising after oxide desorption. The inset shows the SEM image of the top (100) and (111) sidewall region before oxide desorption. The region between Al$_{0.4}$Ga$_{0.6}$As layers numbered 2 and 3 defines a trapezoid-shaped quantum wire with base width 2000 Å and top width 900 Å

shaped groove on the patterned GaAs(100) substrate. Immediately following native oxide desorption in the MBE growth chamber, a 10 ML wide AlAs marker layer (numbered 1 in the main figure) is deposited to delineate the resulting patterned profile. Note the appearance of the (311) facet between the top (100) terrace and the (111) side wall. Subsequent growth of GaAs on the top (100) terrace is then seen to be in the shape of a truncated pyramid due to rapid migration of the cation from the (311) facet to the top (100) terrace under the chosen growth conditions. As a result, (100) "substrates" of smaller and smaller lateral dimensions can be created in situ through control of the amount of initial GaAs buffer deposited. Marker layers 2 and 3 in the figure are 20 ML thick Al$_{0.4}$Ga$_{0.6}$As layers, between which is sandwiched 5 ML of GaAs. The lateral dimensions of the lower and upper barrier layers are $\sim$ 2000 Å and 900 Å, respectively. Once the apex of the pyramid is reached, growth begins on the (311) facets as seen by the subsequent growth of alternating GaAs (170 ML) and Al$_{0.4}$Ga$_{0.6}$As (20 ML) layers to create a MQW structure. This is a remarkable way of achieving, in situ, laterally confined quantum structures without the worry of the direct influence of damage and/or contamination induced by ex situ lithographic or in situ direct-write patterning processes on the nano-structure properties. It is thus clear that the ability to realize nano-structures, including in 2D arrays, is now beginning to emerge so that one may look forward to examination of many proposed nano-structures, their fundamental properties as well as device and systems concepts. The impact of such developments on the side of growth on patterned substrates is likely to be particularly significant for opto-electronic integration and all-optical device concepts of relevance to optical information processing and optical computing technologies of the future. Yet, it should also be clear that the ultimate limitations in such devices will arise from the growth kinetics controlled lateral structural and chemical variations through the accompanying fluctuations in the confining potential.

Acknowledgements. The author gratefully acknowledges the contributions of many former and present Ph.D. students and colleagues which allow this chapter to be written. He also expresses his gratitude to Mrs. Arsho Apardian for her efficient and painstakingly careful typing of the manuscript under often the most trying circumstances. The financial support provided over the last several years by the Air Force Office of Scientific Research (Dr. G. L. Witt and Dr. K. Malloy), Office of Naval Research (Dr. G. B. Wright), and more recently, by the Army Research Office (Dr. M. Stroscio) has made the work at USC possible and is thankfully acknowledged.

References

2.1   L. Esaki, R. Tsu: IBM Jour. Res. Develop. **14**, 61 (1970)
2.2   F. Capasso, K. Mohammed, A. Y. Cho: IEEE J. Quantum Electron. **QE-22**, 1853 (1986) and references therein
2.3   F. Capasso: Ann. Rev. Mat. Sci. **16**, 261 (1986) and references therein
2.4   See, for example, A. C. Gossard (eds. K. N. Tu, R. Rosenberg): *Thin Films: Preparation and Properties*, (Academic Press, New York 1982) Volume 24
2.5   A. Madhukar, S. V. Ghaisas: CRC Critical Reviews in Solid State and Materials Sciences, Vol. 14, p. 1 (1988)
2.6   P. Chen, A. Madhukar, J. Y. Kim, T. C. Lee: App. Phys. Letts. **48**. 650 (1986);
      P. Chen, J. Y. Kim, A. Madhukar, N. M. Cho: Jour. Vac. Sci. Technol. **B4**, 890 (1986)
2.7   P. Chen, A. Madhukar, J. Y. Kim, N. M. Cho: Proc. 18th International Conference on Physics of Semiconductors, (Stockholm, Aug. 11–15, 1986), Ed. Olof Engstrom (World Scientific, Singapore 1987) Vol **1**, p. 109
2.8   P. K. Larsen, P. J. Dobson, J. H. Neave, B. A. Joyce, B. Bolger, J. Zhang: Surf. Sci. **169**, 176 (1986)
2.9   A. Madhukar, T. C. Lee, M. Y. Yen, P. Chen, J. Y. Kim, S. V. Ghaisas, P. G. Newman: App. Phys. Letts. **46**, 1148 (1985);
      see also, A. Madhukar, S. V. Ghaisas, T. C. Lee, M. Y. Yen, P. Chen, J. Y. Kim, P. G. Newman: Proc. of the SPIE Conference, (Los Angeles, Calif., Jan. 20–22, 1985), Vol. 524, p. 78
2.10 B. F. Lewis, F. J. Grunthaner, A. Madhukar, T. C. Lee, R. Fernandez: J. Vac. Sci. Technol. **B3**, 1317 (1985)
2.11 M. Y. Yen, T. C. Lee, P. Chen, A. Madhukar: J. Vac. Sci. Technol. **B4**, 590 (1986)
2.12 T. C. Lee, M. Y. Yen, P. Chen, A. Madhukar: J. Vac. Sci. Technol. **A4**, 884 (1986); Surf. Sci. **174**, 55, (1986);
      see also, T. C. Lee, Ph.D. Dissertation, University of Southern California, Los Angeles, U.S.A., (1986)
2.13 A. Madhukar, S. V. Ghaisas: App. Phys. Lett. **47**, 247 (1985)
2.14 M. Thomsen, S. V. Ghaisas, A. Madhukar: J. Cryst. Growth **84**, 79 (1987)
2.15 M. Thomsen and A. Madhukar: J. Cryst. Growth **84**, 98 (1987)
2.16 S. B. Ogale, M. Thomsen, A. Madhukar: App. Phys. Lett. **52**, 723 (1988)

2.17 F. Voillot, A. Madhukar, J. Y. Kim, P. Chen, N. M. Cho, W. C. Tang, P. G. Newman: App. Phys. Lett. **48**, 1009 (1986)

2.18 F. Voillot, J. Y. Kim, W. C. Tang, A. Madhukar, P. Chen: Superlattices and Microstructures **3**, 313 (1987)

2.19 A. Madhukar, P. Chen, F. Voillot, M. Thomsen, J. Y. Kim, W. C. Tang, S. V. Ghaisas: Jour. Cryst. Growth **81**, 26 (1987)

2.20 F. Voillot, A. Madhukar, W. C. Tang, M. Thomsen, J. Y. Kim, P. Chen: App. Phys. Lett. **50**, 194 (1987)

2.21 J. Y. Kim, P. Chen, F. Voillot, A. Madhukar: App. Phys. Lett. **50**, 739 (1987)

2.22 N. M. Cho, A. Madhukar (Unpublished)

2.23 M. Y. Yen: Ph.D. Thesis, University of Southern California, Los Angeles, California (1986)

2.24 S. B. Ogale, A. Madhukar, F. Voillot, M. Thomsen, W. C. Tang, T. C. Lee, J. Y. Kim, P. Chen: Phys. Rev. **B36**, 1662 (1987)

2.25 A. Madhukar: Proc. MRS Symposium on Epitaxy of Semiconductor Layered Structures, (Nov. 30–Dec. 4, 1987) Vol. 102, ed. by R. T. Tung, L. R. Dawson, R. L. Gunshor (MRS, Pittsburgh, PA 1987) p. 3

2.26 A good review is provided by T. Ando, A. B. Fowler, F. Stern in Revs. Mod. Phys. **54**, 437 (1982)

2.27 R. Dingle, H. L. Stormer, A. C. Gossard, W. Weighmann: App. Phys. Lett. **33**, 665 (1978)

2.28 C. W. Tu, R. Hendel, R. Dingle (ed. D. K. Ferry): *In Gallium Arsenide Technology* (Howard and Sams, Indianapolis, 1985) p. 107

2.29 See the recent review by M. J. Ludowise in J. App. Phys. **58**, R31 (1986)

2.30 For a recent review of gas-source MBE see, M. B. Panish: In *Progress in Crystal Growth and Characterization* (Pergamon, New York 1986)

2.31 C. H. L. Goodman, M. V. Pessa: J. App. Phys. **60**, R65 (1986).

2.32 E. Bauser: In Proceedings of the NATO Advanced Research Workshop, (Brighton, U.K. Sept. 1986), (Plenum, The Netherlands 1987)

2.33 For an overview, see, A. Madhukar: Jour. Vac. Sci. Technol. **20**, 149 (1982)

2.34 W. T. Masselink, Y. L. Sun, R. Fischer, T. J. Drummond, Y. C. Chang, M. V. Klein, H. Morkoc: J. Vac. Sci. Technol. **B2**, 117 (1984)

2.35 R. C. Miller, A. C. Gossard, D. A. Kleinman, O. Munteanu: Phys. Rev., **B29**, 3740 (1984)

2.36 S. Das Sarma, A. Madhukar: J. Vac. Sci. Technol. **19**, 447 (1981)

2.37 A. K. Sood, J. Menendez, M. Cardona, K. Ploog: Phys. Rev. **B32**, 1412 (1985); Phys. Rev. Lett. **54**, 2111 (1985); ibid **54**, 2115 (1985)

2.38 A. Madhukar, P. D. Lao, W. C. Tang, M. Aidan, F. Voillot: Phys. Rev. Lett. **59**, 1313 (1987)

2.39 G. C. Osbourn: J. Vac. Sci. Technol. **B1**, 379 (1983)

2.40 S. B. Ogale, A. Madhukar: J. App. Phys. **56**, 368 (1984) and unpublished results.

2.41 N. M. Cho, S. B. Ogale, A. Madhukar: To be published

2.42 H. Kroemer. RCA Reviews, **18**, 332 (1957)

2.43 R. F. Kazarinov, R. A. Suris: Fiz. Tekh. Poluprov. 5, 797 (1971); translation in Sov. Phys. Semiconductors, **5**, 707 (1971)

2.44 R. F. Kazarinov, R. A. Suris: Fiz. Tekh. Poluprov. 6, 148 (1972); translation in Sov. Phys. Semiconductors, **6**, 120 (1972)

2.45 B. Ricco, M. Ya. Azbel: Phys. Rev. **B29**, 1970 (1984)

2.46 F. J. Grunthaner, M. Y. Yen, R. Fernandez, T. C. Lee, A. Madhukar, B. F. Lewis: App. Phys. Lett. **46**, 983 (1985)

2.47 R. Tsu, G. Dohler: Phys. Rev. **B12**, 680 (1975).
see also, R. Tsu, L. L. Chang, G. A. Sai-Halasz, L. Esaki: Phys. Rev. Lett. **34**, 1509 (1975)

2.48 For a good review of disorder theory, see P. A. Lee, T. V. Ramakrishnan: Rev. Mod. Phys. **57**, 287 (1985)

2.49 A. Chomette, B. Deveaud, A. Regreny: Phys. Rev. Lett. **57**, 1464 (1986)

2.50 A. Madhukar, M. H. Cohen: Phys. Rev. Lett. **38**, 85 (1977)

2.51 A. Madhukar, W. Post: Phys. Rev. Lett. **39**, 1424 (1977)

2.52 D. A. B. Miller, D. S. Chemla, T. C. Damen, T. H. Wood, C. A. Burrus, A. C. Gossard, W. Weigmann: IEEE J. Quantum. Electron. **QE-21**, 1462 (1985)

2.53 A. Madhukar: Surf. Sci. **132**, 344 (1983)
2.54 M. C. Tomargo, R. Hull, L. H. Greene, J. R. Hayes, A. Y. Cho: App. Phys. Lett. **46**, 569 (1985)
2.55 M. Y. Yen, A. Madhukar, B. F. Lewis, R. Fernandez, L. Eng, F. J. Grunthaner: Surf. Sci. **174**, 606 (1986):
      see also, M. Y. Yen: Ph.D. Dissertation, University of Southern California, Los Angeles, CA. (1986)
2.56 A. Y. Cho: J. App. Phys. **41**, 2780 (1970)
2.57 J. H. Neave, B. A. Joyce, P. J. Dobson, N. Norton: App. Phys. **A31**, 1 (1983); ibid **A34**, 1 (1984)
2.58 J. M. VanHove, C. S. Lent, P. R. Pukite, P. I. Cohen: J. Vac. Sci. Technol. **B1**, 741 (1983); ibid **B3**, 564 (1984)
2.59 B. F. Lewis, T. C. Lee, F. J. Grunthaner, A. Madhukar, R. Fernandez, J. Maserjian: J. Vac. Sci. Technol. **B2**, 419 (1984)
2.60 P. Chen, T. C. Lee, N. M. Cho, A. Madhukar: Proceedings of the SPIE Conference on Growth of Compound Semiconductors, Vol. 796, (SPIE, Bellingham, WA 1987) p. 139
2.61 N. M. Cho, P. Chen, A. Madhukar: App. Phys. Lett. **50**, 1909 (1987)
2.62 B. F. Lewis, R. Fernandez, A. Madhukar, F. J. Grunthaner: J. Vac. Sci. Technol. **B4**, 560 (1986)
2.63 N. Sano, H. Kato, M. Nakayama, S. Chika, H. Teranchi: Jpn. J. App. Phys. **23**, L640 (1984)
2.64 T. Sakamoto, H. Funabashi, K. Ohta, T. Nakagawa, N. Kawai, T. Kojima: Jpn. J. App. Phys. **23**, L657 (1984)
2.65 M. Tanaka, H. Sakaki, J. Yoshino: Jpn. J. App. Phys. **25**, L150 (1985) and references therein
2.66 T. Fukunaga, K. L. Kobayashi, H. Nakashima: Jpn. J. App. Phys. **24**, L510 (1985)
2.67 D. Bimberg, D. Mars, J. N. Miller, R. Bauer, D. Oertl: J. Vac. Sci. Technol. **B4**, 1014 (1986)
2.68 R. C. Miller, C. W. Tu, S. K. Sputz, R. F. Kopf: App. Phys. Lett. **49**, 1245 (1986)
2.69 J. R. Arthur: Surf. Sci. **43**, 449 (1974)
2.70 C. T. Foxon, B. A. Joyce: Surf. Sci. **50**, 434 (1975)
2.71 C. T. Foxon, B. A. Joyce: Surf. Sci. **64**, 293 (1977)
2.72 S. V. Ghaisas, A. Madhukar: J. Vac. Sci. Technol. **B3**, 540 (1985)
2.73 S. V. Ghaisas, A. Madhukar: Phys. Rev. Lett. **41**, 1066 (1986)
2.74 See [2.5]
2.75 C. Weisbuch, R. Dingle, A. C. Gossard, W. Weigmann: Solid State Commun. **38**, 709 (1981)
2.76 S. B. Ogale, A. Madhukar, N. M. Cho: J. App. Phys. **62**, 1381 (1987)
2.77 F. J. Grunthaner, L. Eng, B. F. Lewis, R. Fernandez, M. Y. Yen, A. Madhukar: Paper presented at the International Conference on Superlattices, Microstructures and Microdevices (Aug. 1986, Stockholm, Sweden)
2.78 P. M. Petroff, Chapter 11, This volume
2.79 N. M. Cho, D. J. Kim, A. Madhukar, P. G. Newman, D. D. Smith, T. R. Aucoin, G. J. Iafrate: Appl. Phys. Lett. **52**, 2037 (1988)
2.80 P. G. Newman, N. M. Cho, D. J. Kim, A. Madhukar, D. D. Smith, T. R. Aucoin, G. J. Iafrate, J. Vac. Sci. Technol. **B6**, 1483 (1988)
2.81 H. Shtrikman, M Heiblum, K. Seo, D. E. Galbi, L. Osterling: J. Vac. Sci. Technol. **B6**, 670 (1988)
2.82 A. Madhukar, D. J. Kim, W. Chen, K. Z. Hu: To be published
2.83 S. V. Ghaisas, A. Madhukar: Appl. Phys. Lett. **53**, 1599 (1988); J. Appl. Phys. **65**, 1888 (1989)
2.84 S. V. Ghaisas, A. Madhukar: In Proc. of the SPIE Symp. on "Growth of Compound Semiconductor Structures", ed. by A. Madhukar, Vol. 944 (SPIE, Bellingham, WA 1988) p. 16
2.85 S. B. Ogale, A. Madhukar: To be published
2.86 S. V. Ghaisas, A. Madhukar: J. Vac. Sci. Technol., **B7**, 265 (1989)
2.87 A. Y. Cho, W. C. Bellamy: J. Appl. Phys. **46**, 783 (1974)
2.88 W. Tsang, A. Y. Cho: Appl. Phys. Lett. **30**, 293 (1977)
2.89 E. Kapon, M. C. Tamargo, D. M. Hwang: Appl. Phys. Lett. **50**, 347 (1987) and references therein
2.90 K. M. Dzurko, E. P. Menu, C. A. Beyler, J. S. Osinski, P. D. Dapkus: Appl. Phys. Lett. **54**, 105 (1989) and references therein
2.91 S. Guha, A. Madhukar, K. Kaviani, Li Chen, R. Kuchibhotla, R. Kapre, M. Hyugaji, Z. Xie Proc. MRS Spring'89 Symposium on III–V Heterostructures for Electronic/Photonic Devices, Vol. 145, ed. by C. W. Tu, A. C. Gossard, V. D. Matera (MRS Pittsburgh, PA)

3. Nanolithography
for Ultra-Small Structure Fabrication

H. G. Craighead

With 10 Figures

The ability to fabricate structures and devices with dimensions smaller than relevant physical length scales is leading to the discovery and exploitation of new physical phenomena. This chapter describes some of the techniques used for advanced nanofabrication processes along with the physical and practical limits.

3.1 Overview

There has been considerable effort dedicated to the fabrication of increasingly small structures. This is partly motivated by the desire to continue the advances in integrated circuit density and speed that have been so significant in recent years. And it is partly motivated by the quest for observing and understanding the new physical phenomena that occur at increasingly small dimensions, approaching the quantum level, that could lead to entirely new types of devices [3.1]. Some methods of creating very small objects are similar to those used for present day integrated circuit fabrication at dimensions on the order of 1 μm, but the considerations of ultra-high resolution may be different than those of production through-put, alignment and other considerations [3.2]. In this chapter we will consider only the highest resolution processes relevant to fabrication at dimensions less than 100 nm, and we will consider resolution limits of the lithographic techniques.

Control of the structure of materials by control of the growth process, particularly the atomic layer control attainable with MBE [3.3], is dramatic and had lead to new physics and improved devices such as high electron mobility transistors [3.4] and lower threshold quantum well lasers [3.5]. The growth control has the ability to "band gap engineer" revolutionary types of semiconductor structures [3.6]. The technology for lateral patterning of semiconductors is approaching a state where one can begin to consider the possibilities of lateral band gap engineering. We are now just at the edge of seeing lateral quantum confinement effects in a few systems. We can begin to consider the design of lateral devices that operate with elements smaller than scattering lengths. These new types of experiments and devices are made possible by the advances in materials growth and nanofabrication. We should, therefore, consider carefully the limits and possibilities of high resolution fabrication.

There are two steps to consider in the creation of ultra-small devices. The first is the method of defining a desired fine pattern by a lithographic process. This has been given consideration by numerous researchers and has resulted in considerable advances. The second aspect which has been less well studied is the step of creating a desired structure in the material of interest. This is, in general, very material dependent and must be designed for the system of interest. It is this step that is, in many cases, the resolution limiting one. For example, extremely small holes may be drilled in a few nanometer thick free-standing film, and narrow lines can be developed in very thin Langmuir-Blodgett films. These are of limited utility unless the pattern can be transferred into the material of interest, and this remains a difficult problem.

In this chapter I will enumerate the general lithography techniques and discuss the resolution limits of each. Emphasis will be given to those processes that have shown general utility in fabricating ultra-small objects of any desired geometry in a broad class of materials. In particular the creation of nanostructures in semiconductors will be described as it is in these systems that devices can be created with dimensions less than relevant lengths. The layered compound semiconductors such as GaAs/AlGaAs, in particular, are the ones for which the microstructure can be so well controlled by the growth process. Combining this with nanometer lateral patterning suggests the possibility of complete three dimensional control of the materials properties.

This is a dynamic area of research, and there are constant advances in the capability, instrumentation and understanding in the pursuit of ultra small structure study [3.7]. The advances in focused ion beam technology for example have been significant, and while not yet resulting in the smallest structure generation, this area is rapidly moving. The speed and quality of electron beam lithographic instruments constantly improves [3.8]. The invention of the scanning tunnelling electron microscope has recently provided a new method of directly imaging structures at the atomic level, and it is just beginning to be explored as a fabrication tool [3.9]. Most of the small structures examined have been defined by electron beam lithography, and the smallest semiconductor structures have been created by transferring such patterns by ion etching [3.10]. Since electron beam lithography and ion etching have been so productive they will be most thoroughly covered in this chapter, including specific examples.

3.2 Resolution Limits of Lithographic Processes

3.2.1 Lithography

The word lithography comes from the stone plates onto which a pattern was recorded for reproduction by printing. For fabrication, we know lithography as the creation of a pattern in a resist layer, usually an organic polymer film, on a substrate material [3.11]. A latent image, consisting of a chemical change in the

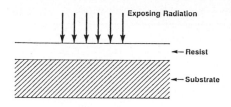

Fig. 3.1. Schematic of the basic lithography steps of exposing a pattern on a substrate and developing the pattern in a resist layer

Development

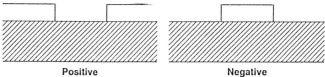

resist is created by exposing the desired area with some form of radiation. The pattern is developed by selectively removing either the exposed resist areas (for a positive resist) or the unexposed areas (for a negative resist). The development of a polymeric resist is usually done with a solvent that brings out the pattern based on the solubility difference created by the exposure. Figure 3.1 shows a schematic of the basic lithographic steps.

Inorganic resist materials also exist and have shown application to the high resolution field. Related processes include vapor or plasma development that operate on difference in gas phase or plasma reactivity rather than liquid development based on solubility differences. Self developing resists are of some importance in the high resolution area. For these materials the exposing radiation volatilizes the resist, creating a pattern in the resist without a development step. It is by exposure of self-developing inorganic resists that the smallest patterns to date have been created. [3.12, 3.13]

The figures of merit for a resist/developer system include: the sensitivity to the exposing radiation, that dictates the speed of exposure, the contrast, that describes the exposure dose dependence of the resist response; the resolution, dictating the minimum feature size; and the suitability of the resist for pattern transfer [3.11]. While the sensitivity and contrast of a system are vital in determining the speed and process latitude, it is the resolution and pattern transfer utility that we want to stress for the application to research level nanostructure fabrication

3.2.2 Resolution Limits of Lithographic Methods

Electrons, ions, and photons can all be used for exposure in the lithographic process. Because of intrinsic scattering mechanisms, in no case can the energy provided by the exposing radiation be confined to arbitrarily small volumes. Firstly, the radiation or particle beam can not be confined arbitrarily because of

Table 3.1. List of lithographic exposure processes and parameters

Lithography type	Wavelength (nm)	Energy	Resolution limiting effect
UV	400–150	3–8 eV	diffraction
X-Ray	0.4–5	0.2–3 eV	diff./scatt.
Electron	0.01–.0003	10–120 keV	scattering
Ion	< 0.001	0.1–1000 keV	scattering

diffraction, Coulomb repulsion among particles, optics limitations or other effects. Secondly, the energy incident on a resist layer spreads in the film, because of intrinsic scattering mechanisms in the solid. There may be other effects that restrict the resolution and applicability of lithographic exposure processes, but let us primarily consider the fundamental limits of electron, ion and photon beam lithography. By considering examples of the present state-of-the-art resolution obtainable with each process we can estimate how close technology is to these ultimate limits.

Table 3.1 shows an outline of lithographic techniques and a list of the particle/radiation energy/wavelength. Listed in this way one can compare the effects of diffraction that depend on the wavelength, and the range of interaction in the resist that depends more directly on the energy. In the following sections we discuss more fully the different limiting processes for each exposure method.

3.2.3 Photolithography and X-Ray Lithography

The use of photons for high resolution lithographic exposure is a broad field that includes most of the lithography in use today. It can be taken to include X-ray lithography and deep and near-UV photolithography. Only the shortest wavelengths are relevant to high resolution fabrication.

In projection lithography a mask containing the desired pattern is demagnified by an optical system and projected on the resist layer (Fig. 3.2a). This is desirable since there is no damaging contact between the mask and wafer and the mask fabrication is not so critical since it is demagnified. The resolution is limited however by diffraction and the quality of the optics. The diffraction limit for the minimum resolvable grating period is usually taken as the Rayleigh criterion for the overlap of the diffraction peaks approximately as

$$\text{minimum line resolvable spacing} \approx \lambda/NA , \qquad (3.1)$$

where λ is the wavelength and NA is the numerical aperture of the optical system, which is on the order of one. The shortest wavelengths to be used with conventional type optics is about 193 nm from an excimer laser source [3.14]. The use of wavelengths much shorter than this is limited by absorption in optical materials. While the technology constantly improves with better optics, improved contrast enhanced resists and shorter wavelength sources, the limit of far field diffraction is a fundamental one that prevents the use for feature sizes smaller than the light wavelength [3.15]. Fabrication at sub 100 nm dimensions is essentially ruled out for photolithography.

Projection systems employing X-rays would reduce diffraction effects but, the problem remains to fabricate optics for use in the X-ray region. This may translate in a circular way into a problem of fabricating zone plates and diffracting optics by a high resolution technique [3.16]. Electron beam written zone plates represent the state of the art. X-ray sources are also a limit, with the best sources in terms of brightness and columation being synchrotrons.

Proximity printing allows the 1:1 replication of a mask pattern. By reducing the distance between mask and substrate the effects of near field diffraction can be arbitrarily reduced (Fig. 3.2b). Qualitatively, the minimum linewidth is

$$d \approx (\lambda s)^{\frac{1}{2}}, \tag{3.2}$$

where s is the mask to substrate separation. A more rigorous estimate [3.17] takes into account the resist thickness b and mask to resist gap distance g as:

$$d = 3[\lambda(g + b/2)]^{\frac{1}{2}}. \tag{3.3}$$

If one could obtain perfect contact ($g = 0$) and zero thickness resist than an arbitrarily fine pattern could be replicated. This was to some extent approximated with a hard contact exposure of a tri-level resist by 157 nm excimer laser radiation to obtain 100 nm linewidth replication [3.18]. Hard contact is undesirable because of damage to the mask and resist.

Proximity printing can be done effectively by X-ray exposure where the shorter wavelengths, on the order of one nanometer, allow much greater mask-substrate separation. With short wavelength X-rays, the diffraction effectively can be ignored for attainable gaps on the order of a few micrometers. However,

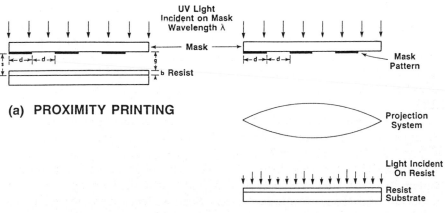

Fig. 3.2. (a) Schematic of proximity printing.
(b) Schematic of projection lithography system

the exposure of polymeric resists by X-rays takes place primarily through the generation of photoelectrons which then expose the resist by the same mechanisms as an electron beam. The range of the photoelectrons in the resist will limit the resolution. Since the photoelectron energy can have energies up to the X-ray energy of hc/λ and the electron range behaves as

$$R_G = (4 \times 10^{-6}/p)E^{1.75} \text{ (in cm)} \tag{3.4}$$

where E is the electron energy in keV, p is the density in g/cm^{-3}. The range can be greater than 100 nm for the shortest wavelengths X-rays [3.19]. We can see qualitatively that there is a trade-off between diffraction and the photoelectron range in limiting the resolution. Perhaps the most significant problem with X-ray printing is the creation of a durable high contrast mask. All materials absorb the X-rays, so the transparent area of the mask must be very thin or nonexistent. An absorbing metal such as gold supported on a thin film such as SiN_4 is one mask type. It is difficult to make structurally stable and durable masks. Some of the smallest features replicated by X-rays were 17.5 nm, fabricated by using edge evaporated metal as a mask [3.20]. Also, some other high resolution process is necessary to generate the mask features, this means in most cases electron beam lithography.

3.2.4 Ion Beams

The use of ion beams is diverse, with a great range in ion species and energies. Both large area col:umated beams and scanned focused beams have applications. The interaction with a solid can be to expose resist, most appropriate for high energy low mass ions. It is also possible to etch away material, change the chemistry by implantation, selectively deposit films, or induce structural changes on a selected area basis.

For ion lithographic printing, the considerations of diffraction are ignorable, because of the extremely small de Broglie wavelengths. High contrast masks are a challenge to fabricate, since the ions are absorbed in all solids. The use of ion channelling masks consisting of absorbers on oriented single crystals and grid supported shadow masks has been demonstrated [3.22]. These masks are usually defined by electron beam lithography. Considerations of ion scattering in solids are similar to those for electrons, but are less severe than for electrons [3.23].

Scanned focused beams can be used to draw patterns of any desired shape. The limits of ion source size and the quality of focusing optics have been the limiting factors of focused beam resolution. The quality of ion optics is poor compared to light optics and aberations along with a beam of broad energy have limited the spot size. Advances with liquid metal field emitter have been significant in producing bright ion sources. Scanned focused systems with liquid metal sources have demonstrated better than 50 nm ion milling resolution capability [3.24, 25].

3.2.5 Electron Beams

Electron beam lithography has developed substantially and been used heavily for the generation of photolithographic masks. Schemes for electron beam 1:1 printing similar to X-rays or ions have been explored but generally not for the creation of nanostructures. Because of the availability of electron sources and the high quality of electron optics, electron beams can be focused to dimensions less than 1 nm and scanned with great accuracy to define arbitrarily shaped patterns. This has been the greatest use and success of electron beam lithography.

In scanned electron beam lithography a small electron source is imaged on the substrate through a series of electromagnetic lens in an electron-optical column. The beam can be rapidly scanned over the sample to trace out any desired pattern. In the normal exposure of organic polymer resists the electron beam causes bond breaking or induces additional chemical bonds to be formed. This results in different molecular sizes in the exposed vs. unexposed areas, and this can be translated into solubility differences in an appropriate developer solvent. Figure 3.3 shows a schematic of the scanned electron beam exposure process.

The problem with electron beams is to confine energy deposition to a small area in the resist. There are several scattering processes in the material that lead to deposition of energy at distances remote from the initial impact point of the electron. This leads to the well known proximity and resolution limiting effects. Figure 3.4 shows schematically the effect of electron scattering in a resist coated substrate.

The longest range scattering effect is the backscattering of electrons, resulting in large angle scattering with energies near the incident electron energy. The range of these can be many micrometers for typical electron beam energies. This range has been determined to have the form of (3.4) over a wide energy range [3.19, 26]. This presents the greatest problem for energies such that the electron range is comparable to the feature spacing.

Forward scattering because of small angle scattering events tends to spread the incident beam passing through the resist. The scattering angles decrease with

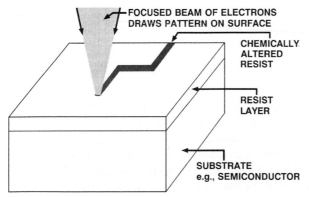

FOCUSED BEAM OF ELECTRONS
DRAWS PATTERN ON SURFACE

CHEMICALLY ALTERED RESIST

RESIST LAYER

SUBSTRATE e.g., SEMICONDUCTOR

Fig. 3.3. Schematic of electron beam exposure process

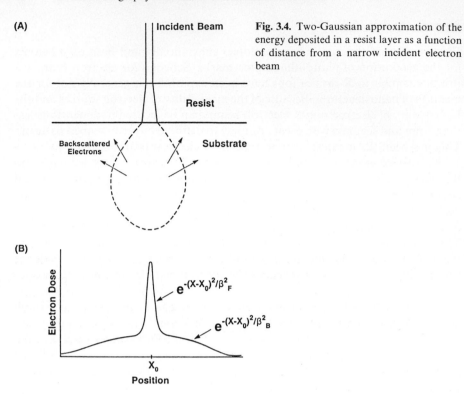

(A)

Incident Beam

Resist

Backscattered
Electrons

Substrate

(B)

Electron Dose

$e^{-(X-X_0)^2/\beta^2_F}$

$e^{-(X-X_0)^2/\beta^2_B}$

X_0

Position

Fig. 3.4. Two-Gaussian approximation of the energy deposited in a resist layer as a function of distance from a narrow incident electron beam

electron energy, and the spread of the beam is obviously more important for thicker resist layers.

The generation of low energy secondaries has an effect analogous to the photoelectrons in the X-ray case. This results in a cylindrical exposed volume around a delta function beam. *Keyser* [3.27] and others have done Monte Carlo calculations that model this effect. This is a fundamental problem with electron beam exposure that can be reduced only by using resists with shorter ranges for these low energy (≤ 50 eV) electrons, or are exposed only by higher energy primary electrons. There have been suggestions that this is the case for the fluoride and oxide self developing films, but these processes are not yet fully understood. The narrowest lines that have been formed in a polymeric resist (PMMA) were about 10 nm wide, [3.28] and this is consistent with the estimates of lateral secondary electron ranges in these systems [3.27, 29].

Figure 3.4 schematically represents the spatial energy deposition by an electron beam incident on a resist coated substrate. This is often approximated as two Gaussians [3.30]. The broad Gaussian results from the backscattered electrons coming primarily from the substrate, and the narrow Gaussian includes the effects of incident beam size, forward scattering and lateral secondary electrons. The width of the broad Gaussian depends on the range of backscattered electrons as

$$\beta_B \sim R_G \propto E^{1.7} \ . \tag{3.5}$$

For low energies, where the range is comparable to the pattern feature size, the contribution to the local exposure can be great. The total exposure from the backscattered electrons is nearly independent of incident energy, since the backscatter coefficient η is approximately independent of energy. For higher energies the range of the backscatter dose can be so large that it is uniform with a value D_B where,

$$D_B = A\eta D_0 \ , \tag{3.6}$$

where D_0 is the incident dose and A is the fraction of area exposed. The peak-to-background exposure is therefore

$$(D_0 + D_B)/D_B = 1 + 1/A\eta \approx 1 + 1/A \ , \tag{3.7}$$

since η is on the order of one. No local proximity corrections are required for sufficiently high energy exposure, but the process latitude decreases for a dense pattern regardless of energy. For these reasons the trend now is to use increasingly high electron energies, with 50 keV in many commercial instruments and 100 keV becoming available.

Thin resists are desirable, as mentioned before, for limiting the effects of forward scattering. This has been exploited in multi-level resists where the thin active layer is deposited atop a thicker spacer or planerizing layer. This spacer layer also reduces the effect of the backscattered electrons and add a thicker useable resist thickness when the exposed pattern is transferred into this layer. With a three level resist, 50 nm and smaller lines widths have been created [3.30, 31].

A method of eliminating the difficulties of electrons backscattered from the substrate is to remove the underlying substrate layer and work with a thin supporting film. This is how all the highest resolution patterning has been done. In addition to eliminating the backscattered electrons and improving the process latitude, as described above, working on an electron transparent membrane allows the use of high resolution transmission electron microscopes for both exposure and imaging. In is with this type of instrument that one obtains the smallest electron beam sizes of down to 0.2 nm. With this type of thin film sample the high resolution imaging capability of the transmission electron microscope can be used to image the ultra-small objects. This is significant because the smallest structures may be difficult to resolve or have little contrast when viewed by conventional scanning electron microscopy.

A variety of resist systems have studied on thin films. These include PMMA [3.28], Langmiur–Blodgett films [3.32, 33], contamination films [3.34, 35], fluoride films [3.12, 36], and alumina [3.13]. Some remarkable work has been done creating functioning field effect transistors on thin films of III–V semiconductors [3.37]. After much work on thin films, it became apparent from studies on bulk materials, that the fundamental resolution limit of electron beam lithography was not affected by the presence of the substrate. This can be seen since 10 nm wide patterns can be developed in a single layer of PMMA on solid semiconductor substrates, as small as those on thin support films [3.38]. It is, however more difficult to work on bulk materials, because of the unwanted electron backscatter. Also the imaging is more difficult with only the electron scattering contrast mechanisms of SEM. There are overwhelming benefits of working on bulk materials in terms of the types and durability of structures that can be created and studied. Many new types of devices and structures have been created on bulk substrates.

With electron beams it is possible to expose such small areas that the molecular size of the resist can become significant. For large organic molecules this can be on the order of 10 nm. The grain size of a polycrystalline layer to be patterned can also become larger than the desired feature size. Clearly there are many new materials considerations at the nanometer dimensions. Another consideration important for the ultra small size range is the time it takes to write, by a scanning serial process. This time inversely related to the pixel size. The smaller the electron beam size the lower the current available for exposure and the longer the exposure time. The highest resolution resists also require higher exposure doses. Fortunately the areas involved for device exposure are small. For experimental devices where a few objects are being written, the time in writing is insignificant, and the benefits and success of scanned electron beam lithography have been great.

3.3 Pattern Transfer

The definition of high resolution patterns in a resist layer is only part of the fabrication process. In fact, pattern transfer is frequently the resolution limiting step in the fabrication process. While holes in thin films as small as 2 nm have been generated by high voltage electron beam lithography [3.12, 13], they have not been transferred into a solid material for study. Also the effects of process induced damage can be devistating on ultra-small structures, and this must be taken into consideration.

The general technique requires an additive or subtractive transfer process, typically an etching or deposition and lift-off step. Figure 3.5 illustrates these methods. The practical limitation in the lift-off procedure is on the aspect ratio and thickness of the film to be patterned in the lift-off step. For a successful removal of the deposited film, the deposited film should be discontinuous over the resist edge. If the deposited film is thick compared to the resist, this will not in general be the case and the lift-off is impossible. For best results a resist profile with an under-cut shape is desirable, but even so the resist thickness must be greater than the deposited film. As noted above the best resolution is obtained

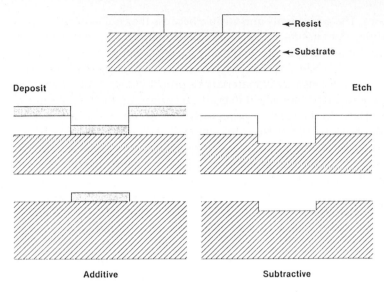

Deposit   Etch

Additive   Subtractive

Fig. 3.5. Schematic of etching and lift-off

with thin resist. The multi-layer resists have been used to improve the resist performance by using a thin imaging layer on a thicker under-layer [3.31, 39, 40]. The pattern exposed and developed in the thin imaging layer can be transferred into the subbing layer by a high resolution process such as reactive ion etching (Fig. 3.6). By appropriately choosing the etching chemistry this can greatly increase the resist utility. As an alternative additive transfer process, electroplating has been used to create 0.8 nm diameter gold wires in narrow cavities [3.39].

Directed ion etching methods of ion milling, reactive ion etching, ion beam etching and ion beam assisted etching have all been used as high resolution

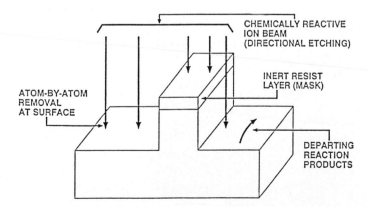

Fig. 3.6. Schematic of anisotropic ion etching process

etching processes. These are highly anisotropic because they use a directed beam of ions. Ion milling does not have the selectivity of etch rates but has been used with contamination lithography to create very narrow 8 nm wide Nb wires and 7 nm diameter Ag disks [3.34, 35]. The reactive techniques are generally superior since they allow selective etching of materials by proper choice of the chemistry. In ion milling the removed atoms will deposit on surfaces in the line of sight of the sputtered surface. In the reactive process the reaction products are volatile and do not deposit on exposed surfaces. In etching GaAs, for example, a relatively non reactive metal can be used as a mask to prevent the under lying material from being removed in a Cl containing plasma [3.41]. Etching narrow grooves can still be a problem because of the required transport into long narrow cavities. The highest aspect ratio structures in semiconductors have been made by ion beam assisted etching [3.42].

Let us consider some examples of nanofabrication that illustrate the possibilities and how the techniques build on each other. In an example of a nanofabrication process using high resolution lithography and a lift-off step, arrays of 20 nm gold particles were fabricated on sapphire substrates for optical measurements [3.43]. The creation of regular arrays of known geometry particles allowed comparison to effective medium theories for the optical response of inhomogeneous media without adjustable parameters. For the creation of these structures a single 60 nm thick layer of PMMA was exposed by a ~ 2 nm diameter 120 keV electron beam in a scanning electron microscope. The beam was focused by imaging a scratch in the resist using the secondary electron signal. The exposed dot resist areas were removed in a solution of cellosolve in methanol. Pure gold was deposited on the resist by vacuum evaporation. The remaining resist was dissolved in acetone to perform the lift-off (Fig. 3.5) and leave the gold disks. Annealing the sample at 125°C caused the gold to consolidate to reduce the surface energy and become more spheroidal. The annealing step made significantly rounder and more regular particles. An

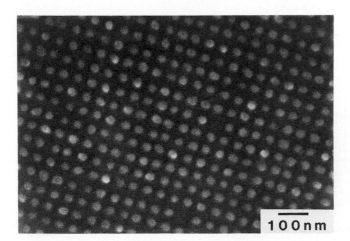

100nm

Fig. 3.7. Scanning electron micrograph of Au particles on sapphire

electron micrograph of a 50 nm period array of gold particles is shown in Fig. 3.7. These particles were sufficiently small that the particle size had to be considered in reducing the electron mean free path.

In another example a technique similar to the previous example was used to define etch masks for creating small GaAs columns [3.41]. In this case NiCr particles were defined similarly to the gold, as described above, by electron beam exposure and lift-off. The NiCr was resistant to anisotropic reactive ion etching in a SiCl$_4$ plasma that anisotropically etches GaAs. By this method 20 nm diameter GaAs columns were formed in square arrays as seen in Fig. 3.8.

The next level of complication involves layered GaAs/AlGaAs materials that require more consideration for etching, because of differing chemistry of the alternating layers. Studies of etching such layers were done [3.44], and the reactive ion etching in the correct BCl$_3$ and Ar gas mixture was used to create arrays of quantum dots and wires for optical studies of dimensionally reduced structures [3.46]. Figure 3.9 shows a transmission electron micrograph of etched multiple quantum well structures.

The ability to etch high aspect ratio structures in GaAs has been used to create high resolution ion masks for selected area disordering of GaAs/AlGaAs heterostructures. In the technologically important case of compound heterostructure materials the effect of impurity and defect induced compositional mixing can be used to define very small lateral geometries. In this process the presence of certain impurities or sufficient amounts of lattice damage substantially reduces the temperature at which the layers of material will interdiffuse.

Much of the work in this area has been motivated by the possibility of fabrication improved heterostructure lasers and waveguides. In the area of nanofabrication, lattice damage induced by Ga or Al ion implantation has been used to locally enhance interdiffusion and modify the mini-band structure to achieve lateral carrier confinement in patterned dots and wires [3.47–50]. With the implantation of Si impurities even greater enhancement of interdiffusion can

0.5 μm

Fig. 3.8. Scanning electron micrograph of reactive ion etched GaAs structures 20 nm in diameter

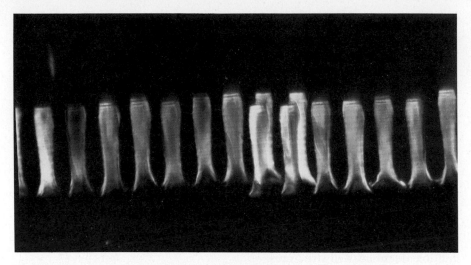

Fig. 3.9. Transmission electron micrograph of etched quantum well structures

be achieved to laterally modify the materials band structure. Si acts as an amphoteric dopant, however and can complicate the electrical modification control. The patterning resolution limit of selected implant induced disorder has been explicitly studied by cross-sectional transmission electron microscopy [3.50], and the indication is that resolution easily better than 30 nm can be achieved (Fig. 3.10). This holds even greater future promise with focused ion beam systems.

The fabrication technology exists to allow fabrication of structures with dimensions on the order of 10–100 nm in a variety of materials. With advanced electron, ion and X-ray techniques the lateral control of semiconductor materials is constantly advancing. With the possibilities of epitaxial growth combined with

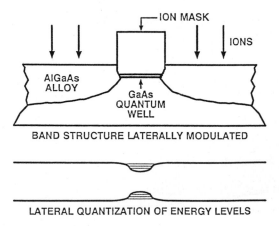

Fig. 3.10. Schematic of the disorder patterning method

these techniques complete three dimensional control of semiconductor structure can be contemplated. This is allowing the exploration of new phenomena.

I acknowledge the valuable collaborations with A. Scherer, E. Clausen, E. Dobisz and others at Bell Communications Research.

References

3.1 H. Sakaki: Jpn. J. Appl. Phys., **19**, L735 (1980);
     R. E. Howard, P. F. Liao, W. J. Skocpol, L. D. Jackel, H. G. Craighad: Science, **221**, 117 (1983);
     M. J. Kelley: In *The Physics and Fabrication of Microstructures and Microdevices*, Ed. by M. J.
     Kelley (Springer, Berlin, Heidelberg 1986) p. 174
3.2 A. N. Broers: Solid State Technology, July 1985, p 119
3.3 Chapter 2 of this book
3.4 T. Mimura, S. Hiyamizu, T. Fujii, K. Napbu: Jpn. J. Appl. Phys. **19**, L225 (1980)
3.5 N. Holonyak, R. M. Kulbas, R. D. Dupuis, D. P. Dapkus: IEEE J. Quantum Elect. **QE-16**, 170
     (1980)
3.6 F. Capasso: In *Semiconductor and Semimetals*, Vol. 24, ed. by R. Dingle (Academic, San Diego
     1987). Chap. 6
3.7 H. G. Craighead: In *The Physics and Fabrication of Microstructures and Microdevices*, Ed. by
     M. J. Kelley (Springer, Berlin, Heidelberg 1986) p. 150
3.8 D. P. Kern: J. Vac. Sci. Technol. **16**, 1686 (1986)
3.9 M. A. McCord, F. W. Pease: J. Vac. Sci. Technol. B **1**, 430 (1987)
3.10 H. G. Craighead: J. Appl. Phys. **55**, 4430 (1984)
3.11 M. J. Bowden: J. Electrochem. Soc. Reviews and News, May 1981, p. 208C
3.12 A. Muray, M. Isaacson, I. Adesida: Appl. Phys. Lett. **45**, 589 (1984)
3.13 I. G. Sailisbury, R. S. Timsit, S. D. Berger, C. J. Humphries: Appl. Phys. Lett. **45**, 1289 (1984)
3.14 K. Jain, C. G. Wilson: Appl. Phys. B **28**, 206 (1982)
3.15 L. F. Thompson, C. G. Wilson, M. J. Bowden: *Introduction to Microlithography* (American
     Chemical Society, Washington D. C. 1983)
3.16 N. P. Economou, D. C. Flanders: J. Vac. Sci. Technol. **19**, 868 (1981)
3.17 D. Widman, K. U. Stein: In *Semiconductor Technologies With Reduced Dimensions, Solid State
     Circuits*, Pro. 2nd Eur. Solid State Circuits Conference., 1976, 29 (1977)
3.18 J. C. White et al.: Appl. Phys. Lett. **44**, 22 (1983)
3.19 Everhait, Hoff: J. Appl. Phys. **42**, 5837 (1971)
3.20 D. C. Flanders: Appl. Phys. Lett. **36**, 93 (1980)
3.21 See for example J. Melngailis, *J. Vac. Sci. Technol. B* **5**, 469 (1987)
3.22 J. Randall, D. C. Flanders, N. P. Economou, J. P. Donnelley, E. I. Bromley: J. Vac. Sci. Technol.
     B**1**, 58 (1985)
3.23 I. Adesida, E, Kratschmer, E. D. Wolf, A. Murray, M. Isaacson: J. Vac. Sci. Technol. B **1**, 45
     (1985)
3.24 M. Kumuro, H. Hiroshima, H. Tanoue: J. Vac. Sci. Technol. B **1**, 985 (1983)
3.25 R. K. Defreez et al.: Electron. Lett. **22**, 919 (1986)
3.26 L. D. Jackel, R. E. Howard, P. M. Mankiewich, H. G. Craighead, R. W. Epworth: Appl. Phys.
     Lett. **45**, 698 (1984)
3.27 D. F. Keyser: J. Vac. Sci. Technol. B **1**, 1391 (1983)
3.28 A. N. Broers: J. Electrochem. Soc. **128**, 166 (1981)
3.29 D. C. Joy: unpublished
3.30 R. J. Hawryluk: J. Vac. Sci. Technol. **19**, 1 (1981)
3.31 D. M. Tennant, L. D. Jackel, R. E. Howard, E. L. Hu, P. Grabbe, R. J. Capik, B. S. Schneider:
     J. Vac. Sci. Technol. B **1**, 1391 (1983)

3.32 A. N. Broers, M. Pomerantz: Thin Solid Films **99**, 323 (1983)

3.33 A. Barraud, C. Rasilio, A. Rauandel-Teixier: Solid State Technology, Aug 1979, p 120.

3.34 A. N. Broers, W. W. Molzen, J. J. Cuomo, N. D. Wittels: Appl. Phys. Lett. **29**, 7188 (1976)

3.35 H. G. Craighaed, P. M. Mankiewich: J. Appl. Phys. **53**, 7188 (1982)

3.36 P. M. Mankiewich, H. G. Craighead, T. R. Harrison, A. H. Dayem: Appl. Phys. Lett. **44**, 468 (1984)

3.37 S. Mackie, S. P. Beaumont: Solid State Commun. **28**, 117 (1985)

3.38 H. G. Craighead, R. E. Howard, L. D. Jackel, P. M. Mankiewich: Appl. Phys. Lett. **42**, 38 (1983)

3.39 W. D. Williams, N. Giordano: Rev. Sci. Instrum. **55**, 410 (1984)

3.40 Gozdz 3 level

3.41 M. B. Stern, H. G. Craighead, P. F. Liao, P. M. Mankiewich: Appl. Phys. Lett. **45**, 410 (1984)

3.42 M. W. Geiss, G. A. Lincoln, N. Efremow, W. J. Piacentini: J. Vac. Sci. Technol. **19**, 1390 (1981)

3.43 H. G. Craighead, G. A. Niklasson: Appl. Phys. Lett. **44**, 1134 (1984)

3.44 E. M. Clausen, Jr., H. G. Craighead, J. M. Worlock, J. P. Harbison, L. M. Schiavone, L. Florez, B. Van der Gaag: Appl. Phys. Lett. **55**, 1427 (1989)

3.45 A. Scherer, H. G. Craighead: Appl. Phys. Lett. **49**, 1284 (1986)

3.46 K. Kash et al.: Appl. Phys. Lett. **49**, 1043 (1986)

3.47 J. Cibert et al.: Appl. Phys. Lett. **49**, 1275 (1986)

3.48 E. A. Dobisz et al.: Proc. Mat. Res. Soc. (1986)

3.49 P. Petroff, Chap. 11 of this book

3.50 E. A. Dobisz, H. G. Craighead, S. A. Schwarz, P. S. D. Lin, K. Kash, L. M. Schiavone, A. Scherer, J. P. Harbison, B. Tell: Proc. SPIE. **797**, 194 (1987)

4. Theory of Resonant Tunnelling and Surface Superlattices

D. K. Ferry

With 16 Figures

One of the attractive features of working with constrained-dimensionality devices is the ability of applying textbook quantum mechanics to their understanding, and still achieving a reasonable degree of success in this task. Perhaps the classic example of this is tunnelling, particularly in the case of the resonant-tunnelling device. The concept of tunnel diodes goes back several decades, and is implemented in very heavily doped p–n junction diodes. In this case the tunnelling is through the forbidden gap region, and involves electrons making transitions from the conduction band to the valence band, and vice versa. In the present context, however, we are concerned with fabricating tunnel barriers by band-gap engineering. Thus, we can separate two GaAs regions by a thin barrier region of GaAlAs, and the tunnel barrier is formed by the conduction (and valence) band discontinuity. In this sense, the barrier formed is a textbook example, and the results on tunnelling current can be calculated in a straight-forward manner.

Interest arises in the ability to combine two or more barriers, and to sandwich thin GaAs regions between the barriers. Here, the small gap GaAs layers are actually quantum wells, weakly coupled to one another. This now sets up the concept of "resonant tunnelling", in which the tunnelling probability is quite low except for the energies of the quantum levels in the individual wells. As we will see below, this opens the possibility of negative differential conductivity in the device characteristics. In fact, the advent of molecular beam epitaxy (and metal-organic CVD) allows one to engineer an entire range of tunnelling and quantum structures within more normal semiconductor devices in each case producing novel or enhanced performance characteristics.

As semiconductor technology continues to pursue the scaling down of integrated circuit dimensions into the submicron and ultra-submicron regimes, many novel and interesting questions will emerge concerning the physics of charged particles for motion along the surface or interface. In particular, the fabrication of the quantum-well superlattice has been possible due to the advent of molecular-beam epitaxy (MBE) and metal-organic CVD (MO-CVD) technology. In the last half of this chapter, we want finally to consider *lateral superlattices*. Lateral superlattices, in which the superstructure lies in a surface or heterostructure layer, offer considerable advantages for obtaining superlattice effects in a planar technology. In the present context, the later superlattices offer us the opportunity to couple a large array of quantum tunnelling structures together in order to study the cooperative effects.

4.1 Tunnelling Probabilities

The tunnelling probability has been calculated in many introductory texts for simple cases, either as rectangular barriers or in the WKB approximation, often called the quasi-classical approximation. In actual devices, the barrier is quite often distorted by the applied bias. In this section, we want to introduce the tunnelling probability, and calculate it in a number of cases. We will begin with a simple single barrier before moving to the more complicated resonant tunnelling structure. Although the double barrier structure is quite old in concept [4.1], it has become a very popular device recently due to measurements showing definite peaks in conductivity (and negative differential conductance) and very high frequency behavior [4.2]. The key factor in this recent success appears to be much better material quality. However, the investigators have not spent any time in optimizing the devices for peak performance. The bias upsets any prior symmetry in the two tunnelling barriers and changes the conditions for resonance. Consequently, optimization must be based upon exact knowledge of the germane peak and the overall structure.

4.1.1 Single Barrier

The general treatment for rectangular barriers to be followed is that of most textbooks, although we will modify this approach through the use of a transfer matrix formulation. Consider, for example, the rectangular barrier of Fig. 4.1. The points A and D represent sites just outside the barrier in which the wave function is allowed to propagate. Points B and C, on the other hand, are points just inside the barrier in which the wave function is strongly attenuated and non-propagating. The transfer-matrix approach sets down a matrix of coefficients that describes the change in the wave functions at the barrier edge and through the barrier (or the propagating region). We differ from some earlier treatments here, by noting that it is possible to have different barrier heights on the two sides of the barrier, as shown in the figure. For this reason, we will write the equations entirely in terms of the wave vectors themselves rather than in terms of the

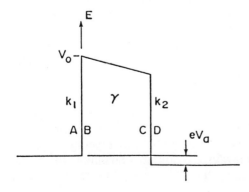

Fig. 4.1. The rectangular single barrier tunnelling structure

potentials. We shall assume that the top row of the matrices refers to the forward wave, propagating in the positive x-direction, and the bottom row refers to the backward wave, propagating in the negative x-direction.

To begin, we must write the wave at C in terms of the wave existing at D. Primarily the transfer matrix at this point just expresses the phase shifts encountered by the waves at the boundary. This matrix for $C(D)$ we will call $2M_0$. It is given by

$$\begin{bmatrix} 1 - ik_2/\gamma & 1 + ik_2/\gamma \\ 1 + ik_2/\gamma & 1 - ik_2/\gamma \end{bmatrix}, \tag{4.1}$$

where $k_2 = (2mE/\hbar^2)^{1/2}$ is the propagating wave vector to the right of the barrier and $\gamma = [2m(V_0 - E)/\hbar]^{1/2}$ is the attenuation constant within the barrier. Within the barrier, we need to now write the wave functions at B in terms of those at C. We call this propagation matrix M_γ, and it is

$$\begin{bmatrix} \exp(\gamma a) & 0 \\ 0 & \exp(-\gamma a) \end{bmatrix}, \tag{4.2}$$

for a constant γ. We remark at this point that (4.2) is an approximation if γ varies with position in the barrier even if γa is replaced by an averaging integral. Rather, the proper treatment is to integrate the incremental exponential operators, which is not the same as the exponential of the integrated operator. In this case, (4.2) is not strictly diagonal anymore. However, we will continue to use the form (4.2), as it is a reasonable approximation that actually improves upon the usual WKB approximation.

Finally, we need a matching matrix for A in terms of B, given by $2M_i$ as

$$\begin{bmatrix} 1 + i\gamma/k_1 & 1 - i\gamma/k_1 \\ 1 - i\gamma/k_1 & 1 + i\gamma/k_1 \end{bmatrix}. \tag{4.3}$$

The total transfer matrix is now $M_i M_\gamma M_0 = M$. If we assume that there is no backward wave at D, then the tunnelling coefficient for the wave function is just $1/M_{11}$, and the probability current is then $1/|M_{11}|^2$. The term M_{11} is just

$$\{(1 + k_2/k_1)\cosh(\gamma a) + 2i[\gamma/k_1 - k_2/\gamma]\sinh(\gamma a)\}/2 .$$

This leads to the tunnelling probability

$$D = 4k_1 k_2/[(k_1 + k_2)^2 + W(k_1,k_2,\gamma)\sinh^2(\gamma a)] , \tag{4.4a}$$

where

$$W = (\gamma^2 + k_1^2)(\gamma^2 + k_2^2)/\gamma^2 . \tag{4.4b}$$

One thing we note immediately is that the tunnelling probability is symmetrical in k_1 and k_2, which is what we assumed at the end of the previous section. This symmetry result is independent of any distortion of the barrier by the field, and is simply a statement that the tunnelling barrier is reciprocal, and hence a linear "resistor". Generally, we may approximate the tunnelling probability by using the fact that γa is a large number. Hence

$$D \simeq [16k_1 k_2 / W(k_1, k_2, \gamma)] \exp(-2\gamma a) . \tag{4.5}$$

Equation (4.5) provides us with the basis for using a WKB type formula for a general barrier, in which we replace the term γa by

$$\gamma a \rightarrow \int_0^a \gamma(x) dx$$
$$= (2m/\hbar^2)^{1/2} (2/3eF) [(E_B - E)^{3/2} - (E_B - eFa - E)^{3/2}], \tag{4.6}$$

where we have assumed that the energy of the barrier top varies linearly with an applied electric field F. Here, E_B is the barrier height (in absolute energy) at $X = 0$, and E is the energy of the tunnelling particle.

What we note from the exponential behavior is that the tunnelling carriers will be those of highest energy on either side of the barrier, yet the current that is calculated is a sum over all of the carriers. If the field is small, $F \ll (E_B - E)/ea$, expansion of (4.6) just yields the result γa, and the role of the field in the barrier can generally be ignored. For $E_B - E = 0.3$ eV, and $a = 3$ nm, we require $F \ll 10^6$ V/cm. While this seems like a substantial field, we note that this is just the field required to lower the barrier on the right-hand side to the energy level E. In fact, these energies and fields can be expected to be routinely encountered in tunnelling problems, and the expansion discussed above cannot be utilized. This means that the field induces a significant change in the quantity in (4.6), which is reflected exponentially in the tunnelling probability, and hence in the current. The second term in an expansion of (4.6) is linear in the field, which means that the current will rise exponentially with the field, as $D = D_0 \exp(F/F_0)$, where D_0 is the tunnelling probability in the absence of the field, and F_0 is a normalization field obtained by the numerical factors in (4.6).

4.1.2 Resonant Tunnelling Rates

The resonant tunnelling structure, for general barriers, is shown in Fig. 4.2. Here, a quantum well is sandwiched between two tunnelling barriers. In its most general, and current, implementation, the tunnelling barriers are GaAlAs, whose composition is adjusted to give a barrier height of about 0.3 V. The quantum well and the two end, or cladding, layers are then usually pure GaAs. In a simple case, the resonant levels correspond to the bound states of the quantum well. For electrons, incident with this energy, the tunnelling probability is considerably larger than that expected from the two barriers. Indeed, in the WKB approximation, with equal barriers and no bias, the tunnelling probability can approach unity. In actual experiments, this has not been found. While the measurements have been carried out on realistic structures, where the barriers are distorted by the applied bias, the assumed theory mentioned above requires pure symmetry.

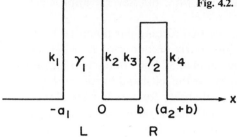

Fig. 4.2. The double-barrier resonant tunnelling device

This can lead to a drastic drop in the effective tunnelling probability for the structure, even on resonance [4.3]. Moreover, the resonances themselves will be shifted by the applied bias [4.4]. In Fig. 4.3, we illustrate a typical $I–V$ curve obtained for a structure with uniform thickness of barriers and well of 5 nm^2.

A second important point that must be made with regard to the actual experiments that have been carried out is that tunnelling can be a time dependent problem. As in any resonant cavity problem in electromagnetics, or quantum mechanics, the population of the resonant level will build up with a characteristic time constant related to the Q of the cavity. This latter quantity is also related to the natural line width of the resonance itself, and this has been suggested as being quite small in resonant tunneling devices [4.4]. However, in the current carrying case, when the device is under bias, we must remember that it is the *loaded Q*, not the natural or un-loaded value, that must be used in computing the time required for the build-up of the resonant level population. The physical device itself, when placed under bias, is an open system. Such systems have not been treated with much consideration in the quantum literature. However, the presence of the bias and external loads will certainly broaden the resonance beyond its natural, or un-loaded, value. In general, this time constant must be found by self-consistent solutions of the bias distribution, local carrier density, and current flow. Not

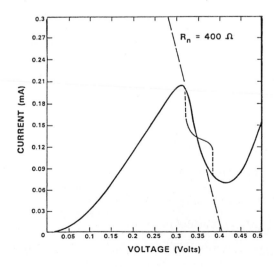

Fig. 4.3. Experimental curves of the tunnelling current through the resonant structure (after *Sollner* et al.) [4.2] The measurements were at 100 K, and the dark line is measured for a stable device, while the light line was measured during oscillations at 4 GHz. The difference is thought to be due to self-detection

much progress has been made in this direction, but several approaches are discussed in following sections.

The general case, shown in Fig. 4.2, for two rectangular potential barriers is the basis for our approach. The tunnelling matrix M for one of these barriers was developed in an earlier section and is given in (4.3). Each of the two barriers has its own matrix. We will denote the matrix for the left-hand barrier in Fig. 4.2 as M_L, and will also take the tunnelling probability for this barrier alone to be $D_L = (k_2/k_1) |M_{L,11}|^{-2}$. This matrix is written in terms of k_1 and k_2 as the propagating wave vectors at the left and right-hand edges, respectively. In a similar fashion, we may write the tunnelling probability of the right-hand barrier in Fig. 4.2 as $D_R = (k_4/k_3)|M_{R,11}|^{-2}$, where M_R is written in terms of k_3 and k_4 as the propagating wave vectors at the left and right-hand edges of the barrier, respectively. For a flat-bottom potential well, as shown in the figure, we of course have $k_2 = k_3$, but retain the difference for generality under applied bias to be treated below.

The overall tunnelling probability can be calculated by connecting the two barrier layers through the equation

$$M_T = M_L U M_R, \tag{4.7}$$

where U is a connection matrix describing the propagation through the quantum well. This latter matrix is given by

$$\begin{bmatrix} \exp(-ikb) & 0 \\ 0 & \exp(ikb) \end{bmatrix}, \tag{4.8}$$

where b is the well thickness and k is an average propagating wave vector (we will of course have to replace the quantity kb by an integral over the region when we apply bias, in keeping with the approximation discussed following (4.2), but for the moment $k = k_2 = k_3$). There are, in addition to (4.7), two propagator matrices which account for the shift in origins of the left and right barriers with respect to the origin assumed in (4.3). However, these matrices are left- and right-multipliers of (4.7), are diagonal as in (4.8), have the same form as (4.8), so that when we take the magnitude squared of M_{11}, they do not play any role. We can therefore ignore them. Finally, we find that the tunnelling probability for the entire structure is now given by

$$D = (k_4/k_1)|M_{T,11}|^{-2} \tag{4.9}$$

$$= (k_4/k_1)|M_{L,11} M_{R,11} \exp(-ikb) + M_{L,12} M_{R,21} \exp(ikb)|^{-2}.$$

We can now expand the denominator term to give

$$D = (k_4/k_1)/[|M_{L,11}|^2|M_{R,11}|^2 + |M_{L,12}|^2|M_{R,21}|^2$$

$$+ 2 \operatorname{Re}\{M_{L,11}^* M_{R,11}^* M_{L,12} M_{R,21}\} \cos(2kb)$$

$$- 2 \operatorname{Im}\{M_{L,11}^* M_{R,11}^* M_{L,12} M_{R,21}\} \sin(2kb)]. \tag{4.10}$$

It is immediately noted that these quantities can be expressed in terms of the tunnelling probabilities for the left and right barriers alone, which means that we can express the result by the properties of these barriers and the quantum well separately. We also note that, because $M_{11} = M_{22}^*$ and $M_{12} = M_{21}^*$ for each of the barriers, the net tunnelling at this point should be symmetrical. This symmetry can not be broken by the applied bias, and we must be careful to distinguish between symmetry of the tunnelling coefficient and symmetry in the current flow for two different directions of the applied bias. This latter result is different and non-symmetric current flow can arise from different positions of the resonant level for the two directions of applied bias. The asymmetry in current for reverse bias can also arise from nonlinear effects associated with charge transfer in the barriers, which we do not treat in this present approach. We return to this point later.

We can examine the denominator in some detail to determine the appropriate terms. We of course want to examine the largest terms in the denominator, as these will create the smallest tunnelling coefficient, as they dominate the overall value of D. We can pursue this somewhat by recognizing that

$$|M_{L,11}|^2 - |M_{L,12}|^2 = k_2\gamma_1/k_1\gamma_2 , \tag{4.11a}$$

$$|M_{R,11}|^2 - |M_{R,12}|^2 = k_4\gamma_3/k_3\gamma_4 , \tag{4.11b}$$

and that we can rewrite a number of the terms as functions of the various "reflection angles," as

$$|M_{11}|^2 = W_1[\cosh(2\overline{\gamma a_1}) - \cos(2\phi_2 - 2\phi_1)] , \tag{4.12}$$

$$M_{11}^* M_{12} = -W_1[\cosh(2\overline{\gamma a_1} - 2i\phi_2) - \cos(2\phi_1)] , \tag{4.13}$$

$$M_{11}^* M_{12}^* = W_1[\cosh(2\overline{\gamma a_1} - 2i\phi_1) \quad (\cos(2\phi_2)] , \tag{4.14}$$

where

$$W_1 = (k_2^2 + \gamma_2^2)(k_1^2 + \gamma_1^2)/8k_1^2\gamma_2^2, \tag{4.15}$$

$$\phi_1 = \arctan(\gamma_1/k_1) , \tag{4.16}$$

$$\phi_2 = \arctan(\gamma_2/k_2) . \tag{4.17}$$

We note here that the quantity $\overline{\gamma a_1}$ is the integrated average over the barrier, as discussed above. These values are of course for the left barrier. For the right barrier, we obtain the equivalent of (4.15–4.17) making the changes $\gamma_1 \rightarrow \gamma_3$, $\gamma_2 \rightarrow \gamma_4$, $W_1 \rightarrow W_2$, $k_1 \rightarrow k_3$, $k_2 \rightarrow k_4$, $\phi_1 \rightarrow \phi_3$, and $\phi_2 \rightarrow \phi_4$. In evaluating the lead terms of the denominator, we need only use the small tunnelling approximation of (4.5). Then the leading term of the denominator is

$$2W_1W_2\exp(2\overline{\gamma a_1} + 2\overline{\gamma a_2})[1 - \cos(2kb - 2\phi_2 - 2\phi_3)] , \tag{4.18}$$

and

$$D \simeq D_L D_R \tag{4.19}$$

reflects the fact that we really have two tunnelling barriers in series. In this case, there is no coherence in the tunnelling wave function. However, this term vanishes at resonance, a condition given by the bracketed term in (4.18); that is, this leading term disappears on resonance when

$$kb = \arctan(\gamma_1/k_2) + \arctan(\gamma_2/k_3) + n\pi , \tag{4.20}$$

where we assume that the integer n is not zero. On resonance, the next leading terms in the series of the denominator are terms of the order of

$$D_L^{-1} + D_R^{-1}, \tag{4.21}$$

but the coefficient of these terms also involves the same bracketed angle dependent terms of (4.18). Thus, these terms also vanish on resonance. In both cases, of (4.18) and (4.21), the form of these terms is not significantly changed by having different barriers. On the other hand, the next leading term, which really governs the tunnelling coefficient on resonance, is one that does not appear in the equal barrier case. This next term is given by

$$C_{RL}\sinh(2\overline{\gamma}a_1 - 2\overline{\gamma}a_2) , \tag{4.22}$$

where

$$C_{RL} = (W_1 W_2/2)\cos(2kb + 2\phi_3 - 2\phi_2) , \tag{4.23}$$

which does not vanish. Thus, on resonance, the tunneling coefficient is given by

$$D_{res} \simeq D_{min}/D_{max}, \tag{4.24}$$

where D_{min} is the smaller of D_L or D_R, and D_{max} is the larger of the two. It may readily be shown that in the case of identical barriers, this quantity goes to unity exactly.

The results obtained above hold even when the incident energy range is quite narrow. We must remember, however, that the tunnelling current is not given by D alone, but is a summation over all of the states that are allowed to tunnel. In the resonant tunnelling device, current begins to flow when the bias is such that the resonant level is brought down to the top of the occupied states on the left cladding layer (assuming the bias is such that the right layer is lowered with respect to the left). The position of the resonance itself is affected by the bias, since this affects the values of the parameters in (4.20). In any case, current flows as long as the resonance energy is sweeping through the occupied states of the left cladding layer. The peak is reached when this energy is reduced to the conduction band edge on the left. Then the current is reduced to the $D_L D_R$ value. One should be careful in estimating the valley current, however, as inelastic processes, transport through a second resonance, and/or emission over one or the other of the barriers can all contribute to the total current.

We also note that in the absence of resonance, the wave function decays continuously from the left to the right of the barrier (assuming the bias is as discussed above). On resonance, however, the wave function has a local maximum in the quantum well. Carrier retention in the well is a dynamic process, while the equations developed above are for the static case. Thus, the number of particles within the well, and the net current flowing through the well, will all be time dependent quantities. This requires that the transient solutions be obtained, which is a somewhat more difficult project. This is especially true, as the bias will force carriers through the barrier in a driven mode. This is a reflection of the fact that it is the loaded-Q of the tunnel structure, and not the unloaded-Q, that is important in determining the time dependent quantities. There is an important feedback mechanism at work as well, as the local shape of the barriers is modified when the number of particles trapped within the well varies. This also affects the resonance time evolution.

In Fig. 4.4, we show a resonant tunnelling barrier with an applied bias. We have assumed that the bias is linearly dropped across the tunnel barriers and the well in the structure, and that the two barriers have equal thicknesses. Then,

$$D_L \simeq \exp\{ - [4(2m)^{1/2}/3heF]\,[\phi_0^{3/2} - \phi_1^{3/2}]\}\,,\tag{4.25}$$

$$D_R \simeq \exp\{ - [4(2m)^{1/2}/3heF]\,[r_2^{3/2} - \phi_3^{3/2}]\}\,,\quad \text{and}\tag{4.26}$$

$$D_{\min}/D_{\max} \simeq \exp\{ - [e(2m)^{1/2}/3heF]\,[\phi_0^{3/2} - \phi_1^{3/2} + \phi_1^{3/2} - \phi_3^{3/2}]\}\,,\tag{4.27}$$

where

$$\phi_0 = eV_{\text{barrier}} - E\,,$$

$$\phi_1 \equiv \phi_0 - eFa\,,$$

$$\phi_2 = \phi_0 - eF(a + b)\,,$$

$$\phi_3 = \phi_0 - eF(2a + b)\,.\tag{4.28}$$

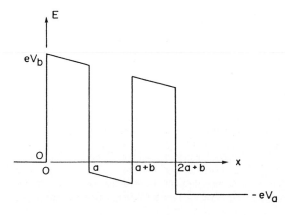

Fig. 4.4. Shift in the double barrier structure under applied bias. Here it is assumed that the bias is linearly distributed across the barriers

We also note that the applied voltage is given by $V_a = F(2a + b)$. In (4.28), the energy is referenced to the left hand conduction band edge, and so the peak in the current is obtained when $E = 0$. Then, resonance is obtained at this same energy and requires

$$[2(2m)^{1/2}/3\hbar eF][(eFa)^{3/2} - (eFa \to eFb)^{3/2}]$$
$$= \tan^{-1}[(\phi_0 - eFa)\}^{1/2} + \tan^{-1}[(\phi_0 - eFa - eFb)/eF(a + b)]^{1/2}. \tag{4.29}$$

Ricco and *Azbel* [4.4] have evaluated this expression for the parameters of [4.2], and obtain a bias voltage of 0.21 V, which agrees well with the experimental data. In Fig. 4.5, we plot the net tunnelling coefficient for the case of barriers of 5 nm and a quantum well of 5 nm, assuming the barrier height is 0.3 eV, in the absence of an applied bias and with a bias of 0.1 V applied. In Fig. 4.6, we plot the resonance energy in this well with applied bias. Here, we find that the peak occurs slightly lower than the Ricco and Azbel value, and is found at about 0.19 V.

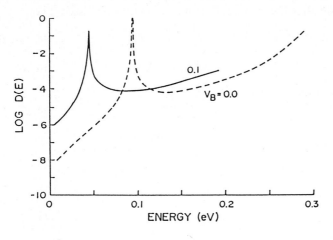

Fig. 4.5. The tunnelling probability as a function of energy for the structure of Fig. 4.4, for zero and 0.1 V of applied bias

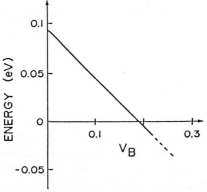

Fig. 4.6. The shift of the resonant level as a function of applied bias for the structure of Fig. 4.4. The energy is measured from the conduction band edge on the left of the structure, as indicated in Fig. 4.4. The peak of the tunnelling current through the structure occurs as the resonance level passes through zero energy

4.2 Tunnelling Time

The very concept of tunnelling through potential barriers is one purely of quantum mechanics, and has no parallel in classical physics. Perhaps it is not surprising therefore that there remain questions in the area of tunnelling for which answers are not immediately obvious, and for which various calculations have proven to be quite controversial. One of these is the question of just how long it takes an *electron* to tunnel through a barrier. The problem is not a simple one, for one must also ask the question as to just what form a wave function must take to simulate an electron. It is not clear that answers to either of these questions have been obtained, although considerable work has addressed the question of how long it takes a wave function (or packet) to "traverse" the barrier. This latter quantity is complicated because of the decaying nature of the wave function within the barrier, and the generally dispersive nature of the propagation throughout the problem.

MacColl [4.5] is thought to be the first to have addressed the question of scattering and propagation of the wave packet through a barrier. His result, for rectangular barriers, is

$$\tau = mX/\hbar K \quad = \int_0^x [m/\hbar k(x')]dx' , \tag{4.30}$$

where k is of course the momentum wave vector of the incident (and transmitted) wave function. *Hartman* [4.6] obtained a similar result for Gaussian wave packets in which the central momentum lay very near to the top of the barrier. However, for packets in which the momentum was not near the top of the barrier, this latter author found a tunnelling time *independent of the barrier thickness*, so that there was no clear velocity associated with the packet. This latter result gave a tunnelling time of

$$\tau = 2m/\hbar k\gamma . \tag{4.31}$$

This result was also obtained for the stationary phase position in wave packets [4.7].

Hagstrom [4.8], on the other hand, pointed out that such wave function approaches neglected the dynamic properties of the potential barrier, in that the quantum mechanics of the system would have the wave function sense the presence of the potential at some distance from the latter. He suggested that the density matrix would be a more appropriate method of investigating the tunnelling time. Nevertheless, he calculated a tunnelling time, for a plane wave, of

$$\tau = \hbar k/2\gamma e V_0 , \tag{4.32}$$

where v_0 is the barrier height. *Barker* [4.9] has picked up on these suggestions, and has calculated the tunnelling by utilizing Wigner functions (discussed below). The Wigner function allows a position and momentum representation of the quantum mechanical density matrix, and can account for the nonlocal behavior of the potential. Yet, the results obtained by *Barker* are those of (4.30).

A more careful analysis of wave function tunnelling has yielded yet another definition. *Büttiker* and *Landauer* [4.10] modulated the potential barrier with a small ac voltage, and then examined the frequency response of the transmitted wave's modulated portion. By looking at the roll-off point of the ac response, they determined a tunnelling time of

$$\tau = mX/\hbar\gamma = \int_{0}^{x} [m/\hbar\gamma(x')]dx' \,. \tag{4.33}$$

They also obtained this same time in considering the tunnelling of a simple wave function or of a packet formed by a few wave functions. *Stevens* [4.11] pointed out the importance of the dispersive nature of the barrier and sought to find the "signal velocity" appropriate for such media. By considering a localized plane wave, he obtained the same result as (4.33).

It is clear from the above discussion that the concept of a tunnelling time may not be as clear as one would like. The nature of non-locality in quantum mechanics is an important concept, in that sharp potentials have Fourier components that can extend quite far from the barrier itself, causing a remote interaction before a wave packet even reaches the barrier. Thus, the proper tunnelling distance may not be easily evaluated for inclusion in the above equations. *Barker* addressed this question by using the asymptotes in position of the tunnelling Wigner packets, but it is not clear that his results are better than normal wave packet studies. In Fig. 4.7, we illustrate the various tunnelling times

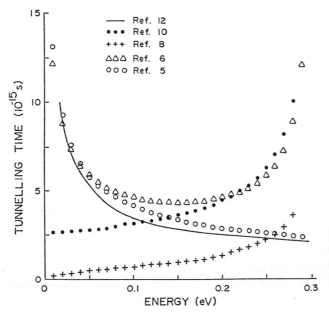

Fig. 4.7. The tunnelling time as a function of the energy, as determined by the various theories discussed in the text

for a barrier height of 0.3 eV and thickness of 3 nm (the other parameters are those for a GaAlAs barrier between GaAs cladding layers). Included in this are our own results for Wigner function tunnelling [4.12], which differ somewhat from those of *Barker*.

In real devices, it is not clear just what the tunnelling time of a wave function, or of a wave packet, means. True devices have degenerate cladding layers, so that a proper treatment requires a full many-electron version of the tunnelling problem. Localization effects in the wave functions, and in the tunnelling properties near the top of the barriers, could be quite important. We turn to this in the next section. Before leaving this topic, however, we want to note one aspect of (4.33). For this approach, it is evident that electrons near the top of the barrier move quite slowly from (4.33), and exhibit quite long tunnelling times. On the other hand, *Hartmann* [4.6] pointed out that electrons near the top of the barrier dominated the tunnelling properties of the Gaussian pulses. The former would suggest electrons near the top of the barrier are 'trapped", while the latter would suggest that they are the fastest ones through. The answer is certainly not clear, and the topic is one that will most probably remain one of contention for some time to come.

4.3 Pseudo-Device Calculations

In calculating the current through a quantum structure such as a resonant tunnelling transistor, we must use a fully quantum transport scheme if we are to accurately reflect the micro-dynamics of the structure. Yet, the understanding of quantum transport applied to far-from-equilibrium, and open, systems like semiconductor devices is still in the primitive state. Consequently, this device – the resonant tunnelling diode – has become the "fruit fly" for quantum studies of device dynamics. In detail, we still can do no better than the direct approach of the Landauer equation. On the other hand, it is to be hoped that the experimental results will actually push the theoretical field forward toward understanding the details of the quantum interference that can go on in this device.

Most quantum transport is developed in terms of either the wave function for a discrete quantum state, or in terms of the density matrix for the mixed system. The density matrix is a non-local function in either the momentum or the position representation, and differs from the normal representations used for classical transport. In classical mechanics, the distribution function is a function of the six dimensions of momentum and position. The normal quantum distribution is the density matrix and does not have this mixed property of describing both position and momentum. On the other hand, we can go to a different, but still proper, quantum description through the introduction of a Wigner distribution function. This latter distribution is written in a mixed representation of both position and momentum, at the expense of introducing quantum interference through negative values and at the expense of introducing non-local terms in the Hamiltonian for the time evolution of the function itself [4.13].

4.3.1 The Wigner Function

Although the Wigner function is normally written in terms of all of the generalized coordinates, we will treat only a single spatial coordinate and a single momentum coordinate. Then we can write it as

$$f_W(x, p) = (2\pi\hbar)^{-1} \int_{-\infty}^{\infty} dy \, \psi^*(x + y/2)\psi \, (x - y/2)\exp(iyp/\hbar), \qquad (4.34)$$

in terms of a general wave function $\psi(x)$, and

$$f_W(w, p) = (2\pi\hbar)^{-1} \int_{-\infty}^{\infty} dy \, \rho(x + y/2, x - y/2)\exp(iyp/\hbar) \,, \qquad (4.35)$$

in terms of the density matrix $\rho(x, x')$. The Wigner function has the proper properties as well. For example, if we integrate f_W over all momenta, we obtain the probability density function, and if we integrate over all position we obtain the momentum probability density.

It follows immediately from (4.34) and (4.35) that the expectation value of an observable $W(x, p)$ is given by

$$\langle W \rangle = \iint W(x, p) f_W(x, p) \, dx dp, \qquad (4.36)$$

which is analogous to the classical expression for the average value. Herein lies the interesting aspect of the Wigner function; the result of (4.36) suggests that it is possible to transfer many of the results of classical transport theory into quantum transport theory by simply replacing the classical distribution function by the Wigner distribtuion function. However, unlike the nonlocal density matrix, the Wigner distribution function itself cannot be viewed as the quantum analog in a simple sense since it is in general not a positive definite quantity. Indeed, general potentials complicate the problem due to the fact that quantum interference appears in the Wigner function through negative regions whose extent in phase space is such that the uncertainty principle is fulfilled. This is to say, the negative regions are sufficiently large that measurements cannot be made in small parts of the phase space that would violate the Heisenberg principle.

The time evolution equation for the Wigner function can be found by substituting for Schrödinger equation into (4.34), integrating the momentum functions by parts, and obtaining

$$\frac{\partial}{\partial t} f_W(x, p) + \frac{p}{m^*} \frac{\partial}{\partial x} f_W(x, p)$$

$$= (1/\pi\hbar^2) \int ds \, dP \, K(s, P) f_W(x, p + p, t) \,, \quad \text{where} \qquad (4.37)$$

$$K(s, P) = [V(x + s\hbar/2) - V(x - s\hbar/2)] \sin(sP) \,. \qquad (4.38)$$

In fact, this equation is not adequate to fully determine the Wigner function, since it does not define the initial condition. It only defines the manner in which the initial function is propagated forward in time, just as the Schrödinger equation does the same for the wave function. One often sees (4.37) with $K(s, P)$ expanded in low order terms of a Taylor series – the classical equation contains only the first two such terms. However, it is through $K(s, P)$ that the nonlocal behavior characteristic of quantum mechanics is evident. (There would be an equivalent form for the kinetic energy if we did not assume parabolic energy bands!) Especially in the case of the tunnelling structures fabricated by molecular beam epitaxy, the potential barriers are quite sharp, and the Taylor series must retain an almost infinite number of terms.

In Fig. 4.8, we illustrate the use of the Wigner distribution by calculating f_W for a narrow Gaussian wave packet, and then propagating it through a double barrier structure. The occupation in the resonant level and the non-positive portions of the distribution are clearly seen in this figure. It is calculations of propagation such as this that have been used to estimate tunnelling times [4.9, 12].

4.3.2 Diode Response

There are a number of problems that must be faced when we get down to actually simulating real devices. The first is the initial distribution function $f_W(x, p)$ that exists within the device. While one might initially expect this to be just a normal classical one, this is incorrect because of the sharp potential barriers that can exist. We illustrate this with the double barrier tunnelling structure. We can

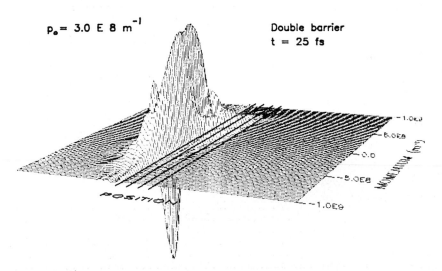

Fig. 4.8. A Gaussian Wigner function impinging upon the structure of Fig. 4.2. Reflection and tunnelling are evident. The center of the momentum of this packet is at $3.0 \times 10^8 \, \mathrm{m}^{-1}$

calculate the initial distribution from the density matrix for the equilibrium situation following the property

$$\rho(x, x') \sim \exp(-\beta\hat{H}),$$ (4.39)

in which $\hat{H}$ is the total Hamiltonian operator that includes the details of the potentials. Both the boundary conditions and the basis set for the expansion must be selected prior to evaluating the density matrix. Once a basis set is selected, the density matrix may be evaluated from the usual expansion

$$\rho(x, x') = \langle x|[1 - \beta\hat{H}/n]^n|x'\rangle$$ (4.40)

in the limit as n goes to infinity. This density matrix can then be transformed with the Wigner transform (4.35) to yield the Wigner distribution function for the device. In Fig. 4.9, a Wigner distribution calculated with periodic (but equilibrium) boundary conditions and with a basis set of a finite number of delta functions for the position representation eigenfunctions. The number was determined by the grid size, but the finite number of these introduces some problems. We see from this figure that the distribution is much broader in momentum range near the barrier than one would expect from just classical considerations. This is because the higher momentum states have a shorter wavelength and therefore penetrate much closer to the barrier. The impact of this on tunnelling currents has not been fully assessed yet, but is thought to relate strongly to some zero-bias anomaly in tunnelling structures. What can also be determined from Fig. 4.9, is the *lack* of sharp resonance levels between the barriers, in distinction to Fig. 4.8. This failure is thought to be due to use of the limited number of delta functions in the initial basis set for evaluating the density matrix. In particular, the delta function basis set excludes nonlocal, off-diagonal terms in the potential energy. In an infinite basis set, this limitation can be overcome, but with a limited basis set, it is felt that the nonlocal contributions to

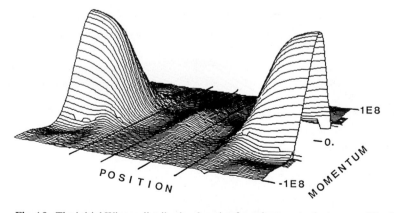

Fig. 4.9. The initial Wigner distribution function for a degenerate electron gas. The dark band at the right is negative-valued. This distribution assumed periodic boundary conditions in which the gradient of the density is zero at the boundary

f_W are restricted. A more proper basis set might justifiably be a set of localized Gaussians in real space. This problem is currently under investigation.

A second problem is the proper boundary conditions that must be introduced into the quantum treatment. As indicated above, this consideration must enter the problem from the very first step. In classical devices, we just use "ohmic" contacts generated by high doping densities (in principle), and do not entertain further complications. In quantum systems, on the other hand, there is no description as to what constitutes an "ohmic" contact. Periodic boundary conditions introduce anomalous quantization levels within the system, and these should be avoided as well. The assumption of some arbitrary equilibrium distribution has also been made; i.e., one can assume that with no applied bias the incoming electrons (positive k at the left boundary and negative k at the right boundary) derive from equilibrium Maxwellians. However, this infers a randomization of electrons at the boundary that introduces dissipation into the system [4.14, 15]. Thus, the boundary condition for the equilibrium system, as well as for the time developing system, is a major concern for the quantum problem.

Still another problem arises from the incorporation of dissipation within the quantum system, as well as at the boundaries. While the introduction of a simple relaxation time approximation is possible [4.12], this avoids the problem that one wants to address with quantum transport in the first place – extended, nonlocal scattering in a dense, many-body system. The problems associated with quantum transport in a general homogeneous system have only now begun to be solved in a general way, without incorporating the details of specific scattering processes. This remains a complicated problem under very active investigation; but, the solution to quantum devices will not be achieved until this problem is solved. The problem is complicated in the device arena because of the possibility that individual device dimensions will be of the size of the electron wavelength. This complicates the scattering problems, and the redistribution of charge accompanying the self-consistent solutions of the Poisson equation for the potential still further complicates the problem.

In summary, while we can talk in quite specific detail about the nature of boundary condition matching and tunnelling probabilities and current formulations, the general problem of actual quantum device simulation is far from being solved. We tend to forget about the many decades that have gone into solving the classical device problem (to the level at which it is currently understood). Extrapolating from this, it will be quite some time until we achieve a comparable understanding of the quantum transport in devices.

4.4 Lateral Superlattices

The concept of a lateral superlattice along a surface has considerable advantages, among which is the ability to control the magnitude of the surface potential seen by an inversion layer. The basic structure is shown in Fig. 4.10, for an MOS

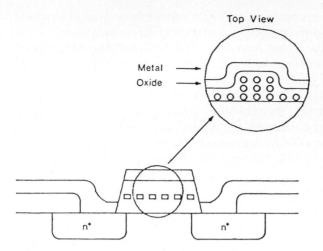

Fig. 4.10. The BlochFET in which a two-dimensional superlatttice array of dots is placed within the gate oxide. This dot array produces a superlattice potential along the interface at the inversion layer

structure (first conceived by T.I.'s Bob Bate). A periodic gate array is buried inside the dielectric and thus differs from a normal CCD array in that the top electrode is a blanket electrode. The top electrode provides energy gap control without requiring critical alignment of successive levels. A one-dimensional (along the surface) implementation of this structure has been achieved [4.16]. If the periodic gates are biased positively, the surface potential for electrons decreases under the gate electrodes, and to a lesser extent in the gaps. Minority carrier generation, injection from an FET source, or optical pumping creates the carriers necessary to form the inversion layer under the gates. Thus, in addition to the normal average surface potential, a periodic superlattice potential is seen by the inversion layer electrons. The presence of the top electrode allows for critical control of the relative strengths of both the average potential and the superlattice potential.

Other possible structures for the lateral surface superlattice can be developed. One is the complement of the MOS structure discussed above, and is fabricated in a GaAs MODFET. A MODFET is usually a depletion mode device, in which the gate is used to push electrons out of a channel, much like a MESFET, rather than drawing them into the channel as in a MOSFET. Thus, we really need the complement of the dot structure shown in Fig. 4.10. In this case, we need a grid, as shown in Fig. 4.11. The grid imposes the periodic potential on the electrons in the channel, and as the device approaches pinch-off, the final electrons are left in pockets which are aligned with the holes of the grid. The electrons are thus sitting in small quantum wells induced by the superlattice potential itself. The grid in Fig. 4.11 was written by electron-beam lithography using single level PMMA, and the pattern transferred by normal lift-off processing. The grid shown has 40 nm lines on 170 nm spacing. The grid is 28 periods in the source-drain direction and 170 periods in the transverse direction, so that the superlattice gate is approximately 5 μm by 30 μm. Devices were then fabricated from typical

Fig. 4.11. Electron micrograph of a grid forming a lateral surface superlattice. The grid is fabricated by lifting off gold with a pattern written in single level PMMA. The lines are approximately 40 nm wide and lie on a 160 nm pitch

modulation-doped heterostructure material commonly employed for MOD-FETs [4.17]. The GaAs active layer was an undoped buffer layer, which was topped with a 5 nm undoped GaAlAs spacer layer. The doping was $3.5 \times 10^{18} \text{ cm}^{-3}$ Si in a GaAlAs layer which was 30 nm thick, and this was topped with a GaAs cap layer 7.5 nm thick and comparably doped. All of the fabrication levels were done with electron-beam lithography, and the active devices were mesa isolated. Ohmic contacts were Au–Ge–Ni and the Schottky was pure Au. The source-drain spacing was 9 μm. We return to a discussion of this device later.

The effective superlattice potential $U(x, y)$ can be expected to vary along the structure in a form given by [4.18]

$$U(x, y) = 4U_0 \cos\left(\frac{2\pi x}{d}\right) \cos\left(\frac{2\pi y}{d}\right) . \tag{4.41}$$

By introducing a change of variables $u = x + y$, $v = x - y$, with

$$\frac{1}{\sqrt{2}}\frac{\partial}{\partial x} = \frac{\partial}{\partial u} + \frac{\partial}{\partial v}, \quad \frac{1}{\sqrt{2}}\frac{\partial}{\partial y} = \frac{\partial}{\partial u} - \frac{\partial}{\partial v} , \tag{4.42}$$

the effective two-dimensional Schrödinger equation for the interface electrons in the inversion layer is given by

$$\left\{\frac{d^2}{du^2} + \frac{d^2}{dv^2} + \frac{2m^*}{\hbar^2}\left[E - 2U_0 \cos\left(\frac{2\pi u}{d}\right) - 2U_0 \cos\left(\frac{2\pi v}{d}\right)\right]\right\} \psi(u, v) = 0 . \tag{4.43}$$

This equation is now separable using a product form of the wave function $\psi_1(u)\psi_2(v)$, which yields two effective one-dimensional Schrödinger equations of the form

$$\left\{\frac{d^2}{du^2} + \frac{2m^*}{\hbar^2}\left[E_1 - 2U_0 \cos\left(\frac{2\pi u}{d}\right)\right]\right\} \psi_1(u) = 0 . \tag{4.44}$$

Introducing the reduced variables

$$\xi = \frac{gu}{2}, \quad a = \frac{8m^* E}{\hbar^2 g^2} = 2\frac{m^* d^2 E}{\hbar^2 \pi^2}, \quad q = 2\frac{m^* d^2 U}{\hbar^2 \pi^2}, \tag{4.45}$$

where $g = 2\pi/d$, (4.44) can be rewritten as

$$\frac{d^2 \psi(\xi)}{d\xi^2} + [a - 2q \cos(2\xi)] \psi(\xi) = 0 . \tag{4.46}$$

This latter form is immediately recognized as the Mathieu equation. For $q = 0$, all values of a (and hence of the energy E) are allowed. However, when $q \neq 0$, gaps open in the spectrum of a. For small q, the lowest gap is centered approximately at the point $a = 1$, and higher gaps occur approximately at $a = 4, 9, \ldots, n^2$. The general energy structure is shown in Fig. 4.12. It is very important to note that the general solution to the Mathieu equation is of Bloch form

$$\psi(\xi) = \exp(ik\xi)p(\xi) , \tag{4.47}$$

where $p(\xi)$ has the periodicity of the superlattice potential. This is, of course, expected for the periodic potential. For the first mini-gap to be centered at a particular energy W, we require $a(W) = 1$, and

$$\hbar^2 \pi^2 / 2m^* d^2 = W, \quad \text{or} \tag{4.48}$$

$$d = (\hbar^2 \pi^2 / 2m^* W)^{1/2} . \tag{4.49}$$

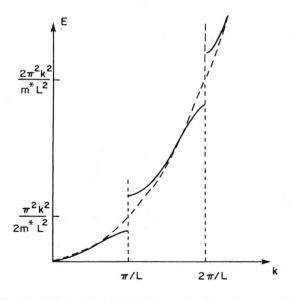

Fig. 4.12. The general conduction band energy structure. Gaps are opened at $k = \pi/d$ due to the perturbation of the surface superlattice potential

The first mini-gap will have a value given approximately by $\Delta_a = a(\Delta) = 1.9q$ for small values of q. For $U = 0.01$ V, we find that $\Delta_a = 2.9\,k_B T$ at 77 K and $52.4\,k_B T$ at 4.2 K, corresponding to rather larger gaps when compared to the miniband energy width. It is clear that relatively small induced superlattice potentials are required to produce the mini-band/mini-gap structure. Indeed, surface band bending corresponding to roughly one trapped electron under each gate could produce sufficient potential to be noticable at 4.2 K in the case of the very light mass InSb. Evidently, lower effective mass material is favoured. Whereas Si requires $d \sim 10$ nm in order to fully produce superlattices, the effects should be observable in InAs and InSb for $d \sim 50$ nm. One caution, however, must be stated here, and this is that the calculations are done for the size of the bands and gaps and not for whether or not the effects will be washed out by thermal effects. Rather, the importance length is not the wavelength, which enters into the equations, but the inelastic mean free path which determines the distance over which the electron wave functions remain coherent.

4.4.1 Transport Effects

As we have seen above, various superlattice structures give rise to energy minibands that vary sinusoidally across the mini-zone, in at least one dimension, and which have relatively narrow widths. The shape of such bands results in interesting electrical properties. The one-dimensional superlattice is one such structure, and the lateral surface superlattice is another. In this section, we want to now talk about the average velocity and energy of the carriers in the superlattice, and the various transport properties that can occur. We will do this in both the steady-state dc conductivity case and later for the small signal ac conductivity case.

The average velocity and energy are found by taking the first and second moments of the Boltzmann transport equation with an assumed form for the distribution function. A constant electric field is assumed to be applied in the plane of the sinusoidal bands, while the energy shape in the other two directions is arbitrary. Here, we shall take a simple Wigner function representation as the initial equilibrium distribution. This treatment is valid for a single energy band at low to moderate electric fields for which the sinusoidal band is less than half-filled with carriers. For a band that is more than half-filled, the Pauli exclusion principle must be taken into account. In addition, we shall use the constant relaxation time approximation, as the effects in which we are interested arise from the properties of the energy bands and not from the energy dependences of the scattering rates. In truth, the relaxation time is not strictly constant, since the density of states for cosinusoidal energy bands in two dimensions show strong Van Hove singularities which lead to strong scattering peaks near mid-band. Nevertheless, we shall see below that the constant relaxation time approximation is not too bad due to the high scattering rates. Lastly, we assume the distribution function is homogeneous in space.

The form of the time-independent, homogeneous Wigner transport equation in the relaxation time approximation is the same as that of the Boltzmann transport equation, and is

$$\frac{eF}{\hbar} \frac{\partial f(\mathbf{k})}{\partial k_z} = - \frac{f(\mathbf{k}) - f_0(\mathbf{k})}{\tau} , \tag{4.50}$$

where the field and the direction of the superlattice are taken to be the z-direction. The quantity $f_0(\mathbf{k})$ is found from the equilibrium quantum density distribution by using the Hamiltonian equivalence principle, followed by a Wigner transformation, which leads to the Bloch form

$$f_0(\mathbf{k}) \sim e^{\beta[\varepsilon - \varepsilon \cos(dk_z)]} f_0(k_x, k_y) , \tag{4.51}$$

in which the energy is

$$E = \varepsilon - \varepsilon \cos(dk_z) , \tag{4.52}$$

ε is the half-width of the energy band and d is related to the periodic spacing of the superlattice.

Taking the first moment of the velocity in the z-direction and the second moment (the total energy) results in the following two equations

$$\frac{eF}{\hbar} \int\!\!\int_{-L}^{L} v_z \frac{\partial f(k)}{\partial k_z} d^3k = - \Gamma \langle v_z \rangle , \tag{4.53}$$

$$\frac{eF}{\hbar} \int\!\!\int_{-L}^{L} E \frac{\partial f(k)}{\partial k_z} d^2k = \Gamma n [\langle E \rangle - \langle E_0 \rangle] , \tag{4.54}$$

where $\Gamma = 1/\tau$, $L = \pi/d$, and $\langle S \rangle$ is defined as the average of the quantity S. Here, E_0 is the equilibrium energy without an applied field.

To proceed, we must now introduce the analytical expressions for the velocity and the energy. For these, we use the assumed energy band shape

$$E = \varepsilon - \varepsilon \cos(dk_z) + E(k_x, k_y) , \tag{4.55}$$

$$v_z = (\varepsilon d/\hbar) \sin(dk_z) . \tag{4.56}$$

The left-hand side of both moment equations may be integrated by parts in the z-direction, and the fact that both the energy and the distribution function are periodic in $2L$ and the velocity vanishes at L, $-L$, to find the results that

$$(eFd^2/h^2) \langle \varepsilon \cos(dk_z) \rangle = \Gamma \langle v_z \rangle , \tag{4.57}$$

$$- eF \langle v_z \rangle = \Gamma [\langle E \rangle - \langle E_0 \rangle] . \tag{4.58}$$

The first bracketed average in (4.57) can be replaced, using (4.55) by $\langle \varepsilon E + E(k_x, k_y) \rangle = \varepsilon - \langle E \rangle + \langle E_t \rangle [E_t = E(k_x, k_y)]$. Solving these equations simultaneously gives the expressions for the velocity and energy as functions of the field as

$$\langle v_z \rangle = \{\varepsilon + \langle E_t \rangle - \langle E_0 \rangle] eF\tau d^2/\hbar^2 (1 + \omega_B^2 \tau^2) \,, \tag{4.59}$$

$$\langle E \rangle = \{\langle E_0 \rangle + (\varepsilon + \langle E_t \rangle)\omega_B^2 \tau^2]/(1 + \omega_B^2 \tau^2) \,, \tag{4.60}$$

where $\omega_B = eFd/\hbar$ is the Bloch frequency. Thus, we see that as the field increases the average energy rises from its equilibrium value $\langle E_0 \rangle$ ($= 3k_B T/2$) to the half-band energy plus the average transverse energy, and the velocity behaves in a corresponding manner.

The velocity has the same field dependence in (4.59) as that obtained earlier by *Lebwohl* and *Tsu* [4.19], except for the energy pre-factor in front of the expression. The difference is caused by the different equilibrium distribution function chosen. In this latter work, the authors assumed the distribution was a zero temperature Fermi-Dirac. Here, on the other hand, the distribution is a real temperature one that includes the details of the band shape. Note that the velocity shows a negative differential conductivity that sets in above $\omega_B \tau = 1$, so that this field corresponds to the current peaks discussed below. Monte Carlo calculations have been performed as well, in which the exact details of the energy dependent scattering processes were included [4.20]. The general shape of the velocity curves of (4.59) are found there as well. In fact, for the same set of material (band) parameters, the curves are very close together, which justifies our earlier assumption of a constant relaxation time. The details of the scattering processes just do not make a significant difference in the present circumstances and the important aspect for negative differential conductivity is the band shape itself.

4.4.2. Bloch Oscillators

The BlochFETs, whose fabrication was discussed above, were tested over a wide temperature range. At 77 K and above, the drain characteristics were typical of standard field effect transistors of this size. On the other hand, when the temperature was lowered to 4.2 K, pronounced negative-differential conductivity was observed, as shown in Fig. 4.13. Here it can be seen that the magnitude of the NDC increased as the devices were pushed towards pinchoff with more negative gate potential. Especially at pinchoff, the curves exhibit exactly the behavior expected for BlochFETs, as discussed in the previous section. As the drain field increases, but remains below that needed for interband tunnelling, an increasing number of electrons are expected to undergo Bloch oscillations and be localized in space. These are removed from the conduction process and the current decreases.

The striking features of these curves is this strong NDC evident at high reverse gate voltages. These features can be further explained as follows. As the device approaches pinchoff, the electrons in the channel are more fully localized in weakly coupled quantum boxes, which are the sites under the holes in the grid.

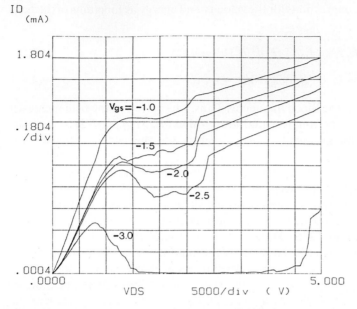

Fig. 4.13. Current-voltage characteristics for the BlochFET formed in a GaAs MODFET. The gate is the grid shown in Fig. 4.11, and imposes a lateral surface superlattice onto the inversion layer at the GaAs/GaAlAs interface. The negative differential conductivity is thought to arise from the onset of Bloch oscillations

Thus, there is a strong superlattice potential that is strengthened by the localization of the electrons in the boxes. As the channel density is increased, by making the gate potential more positive, the superlattice potential is weakened by the screening of the background charge density. To observe the miniband effects, the electrons must have an inelastic mean free path length that is longer than the period of the surface superlattice. The mobility in these layers was such that we estimate the mean free path to be only about 200 nm at 4.2 K, so that the effect is seen only at these low temperature.

While the experiments are highly suggestive of Bloch oscillations, we must be aware that there are other mechanisms that can provide NDC in devices and which may be the cause of that discussed here. One possible one is real-space transfer, in which electrons are scattered out of the inversion layer and into the GaAlAs, where they may be trapped or contribute to lower mobility conduction paths. This mechanism is really not likely as a cause of the effects seen in Fig. 4.13, as this effect should be stronger at more positive values of gate bias, which is opposite to the observations in the figure. Moreover, such an effect should not be sensitive to the grid nature of the gate. In Fig. 4.14, we show the characteristics of a MODFET made in the same manner as the BlochFET except that the gate metalization is continuous. No NDC is seen in these curves, so that we may conclude that the grid nature of the gate is crucial to the existence of the NDC.

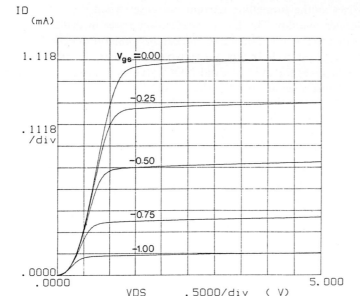

Fig. 4.14. Current-voltage characteristics of a MODFET processed as that for Fig. 4.13, with the exception of using a solid (continuous) gate. Thus, the negative differential conductivity apparent in this previous figure is probably associated with the surface superlattice imposed by the gate

Another possibility for the NDC is sequential resonant tunnelling, in which the tilting of the minibands in the applied drain potential allows electrons to tunnel from full states in one well to empty states in the next well, and subsequently to traverse the entire structure. Such effects have been shown to exhibit negative differential conductivity in layered superlattices [4.21]. For sequential resonant tunnelling, however, the curves of Fig. 4.13 would have to fit certain voltage constraints. For the curve with -3.0 V on the gate, we can estimate that the minibands are 50–60 meV wide and have gaps of 60–80 meV. For this band width and band gap, the conduction would have to take place in the 11th or 12th miniband, based upon the size of the minizone in the grid structure used. That is to say, the physical dimensions of the grid imposes the positions of the minizone boundaries in momentum space, and these set limits upon the allowed band widths of each miniband in the reduced zone scheme. The required band width above occurs only for the 11th or higher minband. If conduction takes place in this miniband, all of the lower minibands must be full. The number of electrons required to fill a miniband is just $2/d^2$, where d is the periodicity of the superlattice (in each direction). In our case, with $d = 170$ nm typically, there are just under 10^{10} cm^{-2} electrons in each miniband, so it is likely that we are filled up to at least the necessary level since MODFETs can reach inversion densities near 10^{12} cm^{-2}. However, it is not clear that sequential resonant tunnelling and Bloch oscillations are different quantities. The negative differential conductivity in the latter case arises as the tunnelling current decreases when the bands in adjacent wells no longer overlap. The Bloch localization arises in principle as electrons are accelerated to the top of the band and can no longer tunnel through to vacant states in the adjacent well. In fact, these two effects seem to supplement each other as possible causes for the observed NDC, and only more extensive experiments can determine a separation for the cause.

4.4.3 High Frequency Response

While the above analysis provides limits within which Bloch oscillations may be seen, it does not provide an existence proof on their presence. We want now to consider several possible routes, besides the normally considered potential negative differential conductivity, by which Bloch oscillations may be experimentally verified. We pursue this by looking at a number of consequences of superimposing a small ac signal on top of the applied dc bias electric field. Here, we will seek first the ac component of the velocity, and hence of the mobility, that relates to the time varying frequency ω at which the applied field is oscillating. To achieve this, we must add the time derivative term to (4.50). We then assume that $\langle E \rangle = \langle E \rangle_0 + E_1, \langle v_z \rangle = \langle v_z \rangle_0 + v_1$. Then, (4.57) and (4.58), for the ac terms, become

$$(i\omega - \Gamma)v_1 = (eF_1 d^2/\hbar^2)\langle \varepsilon \cos(dk_z)\rangle_0 , \tag{4.61}$$

$$(i\omega - \Gamma)E_1 = eF_1 \langle v_z \rangle_0 + eF_0 v_1 , \tag{4.62}$$

from which the resulting ac mobility (the real part of the velocity response to F_1) is given by

$$\mu(\omega) = \mu_0 \frac{(1 - \omega_B^2 \tau^2)[1 + (\omega_B^2 - \omega^2)\tau^2]}{[1 + (\omega_B^2 - \omega^2)\tau^2] + 4\omega^2 \tau^2} , \tag{4.63}$$

where $\mu_0 = e\tau/m$ is the low field dc mobility. In Fig. 4.15, we plot this mobility as a function of frequency for a case in which the dc field lies in the negative differential conductivity regime ($\omega_B \tau = 2$). It is important to note that there is no peak in the conductivity at the Bloch frequency. Rather there is just a fall-off in the negative conductivity to positive values. The lack of a resonance at the Bloch frequency suggests, but does not prove, that the Bloch oscillations are not radiative. In fact, what is probably meant by this result is that the individual Bloch electrons oscillate, but that their phases add incoherently, so that no coherent radiation is produced. This result is somewhat reinforced by Monte Carlo calculations of the velocity correlation function, which show that the noise spectra does exhibit a peak at the Bloch frequency [4.22]. This noise spectra is shown in Fig. 4.16, for a GaAs based simulation. In principle, both the ac conductivity and the spectral density of the noise can be measured, although this is difficult for frequencies close to the Bloch frequency as it lies in the far infrared portion of the spectrum. On the

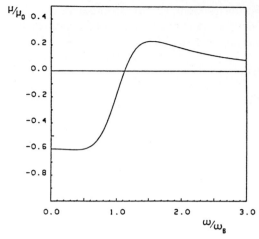

Fig. 4.15. The small signal ac mobility (the real part of the complex mobility) that arises when a small ac electric field is superimposed on the dc electric field. The dc field is large enough to have the device in the negative differential conductivity regime with $\omega_B\tau = 2$. The curve is calculated in the relaxation time approximation, but agrees well with calculations using an ensemble Monte Carlo approach

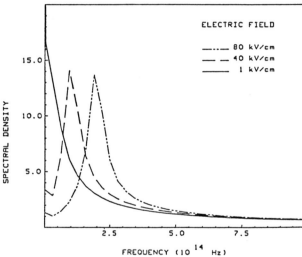

Fig. 4.16. The noise spectrum calculated using an ensemble Monte Carlo approach. The spectrum is calculated from the Fourier transform of the velocity autocorrelation function for the electrons. The peaks occur at the Bloch frequency at each value of the electric field (the parameters are those for GaAs)

other hand, measurements of the noise emission with e.g. an FTIR system can in principle provide evidence of the Bloch oscillations.

The above analysis indicates that it may be difficult to couple directly to the amplitude variations of the Bloch oscillations of the electrons themselves. However, it may be possible to couple to the *phase* of the oscillations. This limitation on amplitude arises due to the fact that the velocity amplitude is limited by the band structure itself, but the phase is not so constrained and may be the preferred coupling scheme. In addition, we note that coupling to the phase has a direct analogy with the flux in the Josephson tunnel junctions and the resulting ac Josephson effect in which steps are produced in the current-voltage characteristics by self-rectification of the ac signal. This result is a direct consequence of the cosinusoidal nature of the energy bands. We illustrate this by treating a single electron confined to the cosinusoidal band described by (4.55), but ignoring the transverse energy for the moment. Under the influence of both a dc electric field F_0 and an ac electric field F_1, the time variation of the momentum wave vector, in the absence of scattering, is given by

$$k(t) = k_0 + eF_0 t/\hbar + (eF_1 t/\hbar)\sin(\omega t) , \qquad (4.64)$$

and the corresponding velocity is just

$$v(t) = v_0 \sin\left[\omega_B t + k_0 d + \frac{\omega_B F_1}{\omega F_0}\sin(\omega t)\right] , \qquad (4.65)$$

where $v_0 = \varepsilon d/h$. This expression can be rewritten as

$$v = v_0 \sum_n J_n(\zeta)\{[\sin(\theta_B + n\theta) + (-1)^n \sin(\theta_B - n\theta)]\cos(\lambda)$$

$$+ [\cos(\theta_B + n\theta) + (-1)^n \cos(\theta_B - n\theta)]\cos(\lambda)\} , \qquad (4.66)$$

where $\zeta = \omega F_1/\omega_B F_0$, $\theta = \omega t$, $\theta_B = \omega_B t$, $\lambda = \lambda_0 d$, and J_n is the Bessel function of order n. A dc component of the velocity, and hence of the current, occurs when $\omega_B = \pm n\omega$. For a fixed ω, we change ω_B by changing the dc electric field, and we then expect to see resonance effects at the critical multiples of the ac frequency. The occurrence of such structures would be an unambiguous demonstration of the existence of the Bloch oscillations, but we caution that these will occur only in the negative differential conductivity region of the dc characteristics. The resonances above arise because the ac signal is inducing transitions, either emission or absorption, across the individual ladder states of the Stark ladder that coexists with the Bloch oscillations. The presence of superlattice implies that the Stark ladder is not a real ladder but a virtual one, and the ac effect is coupled to tunnelling of the electron from one well to the next. In this case, the electron tunnels through to the adjacent well, emits a photon corresponding to the ac frequency, and drops in energy to a new state described by $E - eF_0 d(\omega - \omega_B)$. The absorption response corresponds to first absorbing the photon and then tunnelling to the adjacent well. There is a preferred direction for each of these tunnelling processes, as determined by the symmetry breaking of the applied electric field. It is evident from this that the resonances are very closely tied to the concept of sequential resonant tunnelling in superlattices themselves [4.21, 23]. The importance of the virtual nature of the Stark ladder was only recently clarified [4.24].

References

4.1   L. L. Chang, L. Esaki, R. Tsu: Appl. Phys. Lett. **24**, 593 (1974)
4.2   T. L. L. G. Sollner, W. D. Goodhue, P. E. Tannenwald, C. D. Parker, D. D. Peck, Appl. Phys. Lett. **43**, 588 (1983); **45**, 1319 (1984)

4.3   E. O. Kane: In *Semiconductors and Semimetals*, Vol. 1, Ed. by R. H. Willardson, A. C. Beer (Academic, New York 1966) p. 75

4.4   B. Ricco, M. Ya. Azbel: Phys. Rev. B **29**, 1970 (1984)

4.5   L. A. MacColl: Phys. Rev. **40**, 621 (1932)

4.6   T. E. Hartmann: J. Appl. Phys. **33**, 3427 (1962)

4.7   W. Franz: Phys. Status. Solidi. **22**, K139 (1967)

4.8   W. E. Hagstrom: Phys. Status. Solidi. (b) **116**, K85 (1983)

4.9   J. R. Barker: Physica **134B** + C, 22 (1985)

4.10 M. Büttiker, R. Landauer: Phys. Rev. Lett. **49**, 1739 (1982); IBM J. Res. Develop. **30**, 451 (1986)

4.11 K. W. H. Stevens: Eur. J. Phys. **1**, 98 (1980); J. Phys. C **16**, 3649 (1983)

4.12 N. C. Kluksdahl, A. M. Kriman, D. K. Ferry, C. Ringhofer: Phys. Rev. B **39**, 7720 (1989)

4.13 E. Wigner: Phys. Rev. **40**, 749 (1932)

4.14 M. Büttiker: Phys. Rev. B **33**, 3020 (1986)

4.15 W. Frensley: Phys. Rev. Lett. **57**, 2853 (1986)

4.16 A. C. Warren, D. A. Antoniadis, H. I. Smith, J. Melngailis: In IEEE *Electron Devices Meeting Technical Digest*, (IEEE, New York 1984) p. 866

4.17 G. Bernstein, D. K. Ferry: Superlattices and Microstructures, **2**, 306 (1987)

4.18 D. K. Ferry: Phys. Status. Solidi. (b) **106**, 63 (1981)

4.19 P. A. Lebwohl, R. Tsu: J. Appl. Phys. **41**, 2664 (1970)

4.20 R. K. Reich, R. O. Grondin D. K. Ferry: Phys. Rev. B **27**, 3483 (1983)

4.21 F. Capasso, K. Mohammed, A. Cho: Appl. Phys. Lett. **48**, 478 (1986)

4.22 R. O. Grondin, W. Porod, J. Ho, D. K. Ferry, G. J. Iafrate: Superlattice and Microstructures **1**, 183 (1985)

4.23 R. F. Kazarinov, R. A. Suris: Sov. Phys.-Semiconductors **5**, 707 (1971)

4.24 J. B. Krieger, G. J. Iafrate: Phys. Rev. B **33**, 5494 (1986)

5. The Investigation of Single and Double Barrier (Resonant Tunnelling) Heterostructures Using High Magnetic Fields

L. Eaves, F. W. Sheard, and G. A. Toombs

With 25 Figures

This chapter examines some important properties of single and double barrier tunnelling heterostructures. Particular emphasis is placed on the use of magnetic fields in studying not only the tunnelling process itself, but also the way in which electrons relax their energy and momentum. Four topics are examined in detail. First, LO phonon-related oscillations under reverse bias in the $I(V)$ and $C(V)$ curves of single barrier n^+GaAs/(AlGa)As/n^-GaAs/n^+GaAs and n^+(InGa)As/InP/n^-(InGa)As/n^+(InGa)As heterostructures are explained by the variation of the impedance of the undepleted section of the n^- layers. For the GaAs/(AlGa)As/GaAs structure, a magneto-impurity resonance at 5 T is observed in the oscillation amplitude, indicating that the impedance variation is due principally to impact ionisation of donors, rather than to LO phonon ionisation. The apparently anomalous behaviour of the magnetocapacitance in these devices in reverse bias is also accounted for. In the reverse-biased (InGa)As/InP/(InGa)As structures, the oscillations in $I(V)$ have period ΔV = 33 meV, indicating that the electron energy relaxation occurs almost exclusively via Ga−As mode LO phonons of the n^-(InGa)As layer.

Secondly, the oscillatory structure in the $I(V)$ and $C(V)$ characteristics of the forward biased (InGa)As/InP/(InGa)As heterostructures in the presence of a magnetic field ($\boldsymbol{B}\|\boldsymbol{I}$) is investigated and used to determine the electron concentration in the accumulated two-dimensional electron gas (2DEG) as a function of forward bias voltage.

Thirdly, a new type of tunnelling phenomenon in forward-biased single-barrier n^+(InGa)As/n^-(InGa)As/InP/n^+(InGa)As heterostructures is described for the case when a quantising magnetic field is applied in the plane of the InP barrier ($\boldsymbol{I}\perp\boldsymbol{B}$). The occurrence of two distinct series of resonances in the voltage- or field-dependence of the current is interpreted in terms of electron tunnelling from a 2DEG in the n^- layer into interfacial Landau states in the n^+(InGa)As. These states correspond to classical skipping orbits of an electron along the tunnel barrier interface. For structures in which the n^+(InGa)As doping is relatively low ($\simeq 1 \times 10^{17}$ cm^{-3}) tunnelling into well-defined box-quantised states is observed in the absence of a magnetic field. These observations indicate that a detectable proportion of tunnelling electrons have remarkably long ballistic path lengths (around several thousand angstroms) in n^+(InGa)As.

The fourth topic examined is the recent use of magnetic fields to investigate the electronic properties of double barrier resonant tunnelling devices. A series of structures with different well and barrier widths are examined. In structures in which the quantum well is wide (e.g. 120 nm) we observe up to 70 resonances in the $I(V)$ characteristics. With B applied in the plane of the barriers ($B \perp I$) these resonances evolve into hybrid magneto-electric states. At sufficiently large B, the electron orbits no longer extend to the second barrier and tunnelling occurs into cycloidal interface states which are localized near the emitter barrier. A theoretical model for the observed resonances based on the quantization of the hybrid and cycloidal orbits is presented. Ballistic path lengths of at least 400 nm are observed.

We discuss the controversy concerning intrinsic bistability in resonant tunnelling devices and report what we believe to be a definitive observation of this effect. Finally, we show how quantizing magnetic fields applied perpendicular to the plane of the barriers can be used to reveal the inelastic (LO phonon emission) and elastic scattering processes which tunnelling electrons undergo.

5.1 Background

The development of molecular beam epitaxy (MBE) and metal-organic chemical vapour deposition (MOCVD) as means of growing high quality semiconductor heterostructures has led to a resurgence of interest in electron transport in the direction perpendicular to the plane of the heterojunction interface. In particular, the physics of tunnelling through almost defect-free heterostructure barriers with almost flat interfaces is currently of great interest [5.1].

In addition, tunnelling of electrons through III–V heterostructure barriers is a feature of many new quantum electronic devices (see, for example, [5.1–5]). Most of these devices can be categorised into two broad groupings. The first type are three-terminal devices and use the barrier associated with a heterojunction as a means of injecting fast, hot carriers into a narrow base layer. Ideally the scattering in the base should be small so that the electrons can traverse a collector barrier (also a heterojunction) with a reasonably high efficiency. An example of such a device is the tunnelling hot electron transistor recently studied by *Heiblum* et al. [5.3]. The second type of device is based on "resonant" tunnelling, involving either a superlattice structure [5.1] or double barrier quantum well [5.2]. These are usually two-terminal devices, though several three-terminal transistor variants have recently been proposed [5.4, 5]. Resonant tunnelling devices can exhibit strong negative differential conductivity and have considerable potential as microwave- and millimeter-wave components.

In this chapter, we examine in detail how magnetic fields can be used to probe the electronic properties of single and double barrier tunnelling heterostructures. By quantising the motion of electrons high magnetic fields give rise to oscillatory structure in the current–voltage characteristics. Measurements of this type provide fundamental information about resonant and non-resonant tunnelling, ballistic trajectory lengths and energy- and momentum-relaxation effects. Such detailed information is often impossible to extract from simple electrical measurements at zero magnetic field.

The chapter is organised as follows: In Sect. 5.2 we describe and explain the origin of the longitudinal optic (LO) phonon-related oscillations in the current–voltage $I(V)$ and capacitance-voltage $C(V)$ characteristics of reverse-biased $n^+GaAs/Al_{0.35}Ga_{0.65}As/n^-GaAs/n^+GaAs$ and $n^+(InGa)As/InP/n^-(InGa)As/n^+(InGa)As$ heterostructures. We also account for the apparently anomalous magnetocapacitance observed in these devices at low temperatures. In Sect. 5.3, we describe the oscillatory structure observed in $I(V)$ and $C(V)$ for tunnelling from a two-dimensional electron gas (2DEG) in the presence of a magnetic field perpendicular to the 2DEG plane ($B \| I$). In Sect. 5.4, we describe a new magnetoquantum effect for 2D electrons tunnelling from accumulation layers in $n^+(InGa)As/InP/n^-(InGa)As/n^+(InGa)As/n^+InP$ heterostructures in the presence of a magnetic field transverse to the direction of current flow ($B \perp I$). This configuration is of particular interest because of the Lorentz force acting on the electrons. The two distinct series of oscillations observed in the magnetotunnelling $I(V)$ characteristics for this configuration correspond to tunnelling into localised skipping orbits at the barrier interfaces. The "skipping" orbits of the two series differ in energy due to their different proximities to the barrier. We use these data to determine the ballistic mean free path of injected hot electrons in these structures. As the magnetic field is reduced to zero, oscillatory structure arising from the skipping orbits is replaced by that due to electron tunnelling into box-quantised states of the $InP/n^+(InGa)As/InP$ region. These box-quantised states are the subject of Sect. 5.5.

The final Sect. 5.6 examines resonant tunnelling and negative differential conductivity in a series of double barrier heterostructures based on n-type GaAs/(AlGa)As/GaAs/(AlGa)As/GaAs. The three sub-sections on resonant tunnelling describe:

 (i) ballistic transport and tunnelling into the hybrid magneto-electric orbits of wide quantum wells;
 (ii) the controversy surrounding the existence of intrinsic bistability in the $I(V)$ characteristics and the observation of intrinsic bistability in a device designed to enhance charge build-up in the well at resonance;
(iii) the use of magnetic fields to study inelastic (LO phonon emission) and elastic scattering processes.

5.2 LO Phonon Structure in the $I(V)$ and $C(V)$ Curves of Reverse-Biased Heterostructures

5.2.1 n-GaAs/(AlGa)As/GaAs Heterostructures

In 1984, *Hickmott* et al. [5.6] reported oscillatory structure in the low temperature reverse-bias $I(V)$ curves of single barrier $n^+GaAs/$

(AlGa)As/n^-GaAs/n^+GaAs heterostructures. The two n^+ layers were doped at around 10^{18} cm^{-3}; the n^- layer was 1 μm thick and doped at around 10^{15} cm^{-3}; the (AlGa)As barriers were typically 200 Å thick and undoped. The period ΔV corresponded to the energy ($\hbar\omega_L = 36$ meV) of the LO mode in GaAs. The amplitude of the structure is weak and is best seen in dJ/dV and d^2J/d^2V. The band structure in reverse bias is shown in Fig. 5.1. The figure also shows the equivalent circuit for modelling the device. This will be discussed in greater detail in Sect. 5.2.3. The current in these structures arises from tunnelling of electrons through the (AlGa)As barrier from the n^+GaAs into the n^- layer. *Hickmott* et al. observed the oscillations only at high magnetic fields ($B > 4$ T), though subsequently we demostrated [5.7] that they can be observed at $B = 0$. Typical experimental curves obtained by us at $B = 0$ are shown in Fig. 5.2. Our MBE-grown structures were fabricated as circular mesas with a range of diameters. They consisted of the following layers: n^+GaAs substrate, 200 μm thick, 2 × 10^{18} cm^{-3}; n^+GaAs buffer layer, 1 μm thick, 2 × 10^{18} cm^{-3}; n^-GaAs, 1 μm thick, ∼ 2 × 10^{15} cm^{-3}; (AlGa)As barrier, 170 Å thick, [Al] = 35%, nominally undoped; n^+GaAs top contact, 1 μm thick, with 10^{18} cm^{-3}. Details of their electrical characteristics are described elsewhere [5.7, 8].

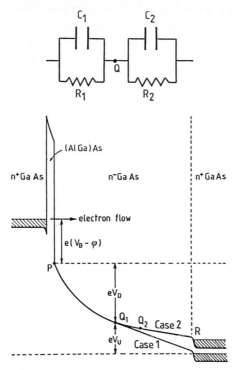

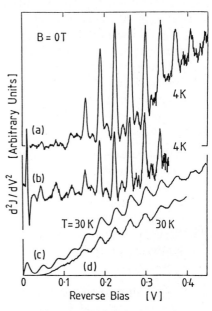

Fig. 5.1. The n^+GaAs/(AlGa)As/n^-GaAs/n^+GaAs structure in reverse bias with equivalent circuit

Fig. 5.2. Plot of d^2J/dV^2 versus reverse bias voltage showing LO phonon related oscillations for a n-GaAs/(AlGa)As/GaAs heterostructure with (AlGa)As barrier thickness of 170 Å. The n^-GaAs layer is 1 μm thick and doped at 10^{15} cm^{-3}

Several competing models [5.8–18] have emerged recently to explain the oscillations.

Our model for the origin of the oscillatory structure [5.8–10], which was outlined in one of our earlier experimental papers [5.7], can be understood from Fig. 5.1 in which the applied voltage $V = V_B + V_D + V_U$ is dropped across three distinct regions: the 170 Å (AlGa)As barrier (V_B), the high-field depleted region of the n^- layer adjacent to the barrier (V_D) and the undepleted n^- region adjacent to the n^+ substrate (V_U). The voltage drop across the n^+GaAs layer is small. A correct description of the potential across the device is important since it determines the $I(V)$ and $C(V)$ curves and the oscillatory LO phonon-related structure. In our model, the potential is determined self-consistently by Poisson's equation and current continuity. The voltage distribution in Fig. 5.1 is maintained in a magnetic field, i.e. magnetic freeze-out does not occur throughout the entire length of the n^-GaAs layer as was originally supposed [5.6]. We stress this point as some models for the oscillatory structure [5.11, 14, 16] have erroneously assumed magnetic freeze-out throughout the n^- layer.

The device characteristics can be modelled by specifying the current through it and determining the resultant voltage drops V_B, V_D and V_U. The current through the barrier at low temperatures $T \ll E_F/k_B$ can be written as

$$J = (4\pi m^* e/h^3) \int_C^{E_F} D(E_z)(E_F - E_z)dE_z ,$$

where E_F is the Fermi energy and m^* the electronic effective mass. Momentum is conserved in the plane of the barrier and the transmission coefficient D depends only on E_z, the energy associated with motion in the z direction perpendicular to the barrier. Electrons can tunnel from the n^+GaAs for all occupied states provided there is an available state in the n^-GaAs. This determines the lower limit C of the integral over E_z. In the WKB approximation

$$D(E_z) = \exp\left\{ -2\int_{z_1}^{z_2}\sqrt{2m^*[V(z) - E_z]/\hbar^2}\, dz \right\},$$

where $V(z)$ is the barrier potential and z_1 and z_2 are the classical turning points. For a trapezoidal barrier, $D(E_z) = \exp(-\alpha f)$ where $\alpha = 2b(2m^*V_0)^{\frac{1}{2}}/\hbar$ and

$$f(V_B) = \frac{2}{3}\left[\left(1 - \frac{e(V_B - V_{fb})}{V_0 + E_F - E_z}\right)^{3/2} - 1\right]\frac{(V_0 + E_F - E_z)^{3/2}}{V_0^{\frac{1}{2}}e(V_B - V_{fb})}$$

where V_0 is the height of the barrier relative to the Fermi energy in the n^+GaAs, b is the thickness of the barrier, V_{fb} is the flat-band voltage and we have assumed that the device is in depletion so that $V_B \gg V_{fb}$. The total current can be determined numerically to give J as a function of V_B and this can be inverted to give $V_B = g(J)$.

The potential drop across the depletion region is

$$V_D = \frac{s}{b}(V_B - V_{fb}) - \frac{(N_D - N_A)es^2}{2\varepsilon_0\varepsilon_r},$$

where $N_D(N_A)$ is the density of donors (acceptors) in the n^-GaAs layer and s is the width of the depletion layer. If the total width of the n^- layer is t then the potential drop across the undepleted portion of length $t - s$ is

$$V_U = (t - s)\frac{J}{\sigma},$$

where the conductivity σ of the undepleted region is not in general ohmic. The depletion width is determined from Gauss's law, which gives

$$(N_D - N_A)es = \varepsilon_r\varepsilon_0\left[\frac{V_B - V_{fb}}{b} - \frac{J}{\sigma}\right].$$

The total voltage drop $V = V_B + V_D + V_U$ may thus be obtained. Calculations of the $I(V)$ characteristics have been made along these lines assuming no charge in the (AlGa)As barrier (which would give $V_{fb} = E_F/e$) and an ohmic conductivity for the undepleted region [5.10]. The results show the general trend of the observed characteristics though there are differences in detail. In determining the depletion width, s, the voltage drop V_U across the undepleted region may, to a good approximation, be neglected. This gives an explicit expression for s in terms of the applied voltage V,

$$s \simeq [(V - V_{fb})2\varepsilon_r\varepsilon_0/(N_D - N_A)e]^{\frac{1}{2}},$$

and will be used in discussing the magnetocapacitance characterisitcs of the structures.

The kinetic energy gained by electrons in the barrier and depletion layer is lost principally by emission of an integral number of LO phonons, since the acoustic-phonon emission rate is much smaller. The energy distribution of the electrons entering the undepleted region will have peaks at kinetic energies $\varepsilon(v) = e(V_B + V_D) - vh\omega_L$, where $v = 0, 1, 2 \ldots v_{max}$ Assuming some inelastic interaction between the incident electrons and the cold electrons in the neutral undepleted layer, the impedance R_U and corresponding potential drop V_U across the neutral region will be periodically modulated as the applied voltage changes. We emphasise that the current through the device is controlled by V_B and the oscillatory structure is due simply to the modulation of V_U. At low temperatures (< 10 K) most of the electrons in the undepleted region are bound in shallow hydrogenic donor states (binding energy $E_D = 5.5$ meV). We have previously suggested impact ionisation of neutral donors by incident hot electrons as a mechanism for modulating the resistance R_U [5.8–10]. We can reliably estimate the change in conduction electron density due to this mechanism from studies of the inelastic scattering of electrons by neutral hydrogen atoms [5.19–21]. Above the appropriate threshold energy E_{th}, the scattering cross-section for $1s \rightarrow 2p$ excitation ($E_{th} = 3E_D/4$) and ionisation ($E_{th} = E_p$) are both $\simeq \pi a_0^2$, where a_0 is the Bohr radius. Excitation to $2s$, $3p$ etc. states have rather smaller cross-sections. However, once a shallow donor is excited to a $2s$, $2p$ etc. state it has a high probability of ionising either by field emission or thermal excitation. This effect is well known in photoconductivity [5.22]. Hence both excitation and ionisation processes contribute to the change in conduction electron density, n. Taking a total cross-section $\sigma_t \sim 3\pi a_0^2$ and equating the rate of impact ionisation $N_D\sigma_t F$, where F is the incident electron flux, to the recombination rate n/τ_r, where τ_r is the recombination time, gives $n = N_D\sigma_t F\tau_r$. At a reverse bias of 0.3 V, the current density $J \sim 10^3 \, \text{A m}^{-2}$ and $F = J/e \sim 0.6 \times 10^{22} \, \text{m}^{-2}$. From time-resolved photoconductivity experiments [5.22], it is known that the rate at which an excited donor relaxes back to the ground state is rather slow due to the phonon "bottleneck" between $n = 2$ and $n = 1$ states, and typically $\tau_r \sim 10^{-8} \, s$ for $N_D = 2 \times 10^{15} \, \text{cm}^{-3}$. This gives $n \sim 10^{14} \, \text{cm}^{-3}$ so that the hot-electron flux can maintain an appreciable ionisation of the shallow donors in the undepleted region. We assume that a significant fraction of the hot-electron flux is associated with the lowest peak in the energy distribution. When, with increasing applied bias, this peak passes the threshold energy for impact ionisation, there is a significant change in conduction electron density and hence resistance R_U of the neutral region.

It is straightforward to test whether this model gives a reasonable value for the oscillatory amplitude, $\Delta I/I$. At $T = 4.2$ K, $B = 0$ and $V = -0.35$ V, we observe that for a 200 μm diameter mesa, $\partial I/\partial V = \times 10^{-4} \, \Omega^{-1}$ and $\Delta I/I = 3 \times 10^{-3}$. The required resistance change of the undepleted layer $\Delta R_U = (\Delta I/I)/(\partial I/\partial V) = 15 \, \Omega$ (for a derivation see [5.8]). In comparison, the equilibrium value of R_U for 0.5 μm of undepleted n^-GaAs at 4.2 K is $R_U \sim 300 \, \Omega$. Therefore the relative change $\Delta R_U/R_U$ required by our model is not unreasonable considering the donor ionisation densities estimated above. The absence of oscillations at $B = 0$ in the devices of *Hickmott* et al. [5.6] can be explained by the much lower current densities which are a consequence of their lower n^+ doping and somewhat thick and higher barriers. The magnetic field in these devices sufficiently increases R_U to a value that it can be modulated over a wide enough range to give observable oscillations in $I(V)$.

An additional mechanism for ionisation of the shallow donors is through interaction with LO phonons [5.14]. The modulation of R_U due to this process can be estimated as follows. An excess LO phonon density N_p arises in the undepleted layer from those hot electrons emerging from the depletion region with energies $\varepsilon(v) > \hbar\omega_L$. The number of hot electrons per unit volume is $n_h = F/v$, where v is a mean velocity $\sim 4 \times 10^5 \, \text{m s}^{-1}$ for electrons of energy $\hbar\omega_L$. Equating the phonon emission rate n_h/τ_{em}^{-1} to the loss rate $N_p(\tau_i^{-1} + \tau_d^{-1})$ gives $N_p = n_h/\tau_{em}(\tau_i^{-1} + \tau_d^{-1})$. Here τ_{em}^{-1} is the emission rate of LO phonons for one electron, τ_i^{-1} is the rate of ionisation of donors and τ_d is the phonon decay time. An estimate based on the known LO-phonon-electron interaction gives $\tau_i \sim 10^{-11} \, s$ for $N_D = 2 \times 10^{15} \, \text{cm}^{-3}$, and taking $\tau_d \sim 10^{-11} \, s$ and $\tau_{em} \sim 0.5$

$\times 10^{-12}$ s [5.23] gives $N_p \sim 10^{11}$ cm^{-3}. Hence in equilibrium the conduction electron density is given by $n = N_p \tau_r / \tau_i \sim 10^{14}$ cm^{-3}. Modulation of n follows when, with increasing bias, the peak in the electron energy distribution passes the threshold for LO phonon emission which alters N_p and hence n. There is considerable uncertainty in this estimate but it indicates that phonon ionisation may be comparable to the impact ionisation mechanism.

We can test whether the impact- or LO phonon-ionisation is the dominant mechanism giving rise to the oscillatory structure in $I(V)$ by examining the amplitude of the LO phonon-related peaks in $d^2 J/dV^2$ as a function of magnetic field. If LO phonon ionisation were dominant, one might expect a series of hot electron magnetophonon resonances (MPR) in the oscillatory amplitude at fields given by $\hbar\omega_L = N\hbar\omega_c + E_D(B)$ where $\omega_c = eB/m^*$ and $N = 1, 2, 3 \dots$ [5.24]. On the other hand, if impact ionisation were dominant, a peak in the amplitude of the oscillations might be expected to occur when $\hbar\omega_c = E_D(B)$. At this magneto-impurity resonance (MIR) field [5.25] the ionisation energy corresponds to the joint density of states maximum for hot electrons falling from the $p = 1$ to $p = 0$ Landau level. Hence the free carrier density n should increase resonantly at $\gamma_B = \hbar\omega_c/2E_D(0) = 0.77$, corresponding to $B_r = 5.2$ T in GaAs. As shown in Fig. 5.3, we observe no MPR in plots of the oscillatory peak amplitude versus B. Instead a maximum occurs around $B = 5$ T, in excellent agreement with the MIR field B_r corredponding to impact ionisation. In addition, as shown in Fig. 5.3 (inset) the widths ΔV of the peaks in the LO structure narrow remarkably at around 5 T, due to the effect of the singularity of the Landau level density of states. The absence of MPR also argues against one of the models recently proposed to explain the oscillatory structure [5.16].

5.2.2 n-(InGa)As/InP/(InGa)As Heterostructures

We have recently extended our work on hot electron effects in single barrier heterostructures to reverse-biased n^+(InGa)As/InP/n^-(InGa)As/n^+(InGa)As devices. The band bending diagram is of the same form as that shown in Fig. 5.1. Typical results are shown in Fig. 5.4. The device was grown by MBE on a

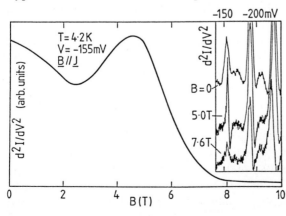

Fig. 5.3. Variation in amplitude of the LO phonon peak at $V = -155$ mV in $d^2 I/dV^2$ plot at 4.2 K. The inset shows a resonant narrowing of peak near the magneto-impurity resonance field, $B_r = 5.0$ T compared with traces at $B = 0$ and 7.6 T

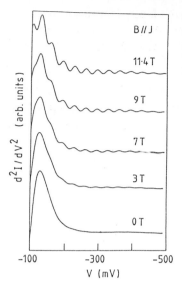

Fig. 5.4. Second derivatives $\partial^2 J/\partial V^2$ of the reverse bias $I(V)$ characteristics of a single barrier $n^+(\text{InGa})\text{As}/\text{InP}/n^-(\text{InGa})\text{As}/n^+\text{InP}$ structure showing the appearance of the oscillatory structure with period $V = 33$ meV at high magnetic fields, $T = 4$ K, $\boldsymbol{I} \| \boldsymbol{B}$

10^{18} cm^{-3} n^+InP substrate with the following layers (in order from substrate): n^+InP, 10^{18} cm^{-3}, 1000 Å; n^+(InGa)As, 4×10^{17} cm^{-3}, 0.5 μm; undoped InP barrier, 160 Å; n^-(InGa)As, low 10^{15} cm^{-3}, 1 μm; n^+(InGa)As, 4×10^{17} cm^{-3}, 1 μm. At zero magnetic field, no clear oscillatory structure is observed. However, as the magnetic field $(\boldsymbol{B} \| \boldsymbol{I})$ is increased, structure appears in $\partial^2 I/\partial V^2$ with characteristic period $\Delta V \sim 33\,meV$. This corresponds to the energy of the Ga-As LO phonon mode in (InGa)As. The predominance of this phonon in optical and electrical measurements has been reported previously [5.26, 27]. Fourier transforms of the oscillatory structure indicate that contribution of the In-As LO mode is at least a factor of 5 weaker. It is interesting to note that the ineffectiveness of the In-As LO phonon mode in relaxing the energy of the hot electrons means that in (InGa)As, the alloying effectively weakens the LO phonon coupling relative to the case for GaAs. This point is relevant to the observation in these devices of the new type of magnetotunnelling phenomenon described in Sect. 5.4 where we present clear evidence for ballistic trajectories of up to 0.3 μm for hot electrons whose energy is well above the LO phonon emission threshold.

It is interesting to note that a magnetic field is required to observe the LO-phonon-related oscillations in our n-(InGa)As/InP/(InGa)As structures, just as *Hickmott* et al. found for their n-GaAs/(AlGa)As/GaAs structure. In the former devices, lower n^+ doping in the n^+(InGa)As layer adjacent to the barrier means that the tunnel current is smaller than in our GaAs/(AlGa)As/GaAs structures. Hence the voltage drop across the undepleted part of the n^-(InGa)As layer will also be small at zero magnetic field. In addition, the shallow donor binding energy in n-(InGa)As is about 60% of its value in n-GaAs. The role of the magnetic field in enhancing the oscillatory structure must be to increase the donor binding energy and hence the impedance of the n^-(InGa)As layer. The variation of the impedance of this layer then modulates the $I(V)$ characteristics of the device in a similar way to that described above for the GaAs/(AlGa)As structures.

5.2.3 Magnetocapacitance and Magnetic Freeze-out

Extensive use of $C(V)$ measurements has been made recently to analyse the distribution of charge in single-barrier heterostructures. *Smith* et al. [5.28] and *Weiss* et al. [5.29] have used capacitance measurements of accumulation layers in GaAs/(AlGa)As heterostructures to study the density of states of a 2DEG in the presence of a perpendicular, quantising magnetic field.

Hickmott et al. [5.6] have used magnetocapacitance measurements to study the distribution of charge in reversed-biased heterostructures. At $B = 0$ they observed that the capacitance fell monotonically with increasing reverse-bias voltage. This occurs as a result of the increasing width of the depletion region in the n^- layer. At high enough reverse-bias voltages, the depletion layer fills the complete length t of the n^- GaAs layer giving a constant capacitance $C_{min} = \varepsilon_r \varepsilon_o /(b + t)$ per unit area, where b is the barrier thickness. However, at high fields ($B > 4$ T), the capacitance even at low reverse bias decreased towards this value C_{min} and at sufficiently high values of B, $C(V)$ remained almost constant and close to C_{min} over a wide range of reverse bias. We have observed similar behaviour as shown in Fig. 5.5a by the experimental values of $C(V)$ measured at 1 MHz for a 200 μm diameter mesa in reverse bias with various values of magnetic field at 4.2 K. However, note that the magnetic field-induced fall in capacitance at 17 K (Fig. 5.5b) is much smaller. For the remainder of this section we refer to the low and essentially voltage-independent values of $C(V)$ measured at 4.2 K and high magnetic fields as the "anomalous" magnetocapacitance. The dependence of the reverse bias $C(V)$ curves on B was interpreted by *Hickmott* et al. as arising from magnetic freeze-out of electrons onto shallow donors. This, it was claimed, neutralised all of the positive space charge in the depletion layer and led to a uniform electric field throughout the length of the n^- region. This interpretation has been followed by several workers who have subsequently attempted to explain the oscillatory structure [5.11, 14, 16]. We have previously pointed out [5.8, 9] that magnetic freeze-out under the high electric field conditions of the experiment is inconsistent with the known electrical behaviour of n^- GaAs. Although magnetic freeze-out of electrons onto shallow donors is a well-established effect and indeed occurs in the low field part of the n^- layers of the single barrier heterostructures, it cannot occur throughout the length of the n^- layer in the presence of the high electric fields (> 1 kV/cm) corresponding to the reverse-bias voltages over which the anomalously low magnetocapacitance values are observed. At these electric fields, electrons are stripped from the donor states by field-emission or avalanche multiplication due to impact ionisation by hot carriers. Since the current through the device is low, the charge due to current carrying electrons in the depletion layer can be neglected and the space charge is given by $(N_D - N_A)e$.

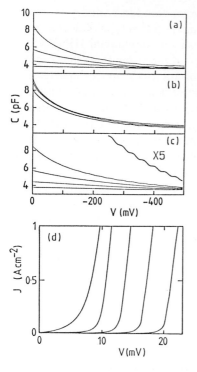

Fig. 5.5. (a) $C(V)$ curves for a 200 μm diameter mesa, T = 4.2 K, top to bottom: B = 0, 3, 5, 11.4 T. (b) As (a), but T = 17 K, top to bottom: B = 0, 5, 11.4 T. (c) Simulation of data for T = 4.2 K of Fig. 5.4 using equivalent circuit shown in Fig. 5.1. The top curve is expanded × 5 to show the oscillatory structure in $C(V)$. Top to bottom the simulations have $R_0(B) = 0.51$, 1.8, 3.2 and 5.9 kΩ. (d) $J(V)$ curves of 1 μm thick $n^+n^-n^+$ GaAs mesas (N_D − $N_A = 2 \times 10^{15}$ cm^{-3} in n^- layer) at 2 K for various magnetic fields, left to right: 0, 2.8, 5.7, 8.6, 11.4 T, $B \perp J$. These test structures lack the (AlGa)As barrier and are used for studying as a function of bias the magnetoresistance of the lightly doped n^-GaAs which forms the undepleted region of the tunnelling structures

Hickmott suggested several factors which may assist in sustaining magnetic freeze-out in the high electric fields [5.30]. One is the magnetic field-induced compression of the donor wavefunction and the associated increased binding energy. However, even if this process occurs to some extent for $B \perp E$, it does not explain the anomalous magnetocapacitance for $B||E$ (H ⊥ in the notation of *Hickmott* and coworkers) since compression of the donor ground state wavefunction along B is relatively small at fields up to 10 T [5.31]. The other mechanisms proposed [5.30] to explain the anomalous magnetocapacitance behaviour (limitation of the current by the barrier and the long mean free path of the electrons in the n^- region) do not address the question of how the donors can remain neutral in the presence of electric fields large enough to cause field emission. This point is illustrated by the data in Fig. 5.5d which show the $I(V)$ curves at various magnetic fields for a specially prepared test structure: a simple $n^+n^-n^+$GaAs sandwich in which the n^- layer is 1 μm thick and doped to the same level ($N_D - N_A = 1 - 2 \times 10^{15}$ cm^{-3}) as the n^- layer in both our and *Hickmott* et al.'s GaAs/(AlGa)As tunnelling structures. This experiment demonstrates that a magnetic field of ∼ 10 T cannot bind the donor in the presence of the large electric fields. It can be seen that even at fields of 11 T the device behaves as a voltage limiter due to field emission processes. (Note also that voltages considerably greater than $kT/e \simeq 0.3$ mV can be sustained since many inelastic processes occur down the 1 μm long conduction channel.)

The apparently anomalous magnetocapacitance data can be understood by a reappraisal of the way the capacitance is measured on this type of device. Both *Hickmott* and ourselves have measured $C(V)$ using a commercial HP4274A or HP4275A multifrequency LCR meter. This type of meter analyses the complex impedance of any circuit or device as a single capacitance C^* and a single resistor R^* either in parallel or series. For the single-barrier heterostructure, the parallel combination is usually more appropriate and is used in the measurements of *Hickmott* et al. and ourselves. However, it must be borne in mind that the electronic behaviour of the device may be more complicated than a two-parameter parallel RC circuit. *Hickmott* noted that the resistance of the undepleted region must, in principle, be taken into account but he neglected its capacitance, C_2. Using a small-signal analysis of the relationships given in Sect. 2.1, it can be shown [5.32] that the equivalent circuit appropriate to the single-barrier heterostructure is the one shown in Fig. 5.1. C_1 and R_1 represent the capacitance and dynamic conductance ($\partial I_r / \partial V$) of the barrier and depletion region (PQ). Here I_r is the current component which is in phase with the modulation voltage. C_1 is given by $\varepsilon_r \varepsilon_0 / (b + s)$, where b is the barrier width and s is the depletion layer width. C_2 and $R_2 (= R_U)$ are the corresponding values for the undepleted region (QR). It is straightforward to express R^* and C^* as measured by the LCR meter in the parallel circuit configuration as functions of R_1, C_1, R_2 and C_2 [5.32]. We can then compare our model with the observed values of R^* and C^* at any voltage, magnetic field or modulation frequency. Using this method, the apparently anomalous magnetocapacitance can be understood. Even at liquid helium temperatures the zero magnetic field value of $R_2 (= R_U)$ is generally small compared to the impedance $1/\omega C_2$ at the measurement frequencies ($0.1 - 2$ MHz). Thus R_2 effectively short-circuits C_2. In addition, R_2 is small compared to R_1, the dynamic impedance of the barrier plus depletion layer so that, to a good approximation, $C^* \sim C_1$ and $R^* \sim R_1$ at zero magnetic field. This explains why the $C(V)$ characteristics of the device at *zero* magnetic field can be modelled successfully in terms of the increase of the depletion layer width with increasing reverse bias voltage [5.6, 30]. This approximation works even better at relatively high temperatures ($4 < T < 60$ K) when R_2 is small but when the temperature is still low enough for thermionic emission over the barrier to be negligible (Fig. 5.5c).

The crucial point apparently overlooked in [5.6, 30] is that at $T \leq 4.2$ K the value of R_2 increases markedly with increasing B. This results from the behaviour of lightly doped semiconductors at low temperatures in which the electrical conduction is dominated by hopping between impurities or by low mobility states close to the edge of the band. When a magnetic field is applied ($E \perp B$ or $E \| B$) the magnetoresistance can increase by several orders of magnitude [5.37]. When the resistance R_2 becomes sufficiently large, it is no longer appropriate to neglect C_2. In fact, at sufficiently high modulation frequencies ($\omega C_1 R_1 \sim 1$ and $\omega C_2 R_2 \sim 1$), $C^{*-} \sim C_1^{-1} + C_2^{-1}$ the value corresponding to two capacitors in series. Thus C^* falls significantly below C_1 even at low reverse bias. C^* is then given approximately by its lowest value, $\varepsilon_r \varepsilon_0 / (b + t)$. This description explains why, at high magnetic fields and low temperatures, the capacitance curves measured by *Hickmott* et al. and by ourselves have low values which are essentially independent of the reverse bias voltage. It is incorrect to assume that because the capacitance at high magnetic fields has a low and constant value, *all* of the n^- GaAs layer is undergoing magnetic freeze-out. We stress that when the magnetic field is applied, a depletion region remains in existence. The measured capacitance decreases because the capacitance of the undepleted region must be taken into account at high magnetic fields. *Hickmott*'s use of the van Gelder-Nicollian equation [5.33] to obtain Fig. 5.5 of [5.30] assumes that the measured capacitance C^* equals C_1 and ignores the impedance of the undepleted layer even in the presence of high magnetic fields. The three curves in Fig. 5.5b taken at 17 K show clearly the effect of the lower value of R_2 where the temperature is high enough to maintain a significant free carrier concentration in the undepleted layer. In this case, the measured C^* approximates more closely to C_1 since C_2 is shorted out by R_2. The equivalent circuit in Fig. 5.1 also explains the frequency-dependent values of C^* reported by *Hickmott* [5.30] and also observed by ourselves. For a simple two-parameter parallel R–C circuit, the measured value of C^* should be independent of frequency. However, C^* and R^* are in fact frequency-dependent [5.32]. This explains why at low modulation frequencies (100 kHz) we observe that the magnetic field has a much smaller effect on the measured capacitance C^* than at 1 MHz since, at low frequencies, R_2 partially shorts out C_2 even when the magnetoresistance of the undepleted layer is large.

These qualitative ideas can be tested by numerically simulating the measured magnetocapacitance using the RC network of Fig. 5.1. The results of such a simulation are shown in Fig. 5.5c. The value of C_1 is taken to be $\varepsilon_r\varepsilon_0/(b + s)$ where $s = [2\varepsilon_r\varepsilon_0|V - V_0|/(N_D - N_A)e]^{1/2}$ is the depletion layer width and V_0 reflects the depletion at zero bias. Similarly $C_2 = \varepsilon_r\varepsilon_0/(t - s)$. The value of R_1 can be estimated from the measured dc reverse bias $I(V)$ characteristics at temperatures (~ 20 K) for which the resistance of the undepleted region is low. The value of this impedance is considerably higher than $1/\omega C_1$ at the measurement frequency. Therefore, the exact choice of R_1 does not have a great effect on the simulated values of $C^*(V)$. For this reason, and for simplicity, we take $R_1 = 10$ kΩ. The simulation of the magnetoresistance therefore involves essentially only one parameter R_2, the resistance of the undepleted region. Since the thickness of the undepleted region decreases with increasing reverse bias we represent R_2 by $R_2(V, B) = R_0(B)(1 - s/t)$. The simulations shown in Fig. 5.5c are obtained with values of $R_0(B) = 0.5$ k$\Omega(B = 0$ T), 1.8 k$\Omega(3$ T), 3.2 k$\Omega(5$ T) and 5.8 kΩ (11 T), chosen to fit the measured capacitance at $V = 0$. These values are consistent with the large magnetoresistance variation of lightly doped n^- GaAs test structures which we have measured at liquid helium temperatures [5.31]. The simulations are in fair agreement with the data for 4.2 K shown in Fig. 5.5a. The slightly greater slope of the observed $C(V)$ at low bias probably arises from non-uniform doping near the barrier [5.33] and from the decrease of R_1 with increasing bias. We note that the ohmic behaviour of $R_0(B)$ is an approximation since at high values of V_U, $R_0(B)$ will voltage-limit as shown in Fig. 5.5d.

Our model also accounts for the oscillatory structure in the observed capacitance C^*. This is due principally to the variation of R_2 rather than the much smaller variations of C_1 and C_2 arising from the modulation of the depletion layer widths. By writing $R_2(V) = R_0(1 - s/t)(1 + a(V)$ $\sin(2\pi V \Delta V)$, we can simulate the weak oscillatory structure observed in the measured C^* which arises from the variation of R_2. A value of $a(V) = 720\ V^2/R_0$ (with V in volts and R_0 in Ω) provides a good simulation to the observed structure in *both* $I(V)$ and $C^*(V)$ *at* 4.2 K, a result which lends strong support to our model. The weak oscillations in C^* induced by varying R_2 can be seen in the upper simulated curve in Fig. 5.5c, also shown in expanded form for clarity.

To summarise this section, the model we have proposed to describe the LO phonon-related oscillatory structure also explains the anomalous magnetocapacitance and magnetic freeze-out originally reported by *Hickmott* and coworkers in [5.6, 30] and the oscillatory structure in the magnetocapacitance.

5.3 Magnetotunnelling from the 2D Electron Gas in Accumulated (InGa)As/InP Structures Grown by MBE and MOCVD

Figure 5.6a shows the band structure of our (InGa)As/InP devices at a small forward bias. A two-dimensional electron gas (2DEG) is accumulated in the potential well adjacent to the InP barrier even at zero bias. The 2DEG can be studied by using the capacitance $C(V)$ and the small tunnel current $I(V)$ flowing through the barrier as a probe. Measurements of this type have been discussed in detail elsewhere [5.28–30, 34]. With a magnetic field perpendicular to the plane of the 2DEG ($I \| B$), pronounced structure is observed in $I(V, B)$, $G(V, B) = \partial J/\partial V$ and $C(V, B)$ as B is swept at constant bias, as shown in Figs. 5.6b, c and 5.7. There are several interesting features of the $I(V, B)$ curves. At each bias, a series of minima in I and G occur at fields given accurately by $B_1/p'(p' = 1, 2, 3 \ldots)$ where B_1 is the fundamental minimum marked by the arrow in the figure. An additional minimum also occurs close to $2B_1$. The value of B_1 increases steadily with V as shown in Fig. 5.8. $I(B)$ and $G(B)$ fall to as low as 30% of their value at $B = 0$ at the fundamental field B_1. All of these features are associated with the 2DEG. This is confirmed by the movement of the peaks as B is tilted away from $B \| I$. There is no evidence that more than one sub-band is occupied. As can be seen from Fig. 5.7, the oscillatory structure in the capacitance is relatively weak. However, the magnetocapacitance shows a clear minimum at B_1 with a much weaker minimum near $2B_1$.

The magneto-oscillations in I and G at low bias V can be understood in terms of the effect of B on the density of states in the 2DEG. Neglecting the prefactor, all

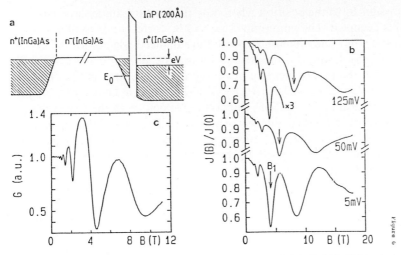

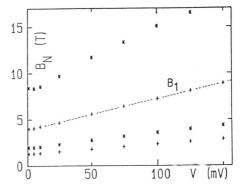

Fig. 5.6. (a) The conduction band of a single barrier n-(InGa)As/InP/(InGa)As device in forward bias V. The n^-(InGa)As is doped low $10^{15}\,\text{cm}^{-3}$ and is $1\,\mu\text{m}$ thick. The n^+ contacts are $4 \times 10^{17}\,\text{cm}^{-3}$. **(b)** The $J(B)$ curves of device shown in 6(a) at 3 fixed forward biases. The InP barrier thickness $b = 200\,\text{Å}$, $T = 4\,\text{K}$. **(c)** Plot of $G(B) = \partial J/\partial V$ around $V = 0$, for a device with InP barrier thickness $b = 170\,\text{Å}$, $T = 2\,\text{K}$

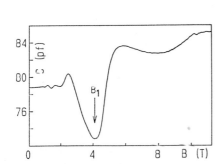

Fig. 5.7. $C(B)$ curve around $V = 0$ for the device shown in Fig. 5. 6(a). The InP barrier $b = 200\,\text{Å}$, $T = 4\,\text{K}$

Fig. 5.8. The variation of the minima in $J(B)$ taken from the curves shown in Fig. 5.6(b) for minimum B_1 and those close to $2B_1$, $B_1/2$ and $B_1/3$

electrons tunnel at the sub-band energy E_0 with the same transmission probability which, by comparison with that of Sect. 5.2.1, is $D \sim \exp(-\alpha y)$ where $\alpha = 2b(2m^*V_0)^{\frac{1}{2}}/\hbar$, V_0 is the barrier height relative to E_0 and $y(V_B)$ is a function of the barrier voltage ($y(0) \simeq 1$). At low temperatures and low bias the tunnel current I is given by an integral over states within eV of the Fermi energy E_F in the 2DEG. The density of these states and hence I and G are modulated by the applied magnetic field and should be a minimum when E_F is between Landau levels. We assign B_1 to the position when only the lowest Landau level (spin up and down) is occupied. The minimum close to $2B_1$ corresponds to filling of the lowest spin state only and is consistent with the enhanced g-factor for the 2DEG in (InGa)As [5.35]. Using this model and noting the slope (dB_1/dV) of the B_1 curve in Fig. 5.8, the rate of increase of charge Q per unit area in the 2DEG is given by $\Delta Q = e(2e\Delta B/h) \sim 2e^2(dB/dV)\Delta V/h$. For a mesa diameter of 200 μm, this gives a capacitance $C = 82$ pF, in good agreement with the $C(V)$ curve in Fig. 5.7 which was measured directly with an LCR meter. The capacitance measurements and the oscillatory structure in $I(V)$ thus give essentially the same value for the increase in the density of the 2DEG in the accumulation layer as the magnetic field is increased.

Within the variational approximation of *Stern* [5.36], the capacitance C per unit area of the 2DEG system is $C^{-1} = b/\varepsilon_r\varepsilon_0 + \gamma z_0/\varepsilon_r\varepsilon_0 + [e^2 D(\varepsilon_F)]^{-1}$ where γ is a numerical factor ~ 1, z_0 corresponds to the mean position of the quantised 2DEG in the potential well and $D(\varepsilon_F)$ is the density of states of the 2DEG at the Fermi energy [5.28, 29]. The $I(V)$ and $C(V)$ cureves are therefore complimentary methods of probing the 2DEG density of states.

Finally, in this section, we note that in the $I(V)$, $G(V)$ and $C(V)$ measurements as a function of B, it is the Fermi energy difference ($= eV$) that is fixed rather than the 2DEG carrier density. As B is increased, the variation of carrier density will modulate the confining potential and hence E_0, thus giving rise to an additional mechanism for modulating $I(V)$.

5.4 Observation of Magnetoquantized Interface States by Electron Tunnelling in Single-Barrier n^-(InGa)As/InP/n^+(InGa)As Heterostructures

In this section we describe a new type [5.38] of tunnelling phenomenon in forward-biased, single-barrier n^+(InGa)As/n^-(InGa)As/InP/n^+(InGa)As structures, which occurs when a quantizing magnetic field $(B||0z)$ is applied in the plane of the barrier, perpendicular to the direction of current flow $(I||0x)$. Two distinct series of resonances in the voltage or field dependence of the current density $I(V, B)$ have been observed and are interpreted in terms of electron tunnelling from an accumulated two-dimensional electron gas (2DEG) into two series of interfacial Landau states which differ in the proximity of the electron to the tunnel barrier. These interface states correspond to classical skipping motion of the electron along the barrier interface and are quite distinct from bulk Landau-level states for which the electron orbits do not intersect the interface.

Under a forward-bias voltage V, as shown schematically in Fig. 5.9, a 2DEG is formed on the left hand side (LHS) of the InP barrier and tunnelling can occur into the RHS n^+(InGa)As layer. The tunnel current I falls rapidly when a magnetic field $(B \perp I)$ is applied, as shown in Fig. 5.10, for a bias voltage of

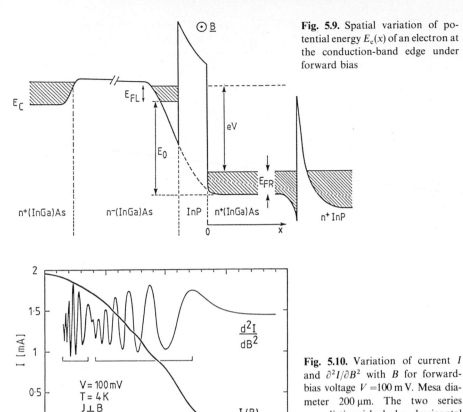

Fig. 5.9. Spatial variation of potential energy $E_c(x)$ of an electron at the conduction-band edge under forward bias

Fig. 5.10. Variation of current I and $\partial^2 I/\partial B^2$ with B for forward-bias voltage $V = 100$ m V. Mesa diameter 200 μm. The two series are distinguished by horizontal brackets

100 mV. In addition, oscillatory structure is observed which is more clearly revealed in $\partial^2 I/\partial B^2$, also shown in Fig. 5.10. The data were obtained at 4 K for a MOCVD-grown device with InP barrier of thickness 170 Å and n^-(InGa)As layer of thickness 0.8 μm, doped in the low 10^{15} cm^{-3} range. Both n^+(InGa)As layers were doped to 10^{17} cm^{-3}. We have obtained similar data for a range of such MBE- or MOCVD-grown structures.

For a given forward-bias voltage, two distinct series of peaks in $\partial^2 J/\partial B^2$ are observed, at fields given by $B_f/B = n + \phi$, where n is an integer and ϕ a (field independent) phase factor. For each series the fundamental field B_f increases steadily with applied voltage V as shown in Fig. 5.11. We stress that the oscillatory structure cannot be understood in terms of tunnelling into *bulk* Landau levels in the RHS n^+ layer. If this were the case, resonances would occur when the Fermi level of the 2DEG coincided with a Landau level on the RHS, which from Fig. 5.9 corresponds to

$$eV + E_{FR} = (n + \tfrac{1}{2})\hbar\,\omega_c, \quad n = 0, 1, 2 \ldots,$$

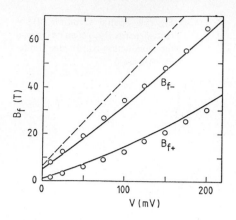

Fig. 5.11. Variation of B_f with bias voltage V for each series. Experiment (*circles*). Theory: bulk Landau states (*dashed line*), interfacial Landau states (*solid lines*)

where $\omega_c = eB/m^*$ and $E_{FR} = eV_{FR}$ is the Fermi energy in the n^+ layer. This would give $B_f = (V + V_{FR})m^*/\hbar$ which indeed predicts an increase of B_f with V, but does not give a fit to either series for any reasonable choice of effective mass m^*. The dashed line in Fig. 5.11 corresponds to $m^* = 0.043m_e$ which is appropriate to an energy $\sim E_{FR} \simeq 17\,\mathrm{meV}$ in the conduction band [5.27]. Owing to nonparabolicity m^* increases with V which would cause this line to deviate further from the data.

To understand the origin of the two series we need to consider in detail the effect of a magnetic field on the electron wave function ψ near the tunnel barrier. Using the vector potential in the Landau gauge $A = (0, Bx, 0)$, we may write $\psi(x, y, z) = \exp[i(k_y y + k_z z)]\psi(x)$. The function $\psi(x)$ is determined by a one-dimensional Schrödinger equation containing the potential energy $E_c(x)$ at the conduction-band edge shown in Fig. 5.9, and the magnetic potential $\frac{1}{2}m^*\omega_c^2(x - X)^2$, where $X = -\hbar k_y/eB$. In the limit of a very high impenetrable barrier the eigenstates on either side can be considered separately. On the LHS the magnetic field only slightly perturbs $\psi(x)$, which is a bound state of the accumulation-layer potential. For convenience we take the origin of coordinates to be the RHS of the barrier. Including motion parallel to the barrier, the energy of this state is then

$$E_L(k_y, k_z) = E_0 + \hbar(k_y'^2 + k_z^2)/2m^* .$$

E_0 is the bound state energy, which is only weakly field dependent [5.37], $k_y' = k_y - k_0, k_0 = eB(b + a_0)/\hbar$, b is the barrier width and a_0 is the mean distance of a bound electron from the LHS of the barrier. The occupied states in the 2DEG correspond to $k_z^2 \leqq k_{FL}^2$, where $k_{FL} = (2m^*E_{FL})^{\frac{1}{2}}/\hbar$ is the Fermi wave vector on the LHS. The shift $\hbar k_0$ is just the momentum change due to the Lorentz force as an electron traverses the barrier region.

In the more heavily doped RHS we take $E_c(x)$ to be constant. The one-dimensional eigenfuctions are bound states of the magnetic potential with energy levels

$$E_R(n, k_y, k_z) = E_n(k_y) + \hbar^2 k_z^2/2m^* .$$

For sufficiently large values of X, we have bulk Landau levels, $E_n = (n + \frac{1}{2})\hbar\omega_c$, whose eigenstates are simple harmonic oscillator (SHO) states centred at $X = -\hbar k_y/eB$. With decreasing X the states become distorted by the presence of the barrier and E_n increases as X decreases (k_y increases). We have calculated $E_n(k_y)$ for these interfacial Landau states using the WKB approximation with the results shown in Fig. 5.12. An additional algebraic approximation (accurate to within 10%) gives an analytic expression for these dispersion curves,

$$\frac{1}{2}(1 - u)E_n(k_y) = (n + \tfrac{3}{4})\hbar\omega_c, \quad n = 0, 1, 2 \ldots, \tag{5.1}$$

where $u = \hbar k_y/[2m^* E_n(k_y)]^{\frac{1}{2}}$. In a semiclassical picture $E_n = \frac{1}{2}m^* v^2$, where v is the orbital speed of an electron, so $u = \hbar k_y/m^* v$. Setting $u = \cos\theta$ gives the angle θ at which the electron strikes the interface in its skipping orbit along the y axis. The range of existence of these Landau interface states is thus $-1 < u < 1$. Bulk Landau states correspond to $u < -1$. Note that for $X = 0$ ($k_y = 0$) the eigenfunctions are just the odd-parity SHO states (since $\psi = 0$ at $x = 0$) and $E_n = (2n + \frac{3}{2})\hbar\omega_c$. The classical skipping orbits then consist of successive semicircles.

For a plane barrier of finite height, tunnelling occurs and the eigenstates on either side, with the same k_y and k_z, are coupled. Under forward bias a current flows as electrons tunnel from the 2DEG into the interfacial Landau states. Current continuity through the device is maintained by scattering processes which allow the electrons to diffuse to and from these localised states. However, the potential drop across the device occurs almost entirely in the accumulation layer and tunnel barrier [5.38].

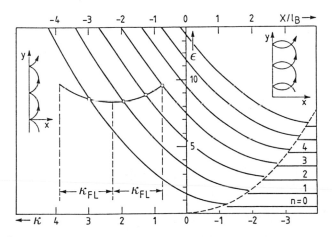

Fig. 5.12. Dispersion relations for interfacial Landau states in terms of scaled variables $\varepsilon = E_n/\hbar\omega_c$ and $\kappa = k_y l_B = -X/l_B$, where $l_B = (\hbar/eB)^{\frac{1}{2}}$. The insets show classical skipping orbits for interface states with $k_y < 0$ and $k_y > 0$. The parabola corresponds to $E = E_0 + \{\hbar^2(k_y - k_0)^2/2m^*\}$, $-k_{FL} < k_y - k_0 < k_{FL}$, and is drawn for $V = 100$ mV and $B = 5$ T. Intersection points $k_y(n)$ are shown as open circles. The dashed line marks the boundary between bulk and interfacial Landau states

We adopt a transfer-Hamiltonian approach [5.39] and write the current density

$$J = \frac{e}{2\pi^2} \sum_n \int \int dk_y dk_z \frac{2\pi}{\hbar} |T_n(k_y)|^2 \delta(\Delta E),$$

where the transfer matrix element $T_n(k_y)$ depends on k_y through the influence of the magnetic potential on the tunnel barrier [5.9] but is independent of k_z. The bias voltage has been taken to be sufficiently large that the electrons tunnel into empty states on the RHS ($V \geqq 10 \, \text{mV}$). Since $\Delta E = E_0 + (\hbar^2 k_y'^2/2m^*) - E_n(k_y)$ is also independent of k_z we may integrate over the occupied states in the 2DEG and obtain

$$J = \frac{2e}{\pi\hbar} \sum_n \int_{-k_{FL}}^{k_{FL}} dk_y' \, (k_{FL}^2 - k_y'^2)^{\frac{1}{2}} |T_n(k_y)|^2 \delta(\Delta E) .$$

The energy conservation condition $\Delta E = 0$ can be interpreted graphically by looking for intersections, in the $E - k_y$ plane, of the parabola $E = E_0 + \hbar^2(k_y - k_0)^2/2m^*$ with the set of dispersion curves $E = E_n(k_y)$ of the interfacial Landau states. As shown in Fig. 5.12, this gives a discrete set of k_y values, $k_y(n)$, which contribute to the above integral and to I. With increasing B the current falls because $T_n(k_y)$ decreases [5.9] and the number of intersection points falls becoming zero at sufficiently high fields. The periodic structure observed in I as B or V is varied corresponds to intersection points entering or leaving the extremities of the parabola when $k_y(n) = \pm k_{FL} + k_0$, which gives $E_n(\pm k_{FL} + k_0) = E_0 + E_{FL} = eV + E_{FR}$, the latter equality following directly from Fig. 5.9. Using these values of E_n and k_y in (5.1) gives

$$\tfrac{1}{2}(1 \mp u_F - u_0) (eV + E_{FR}) = (n + \tfrac{3}{4})\hbar\omega_c ,$$

where $u_F = \hbar k_{FL}/[2m^*(eV + E_{FR})]^{\frac{1}{2}}$ and $u_0 = \hbar k_0/[2m^*(eV + E_{FR})]^{\frac{1}{2}}$. We estimate $k_{FL} = (2\pi n_s)^{\frac{1}{2}}$ from the capacitance per unit area $C = n_s e/(V + V_{FR})$, where n_s is the surface electron density in the 2DEG. This assumes the absence of charge in the barrier so that the flat-band bias is $- V_{FR}$. Hence $u_F = (\pi\hbar^2 C/m^* e^2)^{\frac{1}{2}} = 0.384$ for $m^* = 0.043 m_e$ and $C = 4250 \, \mu\text{F m}^{-2}$ [5.40]. Thus the two series of oscillatory structure in $I(V, B)$ are associated with electrons at the extremities of the Fermi circle $k_y' = \pm k_{FL}$ in the 2DEG and occur at fields given by

$$e(V + V_{FR})\xi_{\pm} = (n + \tfrac{3}{4} + \phi')\hbar\omega_c ,$$

where $\phi' = e(V + V_{FR})u_0/2\hbar\omega_c$ is independent of B and $\xi_{\pm} = \tfrac{1}{2}(1 \mp u_F)$. This gives structure periodic in $1/B$ as observed and the fundamental fields are given by

$$B_{f\pm} = (\xi_{\pm} m^*/\hbar) (V + V_{FR}) , \tag{5.2}$$

where $\xi_+ = 0.31$, $\xi_- = 0.69$ for the $+k_{FL}$, $-k_{FL}$ electrons respectively. Experimental deviations from the linear $B_{f\pm} - V$ relation given by (5.2) can be attributed to (a) variation of capacitance with bias voltage and, of more importance, (b) nonparabolicity of the conduction band. To take account of (a) we have used a voltage-dependent capacitance $C(V)$ obtained from experiment. In the range of forward bias voltage (≤ 0.1 V) for which the conductance of the barrier is low enough, $C(V)$ can be measured directly for $\mathbf{B} \perp \mathbf{J}$. These capacitance values are consistent with the experimental values of n_s obtained from magneto-oscillations in the conductivity observed when $\mathbf{B}||\mathbf{I}$ [5.40]. Our measurements indicate that the capacitance is relatively insensitive to the magnitude and direction of magnetic field. For (b) we have used $m^*/m_e = 0.04(1 + \alpha E)$, where $E = eV + E_{FR}$ is the electron energy. As shown in Fig. 5.11 a good fit to experimental data is obtained with $\alpha = 1.3 \times 10^{-3}$ meV^{-1}. The coefficient α is rather smaller than found from optical measurements [5.27] ($\alpha = 5 \times 10^{-3}$ meV^{-1}, $E < 20$ meV) but is reasonable considering the wide energy range ($40 - 220$ meV) investigated. The oscillations in $\partial^2 J/\partial B^2$ decrease in amplitude as B decreases, the last peak ($-k_{FL}$ series) occurring at $B \sim 1.7$ T for $V = 100$ mV. This gives a length ~ 0.3 μm (time ~ 0.3 ps) between collisions with the interface for the corresponding classical skipping orbit. Although this is a rather long ballistic trajectory [5.3] the time is consistent with typical LO-phonon emission rates for hot electrons in III–V materials [5.41].

Magnetotunnelling oscillations have recently been reported by *Hickmott* [5.42] in forward biased n-GaAs/(AlGa)As/GaAs tunnel structures. Analysis of his data [5.43] indicates that these ocillations also arise from tunnelling into the Landau interface states described in this section.

It is interesting to note that in our heterostructure, tunnelling into bulk Landau levels does not occur since an electron cannot acquire a sufficiently negative k_y to give $u < -1$. By contrast, in a MOS structure the large Fermi momentum in the metal only allows observation of tunnelling into bulk Landau levels in the semiconductor [5.44].

5.5 Box Quantised States

Figure 5.13 shows oscillatory structure in $\partial^2 J/\partial V^2$ under forward bias for a device in which the RHS n^+(InGa)As (see Fig. 5.9) is only 0.36 μm thick and is lightly doped to 1×10^{17} cm^{-3}. The oscillations are not observed in structures where this layer is thicker (0.5 μm) or more heavily doped (5×10^{17} cm^{-3}). Below 2 T the skipping orbit structure disappears and below 1 T a new structure develops with peak separations ~ 6 meV. For $B = 0$ the electrons in the 2DEG tunnel into states of the RHS with energies $E_n + \hbar^2(k_y^2 + k_z^2)/2m^*$, where $E_n = \hbar^2 n^2 \pi^2/2m^*L^2$ are the box-quantised energies for the n^+(InGa)As layer between the two barriers of separation ~ 0.3 μm. This requires significant reflection of electrons at the n^+(InGa)As/n^+InP interface. However the

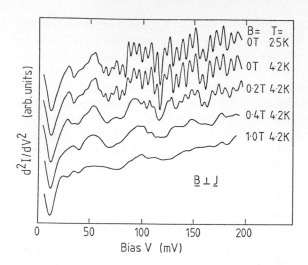

Fig. 5.13. Variation of $\partial^2 I/\partial V^2$ with V for $B = 1\,\mathrm{T}$, $0.4\,\mathrm{T}$ and $0.2\,\mathrm{T}$ at $4.2\,\mathrm{K}$ for $B = 0$ at $4.2\,\mathrm{K}$ and $2.5\,\mathrm{K}$ show the disappearance of the box quantised states in a weak transverse field

impedance at this interface is much less than that of the InP tunnel barrier so that the potential drop due to this reflection is negligible. Since momentum is conserved in the plane of the barrier, resonant peaks in the tunnel current occur when $E_0 = E_n$, or

$$E_n = eV + E_{FR} - E_{FL}. \tag{5.3}$$

We have analysed this condition using the same data as in the previous section for interfacial Landau levels i.e. $E_{FR} = 17\,\mathrm{meV}$, the non-parabolicity factor for m^*, $\alpha = 1.3 \times 10^{-3}\,\mathrm{meV}^{-1}$, and E_{FL} calculated from the same capacitance data. We find excellent agreement with the experimental peak positions. The quantum numbers n form a complete sequence from 29 to 46 for peaks in the range 60 to 170 mV. We therefore identify the $B = 0$ structure as resonant tunnelling from the 2DEG into box-quantised states. *Heiblum* and co-workers [5.45] have observed similar behaviour for well sizes L between 29 and 72 nm.

The observation of resonant tunnelling implies that a detectable proportion of the electrons have long ballistic trajectories $\sim 0.6\,\mu\mathrm{m}$. A similar situation occurs for tunnelling into the interfacial Landau states where a length $\sim 0.3\,\mu\mathrm{m}$ (time $\sim 0.3\,\mathrm{ps}$) between collisions with the interface for a classical skipping orbit is found. This time $\sim 0.3\,\mathrm{ps}$ is comparable with LO phonon emission times for hot electrons in III–V materials [5.41].

We have also investigated the pressure dependence of the peaks in $I(V)$ for pressures up to 6 kbar. Equation (5.3) leads to the following relationship between the voltages V_n of the current peaks and pressure

$$\frac{\partial \ln V_n}{\partial P} = -\frac{\partial \ln m^*}{\partial P} - 2\frac{(V_n - V_{FR})}{V_n}\frac{\partial \ln L}{\partial P} + \frac{V_{FL}}{V_n}\frac{\partial \ln n_s}{\partial P}. \tag{5.4}$$

The right hand side of (5.4) is dominated by the pressure variation of the effective mass in (InGa)As which has been determined by *Gauthier* and co-workers [5.46]. The variation of n_s with pressure is not known but this term contains the small ratio $V_{FL}/V_n \sim 0.14$ throughout the voltage range. If this term is neglected in the RHS of (5.4) then the pressure dependence of the peak positions V_n is in reasonable agreement with experiment. This provides additional support for our interpretation of the $B = 0$ resonances in terms of box-quantised states.

5.6 Double Barrier Resonant Tunnelling Devices

The final section of this chapter deals with some of the properties of double barrier resonant tunnelling structures [5.47–66, 68–72]. The development of our experimental and theoretical understanding of this type of structure is also described in the chapter of *Sollner* et al. *Sollner* and his coworkers in the MIT group have made a major contribution in recent years in highlighting the potential of this type of device for high frequency electronics.

Here we concentrate on some of the interesting physical phenomena that have recently been studied in these devices, particularly those involving the use of a large magnetic field which quantises the motion of the conduction electrons [5.55–57, 66, 70]. We also discuss how these experiments relate to the considerable and sometimes controversial theoretical discussions that have taken place at the same time.

Tsu and *Esaki* [5.47] envisaged the double barrier resonant tunnelling structure as somewhat analogous to the optical Fabry–Pérot resonator. This model has been further developed recently [5.48] but an alternative picture has been proposed by *Luryi* [5.49] who has pointed out that the negative differential conductivity associated with this type of device is resonant only in the sense that the applied voltage brings the electron energy in the emitter contact into resonance with the one-dimensional bound state energy of the quantum well. In this picture, electrons tunnel from the emitter, through the barrier, into the two-dimensional states of the well. The electrons then subsequently tunnel through the collector barrier, possibly after their energy or momentum has changed as a result of scattering processes in the well. Recently, however, it has been pointed out [5.50, 51] that for the parameters generally employed in double barrier structures, both the Fabry–Pérot and sequential tunnelling models lead to the same result for the dc current. In the following sections, we show how the application of a high magnetic field can reveal, under appropriate conditions, both the scattering processes which the tunnelling electrons undergo and also the ballistic nature of the electron trajectories.

5.6.1 Hybrid Magneto-electric States in Resonant Tunnelling Structures

We begin this section on resonant tunnelling devices with a discussion of the effect of a magnetic field ($B \perp I$) on double barrier structures with wide quantum wells [5.70]. The oscillatory structure which we observe in the tunnel current is similar to that for the single barrier described in Sect. 5.4 but more complex due to the effects of the second barrier. We examine two structures, DBS1 and DBS2 with well widths of 60 nm and 120 nm respectively, and each with two (AlGa)As barriers of thickness 5.6 nm with [A1] = 0.4. Their composition is given in detail in Table 5.1.

Figures 5.14a and 5.14b show the $I(V)$ characteristics of the two structures at 4 K. In order to enhance the resonances the differential conductance (dI/dV) is also plotted. Structure DBS1 (60 nm) shows 28 resonances. The first 12 resonances are ascribed to tunnelling into quasi-bound states of the well at an energy below the top of the collector barrier. The others, at higher voltage, are "above-barrier" resonances caused by reflection of the electron waves at the GaAs/(AlGa)As interface. The $I(V)$ characteristics of structure DBS2 show 70 resonances, 23 corresponding to quasi-bound states of the well and 47 corresponding to above-barrier states.

The inset of Fig. 5.14 is a schematic diagram of the electron potential energy in the device. The low doping in the regions adjacent to the barriers leads to the formation of a quasi-two-dimensional electron gas (2DEG) in the emitter contact. Resonant tunnelling occurs whenever the bound state of this 2DEG has the same energy as a state in the quantum well. The highest peak/valley ratio observed is only 1.75 (in structure DBS1 at 4.2 K) and this relatively low value is attributed to the close spacing of the energy levels causing overlap between neighbouring resonances. The beating apparent in the dI/dV curves at high voltages arises from the interference of electron waves scattered from the two interfaces of the collector barrier. The existence of well-defined "standing wave" resonances implies that some electrons traverse distances of at least 240 nm (twice the well width) without scattering even when they are accelerated in the well up to high kinetic energy (≈ 1 eV).

These characteristics make the samples ideal for studying the effect of a confining potential (quantum well) on the electron eigenstates in crossed electric and magnetic fields, i.e. with the electric field perpendicular to the barriers $(E\|x)$ and the magnetic field applied in the plane of the barriers $(B\|z)$. The effect of a magnetic field is to bend the electron orbits in the well by the action of the Lorentz force. The electrons can tunnel through the emitter barrier into two distinct types of magneto-electic states: (a) "skipping" orbits which interact with the emitter barrier only – these correspond to cycloidal motion under the action of crossed E and B; (b) "traversing" states in which the electron wave is repeatedly reflected off both barriers. The two types of orbit are shown in the inset of Fig. 5.15. Note that electrons which tunnel into type (a) states travel parallel to the barrier interface (i.e. perpendicular to the electric field) and only contribute to the measured current if they undergo scattering. The transition from type a to type b orbits occurs when the diameter of the cycloidal cyclotron orbit is greater than the width of the quantum well. This changeover has recently been related to the quenching of the Hall effect in small structures [5.52].

It should be stressed that the skipping states observed in both structures DBS1 and DBS2 develop in an undoped region where there is a large electric

Table 5.1. Compositions, doping levels (cm^{-3}) and thicknesses of the six structures used in this study. The central layers of each structure are undoped. All the layers were grown on an n-type Si-doped GaAs substrate, $n = 2 \times 10^{18}$ cm^{-3}.

Composition	Structures DBS1 & 2	Structure DBS3	Structure DBS4	Structure DBS5	Structure DBS6
n-type GaAs top contact	0.5 μm, 2×10^{18} 50 nm, 2×10^{16}	1.0 μm, 2×10^{17}	0.5 μm, 2×10^{18} 50 nm, 2×10^{16}	0.5 μm, 2×10^{18} 50 nm, 1×10^{17} 50 nm, 1×10^{16}	0.5 μm, 2×10^{18} 50 nm, 2×10^{16}
GaAs	2.5 nm		2.5 nm	3.3 nm	2.5 nm
Al$_{0.4}$Ga$_{0.6}$As	5.6 nm	8.8 nm	5.6 nm	11.1 nm	5.6 nm
GaAs	60 nm & 120 nm (DBS1 & 2 resp.)	5.6 nm	5.0 nm	5.8 nm	11.7 nm
Al$_{0.4}$Ga$_{0.6}$As	5.6 nm	8.8 nm	5.6 nm	8.3 nm	5.6 nm
GaAs	2.5 nm		2.5 nm	3.3 nm	2.5 nm
n-type GaAs	50 nm, 2×10^{16}		50 nm, 2×10^{16}	50 nm, 1×10^{16} 50 nm, 1×10^{17}	50 nm, 2×10^{16}
buffer layer	0.5 μm, 2×10^{18}	1.0 μm, 2×10^{17}	1.0 μm, 2×10^{18}	2.0 μm, 2×10^{18}	2.0 μm, 2×10^{18}

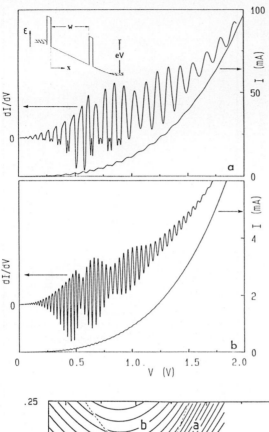

Fig. 5.14. Plots of $I(V)$ and differential conductance dI/dV at 4 K and $B = 0$ for **(a)** structure DBS1 (60 nm well) and **(b)** structure DBS2 (120 nm well). The inset shows the variation of electron potential through the double barrier structure under an applied voltage V

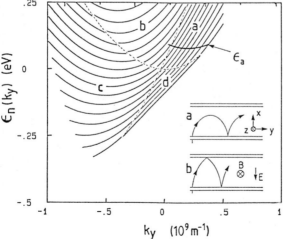

Fig. 5.15. Plot of the energy eigenvalues $\varepsilon_n(k_y)$ of the hybrid magneto-electric states in the 60 nm quantum well of structure DBS1 for $V = 1$ V and $B = 10$ T. The parabola marked ε_a corresponds to the energies of the states in the accumulation layer. The inset shows the ballistic orbits corresponding to skipping (a) and traversing orbits (b)

field. They are therefore essentially different from the skipping states reported in Sect. 5.4 in single-barrier heterostructures in which the electron orbits were in a heavily-doped n^+ region where the electric field was practically zero. This leads to a different quantisation condition although tunnelling in both systems can be analysed using a transfer-Hamiltonian method similar to that outlined in Sect. 5.4.

The tunnelling process is governed by conservation of energy and of momentum components in the plane of the barrier ($\hbar k_z$ and $\hbar k_y = m^*v_y - eBx$). For electrons in the degenerate 2DEG in the accumulation layer, $-\hbar k_F < m^*v_y < \hbar k_F$, where k_F is the Fermi wave vector. If the origin of coordinates is taken to be at the right hand side of the first barrier, the 2DEG is situated at $x = -(b + a)$, where b is the barrier width and a is the mean distance of the 2DEG from the interface between the GaAs emitter and its (AlGa)As barrier. Thus $\hbar k_y = m^*v_y + \hbar k_o$ where $k_o = eB(b + a)/\hbar$. Hence, neglecting the effect of the magnetic field on the quasi-bound state energy ε_o of the 2DEG, the energy of electrons in the emitter accumulation layer is given by

$$\varepsilon_a(k_y) = \varepsilon_o + \frac{\hbar^2}{2m^*}(k_y - k_0)^2 + \frac{\hbar^2 k_z^2}{2m^*},$$

with $k_0 - k_F \le k_y \le k_o + k_F$. The value of k_F at a given bias may be determined from magneto-oscillations in the tunnel current or capacitance in the $\boldsymbol{B}||\boldsymbol{I}$ configuration. The energies $\varepsilon_n(k_y)$ of the quantum well states are determined by the conduction band profile under bias and the magnetic potential $m^*\omega_c^2(x - X_0)^2/2$, where $\omega_c = eB/m^*$ and $X_0 = m^*E/eB^2 - \hbar k_y/eB$. They can be calculated using the WKB approximation. Figure 5.15 shows $\varepsilon_n(k_y)$ for structure DBS1 (with $V = 1$ V and $B = 10$ T) in the simplified case of infinitely high barriers. The dashed curves mark the transitions between states which do and do not interact with the barriers. Region a corresponds to the skipping dates of the emitter barrier, b to hybrid states interacting with both barriers, c to skipping states of the collection barrier and region d corresponds to bulk states which interact with neither barrier. Electrons only tunnel into states in regions a and b.

The parabola labelled ε_a represents the range of energies in the emitter contact. At low temperatures this is sharply cut off at $k_y - k_o = \pm k_F$. The energy and momentum conservation conditions can be interpreted graphically by looking for intersections in the $\varepsilon - k_y$ plane of the parabola ε_a with the set of dispersion curves $\varepsilon_n(k_y)$ of the states in the well. As can be seen in Fig. 5.15 this corresponds to a discrete set of k_y values which are the only ones which can contribute to the tunnel current. Sweeping either the applied voltage or magnetic field causes intersections to enter or leave the parabola (when $\varepsilon_0 + \varepsilon_F = \varepsilon_n(k_0 \pm k_F)$) leading to structure in the tunnel current.

The d^2I/dV^2 versus V characteristics of structure DBS1 at various magnetic fields ($\boldsymbol{B} \perp \boldsymbol{I}$) are shown in Fig. 5.16. Figure 5.17 presents a typical $I(B)$ curve at $V = 600$ mV for structure DBS2. In order to enhance the resonant structure the second derivative d^2I/dB^2 is also plotted. The series of oscillations at low voltage in Fig. 5.16 (7 and 10 T curves) is due to tunnelling into skipping states with $k_y = k_0 - k_F$ (type (a_-) orbits) in which the electron interacts with the emitter barriers only. The oscillations at higher bias are due to hybrid magneto-electric states which traverse the well (type b orbits). The largest skipping orbit observed

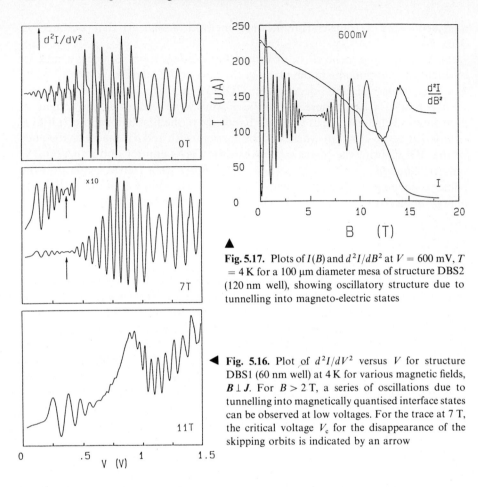

Fig. 5.17. Plots of $I(B)$ and d^2I/dB^2 at $V = 600$ mV, $T = 4$ K for a 100 μm diameter mesa of structure DBS2 (120 nm well), showing oscillatory structure due to tunnelling into magneto-electric states

Fig. 5.16. Plot of d^2I/dV^2 versus V for structure DBS1 (60 nm well) at 4 K for various magnetic fields, $B \perp J$. For $B > 2$ T, a series of oscillations due to tunnelling into magnetically quantised interface states can be observed at low voltages. For the trace at 7 T, the critical voltage V_c for the disappearance of the skipping orbits is indicated by an arrow

in structure DBS2 corresponds to a ballistic path length of at least 400 nm. In the $I(B)$ curve at $V = 600$ mV, shown in Fig. 5.17, three different series of oscillations can be observed: the two series of 0–2 T and 2–5 T correspond to type $(b_\pm)$ orbits with $k_y = k_0 \pm k_F$ respectively and the series above 6 T corresponds to type (a_-) orbits. The different tunnelling probability for $k_y = k_0 \pm k_F$ in the presence of a transverse field [5.9] means that only one k_F value is observed for the a-orbits. Note that at high B (> 15 T at this voltage) the tunnel current is quenched (since the strong quantum confinement raises the energy of the skipping states above the emitter Fermi energy). The fan chart in Fig. 5.18 shows the positions of the maxima in the current illustrating how the states evolve with magnetic field and applied voltage. The dashed lines define the regions in $B - V$ space corresponding to the different types of orbit. In order to obtain more than qualitative agreement with the data, the outline theory presented here needs to be extended to include the effects of a finite barrier height and the nonparabolicity and anisotropy of the conduction band of GaAs at these high injection energies, as

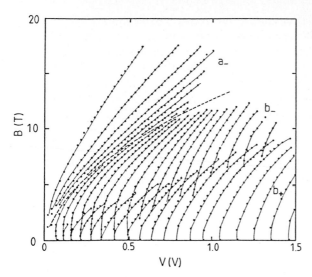

Fig. 5.18. Fan chart showing the positions of the maxima in I in $B - V$ space for DBS1 (60 nm well). The dashed lines define the regions corresponding to different types of orbit. The solid lines act as guides to the eye

well as a detailed calculation of the matrix elements for transitions between the emitter and the quantum well.

Our measurements on this type of structure show that high energy electrons travel ballistically over remarkably long distances (≈ 500 nm) in the wide quantum wells of double barrier structures based on n-GaAs/(AlGa)As. In the presence of a quantising magnetic field applied parallel to the plane of the barriers electrons tunnel into two distinct types of hybrid magneto-electric states with conservation of energy and momentum. These hybrid states are closely related to those responsible for edge currents in the Quantum Hall Effect.

5.6.2 Intrinsic Bistability in Resonant Tunnelling Devices

Recently, *Goldman* et al. [5.53] reported the observation of bistability in the current–voltage characteristics $I(V)$ of double barrier resonant tunnelling semiconductor heterostructures. This bistability occurs in the region of negative differential conductivity (NDC). It was interpreted as an intrinsic feature arising from the electostatic effects due to the build-up of negative space-charge in the quantum well between the two barriers.

This conclusion was challenged by *Sollner* [5.54] who claimed that the observed bistability in $I(V)$ was a common characteristic of devices exhibiting NDC and was due to current oscillations in the device and in the external circuit. In this case, bistability arises because of the difference between the turn-on and turn-off points for oscillatory behaviour when sweeping the applied dc voltage up or down through the NDC region. The range of applied dc voltage over which the bistability occurs then depends on the external circuit parameters as well as on the intrinsic characteristics of the device itself.

Recently, we investigated the magnetic field dependence $(\boldsymbol{B} \| \boldsymbol{I})$ of the current–voltage characteristics [5.55, 56] of resonant tunnelling double barrier structures based on *n*-(AlGa)As/GaAs. Our measurements confirmed the build-up of charge in the well at the resonant tunnelling voltages. In the region of NDC, the devices exhibited a current bistability similar to that originally reported by *Goldman* et al. [5.53]. We also reported [5.56] that the form of the $I(V)$ curves in the bistable region can be simulated quite well by numerical calculation of the current oscillations in an equivalent circuit consisting of a device exhibiting NDC in parallel with a capacitor and connected by resistive and inductive leads to a steady voltage source. This is consistent with *Sollner*'s point of view. *Sollner* also pointed out that if the magnitude of the negative differential resistance $|dV/dI|$ is sufficiently large, the current oscillations should be suppressed by a capacitor placed in parallel with the device. In order to study this, we have made further measurements on double-barrier devices [5.71] which have a higher impedance than those used by *Goldman* et al. [5.53].

The structure, DBS3, was fabricated into a mesa of 100 μm diameter. The composition and thickness of the various layers are given in Table 5.1.

The $I(V)$ characteristics shown in Fig. 5.19 were measured at 77 K with the mesa mounted on a standard transistor header. The upper curve of Fig. 5.19 was obtained with no external capacitance across the device and a region of hysteresis is clearly observable. An oscilloscope connected across the device indicated the presence of oscillations in the NDC region. The oscillations were not suppressed and the bistability persisted if a capacitor was connected across the leads emerging from the cryostat. When, however, a 0.28 μF chip capacitor was mounted directly on the transistor header so as to minimise the length of the inductive connecting leads, then the smooth $I(V)$ curve shown in the lower curve

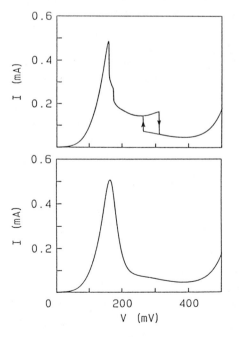

Fig. 5.19. The current-voltage characteristics at 77 K of a 100 μm mesa fabricated from the double barrier structure DBS3 (5.6 nm well) described in the text. The upper curve shows the dc current with no external capacitor across the mesa. In the voltage range corresponding to current bistability, the device is oscillating at a high frequency. In the lower curve, the oscillations and bistability are completely suppressed by placing a 0.28 μF capacitor directly across the mesa

of Fig. 5.19 was obtained. In this case, there was no bistability and no oscillations were observed throughout the NDC region.

An alternative method of suppressing the oscillations in the region of NDC is to connect, in parallel with the device, a small chip resistor r (25 Ω) of sufficiently low impedance that $r < |dV/dI|$ throughout the region of NDC. It is necessary to mount the resistor in close proximity with the device with very short connecting leads. A stable $I(V)$ plot of the device and resistor in parallel can then be obtained by applying a ramped voltage V. Even in the region of NDC, the circuit does not break into oscillation. The stable $I(V)$ characteristics of the tunnelling device alone are calculated by subtracting, from the total current, the current V/r flowing through the parallel resistor. Typical results obtained at 77 K with this simple procedure are shown in Fig. 5.20 for a 5 μm diameter mesa device (structure B, fabricated from structure DBS4 (see Table 5.1)).

We conclude that our measurements support the objections raised by *Sollner* concerning the reported observation by *Goldman* et al. of intrinsic bistability in double barrier resonant tunnelling devices. However, the magneto-oscillation studies [5.55–57] show clearly the existence of space-charge build-up in the quantum well. Thus intrinsic bistability driven by electrostatic feedback remains a theoretical possibility. Theoretical modelling [5.58] shows that the intrinsic bistability is removed by sufficient inhomogeneous broadening of the bound state level. A carefully designed structure which enhances the electrostatic feedback is therefore required to observe the intrinsic bistability effect.

To enhance the electrostatic feedback we have prepared and investigated [5.68, 69] a structure (DBS5) in which the two barriers have different widths, 8.3 nm and 11.1 nm. Details of the structure are given in Table 5.1. The device is shown schematically in Fig. 5.21 under reverse bias, that is when electrons are tunnelling into the well through the thinner of the two barriers. Note that the GaAs well width of 5.8 nm gives rise to two quasi-bound states in the well.

The $I(V)$ characteristics of the device (200 μm diameter mesa) at 4 K are shown in Fig. 5.22. There is a pronounced difference between forward and reverse

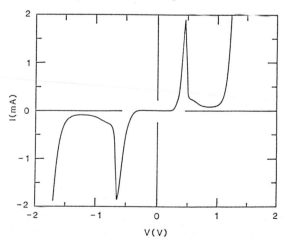

Fig. 5.20. The current-voltage characteristics at 77 K of a 5 μm diameter mesa fabricated from the double barrier structure DBS4 (5 nm well) described in the text. The oscillation and circuit bistability are suppressed by connecting a small resistor (25 Ω) in parallel with the device

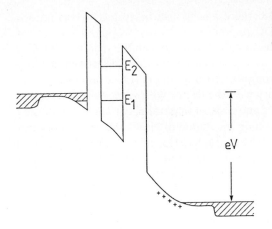

Fig. 5.21. Spatial variation of electron potential energy through an asymmetric double-barrier structure

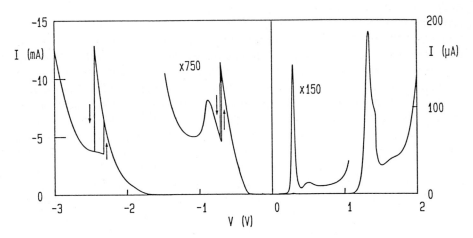

Fig. 5.22. The current-voltage characteristics at 4 K of a 200 μm diameter mesa fabricated from the asymmetric double barrier structure described in the text

bias (forward bias = substrate positive, thick emitter barrier, thin collector barrier). In forward bias both resonances are very narrow (the first resonance has a full width half maximum height of 40 mV) and show no bistability. In reverse bias the two resonances are much broader and both show regions of bistability (30 mV on the first peak and 140 mV on the second). The small tunnelling probability through the thicker collector barrier enhances the charge build-up in the well and leads to pronounced bistability in $I(V)$. The form of the bistabilities observed in reverse bias is quite different from that in *Goldman* et al. [5.53]. In particular, the current does not oscillate and the $I(V)$ characteristics remain unchanged when a parallel capacitor or resistor is connected. Note also that on both high and low current branches of the hysteresis loop, $dI/dV > 0$. The curve resembles a load-line effect but such a similarity is expected from our theoretical analysis of the effect of electrostatic feedback on the $I(V)$ characteristics [5.58]. The bistabilities in the $I(V)$ characteristics cannot be explained by the presence of an ohmic series resistance.

Our asymmetric DBS differs from the idealised structure analysed by *Sheard* and *Toombs* [5.58]. The light doping in the contact layers and the large threshold voltage lead to the formation of a two-dimensional electron gas (2DEG) in the emitter accumulation layer and a significant voltage drop across the collector depletion layer, as shown in Fig. 5.21. This depletion layer voltage magnifies the electrostatic feedback effect.

5.6.3 Magnetic Field Studies of Elastic Scattering and Optic Phonon Emission in Resonant Tunnelling Devices

The relatively low values of the peak-to-valley ratios found in real devices are generally attributed to a combination of "over the barrier" thermionic current [5.59, 60] and the effects of scattering processes on the tunnelling electrons [5.61, 62, 72]. The former process is important only at and around room temperature and can be neglected at liquid nitrogen temperature and below. In this section we investigate the nature of the scattering processes that contribute to the current in the valley region of the $I(V)$ curve, at voltages beyond the resonant peak in the current. By applying a high magnetic field perpendicular to the plane of the tunnel barriers (i.e. $\boldsymbol{B} || \boldsymbol{I}$), the density of electron states is quantised into discrete Landau levels. This allows us to investigate the scattering processes spectroscopically and to distinguish between contributions to the valley current arising from elastic scattering and from inelastic scattering processes due to the emission of longitudinal optic (LO) phonons by the tunnelling electron [5.72].

Three structures, DBS4, 5 and 6, with different well widths and barrier thicknesses were studied. Their compositions are given in Table 5.1. The layers were fabricated into mesas of various sizes, using standard photolithographic techniques. Note that structure DBS5 is the asymmetric device described in Sect. 5.6.2, i.e. the tunnelling barriers have different widths.

For all three of these structures the contact regions adjacent to the barriers are lightly doped. This appears to enhance the peak-to-valley ratio [5.63]. It also means that under bias a quasi-two-dimensional electron gas (2DEG) forms in the accumulation layer adjacent to the emitter barrier. Electrons are continually removed from the accumulation layer by tunnelling. Due to the relatively low current density the mean electron lifetime in the accumulation layer is long (3 μs for structure DBS4 at 1 V and 300 μs for structure DBS6 at 400 mV) compared to the energy relaxation time due to acoustic phonon emission. Hence incoming electrons have suffiecient time to thermalise in the accumulation layer and at low temperatures the 2DEG formed there is degenerate. This is confirmed by the existence in the tunnel current for $\boldsymbol{I} || \boldsymbol{B}$ of Shubnikov-de Haas-like oscillations associated with this 2DEG.

Structure DBS4, with the 5 nm quantum well, shows only one resonant peak in $I(V)$ at 470 mV; structure DBS6 with well width 11.7 nm exhibits three, at 70,

420 and 890 mV; the asymmetric structure DBS6 exhibits two peaks at 300 and 1300 mV in forward bias (substrate positive). In order to study the valley current it is necessary to suppress the current oscillations that can occur when a device is biased in the region of NDC, as discussed in Sect. 5.6.2. Stability is achieved by connecting, in parallel with the device, a small chip resistor of sufficiently low impedance that $r < |dV/dI|$ throughout the region of NDC. The stable $I(V)$ characteristics of the tunnelling device are calculated by subtracting the current V/r flowing through the parallel resistor from the total current. Typical results obtained at zero magnetic field are shown for the three structures in Figs. 5.23 and 24 for DBS6 and 5 respectively. Due to its high impedance, structure DBS6 did not require a parallel resistor to stabilise the current.

The $I(V)$ curves for all three structures exhibit a subsidiary peak (or shoulder) beyond the main resonant peak. *Goldman* et al. [5.61] and *Bando* et al. [5.64] have attributed this feature to LO-phonon-assisted tunnelling into the quantum well. Note also that LO-phonon assisted scattering between the subbands of the quantum well has been observed in resonant tunnelling structures [5.65, 66].

If an electron traverses the barriers without scattering, which is assumed to be the case for the majority of electrons contributing to the main resonant peak, the k-vector component, $k_\perp$, perpendicular to the tunnelling direction is conserved. The emission of an LO phonon (energy $\hbar\omega_{LO}$) or an elastic scattering process violates this conservation rule. The LO-phonon-assisted peak and the contribution to the valley current of elastic scattering can be revealed more clearly by

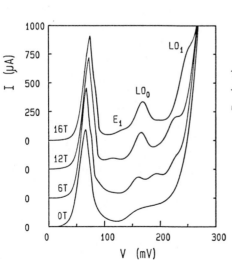

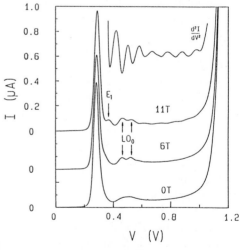

Fig. 5.23. The current-voltage characteristics at 4 K and at various magnetic fields $B \| J$ of a 100 μm diameter mesa fabricated from structure DBS6 (11.7 nm well). The curves show only the region of the first resonance

Fig. 5.24. The current-voltage characteristics of the first resonance in forward bias at 4 K and various magnetic fields $B \| J$ for a 200 μm diameter mesa fabricated from the asymmetric structure DBS5. The inset shows d^2I/dV^2 for the 11 T curve, emphasising the magneto-oscillatory structure

applying a quantising magnetic field B parallel to the direction of the tunnel current. This quantises the energy of motion in the plane of the barriers so that the energy of electrons in the accumulation layer of the emitter and in the quantum well are given by

$$\varepsilon = \varepsilon_0 + (n + \tfrac{1}{2})\hbar\omega_c \quad \text{Accumulation layer, and}$$

$$\varepsilon = \varepsilon_1 + (n' + \tfrac{1}{2})\hbar\omega_c \quad \text{Quantum well,}$$

where n and n' are the Landau level quantum numbers, $\omega_c = eB/m^*$, and ε_0 and ε_1 are the lowest quasi-bound state energies in the emitter and well respectively. The conservation of $k_\perp$ for $B = 0$ corresponds to the requirement that $p = n' - n = 0$ at finite B, so that resonant tunnelling occurs at an applied voltage for which $\varepsilon_0 = \varepsilon_1$, independent of B. Figure 5.23 shows the effect of a quantising magnetic field $B \| I$ on the $I(V)$ characteristics of structure DBS6. The following features are noteworthy. Firstly, the magnetic field increases the amplitude of the strongest LO-phonon-assisted peak, which has a peak-to-valley ratio of 2.6 at 18 T. Secondly, a weak secondary peak (E_1) emerges from the main resonant peak in the $I(V)$ curve as the magnetic field is increased. Similar subsidiary peaks also evolve from the LO phonon feature with increasing B. Thirdly, the magnetic field increases the peak-to-valley ratio (from 15 at $B = 0$ to 25 at $B = 18$ T). The fan chart in Fig. 5.25 shows the evolution of the magnetoquantum peaks in the $I(V)$ characteristics.

Transitions for which $k_\perp$ (or n) is not conserved are governed only by energy conservation. Therefore

$$\varepsilon_0 = \varepsilon_1 + \frac{pheB}{m^*} + ih\omega_{LO},$$

where $i = 0$ for elastic scattering and $i = 1$ for LO phonon emission. We have no evidence for multi-phonon emission ($i > 1$). The chart shows two clearly

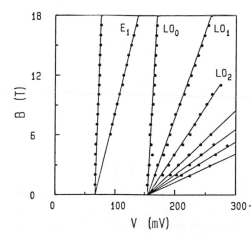

Fig. 5.25. Fan chart showing the magnetic field dependence ($B \| J$) of the peaks in $I(V)$ for structure DBS6. The elastic and inelastic (LO phonon) scattering processes giving rise to the oscillations are discussed in the text

identifiable groups of lines. In the limit $B \rightarrow 0$, peak E_1 extrapolates back to the main resonant peak at 70 mV. The peaks LO_p extrapolate back to the satellite corresponding to single LO phonon emission at 160 mV. The main resonant peak, which shifts very slightly to higher bias with increasing B, corresponds to tunnelling processes for which n is conserved. The slight shift may be due to the magnetoresistance of the contact layers. The weak peak marked E_1 is due to a non-resonant tunnelling transition involving elastic (or quasi-elastic) scattering from the nth Landau level in the emitter contact to the $(n + 1)^{th}$ Landau level in the well. Such a transition could be caused by scattering due to ionised impurities or interface roughness (elastic) or by acoustic phonon emission (quasi-elastic). The peaks marked LO_p correspond to transitions of electrons from the nth Landau level in the emitter to the $(n + p)^{th}$ Landau level in the well, with the emission of an LO phonon. The relative intensities of the main resonant peak and peaks E_1 and LO_p provide a qualitative indication of the contribution of the various charge transport processes to the measured current.

It is interesting to note that the effect of the magnetic field is to suppress the (quasi-)elastic scattering-induced transitions at certain voltages below and above E_1 and to enhance it at other voltages, corresponding to the peak E_1. In zero magnetic field such processes are allowed energetically for all voltages beyond the main resonant peak in the tunnel current. At these voltages the lowest energy bound state in the well is below the energy of the electrons in the emitter. However, a large magnetic field quantises the electron motion in the plane of the barriers, thus giving rise to sharp peaks in the densities of states. Therefore, energy conservation allows elastic scattering into the well only at certain voltages (E_1) and inhibits it elsewhere. This explains the enhancement of the peak-to-valley ratio with increasing B which is evident in Fig. 5.23.

Figure 5.24 shows the forward bias $I(V)$ characteristics of the asymmetric double barrier device, structure BDS5, at $B = 0$ and in the presence of a longitudinal magnetic field. The inset shows the second derivative, d^2I/dV^2, which reveals the magneto-oscillations more clearly. At 0 T the phonon satellite peak has a "flat top" structure. Application of a magnetic field clearly resolves two distinct phonon-assisted peaks at voltages (470 and 530 mV) which do not shift with increasing B. They must arise from optical phonon emission with no change in Landau level number. We attribute the two components to the two LO phonon modes in (Al, Ga) As [5.67]. Structure due to the elastic scattering process (E_1) and LO phonon emission accompanied by a change of Landau quantum number is also observed, but is complicated by the overlapping of two different phonon series. Very similar structure is observed in structure DBS4, with two LO-phonon-assisted peaks, at 570 and 630 mV, being resolved by the application of a magnetic field.

The difference in voltage between the phonon satellites and the main resonant peak is considerably larger than $\hbar\omega_{LO}$. This is because only a fraction (e.g. $\simeq 30\%$ for structure DBS6) of the total applied voltage V is dropped between the emitter contact and the quantum well, with a large portion of the voltage being dropped across the collector barrier and the depletion layer in the collector contact. The potential distribution across the device varies with applied bias. Fairly accurate estimates of the potential difference V_1 between the emitter contact and the well can be obtained over a range of applied voltage V by noting that the separations between the main resonance and E_1 and between the peaks LO_p and LO_{0+1} correspond to $\Delta V_1 = \hbar\omega_c$. Using this procedure we can estimate the energy of the LO phonons involved in the phonon-assisted tunnelling process. For structure DBS6 we obtain $\hbar\omega_{LO} = 35$ meV, in good agreement with the LO phonon energy of GaAs. For structure DBS5 the two phonon peaks correspond to $\hbar\omega_{LO_1} = 35.5$ meV and $\hbar\omega_{LO_2} = 48$ meV, and to $\hbar\omega_{LO_1} = 34.5$ meV and $\hbar\omega_{LO_2} = 48.5$ meV for structure DBS4. These values are in good agreement with the energies of the GaAs-like and AlAs-like LO phonon modes of (AlGa)As with $[A1] = 0.4$ [5.67].

A possible explanation for the observation of two phonon modes in structures DBS4 and DBS5 but only one in structure DBS6 is that structures DBS4 and DBS5 have narrower quantum wells so the wavefunction of the quasi-bound state in the well penetrates further into the (AlGa)As barrier. Tunnelling electrons would then couple more effectively to the AlAs-like mode. Note that structures DBS4 and DBS6 have the same barrier widths but only the narrower well (DBS4) shows the two phonon modes. In conclusion, we have used a quantising magnetic field to investigate elastic and inelastic scattering processes in the valley region of resonant tunnelling devices. We have observed coupling of the tunnelling electrons to both the GaAs-like and AlAs-like LO phonon modes of the (AlGa)As barrier region.

We acknowledge many helpful discussions with our colleagues who have been involved in our tunnelling programme: E. Alves, S. Bass, K. S. Chan, P. Claxton, M. Davies, T. J. Foster, P. S. S. Guimaraes, M. Heath, M. Henini, G. Hill, O. H. Hughes, M. L. Leadbeater, D. K. Maude, M. A. Pate, C. A. Payling, J. C. Portal, K. E. Singer, P. E. Simmonds, B. R. Snell, K. W. H. Stevens and D. C. Taylor.

References

5.1 L. Esaki: "Semiconductor superlattices and quantum wells", Proc. 17th Int. Conf. on The Physics of Semiconductors, San Francisco, 1984, Eds. J. D. Chadi, W. A. Harrison, p. 473 (Springer, New York, 1985)

5.2 T. C. L. G. Sollner, P. E. Tannenwald, D. C. Peck, W. D. Goodhue: App. Phys. Lett. **45**, 1319–21 (1984)

5.3 M. Heiblum, M. I. Nathan, D. C. Thomas, C. M. Knoedler: Phys. Rev. Lett. **55**, 2200–3 (1985)

5.4 A. R. Bonnefoi, D. H. Chow, T. C. McGill: App. Phys. Lett. **47**, 888–90 (1985)

5.5 S. Luryi, F. Capasso: App. Phys. Lett. **47**, 1347 (1985)

5.6 T. W. Hickmott, P. M. Solomon, F. F. Fang, F. Stern, R. Fischer, H. Morkoc: Phys. Rev. Lett. **52**, 2053 (1984); also T. W. Hickmott, P. M. Solomon, F. F. Fang, R. Fischer, H. Morkoc: Proc. 17th Int. Conf. on Physics of Semiconductors, San Francisco (Springer, New York, 1984) p. 417; T. W. Hickmott, P. M. Solomon, R. Fischer, H. Morkoc: J. Appl. Phys. **57**, 2844 (1985)

5.7   L. Eaves, P. S. S. Guimaraes, B. R. Snell, D. C. Taylor, K. E. Singer: Phys. Rev. Lett. **53**, 262 (1985); P. S. S. Guimaraes, D. C. Taylor, B. R. Snell, L. Eaves, K. E. Singer, G. Hill, M. A. Pate, G. A. Toombs, F. W. Sheard: J. Phys. C: Solid State, **18**, L605–9 (1985).

5.8   L. Eaves, P. S. S. Guimaraes, F. W. Sheard, B. R. Snell, D. C. Taylor, G. A. Toombs, K. E. Singer: J. Phys. C **18**, L885–9 (1985); D. C. Taylor, P. S. Guimaraes, B. R. Snell, L. Eaves, F. W. Sheard, G. A. Toombs, K. E. Singer: Physica B **134**, 12 (1985); L. Eaves, P. S. S. Guimaraes, B. R. Snell, F. W. Sheard, D. C. Taylor, G. A. Toombs, J. C. Portal, L. Dmowski, K. E. Singer, G. Hill, M. A. Pate: Superlattices and Microstructures **2**, 49 (1986)

5.9   L. Eaves, D. C. Taylor, J. C. Portal, L. Dmowski: In *Two Dimensional Systems: Physics and New Devices*, ed. G. Bauer et al., Springer Ser. Solid State Sci. Vol. 67 (Springer, Berlin, Heidelberg 1986); L. Eaves, F. W. Sheard, K. W. H. Stevens: In *The Physics and Fabrication of Microstructures and Microdevices*, Springer Proc. Phys. Vol. 13, ed. M. J. Kelly, C. Wiesbuch (Springer, Berlin, Heidelberg 1986)

5.10 D. C. Taylor, P. S. S. Guimaraes, B. R. Snell, F. W. Sheard, L. Eaves, G. A. Toombs, J. C. Portal, L. Dmowski, K. E. Singer, G. Hill, M. A. Pate: Proc. Int. Conf. on Modulated Semiconductor Structures, Kyoto (1985), Surf. Sci. **174**, 472 (1986); G. A. Toombs, F. W. Sheard and L. Eaves: *Phonon Physics* (World Scientific, Singapore 1985) p. 561

5.11 J. P. Leburton: Phys. Rev. B **31** 4080 (1985)

5.12 J. R. Barker: Physica B **134**, 22 (1985)

5.13 E. S. Hellman, J. S. Harris, C. Hanna, R. B. Laughlin: Physica B **134**, 41 (1985)

5.14 J. P. Leburton: Physica B **134**, 32 (1985)

5.15 E. S. Hellman, J. S. Harris: Phys. Rev. B**33**, 8284 (1986)

5.16 J. Ihm: Phys. Rev. Lett., **55**, 999 (1985); ibid **56**, 2548 (1986)

5.17 C. B. Hanna, R. B. Laughlin: Phys. Rev. Lett. **56**, 2547 (1986)

5.18 T. Wang, J. P. Leburton, K. Hess, D. Bailey: Phys. Rev. B**33**, 2906 (1986)

5.19 R. L. F. Boyd, A. Boksenberg: Proc. Int. Conf. on Ionisation Phenomena in Gases Uppsala, North Holland, Amsterdam (1959) p. 529

5.20 J. E. Golden, J. H. McGuire: Phys. Rev. Lett. **32**, 1218 (1974)

5.21 J. W. McGowan, J. F. Williams E. Curley: Phys. Rev. **180**, 132 (1969)

5.22 J. M. Chamberlain, A. A. Reeder, L. M. Claessen, G. L. J. A. Rikken, P. Wyder: Physica **134B**, 426 (1985) and references therein

5.23 J. A. Kash, J. C. Tsang, J. M. Huan: Phys. Rev. Lett. **54**, 2151 (1985)

5.24 R. A. Stradling, L. Eaves, R. A. Hoult, A. L. Mears, R. A. Wood, Proc, Int. Conf. on Semiconductors, Boston (USAEC/DTI 1970) p. 369; R. J. Nicholas, R. A. Stradling: J. Phys. C. **9**, 1253 (1976)

5.25 L. Eaves, J. C. Portal: J. Phys. C **12**, 2809 (1979)

5.26 K. J. Nash, M. S. Skolnick, S. J. Bass: to be published

5.27 C. K. Sarkar, R. J. Nicholas, J. C. Portal, M. Razeghi, J. Chevrier, J. Massies: J. Phys. C **18**, 2667 (1985)

5.28 T. P. Smith III, W. I. Wang P. J. Stiles: Phys. Rev. B **34**, 2995 (1986)

5.29 D. Weiss, K. V. Klitzing, V. Mosser: In Springer Ser. Solid State Sci. Vol. 67 (Springer, Berlin, Heidelberg 1972) p. 204

5.30 T. W. Hickmott: Phys. Rev. B, **32**, 6531 (1985); Physica **134B**, 3, (1985)

5.31 See for example B. I. Shkovskii, A. L. Efros: Springer Series in Solid State Sciences, Vol. 45 (Springer, Berlin, Heidelberg 1984); H. Kahlert, G. Landwehr, A. Schachetzski, H. Salow: Z. Phys. B**24**, 361 (1976); D. C. Taylor et al. to be published

5.32 The derivation of the equivalent circuit in Figure 1 a will be described in a paper by F. W. Sheard, G. A. Toombs and L. Eaves submitted to Semiconductor Science and Technology. The circuit in Figure 1 can be represented by a single capacitor C^* and resistance R^* in parallel where
$$C^* = [(R_1 + R_2)(C_1R_1 + C_2R_2) - (C_1 + C_2)R_1R_2(1 - \omega^2 C_1 R_1 C_2)]/F^2,$$
$$R^{*-1} = [(R_1 + R_2) + \omega^2 R_1 R_2 (C_1^2 R_1 + C_2^2 R_2)]/F^2,$$
$$F^2 = (R_1 + R_2)^2 + \omega^2(C_1 + C_2)^2 R_1^2 R_2^2$$

5.33 E. H. Nicollian, J. R. Brews: MOS *Physics and Technology* (Wiley, New York 1982) pp. 385–90

5.34 L. Eaves, B. R. Snell, D. K. Maude, P. S. S. Guimaraes, D. C. Taylor, F. W. Sheard, G. A. Toombs, J. C. Portal, L. Dmowski, P. Claxton, G. Hill, M. A. Pate, S. Bass: Proc. Int. Conf. on Physics of Semiconductors, Stockholm, Ed. by O. Engstrom (World Scientific, Singapore 1986) pp. 1615–1622.

5.35 R. J. Nicholas, M. A. Brummel, J. C. Portal, K. J. Cheng, A. Y. Cho, T. P. Pearsall: Solid State Commun. **45**, 911 (1985)

5.36 F. Stern: Phys. Rev. **B5**, 4891 (1972)

5.37 F. Stern, W. E. Howard: Phys. Rev. **163**, 816 (1967)

5.38 B. R. Snell, K. S. Chan, F. W. Sheard, L. Eaves, G. A. Toombs, D. K. Maude, J. C. Portal, S. J. Bass, P. Claxton, G. Hill, M. A. Pate: Phys. Rev. Lett. **59**, 2806 (1987)

5.39 C. B. Duke: "Tunnelling in Solids" *Solid State Physics.* Suppl. **10**, eds. H. Ehrenriech, F. Seitz, D. Turnbull (Academic, New York 1969)

5.40 L. Eaves, B. R. Snell, D. K. Maude, P. S. S. Guimaraes, D. C. Taylor, F. W. Sheard, G. A. Toombs, J. C. Portal, L. Dmowski, P. Claxton, G. Hill, M. A. Pate, S. J. Bass: Proc. 18th Int. Conf. on Physics of Semiconductors, ed. O. Engstrom (World Scientific, Singapore 1987) p. 1615

5.41 J. A. Kash, J. C. Tsang, J. M. Huan: Phys. Rev. Lett. **54**, 2151 (1985)

5.42 T. W. Hickmott: Solid State Commun. **63**, 371 (1987)

5.43 F. W. Sheard, K. S. Chan, G. A. Toombs, J. C. Portal, L. Eaves: 14th Int. Symposium on GaAs and Related Compounds (Crete 1987). Institute of Physics Conf. Series **91**, 387 (1988)

5.44 D. C. Tsui: Phys. Rev. **B12**, 5739 (1975)

5.45 M. Heiblum, M. V. Fischetti, W. P. Dumke, D. J. Frank, I. M. Anderson, C. M. Knoedler, L. Osterburg: Phys. Rev. Lett. **58**, 816 (1987)

5.46 D. Gauthier, L. Dmowski, S. Ben Amor, R. Blondel, J. C. Portal, M. Razeghi, P. Maurel, F. Omnes, M. Laviron: Semicond. Sci. Technol. **1**, 105 (1986)

5.47 R. Tsu, L. Esaki: Appl. Phys. Lett. **22**, 562 (1973)

5.48 B. Ricco M. Ya Azbel: Phys. Rev. B **29**, 1970 (1984)

5.49 S. Luryi: Appl. Phys. Lett. **47**, 490 (1985)

5.50 M. C. Payne: J. Phys. C **19**, 1145 (1986)

5.51 T. Weil, B. Vinter: Appl. Phys. Lett. **50**, 1281 (1987); M. Jonson, A. Grincwajg: Proc. EPS Condensed Matter Meeting, Pisa (1987)

5.52 C. W. J. Beenakker, H. van Houten: Phys. Rev. Lett. **60**, 2406 (1988)

5.53 V. J. Goldman, D. C. Tsui, J. E. Cunningham: Phys. Rev. Lett. **58**, 1256 (1987); ibid. **59**, 1623 (1987)

5.54 T. C. L. G. Sollner: Phys. Rev. Lett. **59**, 1622 (1987)

5.55 C. A. Payling, E. S. Alves, L. Eaves, T. J. Foster, M. Henini, O. H. Hughes, P. E. Simmonds, F. W. Sheard, G. A. Toombs: Proc. 7th Int. Conf. on the Electronic Properties of Two Dimensional Systems, Santa Fe, 1987. Surf. Sci. **196**, 404 (1988); C. A. Payling, E. Alves, L. Eaves, T. J. Foster, M. Henini, O. H. Hughes, P. E. Simmonds, J. C. Portal, G. Hill, M. A. Pate, Proc. 3rd Int. Conf. on Modulated Semiconductor Structures, Montpellier, France, J. Physique **C5**, 289 (1987)

5.56 G. A. Toombs, E. S. Alves, L. Eaves, T. J. Foster, M. Henini, O. H. Hughes, M. L. Leadbeater, C. A. Payling, F. W. Sheard, P. A. Claxton, G. Hill, M. A. Pate, J. C. Portal: 14th Int. Symposium on Gallium Arsenide and Related Compounds, Crete 1987. Institute of Physics Conf. Series **91**, 581 (1988)

5.57 V. J. Goldman, D. C. Tsui, J. E. Cunningham: Phys. Rev. **B35**, 9387 (1987)

5.58 F. W. Sheard, G. A. Toombs: Appl. Phys. Lett. **52**, 1228 (1988)

5.59 O. H. Hughes, M. Henini, E. S. Alves, L. Eaves, M. L. Leadbeater, T. J. Foster, F. W. Sheard, G. A. Toombs: J. Vac. Sci. Technol. **B6**, 1161 (1988)

5.60 M. A. Reed, J. W. Lee, H.-L. Tsai: Appl. Phys. Lett. **49**, 158 (1986)

5.61 V. J. Goldman, D. C. Tsui, J. E. Cunningham: Phys. Rev. **B36**, 7635 (1987)

5.62 E. Wolak, K. L. Lear, P. M. Pitner, E. S. Hellman, B. G. Park, J. S. Harris, D. Thomas: Appl. Phys. Lett. **53**, 201 (1988)

5.63 C. I. Huang, M. J. Paulus, C. A. Bozada, S. C. Dudley, K. R. Evans, C. E. Stutz, R. L. Jones, M. E. Cheney: Appl. Phys. Lett. **51**, 121 (1987)

5.64 H. Bando, T. Nakagawa, H. Tokumoto, K. Ohta, K. Kajimura: Proc. 18th Int. Conf. on Low Temperature Physics, Kyoto 1987, Jpn. J. Appl. Phys. **26** (Supplement 26-3), 765 (1987)

5.65 L. Eaves, G. A. Toombs, F. W. Sheard, C. A. Payling, M. L. Leadbeater, E. S. Alves, T. J. Foster, P. E. Simmonds, M. Henini, O. H. Hughes, J. C. Portal, G. Hill, M. A. Pate: Appl. Phys. Lett. **52**, 212 (1988)

5.66 E. E. Mendez, L. Esaki, W. I. Wang: Phys. Rev. **B33**, 2893 (1986)

5.67 O. K. Kim, W. A. Spitzer: J. Appl. Phys. **50**, 4362 (1979)

5.68 E. S. Alves, L. Eaves, M. Henini, O. H. Hughes, M. L. Leadbeater, F. W. Sheard, G. A. Toombs, G. Hill, M. A. Pate: Electron. Lett. **24**, 1190 (1988)

5.69 M. L. Leadbeater, E. S. Alves, L. Eaves, M. Henini, O. H. Hughes, F. W. Sheard, G. A. Toombs; Semicond. Sci. Technol. **3**, 1060 (1988)

5.70 E. S. Alves, M. L. Leadbeater, L. Eaves, M. Henini, O. H. Hughes, A. Celeste, J. C. Portal, G. Hill, M. A. Pate: Proc. Int. Conf. on Superlattices and Microstructures, Trieste 1988, Superlattices and Microstructures **5**, 527 (1989)

5.71 T. J. Foster, M. L. Leadbeater, L. Eaves, M. Henini, O. H. Hughes, C. A. Payling, F. W. Sheard, P. E. Simmonds, G. A. Toombs, G. Hill, M. A. Pate: Phys. Rev. **B39**, 6705 (1989)

5.72 M. L. Leadbeater, E. S. Alves, L. Eaves, M. Henini, O. H. Hughes, A. Celeste, J. C. Portal, G. Hill, M. A. Pate: Phys. Rev. **B39**, 3438 (1989)

6. Microwave and Millimeter-Wave Resonant-Tunnelling Devices

T. C. L. G. Sollner, E. R. Brown, W. D. Goodhue, and H. Q. Le

With 23 Figures

The concept of particles interacting coherently with finite multiple-barrier structures is over 35 years old, and yet it forms the basis for an area of intense activity today, both for practical devices and for studies of the underlying physics. An example is the two barrier structure shown in Fig. 6.1. In the quantum theory textbook written by *Bohm* [6.1] in 1951, the double-barrier problem was solved in the WKB approximation. He showed that, at certain energies, unity transmission resonances (resonant tunnelling) occur for particles incident upon the structure. Ten years elapsed before it was recognized that this phenomenon could be useful for devices. The first suggestion for a resonant-tunnelling transistor was made by *Davis* and *Hosack* [6.2] and *Ioganson* [6.3] in 1963, following the suggestion by *Mead* [6.4] in 1960 of a nonresonant double-barrier transistor. Early in the next decade *Esaki* and *Tsu* [6.5] pointed out that superlattices should show negative resistance, and *Kazarinov* and *Suris* [6.6] showed that negative resistance could arise from a finite superlattice. In 1973 *Tsu* and *Esaki* [6.7] derived the two-terminal current-voltage $(I–V)$ curves for finite multiple-barrier structures using a wave function matching formulation based on a method of *Kane* [6.8]. This technique has been remarkably successful at explaining experimental results, as will be discussed in Sect. 6.7. In 1974 *Chang* et al. [6.9] were the first to observe resonant tunnelling in a mono-crystalline semiconductor. They used a two-barrier structure and observed the resonances in the current by measuring the $I–V$ curve. A decade later, interest in the field was renewed when *Sollner* et al. [6.10] showed that the intrinsic charge transport mechanism of a two-barrier diode could respond to voltage changes in times of the order of 0.1 ps. More recently, the negative differential resistance characteristic of resonant tunnelling has been obtained at room temperature [6.11–13]. At present, several laboratories are actively investigating resonant-tunnelling devices.

The conduction-band edge of a double-barrier structure is shown in Fig. 6.1. These structures have usually been implemented in the AlGaAs system, although recently the group at Fujitsu has shown that excellent devices can be made from $In_{0.52}Al_{0.48}As/In_{0.53}Ga_{0.47}As$ material [6.14]. In both cases the barriers are provided by regions containing higher concentrations of aluminum, and the layers have been grown by molecular beam epitaxy (MBE) because thin layers and sharp interfaces are required. Some workers have also used organometallic chemical vapor deposition (OMCVD) to prepare the layers [6.15, 16]. Other material systems may be possible, and may have some advantages. However, it appears to be important to eliminate scattering centers as much as possible, so the

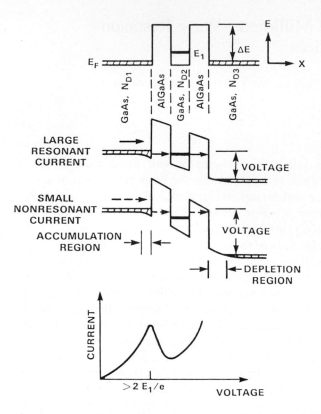

Fig. 6.1. Electron energy as a function of position in a double-barrier resonant-tunnelling structure

cleanest materials will be the most useful. The ability to make high quality structures on the scale of only a few layers of atoms has been essential to the growth of this field. The material used for the devices described in later sections is discussed more fully by *Goodhue* et al. [6.13].

Figure 6.1 also shows the essential features of resonant tunnelling. A thin layer of GaAs (2–6 nm) is sandwiched between two thin layers of $Al_xGa_{1-x}As$. The addition of aluminum raises the band gap above that of GaAs so these regions act as partially transparent mirrors to electrons. The charge transport takes place by tunnelling through the thin (1–5 nm) barriers. These mirrors form a sort of electron Fabry–Perot resonator, resulting in peaks in the electron transmission (current) as the incident electron energy (voltage) is changed, as shown schematically at the bottom of Fig. 6.1. The calculation of the current–voltage ($I–V$) relationship using this model is described in more detail in Sect. 6.7.

It is clear from the Fabry–Perot analogy that coherence of the electron wave function is required across the entire double-barrier region. Any scattering that occurs in either the well or the barriers will randomly alter the wavefunction phase, destroying the coherence. It has been suggested by *Luryi* [6.17] that a different picture, one which does not require coherence between the parts of the wave function outside and inside the well, could produce negative resistance. This possibility will also be discussed further in Sect. 6.7.

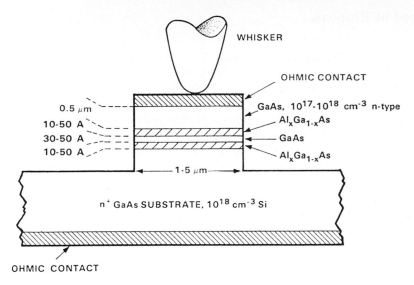

Fig. 6.2. Cross-sectional view of completed double-barrier diode

The physical embodiment of these principles is summarized in Fig. 6.2. The layered material is grown in wafer form, then the active regions are defined by ohmic contacts. These contacts are then used as a mask to isolate the region under the contact, either by etching mesas as shown in Fig. 6.2, or by proton implantation to render the surrounding material nonconductive. Electrical connection is made to the ohmic contact with a pointed wire (whisker) since the diameter of the contact is only a few microns. In some cases this whisker acts as an antenna to couple ac fields to the double-barrier diode, as discussed in the next section.

In the remainder of this chapter we will discuss various aspects of the physics and several applications of resonant tunnelling. This is not meant to be a comprehensive review of this rapidly developing field, but will emphasize the high-frequency applications that have been studied by the authors. The next section considers the ultimate speed of devices based on resonant tunnelling, Sect. 6.2 describes the exploitation of the negative differential resistance for oscillators, Sect. 6.3 discusses devices that combine the negative differential resistance with the intrinsic nonlinearity of the resonant-tunnelling $I-V$ curve to produce self-oscillating mixers, Sect. 6.4 deals with harmonic multipliers that make use of the peaks and valleys in the $I-V$ curve to produce power at high harmonics of a pump signal, and Sect. 6.5 describes an interesting observation of absolute negative resistance. A three-terminal device is proposed in Sect. 6.6, and the state of the theory of resonant tunnelling is summarized in Sect. 6.7. A look into the future concludes the chapter.

6.1 Speed of Response

The maximum useful frequency for the negative differential resistance in the $I-V$ curve is of importance for many applications. We will estimate this maximum frequency by examining the time required for the double-barrier current to respond to a sudden change in voltage.

Suppose that the voltage is instantaneously changed so that the current will decrease to a lower steady-state value. As in a Fabry–Perot resonator, the steady-state charge in the well must also decrease if the current decreases. As is well known from scattering theory, the lifetime of any resonant state, including the one represented by an electron initially placed in the well between the two barriers of a resonant-tunnelling structure, is given by $\tau = \hbar/\Delta E$, where ΔE is the energy half-width of the transmission probability function through the resonant state (see, for example, *Blatt* and *Weisskopf* [6.18]). Approximately this time will be required to fill or empty the well to a new steady-state value. Since the carrier transmission probability is determined by the amplitude of the wavefunction inside the well, the current will reach its new steady-state value on the same time scale. This time has been calculated for three representative structures by *Sollner* et al. [6.19] who find a range of 4 ps for 2.5-nm-thick AlAs barriers to 0.16 ps for 3.0-nm-thick $Ga_{0.7}Al_{0.3}As$ barriers. These values are listed as $f_{\Delta E} = (2\pi\tau)^{-1}$ in Table 6.1, along with a summary of other material and derived parameters for three double-barrier diode structures. (Note that the values of $f_{\Delta E}$ are half those of Ref. [6.19] since the full width of the transmission peak was taken there.)

The transit of the electrons across the depletion region shown in Fig. 6.1 produces an additional delay. This delay will increase the phase delay of the current relative to the voltage at high frequencies. The thickness of the depletion region depends primarily on the doping density in the regions just outside the barriers. As shown in Table 6.1, calculated values for this time delay, assuming a drift velocity of 10^7 cm/s, range from 0.16 to 0.69 ps. These times may be overestimated by as much as a factor of 5 since ballistic motion has been neglected. We will call the sum of this time and the resonant state lifetime the *intrinsic* response time to distinguish it from other delay times associated with circuit considerations.

The equivalent circuit for a double-barrier diode is shown in Fig. 6.3. Included in the equivalent circuit are the voltage-dependent dynamic conductance $G(V)$, the series resistance R_s, and the parallel capacitor C inherent to the device structure. To a good approximation, the capacitance occurs across the two barriers and the depletion region on the anode side of the biased device. The $I-V$ curve measured at low frequencies approximately gives the conductance from its slope, i.e., $(dI/dV)^{-1} = R_s + 1/G \cong 1/G$. As the frequency of an applied signal increases, a larger fraction of the current will flow as displacement current through the capacitor, with a smaller fraction flowing as conduction current through the double-barrier region. The conductance G is much more strongly dependent on the voltage than the capacitor C. (The capacitance varies inversely

Table 6.1 Measured and calculated parameters for three different wafers of double-barrier diodes

	Wafer		
	1	2	3
Material Parameters:			
Barrier material	AlAs	$Ga_{0.7}Al_{0.3}As$	AlAs
Barrier thickness (nm)	2.5	3.0	1.5
Well thickness (nm)	4.5	4.5	4.5
Doping outside barriers (cm^{-3})	1×10^{18}	2×10^{17}	2×10^{17}
Electrical Parameters:			
Peak-to-valley ratio, 300 K	1.7/1	1.3/1	3.5/1
Peak current density ($\times 10^4$ A cm^{-2})	0.8	1.2	4.0
Depletion layer at bias (nm)	15	30	70
Capacitance (fF)[a]	100	50	20
Max. negative conductance (mS)[a]	5.0	8.0	13.0
Series resistance (Ω)[a]	10	15	15
Oscillation Characteristics:			
DC bias I_B, V_B (mA, V)	0.7, 0.40	2.7, 0.32	3.0, 0.95
f_{osc} (GHz)	20.7	43.7	201
	Theoretical		
Max. Oscillation Frequency:			
f_{max} (GHz)[c]	35	70	270
f_{depl} (GHz)[d]	1000	500	230
$f_{\Delta E}$ (GHz)[e]	40	1000	400

[a] Typical values for a circular mesa of 4 µm diameter.
[b] Maximum observed fundamental oscillation frequency.
[c] $f_{max} = (2\pi C)^{-1}(-G_{max}/R_s - G_{max}^2)^{1/2}$.
[d] From depletion layer drift time assuming a drift velocity of 10^7 cm/s.
[e] From calculation of energy width of transmission through double-barrier structure. See Secs. 6.2 and 6.8.

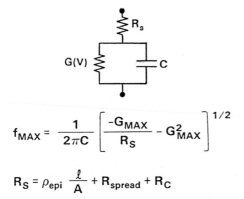

$$f_{MAX} = \frac{1}{2\pi C}\left[\frac{-G_{MAX}}{R_S} - G_{MAX}^2\right]^{1/2}$$

$$R_S = \rho_{epi}\frac{\ell}{A} + R_{spread} + R_C$$

$$C = \epsilon\frac{A}{L_{depl}}$$

Fig. 6.3. Equivalent circuit for the structure shown in Fig. 6.2

as the square root of the voltage plus a constant, so the displacement current will decrease slowly as the voltage is increased.) Thus, it is possible to observe nonlinearities in G even for frequencies at which most of the current is displacement current. Above a frequency f_{max} (defined in the next section) the fraction of the current through the capacitor becomes so large that the terminal conductance becomes positive even when G is negative. However, it is easy to show that the second derivative d^2I/dV^2 has the voltage dependence of $g(V)$ if we neglect the voltage dependence of C. As shown in Table 6.1, f_{max} for these structures corresponds to frequencies in the range between 20 and 300 GHz, so it will be necessary to operate well above f_{max} to probe the intrinsic response of less than 1 ps.

The intrinsic response time was first measured experimentally by examining the difference between the $I-V$ curve measured at dc and that inferred from high-frequency measurements [6.10]. This necessitated operating at frequencies up to the terahertz region. For signals with periods much shorter than the intrinsic response time, the current cannot follow the applied voltage and the $I-V$ curve thus measured is expected to deviate markedly from the dc $I-V$ curve.

One obvious method to determine the frequency response is to sweep through the $I-V$ curve at increasing speed until the measured $I-V$ curve changes from the one measured at dc. Unfortunately, it is very difficult to measure the current at frequencies above those accessible to sampling oscilloscopes ($\cong 100$ GHz). The approach taken by *Sollner* et al. [6.10] involved a differential method in which a large low-frequency voltage was used to sweep over the measured range, and a small high-frequency signal was applied at the same time. The high-frequency voltage caused a change in the measured low-frequency current proportional to the curvature of the $I-V$ curve at the bias point. For devices utilizing the negative differential resistance, this method closely resembles the actual operating conditions, i.e., the device is biased into the negative differential resistance region by a large dc bias, and the voltage excursions do not extend far outside that region.

It can easily be shown [6.20] that at high frequencies the current responsivity R_i, i.e., the change in dc current ΔI divided by the change in ac power applied ΔP_{ac} is given by

$$R_i(V) = \frac{\Delta I(V)}{\Delta P_{ac}} = \frac{2I''(V)Z_A}{(1 + Z_A/R_s)^2} \left[\frac{1}{\omega R_s C}\right]^2. \tag{6.1}$$

(This expression corrects an error of a factor of 2 in Ref. [6.10].) In this formula I'' is the second derivative of the $I-V$ curve *at the ac frequency of interest*. The mismatch between the antenna impedance Z_A and the device impedance has been taken into account, and it has been assumed that at the higher frequencies $\omega R_s C \gg 1$ and $R_s \ll (dI_{dc}/dV)^{-1}$. This expression can be trivially inverted to yield I'' and then integrated twice to obtain the $I-V$ curve from current responsivity measured over the voltage range of interest. Measurements were made at 1, 138, 761, and 2500 GHz on a double-barrier diode with nominally 5.0-

nm-thick well and barriers [6.10]. Scanning transmission electron micrographs and subsequent calculations indicate that the actual well and barrier widths were probably closer to 3.0 nm. The results at dc, 1 GHz and 2.5 THz are shown in Fig. 6.4. The results for 138 and 761 GHz were essentially the same as the 1 GHz curve. The reason for the discrepancy between dc and 1 GHz is not known, but is probably due to slow traps. It is clear that by 2.5 THz the curve looks quite different from the dc curve in that the negative differential resistance in one direction has vanished, while it remains in the other direction. *Sollner* et al. [6.10] take this as evidence that the charge transit time for this device is of the order of $\tau = (2\pi f)^{-1} = 6 \times 10^{-14}$ s. This is in approximate agreement with the theoretical expectations from Table 6.1 for 3 nm barriers of $Al_{0.25}Ga_{0.75}As$. The asymmetry of both the dc I–V curve and the response may indicate that the two barriers or perhaps the two depletion regions are not identical. The dependence of the extrinsic speed of response on material parameters will be discussed in more detail in Sect. 6.2.

The circuit employed for applying ac and dc fields to the double-barrier diode is shown in Fig. 6.5. This corner-reflector mount was originally developed for Schottky diode mixers in the far infrared [6.21]. Frequencies between dc and about 20 GHz can be applied through the OSM coaxial connector via the whisker that contacts the active area. The GaAs substrate is soldered to the chip stud, which is at the same ground potential as the corner reflector. For frequencies from about 100 GHz to a few terahertz the long whisker acts as an antenna, and the conducting surfaces cause images of the whisker to produce an antenna array. This array will receive energy in a beam. The direction depends on frequency, but is approximately 45° from all surfaces of the cube. The full cone-angle of the beam is of the order of 20°. For the 2.5-THz measurements, for example, the power produced by an optically pumped methanol laser (about 100 mW) was matched to the antenna pattern with a lens, thus coupling about

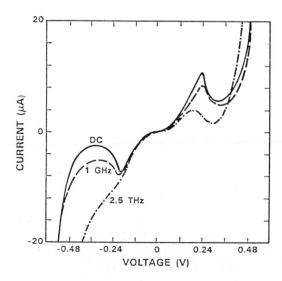

Fig. 6.4. Current-voltage (I–V) curves taken at low frequency (labeled dc) and reconstructed by integrating (6.1) for 1 GHz and 2.5 THz

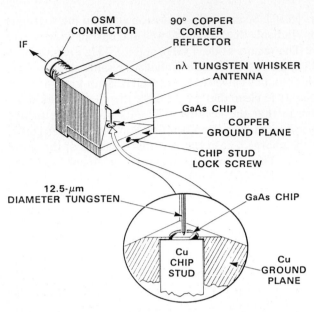

OSM
CONNECTOR

90° COPPER
CORNER
REFLECTOR

IF

nλ TUNGSTEN WHISKER
ANTENNA

GaAs CHIP

COPPER
GROUND PLANE

CHIP STUD
LOCK SCREW

12.5-μm
DIAMETER TUNGSTEN

GaAs CHIP

Cu
CHIP
STUD

Cu
GROUND
PLANE

DETAIL OF CHIP STUD MOUNTING

Fig. 6.5. Corner reflector antenna mount used to supply dc bias and ac signals to the resonant-tunnelling diode

50% of the incident power onto the antenna and producing the ac signal across the double-barrier structure. The extensive characterization of the corner reflector mount at lower frequencies by Fetterman et al. [6.21] led to an estimate of 50 Ω for the antenna impedance Z_A used in (6.1) to calculate the curves of Fig. 6.4.

The demonstration that resonant tunnelling could be a fast process has spurred the conception and development of several devices based on the effect, as summarized in the introduction. In the next sections we will outline some of the work on microwave and millimeter-wave devices that has occurred to date.

6.2 Resonant-Tunnelling Oscillators

The negative differential resistance (NDR) displayed by the double-barrier diode can act as the basis for a very fast and simple two-terminal oscillator. In the previous section it was shown that effects of the negative differential resistance persist on time scales as short as the lifetime of an electron in the resonant state between the barriers. But the other inherent circuit elements, in particular the series resistance and the device capacitance shown in Fig. 6.3, must be considered for circuit applications. The conductance, $G(V_0)$, is assumed to be frequency independent but should depend strongly on the voltage amplitude V_0 across the device. The real part of the impedance Z_D measured across the equivalent circuit of Fig. 6.1 will be negative up to a frequency given by the expression

$$f_{max} = \frac{1}{2\pi C}\left[\frac{-G_{max}}{R_S} - G_{max}^2\right]^{1/2} \tag{6.2}$$

where G_{max} is the maximum negative value of dynamic conductance in the NDR region of the $I - V$ curve. For all frequencies above f_{max}, the real part of the terminal impedance will be positive, making it impossible for oscillations to occur.

Interest in the oscillator application stems first from a desire for a new solid-state source for frequencies above about 300 GHz. In this region the availability of fundamental solid-state sources is very poor, so that the double-barrier diode could be useful in a variety of applications requiring only modest amounts of power. A second reason for studying oscillators is that they provide a direct and unmistakable indication of the speed of the device. Although the simple circuit model shown in Fig. 6.3 has been tentatively adopted, this model may fail at higher frequencies or with devices having larger current densities than those used to date, as discussed in Sect. 6.7. In fact, one group has suggested different equivalent circuits even at relatively low frequencies [6.22]. Careful study of oscillator behavior may pinpoint failure of the current model, if it occurs, and lead to the formulation of a more accurate model.

Figure 6.6 shows the waveguide resonator used for most of the oscillators described by *Brown* et al. [6.23], along with the equivalent circuit. The optimum parameters for the elements of the equivalent circuit were obtained using the analysis described below.

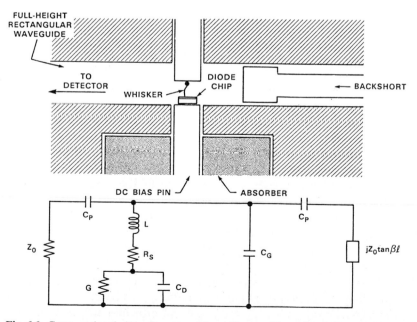

Fig. 6.6. Cross-sectional view of a waveguide oscillator with an electrically equivalent circuit

In order for oscillations to begin and to be stable, the circuit in which the diode is mounted must satisfy certain stringent conditions. First of all, the diode must be dc stable; that is, the load line must intersect the $I-V$ curve in only one point across the entire NDR region. If it intersects both a positive and negative resistance point simultaneously, the diode will switch to the positive resistance point even if initially biased at the negative resistance point. We define Y_D as the admittance seen looking toward the device from the device terminals and Y_L as the admittance seen looking toward the load (the partition of the circuit into device and load is arbitrary). A sufficient condition for dc stability is that the load admittance Y_L be purely real and satisfy $(\mathrm{Re}\{Y_L\}) > |G_{max}|$ for all frequencies below the range in which one desires oscillation. Within this range, instabilities or oscillations will begin provided that $\mathrm{Re}\{Y_D\} + \mathrm{Re}\{Y_L\} < 0$. Application of Kirchoff's voltage law leads to the conclusion that the oscillations will be periodic if and only if $Y_D + Y_L = Y_T = 0$ at some frequency and amplitude of oscillation.

The stability of oscillations is determined by the following conditions derived by *Kurokawa* [6.24].

$$\frac{\partial(\mathrm{Im}\{Y_T\})}{\partial\omega} > 0$$

$$\frac{\partial(\mathrm{Re}\{Y_T\})}{\partial V_0} > 0$$

(6.3)

where V_0 is the voltage amplitude. These equations result from the requirement that small voltage perturbations during oscillation decrease rather than increase with time. Assumed here is that the voltage waveform is sinusoidal. This is a good assumption for the resonant-tunnelling diode if the current components at higher harmonics are loaded by impedances much lower than the output impedances of the diode at these harmonics. Figure 6.7 is a plot for the 100-GHz resonator used by *Brown* et al. [6.23] of the imaginary versus the real part of the total admittance $(Y_D + Y_L)$ for different frequencies with the large-signal negative conductance G (corresponding to different amplitudes) as a parameter. Clearly the conditions of (6.3) are satisfied just below 100 GHz. Similar diagrams have been used by Brown et al. to design all of their oscillators.

The output power of these oscillators is limited by the voltage range over which negative resistance exists. *Kim* and *Brandli* [6.25] have shown that the maximum output power is $P_{max} = a^2/6b$, having assumed an $I-V$ curve about the center of the negative differential resistance region of the form $I \sim -aV + bV^3$ and a sinusoidal voltage waveform. It is also easy to show that $a = 3\Delta I/2\Delta V$ and $b = 2\Delta I/\Delta V^3$, so we get the well-known [6.26] relation $P_{max} = (3/16)\Delta I\Delta V$, where ΔI and ΔV are the current and voltage ranges of the negative resistance region. For the 4-μm-diameter diodes of Wafer 3 in Table 6.1, to be discussed further below, this latter relation gives $P_{max} \cong 225\,\mu W$. In principle one could obtain more power by using diodes of larger area. However, G_{max} scales linearly with

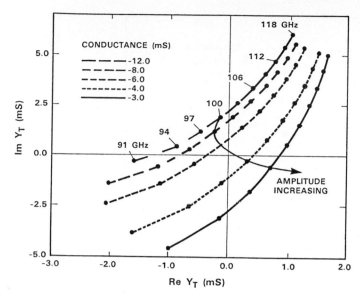

Fig. 6.7. Oscillation diagram showing that the circuit will oscillate near 100 GHz using the conditions of (6.3)

diode area, making it very difficult to obtain dc stability with the larger devices. All of the 4-μm-diameter devices tested to date have been stabilized with standard 50-Ω coaxial loads.

A variety of double-barrier diode oscillators have been demonstrated, covering the frequency range from 20 to 200 GHz. Figure 6.8 shows the experimental results obtained in this range with diodes from the three wafers listed in Table 6.1. The initial experiments were performed with a device from Wafer 1 in a coaxial resonator, yielding an oscillation frequency of 20.7 GHz and an output power far below 1 μW. Attempts to achieve oscillation with this device at frequencies near 40 GHz in a WR-22 waveguide resonator were unsuccessful, consistent with the device having a theoretical f_{max} of only 35 GHz. The first millimeter-band results [6.23] were obtained in the vicinity of 30 and 40 GHz in WR-22 and WR-15 waveguide resonators, respectively, with a device from Wafer 2. This device probably could have achieved higher oscillation frequencies, but such an effort was not undertaken because of the relatively low peak-to-valley ratio at room temperature of devices from Wafer 2.

The highest frequency and most powerful oscillations to date have been obtained with diodes from Wafer 3. This wafer extended the maximum observed oscillation frequency of resonant-tunnelling diodes from 56 to 201 GHz. Oscillations in the range 49–56 GHz were obtained in a WR-15 resonator, with a peak output power of 60 μW occurring at the high end of this range (see Fig. 6.8). Subsequently a different diode from the same wafer oscillated in a WR-6 resonator between about 101 and 112 GHz. The peak output power in this range

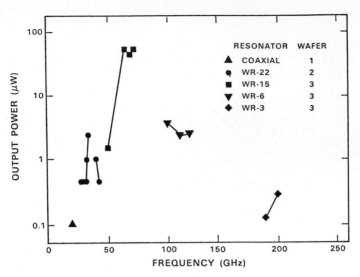

Fig. 6.8. Output power from several oscillators (indicated by different symbols) using three different double-barrier structures as a function of frequency

was about 5 µW. Most recently, the same wafer has led to oscillations in a WR-3 resonator between 187 and 201 GHz [6.27]. The highest output power was about 0.2 µW, and several of the diodes tested could not be made to oscillate at all. The difficulty in initiating oscillation near 200 GHz is consistent with (6.2), which predicts that $f_{max} \cong 270$ GHz for this diode.

The simple model of Fig. 6.3 is identical to that used extensively for the p–n junction tunnel diode. Indeed, the two devices are very similar, displaying similar I–V characteristics and similar behavior in circuits like those discussed above. The major difference between the two is the magnitude of parasitics. In the tunnel diode, very high doping densities are required on both sides of the junction ($N \gtrsim 1 \times 10^{19}$ cm^{-3}) to achieve a high tunnelling current density. This results in a short depletion layer, which gives the device a relatively large specific capacitance. The double-barrier diode can achieve high current density with much lower doping densities on both sides of the structure ($N \cong 10^{17}$–10^{18} cm^{-3}). A good figure of merit for comparing the speed of different diodes is the ratio of specific capacitance to the peak current density, $\gamma = C_S/J_P$. This ratio is known as the speed index [6.28] because it is a measure of the current available for charging the device capacitance. For Wafer 3 this quantity is $\gamma \cong 1 \times 10^5$ pF cm^{-2}/4.0 $\times 10^4$ A cm^{-2} = 3.0 ps/V. The fastest tunnel diodes ever reported [6.29] were made of GaAs and yielded $\gamma = 14$–16 ps/V, nearly a factor of five worse. These tunnel diodes [6.30] achieved a maximum experimental oscillation frequency of 103 GHz with an output power far below 1 µW. (See Note Added in Proof.)

6.3 Self-Oscillating Mixers

The resonant-tunnelling diode has the ability to act as an efficient mixer because of the rapid variation of the dynamic conductance with voltage near the negative differential resistance region of the $I–V$ curve. For a diode oscillating with a dc bias at the center of this negative differential resistance range, the time-varying small-signal dynamic conductance $g(t)$ changes from a large negative value at the dc bias point to a smaller, perhaps positive, value at both extrema of the oscillation amplitude. The Fourier series of the conductance then has large coefficients at the oscillation frequency f_O and its first few harmonics, especially the even harmonics if the $I–V$ curve is antisymmetric about the bias point. The relative strength of these components will determine the efficiency for conversion of power from the signal frequency f_s to the intermediate frequency (IF) f_I, where we assume that $f_s > f_I$. In the fundamental mode of conversion, the signal has frequency $f_s = f_O \pm f_I$, and in the second-harmonic mode, the signal frequency is $f_s = 2f_O \pm f_I$. We expect the most efficient conversion in the second-harminic mode at the dc bias point of maximum negative resistance, since this a point of approximate antisymmetry in the $I–V$ curve. On the other hand, the fundamental mode should achieve maximum efficiency at bias voltages nearest the regions of greatest curvature, where the Fourier series of $g(t)$ has a predominant coefficient at the oscillation frequency.

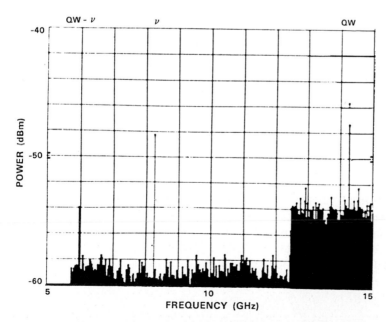

Fig. 6.9. Frequency down-conversion of a signal at frequency v by a double-barrier diode oscillating . at the frequency marked QW to produce the difference frequency QW-v

Experimental work on the fundamental mode of conversion has been carried out with coaxial resonant-tunnelling oscillators in the microwave region. Shown in Fig. 6.9 is the mixing spectrum with oscillation frequency at 14.2 GHz, signal at 8.2 GHz, and IF at 6.0 GHz. The single-sideband conversion loss in this case is just under 6 dB, which is only about 3 dB higher than the best results for room-temperature Schottky diode mixers in the same frequency region. The experiments on the second-harmonic mode have just begun with a waveguide oscillator in the millimeter band. The best conversion loss achieved to date is about 12 dB for an oscillation frequency of 50 GHz and a signal frequency of 100 GHz. This performance is comparable to the best results reported for a pair of Schottky diodes in the antiparallel configuration [6.31].

Perhaps the most intriguing aspect of the self-oscillating mixer is its intrinsic capability to achieve conversion gain (efficiency > 1). This can be demonstrated theoretically following a derivation developed for fundamental mode conversion with the p–n junction tunnel diode mixer by *Kim* [6.32]. This calculation assumes that the large signal voltage across the diode is sinusoidal and that the only nonvanishing terms of the conductance series are the dc term g_0, the fundamental term g_ω, and the second-harmonic term $g_{2\omega}$. In addition to the large-signal currents at the local oscillator frequency f_0, the current through the diode consist only of components at the IF, f_1, the signal frequency, $f_0 + f_1$, and the image frequency, $f_K = f_0 - f_1$. In general, the current i_m at frequency m is linearly related to the voltages $v_{m'}$ at frequency m' for small signals by an admittance matrix Y,

$$i_m = \sum_{m'} Y_{mm'} v_{m'}. \tag{6.4}$$

The elements of this matrix are the Fourier components of the conductance for the diode in the presence of the local oscillator drive. We define an augmented matrix that includes the mixer termination admittances y_m at each frequency m as $Y_{mm'}^A = Y_{mm'} + y_m \delta_{mm'}$. In the present case, Kim finds

$$Y^A = \begin{bmatrix} y_S + g_0 & g_\omega & g_{2\omega} \\ g_\omega^* & y_1 + g_0 & g_\omega \\ g_{2\omega}^* & g_\omega^* & y_K^* + g_0 \end{bmatrix}. \tag{6.5}$$

In this expression, y_S (y_1, y_K) is the admittance presented to the ideal nonlinear element across its terminals at the signal (IF, image) frequency. Ignoring the diode parasitic capacitance, we can write $y_S = [R_S + Z_L(\omega_S)]^{-1}$, where R_S is the series resistance and Z_L is the load impedance. The conversion gain, defined as the ratio of the power delivered to the IF to the power available from the signal, is given by

$$G_c = \frac{4 \text{Re}\{y_S\} \text{Re}\{y_1\} |g_\omega(y_K^* + g_\omega - g_{2\omega})|^2}{|\det Y^A|^2} \tag{6.6}$$

where det specifies that the determinant is to be taken.

By fitting a fourth order polynomial to the negative resistance region for the diode used for the results shown in Fig. 6.9, the curve shown in Fig. 6.10a results. If this device is biased to 0.4 V and placed in a circuit such that the voltage amplitude is 20 mV, then the resulting dynamic-conductance waveform is shown in Fig. 6.10b. The large-signal conductance of the oscillator is found to be -0.0061 S, so the following terminations are assumed: $y_S = (0.0061, 0.0)$, $y_K = (0.0061, 0.0)$, $y_I = (0.02, 0.0)$. Upon substitution of these values into (6.6), a fundamental conversion gain of 18.4 or $+12.6$ dB is obtained. Mixers such as the standard Schottky diode are not capable of gain and, in fact, usually show loss of several decibels.

We suspect that the discrepancy between the theory and the experimental result is due in part to the fact that the circuits used to date have been optimized for oscillators instead of for mixers. The primary concern has been maximizing the oscillation frequency. In addition, the theory given above is oversimplified in that it assumes a sinusoidal oscillator voltage in calculating the dynamic conductance waveform. To go beyond this assumption, large-signal harmonic balance techniques must be applied [6.33], for which one must know the impedance seen by the oscillator at the second and higher harmonics.

The resonant-tunnelling self-oscillating mixer has the potential to displace the Schottky diode in many millimeter-wave applications. To do this, it must demonstrate a competitive noise figure, roughly 3 to 6 dB in the microwave region or 6 to 10 dB in the millimeter band. Although no experimental results of noise figure yet exist, separate measurements on stable resonant-tunnelling diodes indicate that it has very low intrinsic noise [6.34]. In fact the measured noise power is *less* than expected from the full shot noise expression, for reasons that are not fully understood. This will probably prove beneficial to the noise figure of the self-oscillating mixer.

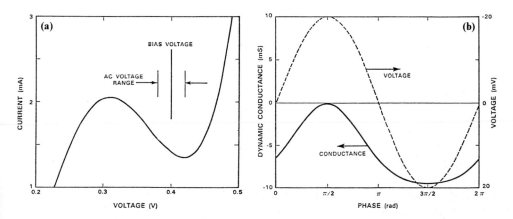

Fig. 6.10. (a) $I-V$ curve of negative differential resistance region showing dc bias and ac amplitude, producing the voltage and conductance curves shown in (b)

6.4 Resistive Multipliers

The presence of a peak and valley in the $I–V$ curve, combined with the overall antisymmetry of the $I–V$ curve about the origin [i.e., $I(V) = -I(-V)$], offers the potential for efficient odd-harmonic generation with an unbiased resonant-tunnelling diode. The key lies in pumping the diode so that the peak amplitude of the voltage across the diode occurs above the resonant current peak. This causes at least three local maxima to occur in the diode current waveform over one cycle, corresponding to third or higher odd-harmonic generation. To demonstrate this effect, we model an $I–V$ curve with a seventh order polynomial. The diode is assumed to be driven by a source having internal impedance less than the minimum negative resistance of the double-barrier diode, so that the current across the diode is a single-valued function of the drive voltage. Shown in Fig. 6.11 is the numerically determined current waveform for a source amplitude of 0.5 V. The local maxima in this waveform, if equally spaced in phase, should lead to a strong fifth harmonic component in the current power spectrum. This spectrum, shown in Fig. 6.12, verifies our expectation and shows the magnitude of fifth-harmonic power to be 0.13 times that at the fundamental.

Shown in Fig. 6.13 is the experimental power spectrum for a resonant-tunnelling diode when mounted in a 50-Ω coaxial circuit and pumped at 4 GHz. As expected, there is a complete absence of even harmonics and a predominance of the fifth among the odd harmonics. However, the measured efficiency was only about 0.5%, significantly less than the theoretical prediction. This discrepancy can possibly be attributed to the circuit, which does not allow independent tuning of the harmonics. Ideally, one would want to terminate the fifth harmonic with a resistance greater than the source resistance, and terminate the third harmonic with a reactance to eliminate power dissipation and reinforce the fifth-harmonic voltage.

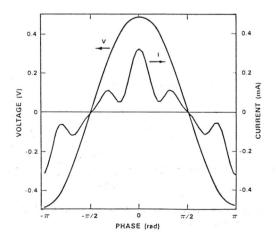

Fig. 6.11. Voltage and current waveforms from a double-barrier diode biased at zero dc voltage

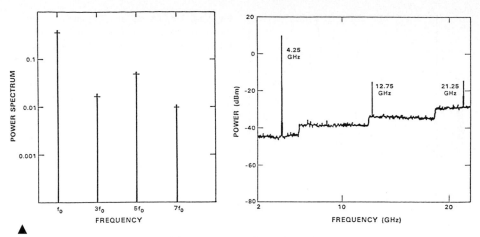

Fig. 6.12. The power spectrum of the current waveform of Fig. 6.9

Fig. 6.13. Power spectrum from a coaxially mounted double-barrier diode showing the input at 4.25 GHz and the output at the third and fifth harmonics

The resonant-tunnelling multiplier has two distinct advantages over existing resistive multipliers, which are usually based on Schottky barrier diodes. First, the absence of even harmonics greatly simplifies the circuit design, particularly in the millimeter-wave region. Second, the maximum theoretical generation efficiency of a double-barrier diode is significantly higher than the n^{-2} (n is the harmonic number) value that applies to ideal diodes [6.35] because of its negative resistance.

6.5 Variable Absolute Negative Conductance

In the course of studying the multiplier discussed above, *Sollner* et al. [6.36] found that the device displayed an absolute negative conductance to dc at and near $V = 0$ when the applied pump power was within a small range. Figure 6.14 shows the unpumped $I-V$ curve as well as that displaying the maximum negative conductance with a 1-GHz pump. The maximum negative conductance occurred when the peak pump amplitude at the device terminals was about 0.35 V. The value of the negative conductance is approximately the same as that found in the differential negative conductance regions and the voltage range over which it occurs is somewhat smaller. This phenomenon can be understood qualitatively from Fig. 6.15. This diagram shows that if the pump waveform is approximated by a square wave, and a linear approximation is made for the unpumped $I-V$ curve, absolute negative conductance occurs at dc when the pump amplitude is greater than the peak voltage, but not greater than the valley voltage. In the actual experiment, the positive conductance regions are weighted more heavily

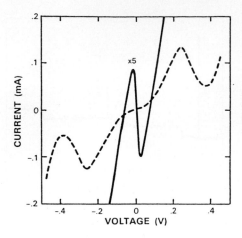

Fig. 6.14. Unpumped dc $I–V$ curve (*dashed*) showing differential negative resistance, and absolute negative resistance (*solid*) that occurs when ac power is applied

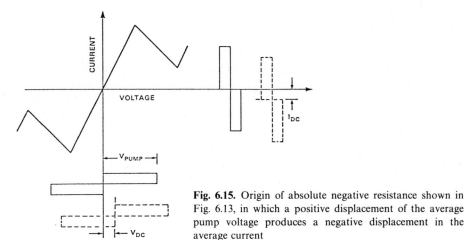

Fig. 6.15. Origin of absolute negative resistance shown in Fig. 6.13, in which a positive displacement of the average pump voltage produces a negative displacement in the average current

than in the case of a square-wave pump, but the principle is the same as shown in Fig. 6.15.

From the explanation given above, one would expect to find absolute negative conductance whenever a material with negative differential conductance and an $I–V$ curve symmetric about the origin is driven with a pump of the right amplitude and frequency. In fact, this effect was predicted in 1971 by *Banis* et al. [6.37] for any N-shaped $I–V$ curve and observed for a sample of bulk GaAs. *Pozhela* [6.38] reviews these observations, in which the negative differential mobility for electric fields above about 1 kV/cm is the basis for the absolute negative conductance.

The origin and the frequency dependence of the absolute negative conductance in the present case can be better understood if the $I–V$ curve is represented by a polynomial. A reasonable fit to the $I–V$ curve shown in Fig. 6.14 is obtained with

$$i = \sum_{n=1}^{4} a_{2n-1}e^{2n-1} \quad (e < 0.5 \text{ V}). \tag{6.7}$$

Only odd powers of the voltage e appear because the $I–V$ curve is antisymmetric. Suppose the total voltage consists of a large pump amplitude, e_1, at frequency ω_1, and a small signal amplitude, e_2, at frequency ω_2, i.e.,

$$e = e_1 \cos\omega_1 t + e_2 \cos\omega_2 t. \tag{6.8}$$

There will, of course, be harmonics of the pump generated by the nonlinearity of the $I–V$ curve, and they should be calculated in a self-consistent manner (see, for example, *Kerr* et al. [6.33]) to do this analysis properly. These harmonics will be neglected here to obtain a simple physical picture of the device behavior, although some quantitative information will be lost. By keeping terms to first order in e_2 from (6.8),

$$e^{2n-1} \cong (e_1 \cos\omega_1 t)^{2n-1} + (2n-1)e_2 \cos\omega_2 t(e_1 \cos\omega_1 t)^{2n-2}. \tag{6.9}$$

Then the signal conductance is

$$\frac{di}{\partial e_2} = \sum_{n=1}^{4} \{a_{2n-1}(2n-1)(e_1 \cos\omega_1 t)^{n-2}\} \cos\omega_2 t. \tag{6.10}$$

Unless $\omega_2 = (2n-2)\omega_1$, the only terms in (6.10) at frequency ω_2 arise from the constant terms inside the braces. These terms have been plotted in Fig. 6.16. This behavior is essentially what was observed in the experiment leading to Fig. 6.14.

The foregoing asserts that at any frequency, even those well above the pump frequency ($\omega_2 > \omega_1$), the conductance of the pumped device will be negative at

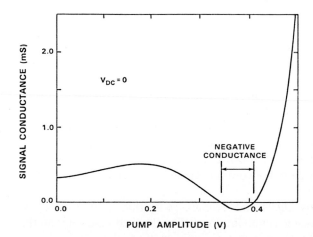

Fig. 6.16. Signal conductance from (6.10) using the $I–V$ curve shown in Fig. 6.13

the signal frequency when the pump amplitude is within the region shown in Fig. 6.16. Furthermore, the magnitude of the negative conductance can be adjusted by varying the pump amplitude, a very useful circuit property. In addition, when $\omega_2 = 2\omega_1$ there is a slight increase in the negative conductance above that calculated in Fig. 6.16 for the parameters used here. This increase in negative conductance at a specified frequency could simplify frequency selection for an oscillator based on this effect. Finally, it should be noted that little in the way of negative conductance or dynamic range has been sacrificed, and the advantage of operating with zero dc bias voltage has been gained. It appears that the variable absolute negative conductance recently observed in double-barrier diodes can be used as the bias for oscillators up to the cutoff frequency of the diode.

6.6 Persistent Photoconductivity and a Resonant-Tunnelling Transistor

Persistent photoconductivity has also been observed in resonant-tunnelling structures [6.39], as shown in Fig. 6.17. The cause of the shift in the I–V curves with successively greater exposure to light is the photoionization of DX centers in the $Al_{0.3}Ga_{0.7}As$ barriers. (For a detailed discussion of DX centers, see *Nelson* [6.40] or *Lang* et al. [6.41]). This ionization creates a dipole region with fixed positive charge in the barriers and free electrons outside the barriers. Any electrons that reside initially in the well quickly escape because of the higher energy of the confined band edge there and the short resonant-state lifetime. These dipoles produce the band bending shown in Fig. 6.18. The well is lowered in potential by an amount $\Delta\phi$, and the barriers are also lowered. The resulting shifted I–V curve shows a peak transmission that has been moved to lower voltage by the lowered well and a higher current density due to the lower effective barriers.

Theoretical I–V curves are also shown in Fig. 6.17 and agree qualitatively with the experimentally observed ones, suggesting that ionized DX centers provide the correct interpretation. The excess current observed at higher voltages probably results from non-resonant tunnelling assisted by defects in the barriers. Also, the currents in the predicted curves are significantly larger than those observed, but this is the usual situation (more discussion on this point occurs in Sect. 6.7). Additional confirmation of the accuracy of this interpretation is provided by the agreement between the observed spectral response shown in Fig. 6.19 to the response of silicon DX centers in $Al_{0.4}Ga_{0.6}As$, measured by *Lang* and *Logan* [6.42]. The silicon impurities in the barriers are not intentional, but presumably diffuse there from the contact regions, where they are the major dopant.

Since the recognition by *Davis* and *Hosack* [6.2] that a double-barrier structure could exhibit resonant tunnelling and that the well could act as the

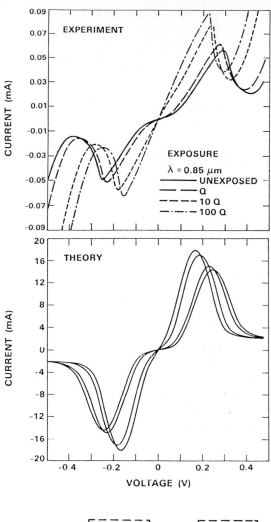

Fig. 6.17. Observed and calculated *I–V* curves for a double-barrier diode that has been cooled to 20 K in the dark and then given progressively greater exposure to light

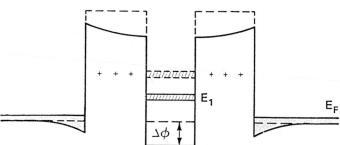

Fig. 6.18. Electron energy as a function of position in a double-barrier diode showing the shift from the dashed to the solid lines due to positive charge in the barriers

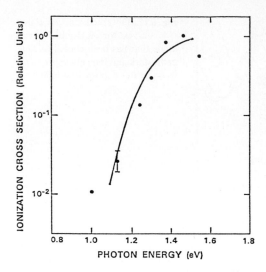

Fig. 6.19. Observed (*dots*) photon energy dependence of the relative ionization cross-section for the persistent photoconductive effect shown in Fig. 6.16 compared with the measured spectrum (*line*) for Si DX centers in $Al_{0.4}Ga_{0.6}As$ from [6.42]

control electrode, several similar transistor structures have been suggested that have unique characteristics. The year 1985 saw particular activity; *Jogai* and *Wang* [6.43] analyzed the configuration suggested by Davis and Hosack, *Bonnefoi* et al. [6.44] proposed a variation in which the original collector becomes the control electrode via the Stark effect, *Yokoyama* et al. [6.45] designed and tested a transistor that used a double-barrier structure for the emitter, and *Capasso* and *Kiehl* [6.46] proposed a transistor with a double-barrier structure in the base. Also *Sollner* et al. [6.47] used the results of the persistent photoconductivity studies just described to estimate the performance of the original double-barrier resonant-tunnelling transistor. This last work will be described in more detail in the remainder of this section.

From Fig. 6.18 it is clear that DX centers in the barriers provide a way of adjusting the well potential relative to the outer contact regions. This is a similar effect to attaching an electrical connection to the well so that the device can be operated as a transistor, with the well serving as the control electrode. Figure 6.20 shows one geometry for a resonant-tunnelling transistor.

The transconductance can be calculated using some reasonable assumptions. The transconductance G_m is related to the change in collector current density ΔJ_c and the change in well potential $\Delta\phi$ by

$$G_m \equiv \frac{\partial I_c}{\partial V_{BE}} = \frac{A \, \Delta J_C}{\Delta\phi} \tag{6.11}$$

where A is the emitter area. The shift in the well potential is related to the shift in the current peak ΔV_p by

$$\Delta V_p \cong 4\Delta\phi \, . \tag{6.12}$$

This expression is valid only for the specific diode of *Sollner* et al. [6.47] because

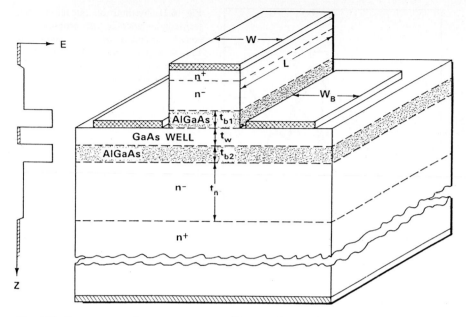

Fig. 6.20. One geometry for a resonant tunnelling transistor with the spatial dependence of the conduction band energy

one factor of two on the right side approximately accounts for the depletion region on the collector side when biased to the current peak. The other factor of two arises from the fact that the base-to-emitter voltage is at most half of that applied between the base and collector. So, the transconductance becomes

$$G_m = \frac{4A\,\Delta J_c}{\Delta V_p}. \tag{6.13}$$

There is one complication, however. The excess current discussed above also changes with $\Delta\phi$, but this leakage current change is probably related to the presence of DX centers in the barriers rather than the modulation of the well potential. To account for this contribution it is assumed that at voltages below the current peak the transistor output impedance would be large and positive, and the excess current at high voltage is extrapolated smoothly back toward zero keeping the output impedance positive. These extrapolations are shown in Fig. 6.21. Using this figure an intrinsic transconductance of 4000 mS/mm is obtained for an emitter width of 1 μm. Specific contact resistances of the order of $10^{-7}\,\Omega\,\mathrm{cm}^2$ would be necessary to realize such a high extrinsic transconductance.

The frequency above which the small-signal short-circuit current gain drops below unity is

$$f_T = \frac{C}{2\pi G_m}. \tag{6.14}$$

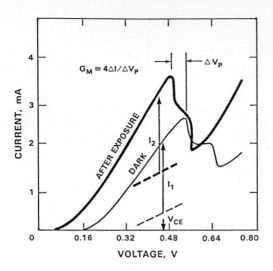

Fig. 6.21. Method of calculating the transconductance of the proposed resonant tunnelling transistor shown in Fig. 6.19 from the two-terminal I–V measurements with persistent photoconductive effects

where C is the total input capacitance. Using a 1-μm-wide gate contact and 40-nm-thick n^- regions shown in Fig. 6.20, we find $f_T = 110$ GHz.

The maximum frequency of oscillation f_{max} will also depend on the base resistance,

$$f_{max} = \frac{f_T}{4R_B C_C} \tag{6.15}$$

where R_B is the base resistance and C_C is the base-to-collector capacitance. Since the base is very thin and lightly doped, it might be expected that the base resistance would be quite high. However, there are some fortunate aspects to the quantum-well geometry that reduce its resistance considerably. It is well known that electron mobilities in modulation-doped quantum wells are very high at temperatures less than 100 K. Although this structure is not a modulation-doped well in the usual sense, near the resonant current peak the base layer acquires charge from the transiting carriers without any direct doping [6.48, 49]. For present samples an average well charge density of approximately 10^{17} cm^{-3} can be estimated. Using the best reported [6.50] mobility in 1984 at 50 K of 5×10^5 cm^2/Vs, a base carrier density of 2×10^{17} cm^{-3}, a 1 × 20-μm emitter, and a 4.0-nm-thick well, a base resistance of less than 10 Ω results. This gives an $R_B C_C$ product of about 0.5 ps, resulting in an f_{max} of 330 GHz.

Any increase in current density would increase f_T and f_{max} proportionally, and theoretically predicted currents (Sect. 6.7) are several times higher than presently observed values. It seems, then, that a transistor based on a double-barrier resonant-tunnelling structure promises performance that could improve the present state of the art considerably. The main challenge is a contact to the thin well region that will not also contact the surrounding regions. This is a problem that is generic to many heterostructure devices, so a solution will probably be found in the near future.

6.7 A Look at Resonant-Tunnelling Theory

The theory of resonant tunnelling is currently dynamic and still evolving. The full problem is complicated, involving self-consistent solution of Poisson's equation and the time-dependent Schrödinger equation. The spatial quantization that creates the effects of interest also renders many of the usual approximations inadequate. To further complicate matters, scattering from impurities, defects, other carriers, and collective excitations is almost certainly important, but the inclusion of these effects in detail is a difficult theoretical problem. On the positive side, however, the simplest calculations seem to explain the general outline of the experimental observations. It is hoped that some of the unexplained aspects will be illuminated by more complete treatments in the near future.

Here we will outline the simple stationary-state approach and compare this with observations. Then we will summarize the time-dependent calculations that have yielded results to date, and finally mention the thoughts of some workers on the importance and implications of scattering.

6.7.1 Stationary-State Calculation

The treatment to be described here is based on the approach first applied to finite superlattices by *Tsu* and *Esaki* [6.7] after a method of *Kane* [6.8]. The specific calculation incorporates some refinements by *Le* and *Sollner* [6.51]. For a first-order solution to the problem, the following assumptions have been made:

1) Electrons interact only with the potential discontinuities of the conduction band, and no other scattering is included. The only carriers considered are electrons.
2) The effective mass model is used, and parabolic energy bands are assumed. The different effective masses in different semiconductors are accounted for (but see below for an exception), and the matching of wave functions at heterointerfaces is based on the conservation of probability current.
3) The potential profile of the structure as experienced by an electron is the sum of the potential due to the conduction band offsets and the electrostatic potential due to the applied bias and any localized charges.
4) In the regions outside the barriers there is an electron gas, and the field screening behavior is described by the Thomas–Fermi approximation.

Dynamic charge storage, i.e., the accumulation of electrons in a well near resonance and the resulting potential modification, has also not been included here. This effect is thought to be small at current densities that have been obtained so far. However, two groups have performed self-consistent calculations [6.52, 53] and predict discontinuities and hysteresis in the $I–V$ curves as a direct result of the charge build-up in the well at resonance. No discontinuities have so far (1987) been observed experimentally that could not be explained by oscillations. The one experimental manifestation of this effect that is claimed to have been observed [6.54] could also be due to oscillations, as discussed by *Sollner* [6.55].

The first step in the calculation of a resonant-tunnelling I–V curve is to determine the spatial variation of the potential experienced by electrons. In addition to the potential change produced by the barrier regions, there will be an electrostatic potential applied by an external field. This will produce accumulation and depletion regions that will further perturb the potential. The spatial dependence of the electrostatic potential $\phi(x)$ is calculated in the barrier region using the self-consistent Thomas–Fermi equation (cgs units)

$$\phi''(x) = \frac{4\pi q n_0}{\varepsilon}\left[1 - \left(1 - \frac{q\phi(x)}{E_F}\right)^{3/2}\right] \tag{6.16}$$

where E_F is the Fermi energy, ε is the dielectric constant, and n_0 is the average volume doping density. This expression is solved analytically in the regions with nonzero net charge, then matched numerically at the boundaries. In practice, a parabola is fit to the solution in the cathode so that the band-bending region is finite. The spatial extent of the fitted region is taken as about twice the Thomas–Fermi screening length. A potential profile calculated for a double-barrier structure with doping carrier density of 10^{17} cm^{-3} in the outer regions is shown in Fig. 6.22.

It should be noted that while this is a convenient approximation to the potential in the accumulation region, strictly it is only valid when the potential changes very little on the scale of the electron wavelength, $h/\sqrt{2m_e E_F}$, where m_e is the electron effective mass. This is not the case for the structures of Table 6.1, so a more correct solution would include the quantization of the accumulation region in the determination of the potential distribution.

Once the potential has been found, the transmission coefficient for an electron with a given energy is determined by matching boundary conditions with the transfer matrix method, and the current is then found by integrating over the incident electron distribution and the density of available final states, as outlined

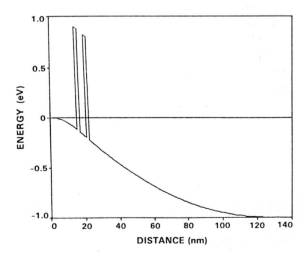

Fig. 6.22. Calculated potential energy for an electron in the conduction band of a double-barrier diode including accumulation and depletion regions

by *Tsu* and *Esaki* [6.7]. The transfer matrix is numerically calculated for an arbitrary parabolic potential profile. To guarantee rapid convergence the potential is divided into a few (< 10) spatial segments with transfer matrices calculated for each partition. Since the cathode contains an accumulation region, there is a question of what energy distribution should be used for the incident electrons in the current calculation. Better agreement with measurements is obtained if the equilibrium Fermi distribution of the cathode material is used, ignoring possible tunnelling of the accumulated electrons. This may be caused by the fact that it is improbable for electrons to scatter (inelastically) into the accumulation region, so the lifetime for tunnelling out is shorter than the time to scatter in, but in that case there would be much less band bending than has been assumed.

In spite of some unsatisfactory aspects of this simple calculation, the agreement with experiment is, perhaps fortuitously, rather good. Shown in Fig. 6.23 are the calculated [6.51] and measured *I–V* curves for a double-barrier structure consisting of two 1.5-nm-thick A1As barriers with a 4.5-nm-thick well between them. For barriers only three lattice constants thick, there is some question about the validity of the effective mass theory. In this calculation *Le* and *Sollner* [6.51] used the effective mass for GaAs and assumed that the electrons retained symmetry of the *Γ*-valley. The use of a larger effective mass would decrease the predicted current. The other growth parameters correspond to Wafer 3 in Table 6.1.

While the general shapes of the two curves of Fig. 6.23 are similar, there are some differences. Firstly, the calculated current is higher than measured by about a factor of three. *Coon* and *Liu* [6.56] have pointed out that an approach that includes two-body terms can enhance the calculated current by as much as a factor of two. Thus the discrepancy in predicted and measured current may be somewhat greater than shown here, although as mentioned above a larger effective mass would reduce the difference. The observation of less current than

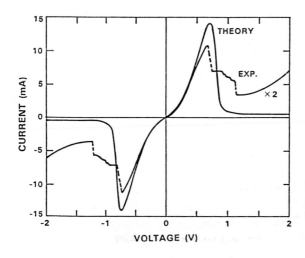

Fig. 6.23. Predicted and observed *I–V* curve for a double-barrier structure with AlAs barriers

predicted may be due to scattering of the carriers during transit, which would destroy the phase coherence needed for resonance and presumably reduce the transmission coefficient. (But see below for a discussion of scattering.) Secondly, the measured currents at voltages above the current peak are higher than the calculated curve would suggest. This may be due to nonresonant tunnelling, perhaps via impurities in the barriers. Nevertheless, for such a simple calculation the results give the general features of the measured curves.

6.7.2 Temporal Behavior

Time evolution of the system has been eliminated from the stationary-state calculation above. However, it is possible to obtain the lifetime of a transiting electron in the resonant state that it occupies while it is between the two barriers, as discussed in Sect. 6.2. The approach, first derived for atomic and nuclear resonances (see, for example, *Blatt* and *Weisskopf* [6.18]) is generally applicable to any resonant state, and has been applied to resonant tunnelling by *Ricco* and *Azbel* [6.57] and by *Coon* and *Liu* [6.58]. The result is that the lifetime is given by the uncertainty relation, $\tau = \hbar/\Delta E$, where ΔE is the half-width of the peak in the transmission coefficient $T(E)$. Frequencies corresponding to $f_{\Delta E} = (2\pi\tau)^{-1}$ are calculated for the three structures and listed in Table 6.1.

A time-dependent calculation of the electron distribution has been performed by *Frensley* [6.49] using the Wigner function approach. He finds the time required to reach equilibrium after an impulse to the system to be comparable to those estimated by the resonant-state lifetime above. The advantage of Frensley's calculation is that the time evolution of the wave functions are predicted for all times. The complete time-dependent solution should take account of charge redistribution from applied electric fields and motion of carriers through the depletion and accumulation regions. Scattering clearly plays an important part in these processes.

6.7.3 Scattering

Scattering in the barriers will remove the assumed condition of conservation of transverse momentum during tunnelling, and scattering in the well region(s) destroys the coherence of a carrier wave function over the structure. In either case, the simple analysis above does not consider such processes. Possible scattering centers include impurities, dislocations, other carriers, phonons, and in the barriers surface roughness and alloy fluctuations could be important. When there is more than one resonant state in the well, something akin to intersubband scattering may also occur. The importance of scattering in resonant tunnelling has been recognized [6.59] since 1965. It was pointed out by *Luryi* [6.17], soon after the most recent revival of interest in resonant tunnelling, that scattering may in fact dominate the charge transport process through a double-barrier structure. He proposed that all phase coherence is lost before the electron leaves the well, and that the negative resistance in this case results from the conservation of momentum, making it impossible for electrons to tunnel into the well when the peak in the density of state in the well (for momentum perpendicular to the well) is below the conduction band-edge of the cathode. There has been considerable informal discussion of the relative merits of the two models, but it has been difficult to conceive an experimental test, at least in part because an explicit calculation of the $I–V$ curve did not exist for the sequential tunnelling model.

Very recently *Weil* and *Vinter* [6.60] have calculated that the peak current densities should be the same for both the ballistic and the sequential models. However, it may be that the two models are actually equivalent as they are presently defined. In the sequential model, as described by Luryi and by Weil and Vinter, scattering is not included explicitly; it is accounted for by a presumed lack of phase coherence of the wave function representing a carrier iinside and outside of the well. However, in the sequential-tunnelling calculation of Weil and Vinter, coherence of the wave function across the incoming barrier is established by the use of the same boundary conditions as those used for the resonant model (see Ref. 8 in their paper). The effects of the second barrier enter via the width of the quasibound state in the well, again with a calculation that assumes coherence across the barrier. Perhaps it is not surprising that, with no scattering in the well, these calculations of resonant and sequential tunnelling give the same result.

Weil and Vinter do attempt to include the effects of scattering in the well via a broadening of the quasibound state. They conclude that, as long as the energy width of this state is small compared to the energy width of the incoming carriers (the usual experimental situation), the lower peak transmission is offset by the additional width. Thus the integral determining the peak current is unaffected. However, this technique of including scattering still implicitly assumes the phase coherence discussed above, in spite of the fact that scattering would in general alter the phase after the scattering event.

This calculation does not seem to represent the model that *Luryi* originally suggested, since it does not perturb the phase coherence across the structure. There are also important scattering processes that are not in *Luryi*'s model, for example, scattering in the barriers. The role of scattering remains one of several important unanswered questions in resonant tunnelling.

6.8 Concluding Remarks

There is still much fertile yet uncultivated territory in the realm of multiple-barrier tunnelling. Three-terminal devices are in their infancy, as are devices for digital applications. The possibility of electrooptical effects has received some attention, and several novel devices have resulted [6.61]. Most structures to date have contained only two barriers, but the investigation of the interaction of three or more barriers may yield even more interesting and useful phenomena.

Multiple-barrier structures, carried to one natural conclusion, become superlattices. These have presented problems as electrical devices in the past because of domain formation. There are many variations that remain untested, even unanalyzed; for example, the "CHIRP" superlattice [6.62] has been looked at in some detail, but only one type of period variation was investigated. There are probably some interesting structures that would overcome or control the domain formation that has limited this field to date.

All of the devices discussed in this chapter have been small compared to their operating wavelength, i.e., they are lumped elements rather than transmission media. A bulk material that could provide large, fast impedance nonlinearities would be very useful at the higher frequencies. This is difficult with two-barrier structures, but some variety of superlattice may provide the material necessary for travelling-wave devices.

The materials growth that makes possible the high spatial resolution in heterostructure formation is well advanced and progressing rapidly, but there is still much room for improvement. Only for the past two years have we had material of sufficient quality to observe reasonable peak-to-valley ratios at room temperature. Theoretically this ratio should be much greater, as shown in Fig. 6.23. Materials of greater purity would make valid most of the assumptions leading to the calculated curve of Fig. 6.23.

In short, the future of multiple-barrier tunnelling structures appears bright, especially in view of the high level of current interest in the field. We believe that some of the devices that are just demonstrating feasibility will be commercially exploited in the next several years, and that there remain many yet to be invented that will reach the same goal in the years to come.

Note Added in Proof

Since this chapter was written, the highest oscillation frequency of resonant-tunnelling diodes has reached 425 GHz (Brown et al.: Appl. Phys. Lett. **55**, to be published), and effects of the finite lifetime of the resonant state have been incorporated in the equivalent circuit [Brown et al.: Appl. Phys. Lett. **54**, 934 (1989)].

List of Symbols

Units are shown in brackets and equation numbers are in parentheses. Greek symbols follow the English ones.

A Cross-sectional area of a device [cm^2] (6.11)
a_n Polynomial coefficient [S] (6.7)
C Capacitance [F]
C_C Collector capacitance [F] (6.15)
C_S Capacitance per unit area [F/cm^2]
E_F Fermi energy [J] (6.16)
e Voltage [V] (6.7)

e_n Voltage amplitude at frequency ω_n [V] (6.8)

f_I Intermediate frequency [Hz]

f_K Image frequency [Hz]

f_{max} Frequency above which the terminal conductance is positive for all voltages, hence maximum oscillation frequency [Hz] (6.2, 15)

f_O Output frequency [Hz]

f_S Signal frequency [Hz]

f_T Frequency above which the small-signal short-circuit current gain is below unity [Hz] (6.14)

$f_{\Delta E}$ Frequency corresponding to resonant-state lifetime [Hz]

G_{max} Maximum negative value of voltage-dependent conductance [S]

$G(V)$ Voltage-dependent conductance of a resonant-tunnelling diode [S]

$g(t)$ Conductance of a diode modulated by a changing voltage [S] (6.5)

g_ω Fourier components of the conductance $g(t)$ [S] (6.5)

I Current [A]

IF   Intermediate frequency [Hz]

i Current [A] (6.7)

i_m Current at frequency m [A] (6.4)

J_C Collector current density [A/cm^2] (6.11)

J_p Peak current density [A/cm^2]

m_e Effective mass of the electron [kg]

n_0 Carrier concentration [cm^{-3}] (6.16)

P_{max} Maximum output power attainable from a negative-resistance amplifier [W]

q Charge on the electron [C] (6.16)

R_B Base resistance [Ω] (6.15)

$R_i(V)$ Current responsivity [A/W] (6.1)

R_s Series resistance [Ω]

V Voltage [V]

v_0 Voltage amplitude [V] (6.3)

v_m Voltage at frequency m [V] (6.4)

Y^A Augmented admittance matrix [S] (6.5)

Y_D Device admittance [S] (6.3)

Y_L Load admittance [S] (6.3)

$Y_{mm'}$ Element of admittance matrix Y [S] (6.4)

Y_T Total admittance [S] (6.3)

Y_m Termination admittance at frequency m [S] (6.5)

Z_A Antenna impedance [Ω] (6.1)

Z_D Device impedance [Ω]

Z_L Load impedance [Ω]

ΔE Energy half-width of transmission function [J]

ΔI Current excursion of negative differential resistance region [A]

$\Delta I(V)$ Change of current [A] (6.1)

ΔP_{ac} Change of ac power [W] (6.1)

ΔV_p Shift of the voltage of the current peak from ionized charges in the barriers [V] (6.12)

ΔV Voltage excursion of negative differential resistance region [A]

$\Delta \phi$ Shift in potential of the well from ionized charges in the barriers [eV] (6.11)

ε Dielectric constant [F/cm] (6.16)

γ Speed index [s/V]

ω Angular frequency [s^{-1}] (6.3)

$\phi(x)$ Electrostatic potential energy [eV] (6.16)

Acknowledgements. None of the experimental work summarized here could have been accomplished without help from many people skilled in the art of material growth and fabrication. We are especially indebted to W. D. Goodhue for producing excellent quality heterostructures grown by MBE, for suggesting useful structures, and for overseeing much of the processing. C. L. Chen has also been very helpful in processing, as have G. D. Johnson, K. M. Molvar, W. F. DiNatale, and R. F. Murphy. Expert packaging help has been provided by N. Usiak, D. J. Landers and P. J. Daniels. C. D. Parker has provided considerable expertise with the measurements.

Similarly, we owe much to the environment of ideas in which we work. P. E. Tannenwald, B. Lax, C. O. Bozler, A. R. Calawa, B. J. Clifton, M. W. Geis, M. A. Hollis, R. A. Murphy and H. J. Zeiger at Lincoln Laboratory, F. Capasso and S. Luryi at AT&T Bell Laboratories, W. R. Frensley, R. T. Bate and M. A. Reed at Texas Instruments, M. Heiblum and R. A. Kiehl at IBM, D. D. Coon at U. Pittsburgh, H. Fetterman at UCLA, H. Sakaki at U. Tokyo and L. F. Eastman at Cornell have all contributed to useful technical discussions.

This work was sponsored by the U.S. Army Research Office, the U.S. Air Force, and by NASA.

References

6.1   D. Bohm: *Quantum Theory* (Prentice-Hall, Engelwood Cliffs, N.J. 1951) p. 283

6.2   R. H. Davis, H. H. Hosack: *J. Appl. Phys.* **34**, 864 (1963)

6.3   L. V. Ioganson: Zh. Eksp. Teor. Fiz. **45**, 207 (1963) [English transl. Sov. Phys.-JETP **18**, 146, (1964)]

6.4   C. A. Mead: *J. Appl. Phys.* **32**, 646 (1961)

6.5   L. Esaki, R. Tsu: *IBM J. Res. Develop.* **14**, 61 (1970)

6.6   R. F. Kazarinov, R. A. Suris: *Sov. Phys. Semicond.* **5**, 707 (1971)

6.7   R. Tsu, L. Esaki: *Appl. Phys. Lett.* **22**, 562 (1973)

6.8   E. O. Kane: "Basic Concepts of Tunnelling," in *Tunnelling Phenomena in Solids*, ed. E. Burstein, S. Lundqvist (Plenum, New York 1969)

6.9   L. L. Chang, L. Esaki, R. Tsu: *Appl. Phys. Lett.* **24**, 593 (1974)

6.10   T. C. L. G. Sollner, W. D. Goodhue, P. E. Tannenwald, C. D. Parker, D. D. Peck: *Appl. Phys. Lett.* **43**, 588 (1983)

6.11   M. Tsuchiya, H. Sakaki: IEEE Int. Electron Devices Meeting, Washington DC, 1985 p. 662

6.12   T. J. Shewchuck, P. C. Chaplin, P. D. Coleman, W. Kopp, R. Fischer, H. Morkoc: *Appl. Phys. Lett.* **46**, 508 (1985)

6.13   W. D. Goodhue, T. C. L. G. Sollner, H. Q. Le, E. R. Brown, B. A. Vojak: *Appl. Phys. Lett.* **49**, 1086 (1986)

6.14   S. Muto, T. Inata, Y. Nataka, S. Hiyamizu: Int. Workshop on Future Electron Devices – Superlattice Devices, Tokyo, Japan, Feb. 9–11, 1987, p. 33

6.15 A. R. Bonnefoi, R. T. Collins, T. C. Collins, T. C. McGill, R. D. Burnham, F. A. Ponce: Appl. Phys. Lett. **46**, 285 (1985)
6.16 S. Ray, P. Ruden, V. Sokolov, R. Kolbas, T. Boonstra, J. Williams: Appl. Phys. Lett. **48**, 1666 (1986)
6.17 S. Luryi: Appl. Phys. Lett. **47**, 490 (1985)
6.18 J. Blatt, V. F. Weisskopf: *Theoretical Nuclear Physics* (Springer, Berlin, Heidelberg 1979)
6.19 T. C. L. G. Sollner, E. R. Brown, W. D. Goodhue, H. Q. Le: Appl. Phys. Lett. **50**, 332 (1987)
6.20 H. C. Torrey, C. A. Whitmer: *Crystal Rectifiers*, New York, 1948, p. 336
6.21 H. R. Fetterman, P. E. Tannenwald, B. J. Clifton, C. D. Parker, W. D. Fitzgerald, N. R. Erickson: Appl. Phys. Lett. **33**, 151 (1978)
6.22 P. D. Coleman, S. Goedeke, T. J. Shewchuk, P. C. Chapin, J. M. Gering, H. Morkoc: Appl. Phys. Lett. **48**, 422 (1986)
6.23 E. R. Brown, T. C. L. G. Sollner, W. D. Goodhue, C. D. Parker: Appl. Phys. Lett. **50**, 83 (1987)
6.24 K. Kurokawa: Bell Syst. Tech. J. **48**, 1937 (1969)
6.25 C. S. Kim, A. Brandli: IRE Trans. Circuit Theory **CT8**, 416 (1961)
6.26 R. F. Trambarulo: International Solid-State Circuits Conference, Philadelphia, PA, 1961.
6.27 E. R. Brown, T. C. L. G. Sollner, W. D. Goodhue, C. D. Parker: Device Research Conference, Santa Barbara, CA, June 1987. Paper IVA-2
6.28 P. E. Davis, G. Gibbons: Solid State Electron. **10**, 461 (1967)
6.29 D. T. Young, C. A. Burrus, R. C. Shaw: Proc. IEEE **52**, 1260 (1964)
6.30 C. A. Burrus: J. Appl. Phys. **32**, 1031 (1961)
6.31 D. Carlson, M. V. Schneider: IEEE Trans. Microwave Theory Tech. **MTT-26**, 706 (1978)
6.32 C. S. Kim: IRE Trans. Electron Dev. **ED-8**, 394 (1961)
6.33 A. R. Kerr: IEEE Trans. Microwave Theory Tech. **MTT-23**, 828 (1975)
6.34 E. R. Brown, T. C. L. G. Sollner, W. D. Goodhue: *Solid Research Report, MIT Lincoln Laboratory* **1986:1**, 37 (1986)
6.35 C. H. Page: Proc. IRE **46**, 1738 (1958)
6.36 T. C. L. G. Sollner, E. R. Brown, W. D. Goodhue: Optical Soc. Am. Topical Meeting on Picosecond Electronics and Optoelectronics, Incline Village, NV, Jan 14–16, 1987, p. 143
6.37 T. L. Banis, I. V. Parshelyunas, Yu. K. Pozhela: Litov. Fiz. Sb. **11**, 1013 (1971)
6.38 J. Pozhela: *Plasma and Current Instabilities in Semiconductors*, Intern. Ser. Sci. Solid State, **18** (Pergamon, Oxford 1981)
6.39 T. C. L. G. Sollner, H. Q. Le, C. A. Correa, W. D. Goodhue: Appl. Phys. Lett. **47**, 36 (1985)
6.40 R. J. Nelson: Appl. Phys. Lett. **31**, 351 (1977)
6.41 D. V. Lang, R. A. Logan, M. Jaros: Phys. Rev. B, 1015 (1979)
6.42 D. V. Lang, R. A. Logan: Inst. Phys. Conf. Ser. **43**, 433 (1979)
6.43 B. Jogai, K. L. Wang: Appl. Phys. Lett. **46**, 167 (1985)
6.44 A. R. Bonnefoi, D. H. Chow, T. C. McGill: Appl. Phys. Lett. **47**, 888 (1985)
6.45 N. Yokoyama, K. Imamura, S. Muto, S. Hiyamizu, H. Nishii: Jpn. J. Appl. Phys. **24**, L583 (1985)
6.46 F. Capasso, R. A. Kiehl: J. Appl. Phys. **58**, 1366 (1985)
6.47 T. C. L. G. Sollner, H. Q. Le, C. A. Correa, W. D. Goodhue: IEEE/Cornell Conf. Advanced Concepts in High Speed Semicond. Devices and Circuits, Ithaca, NY, 1985, p. 252
6.48 W. Frensley: IEEE Int. Electron Devices Meeting, Washington, DC, 1986. Paper 25.5
6.49 W. Frensley: Phys. Rev. B **36**, 1570 (1987)
6.50 A. C. Gossard: Inst. Phys. Conf. Ser. **69**, 1 (1984)
6.51 H. Q. Le, T. C. L. G. Sollner: unpublished
6.52 H. L. Berkowitz, R. A. Lux: *Proc. Phys. Chem. Semicond. Interfaces* **XIV**, Salt Lake City, UT (Jan. 1987). To be published in *J. Vac. Sci. Technol.*
6.53 S. Wingreen, J. W. Wilkins: Bull. Am. Phys. Soc. **32**, 833 (1987)
6.54 V. J. Goldman, D. C. Tsui, J. E. Cunningham: *Phys. Rev. Lett.* **58**, 1256 (1987)
6.55 T. C. L. G. Sollner: Phys. Rev. Lett. **59**, 1622 (1987)
6.56 D. D. Coon, H. C. Liu: Appl. Phys. Lett. **47**, 172 (1985)

6.57 B. Ricco, M. Ya. Azbel: Phys. Rev. B **29**, 1970 (1984)
6.58 D. D. Coon, H. C. Liu: Appl. Phys. Lett. **49**, 94 (1986)
6.59 L. V. Ioganson: Usp. Fiz. Nauk **86**, 175 (1965). [English transl. in Sov. Phys-Usp. **8**, 413 (1965)] ·
6.60 T. Weil, B. Vinter: Appl. Phys. Lett. **50**, 1281 (1987)
6.61 F. Capasso: Surface. Sci. **142**, 513 (1984)
6.62 T. Nakagawa, N. J. Kawai, K. Ohta: Superlattices and Microstructures **1**, 187 (1985)

7. Resonant Tunnelling and Superlattice Devices: Physics and Circuits

F. Capasso, S. Sen, F. Beltram, and A. Y. Cho

With 57 Figures

Resonant tunnelling (RT) through semiconductor double barriers (DB's) was first demonstrated by *Chang* et al. [7.1] in 1974. With the development of modern crystal growth techniques, like molecular beam epitaxy (MBE), there has been renewed interest in the subject in recent years [7.2–23]. Material quality has improved to the point that negative differential resistance (NDR) can be observed at room temperature [7.2]. Intense research efforts are directed towards the optimization of the performances of the RT DB's and their utilization as the building blocks of novel electronic and optical devices.

Recently peak-to-valley ratios of nearly 4:1 in the current through a single double barrier quantum well (DBQW) were reported at room temperature [7.11, 12]. At 77 K, peak-to-valley as high as 15:1 was observed [7.12]. Further improvement in the peak-to-valley ratio (14:1 at room temperature) was obtained by the use of pseudomorphic structures [7.13]. *Mendez* et al. have also observed RT of holes [7.15]. Recently, *Reed* et al. [7.16] showed that the replacement of AlGaAs in the barriers with an AlAs/GaAs superlattice with the same average composition considerably improves the current-voltage ($I–V$) characteristics of RT diodes by making it symmetric. *Nakagawa* et al. have also reported RT of electrons and holes in triple barrier diodes [7.17, 18]. The RT of electrons from two-dimensional (2-D) quantized states in the valence band to 2-D states in the conduction band (resonant Zener tunnelling) has been investigated by *Allam* et al. [7.19]. *Sen* et al. have recently observed RT through parabolic quantum wells [7.20]; as many as 14 resonances were observed in the $I–V$ of one such sample. Unlike rectangular quantum wells, the multiple resonances of the parabolic well were nearly equally spaced.

The first practical application of RT diodes was demonstrated by *Sollner* et al. at the MIT Lincoln Laboratories in 1983 [7.21]. They used the NDR of RT diodes in detectors and mixers at frequencies up to the terahertz range. With the improvement of technology, the parasitic series resistance was reduced and RT diodes could be used for microwave generation [7.22] as well. Recently, *Brown* et al. have also reported oscillation frequencies up to 200 GHz [7.23] using RT diodes. The work of the Lincoln Labs group is discussed in the chapter by Sollner and coworkers.

Apart from the above, RT structures have assumed importance in recent years as functional devices for circuit applications [7.24]. The first proposal of including a RT structure in a bipolar transistor came from *Capasso* and *Kiehl* [7.25] in 1985. Following this a variety of three terminal devices (both unipolar and bipolar) have been proposed and implemented [7.26–40]. The RT approach to circuits is one of several proposed to circumvent the limits imposed by scaling laws to the ever increasing functional density [7.41]. In fact, *Sen* et al. have shown that through the use of RT devices, many circuits can be implemented with less devices per function [7.42]. In particular, RT devices with multiple negative resistance regions are of considerable interest for a variety of potential applications which could be realized with greatly reduced circuit complexity.

This chapter deals with the physics of RT and its device and circuit applications.

7.1 Resonant Tunnelling Through Double Barriers and Superlattices

7.1.1 The Origin of Negative Differential Resistance

RT through a DB occurs when the energy of an incident electron in the emitter matches that of an unoccupied state in the quantum well (QW) corresponding to the same lateral momentum. Negative differential resistance arises simply from

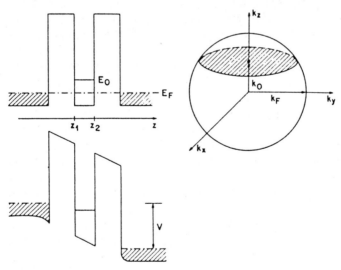

Fig. 7.1. Illustration of the operation of a double-barrier RT diode. The top left part shows the electron energy diagram in equilibrium. Below it is displayed the band diagram for an applied bias V, when the energy of certain electrons in the emitter matches unoccupied levels of the lowest subband E_0 in the QW. The right part illustrates the Fermi surface for a degenerately doped emitter. Assuming conservation of the lateral momentum during tunnelling, only those emitter electrons whose momenta lie on a disk $k_z = k_0$ (shaded disk) are resonant. The energy separation between E_0 and the bottom of the conduction band in the emitter is given by $\hbar^2 k_0^2/2m^*$. In an ideal double barrier diode at zero temperature, RT occurs in a voltage range during which the shaded disk moves down from the pole to the equatorial plane of the emitter Fermi sphere. At higher V (when $k_0^2 < 0$) resonant electrons no longer exist

momentum and energy conservation considerations and does not require the
coherence of the electron wave function (as is the case for the electronic analog
of the Fabry–Pérot effect). This has been clarified by *Luryi* [7.43] and is
illustrated in Fig. 7.1.

Consider the Fermi sea of electrons in the degenerately doped emitter. Their
energy can be expressed as

$$E_{3\text{-D}} = E_C + \frac{\hbar^2 k_z^2}{2m^*} + \frac{\hbar^2 k_\perp^2}{2m^*} \tag{7.1}$$

where E_C is the bottom of the conduction band and $k_\perp^2 = k_x^2 + k_y^2$. In doing so,
we are neglecting quantization in the emitter accumulation layer. This would
simply add further structure to the peaks in the I–V without altering the main
finding, i.e. the NDR. The energy in the 2-D target states in the QW, on the other
hand, is given by

$$E_{2\text{-D}} = E_n + \frac{\hbar^2 k_\perp^2}{2m^*} \tag{7.2}$$

where E_n is the bottom of the relevant subband in the QW. The RT of electrons
into the 2-D states requires the conservation of energy and of lateral momentum
($k_\perp$). It is of course assumed that the barriers are free from impurities and
inhomogeneities. The momentum conservation condition requires that the last
term in (7.1) and (7.2) be equal. So from energy conservation we find that
tunnelling is possible only for electrons whose momenta lie in a disk
corresponding to $k_z = k_0$ (shaded disk in the figure where the case $n = 0$ is
illustrated) where

$$k_0^2 = \frac{2m^*}{\hbar^2}(E_0 - E_C) . \tag{7.3}$$

Only those electrons have isoenergetic states in the quantum well with the same
$k_\perp$. This is a general feature of tunnelling into a two-dimensional system of
states. As the emitter-base potential rises, so does the number of electrons which
can tunnel; the shaded disk moves downward to the equatorial plane of the
Fermi sphere. For $E_n = E_C$, which corresponds to $k_0 = 0$, the number of
tunnelling electrons per unit area is maximum and equals $m^* E_F / \pi \hbar^2$. When E_C
rises above E_n, then at $T = 0$ K temperature, there are no electrons in the
emitter which can tunnel into the quantum well while conserving their lateral
momentum. Therefore, one can expect an abrupt drop in the tunnelling current.
NDR then, arises from the reduction of the dimensionality of electronic states in
tunnelling into the QW, and the presence of two tunnelling barriers is not
essential. This has been experimentally observed unambiguously by *Beltram* et
al. [7.40] in the operation of the gated QW transistor, described in the last
section of this chapter. Of course, similar arguments of conservation of lateral
momentum and energy leading to NDR apply also to systems of lower

dimensionality, e.g., to tunnelling of two-dimensional electrons through a quantum wire and to RT in one dimension.

7.1.2 Coherent (Fabry–Perot-Type) Resonant Tunnelling

Let us now consider the electronic Fabry–Pérot effect. In the presence of negligible scattering of the electrons in the well, the above NDR effect is accompanied by a coherent enhancement of the transmission, analogous to that occurring in an optical Fabry–Pérot. In the case of symmetric structure (such as the one discussed in Sect. 7.2), after a transient in which the electron wave function builds up in the quantum well, an equilibrium is reached where the portion of the incident wave reflected by the first barrier is exactly cancelled by the fraction of the electron wave function leaking from the QW to the left. The net effect is a total transfer of electrons from the left to the right through the DB. This is shown in Fig. 7.2 by the unity transmissivity peaks. In this case of coherent RT, the peak transmission at resonance is given approximately by T_{min}/T_{max} where T_{min} is the smaller among the transmission coefficients of the two barriers and T_{max} is the larger [7.44]. It is, therefore, possible to achieve unity transmission at the resonance peaks as discussed above, by making the transmission of the left and right barriers equal. This role of symmetry has been discussed in detail by *Ricco* and *Azbel* [7.44]. Application of an electric field to a symmetric DB introduces a difference between the transmissions of the two barriers, thus significantly decreasing below unity the overall transmission at the resonance peaks. Unity transmission can be restored if the two barriers have different and appropriately chosen thicknesses; obviously, with this procedure, one can optimize the transmission of only one of the resonance peaks. This is

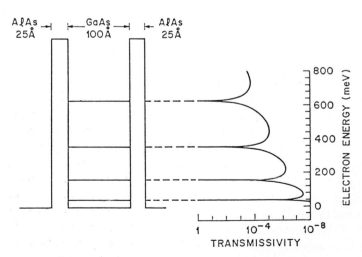

Fig. 7.2. Schematic conduction band energy diagram of an AlAs/GaAs/AlAs RT double barrier with 25 Å barriers and 100 Å well (*left*) and the calculated transmissivity as a function of incident electron energy (*right*)

because the exit barrier becomes lower under application of an electric field, and therefore has a higher transmission than the input barrier. Unity transmission can be restored by making the exit barrier thicker. However, as discussed by *Weil* and *Vinter* [7.45] and *Jonson* and *Grincwajg*) [7.46] and recently elaborated by *Luryi* [7.47], these arguments do not usually apply to DB's. In fact, in order to calculate the current one must average over the energy distribution of incoming electrons, which typically is much broader than the resonance width of the quantum state. As shown in [7.45–47] in this case the peak current is proportional to T_{min} only and the above considerations do not apply.

In a recent experiment, *Choi* et al. have obtained the first strong evidence of coherent tunnelling [7.48]. The band diagrams of the structure used in their experiments under different bias conditions are shown in Fig. 7.3. The sample, grown by MBE, consists of a superlattice with fifty periods, sandwiched between two heavily doped n^+-GaAs ($1 \times 10^{18}/\text{cm}^3$) contact layers. Each period of the superlattice is composed of 72 Å n-type GaAs quantum wells ($1 \times 10^{18}/\text{cm}^3$), 39 Å undoped $\text{Al}_{0.33}\text{Ga}_{0.67}\text{As}$ barrier, followed by a second well of undoped 18 Å GaAs and a second barrier of 154 Å undoped $\text{Al}_{0.33}\text{Ga}_{0.67}\text{As}$. Neglecting the coupling between QW's, the calculated energy levels for the thicker wells (W_1) are $E_1 = 47$ meV and $E_2 = 183$ meV, while for the thinner wells (W_2) only one subband is present whose bottom is at $E_1' = 174$ meV. For electrons photoexcited from the state E_1 to the state E_2, *Choi* et al. [7.48] have calculated

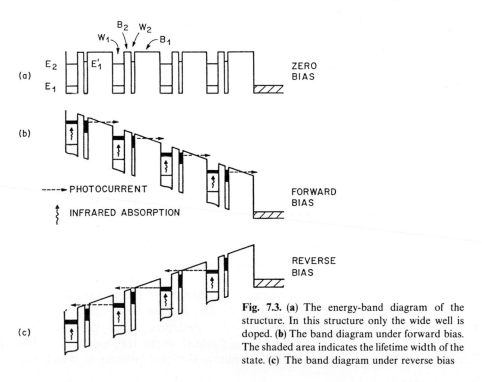

Fig. 7.3. (a) The energy-band diagram of the structure. In this structure only the wide well is doped. (b) The band diagram under forward bias. The shaded area indicates the lifetime width of the state. (c) The band diagram under reverse bias

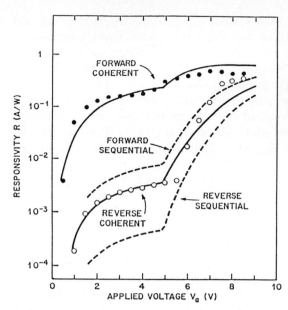

Fig. 7.4. The experimental results of the responsivity (R) in forward bias (*filled circles*) and reverse bias (*open circles*), and theory with the assumptions of coherent tunnelling (*solid curves*) under forward bias and reverse bias and of sequential tunnelling (*dashed curves*) under forward bias and reverse bias for the structure of Fig. 7.3

the transmission coefficients of the two barriers for opposite bias polarities. Under suitable forward bias conditions (Fig. 7.3b), it was shown that the transmission coefficient of the two barriers are nearly equal, resulting in a large coherent resonant enhancement of the photocurrent (Fig. 7.4). On the contrary, for reverse polarity, the transmission coefficient of the thicker barrier is always much smaller than that of the thinner one. Theoretical calculations [7.48] also indicate that the maximum ratio of the forward and reverse bias transmissivities would be 10 and 100 respectively under sequential and coherent tunnelling conditions. The nearly two orders of magnitude enhancement of the photocurrent measured under forward bias over that in reverse bias (Fig. 7.4) confirms the presence of coherent RT.

7.1.3 The Role of Scattering: Sequential Resonant Tunnelling Through Double Barriers and Superlattices

RT through a DB has been investigated experimentally by many researchers [7.1–16]. All of these investigations assumed that a Fabry–Pérot-type enhancement of the transmission was operational. However, as previously discussed, the observation of NDR does not imply a Fabry–Pérot mechanism. Other types of tests are necessary to show the presence of the coherence of the wave function.

The presence of scattering gives rise to another physical picture for RT. Once the electrons are injected into the QW as discussed in Sect. 7.1.1, scattering events can randomize the phase of the electronic wave function; this considerably weakens the coherent enhancement of the transmission. In the limit of very strong scattering RT is then a two-step process in which the electrons first tunnel into the well and then out of it through the second barrier. *The first step is the one that gives rise to NDR.* A lucid discussion of scattering has recently been given by *Stone* and *Lee* [7.49] in the context of RT through an impurity center. Unfortunately, their work has gone unnoticed among researchers in the area of QW structures. Their conclusions can also be applied to RT through QW's and we shall discuss them in this context.

To achieve the resonant enhancement of the transmission (Fabry–Pérot effect), the electron probability density must be peaked in the well. The time constant for this phenomenon, τ_0, is of the order of $\hbar/\Gamma_r$, where Γ_r is the full width at half maximum of the transmission peak. Collisions in the DB tend to destroy the coherence of the wave function, and therefore the electronic density in the well will never be able to build up to its full resonant value. If the scattering time τ is much shorter than τ_0, the peak transmission at resonance is expected to be decreased by the ratio τ_0/τ. The principal effects of collisions are to decrease the peak transmission by the ratio $\tau_0/(\tau_0 + \tau)$ and to broaden the resonance. In addition, the ratio of the number of electrons that resonantly tunnel without undergoing collisions to the number that tunnel after undergoing collisions is equal to τ/τ_0 [7.49]. To summarize, coherent RT is observable when the intrinsic resonance width ($\approx \hbar/\tau_0$) exceeds or equals the collision broadening ($\approx \hbar/\tau$). In the opposite limit ($\tau \ll \tau_0$), electrons will always tunnel through one of the intermediate states of the well, but they will do it incoherently without resonant enhancement of the transmission. We shall apply now the above criterion to RT through AlGaAs/GaAs DB investigated in several experiments.

Consider a 50 Å thick GaAs well sandwiched between two $Al_{0.30}Ga_{0.70}As$ barriers. Table 7.1 shows the ground state resonance widths Γ_r as defined above calculated for different values of the barrier thicknesses L_B (assumed equal). Note the strong dependence of Γ_r on L_B. This is due to the fact that Γ_r is proportional to the transmission coefficient of the individual barriers which decreases exponentially with increasing L_B. The case $L_B = 50$ Å corresponds to the microwave oscillator reported by *Sollner* et al. [7.22].

Because of dimensional confinement in the wells and because the wells are undoped, one can obtain a good estimate of the scattering time of electrons in the wells from the mobility of a two-dimensional electron gas (in the plane of the

Table 7.1. Resonance and collision widths of $Al_{0.30}Ga_{0.70}As$/GaAs RT diode (at zero bias) for different barrier thicknesses

L_W [Å]	L_B [Å]	Γ_r [meV]	Γ_r/Γ_C (= Resonance width/collision broadening)		
			300 K	200 K	70 K
50	70	1.28×10^{-2}	6×10^{-3}	1.93×10^{-2}	2.6×10^{-1}
50	50	1.5×10^{-1}	7.5×10^{-2}	2.26×10^{-1}	3.08
50	30	1.76	8.8×10^{-1}	1.32	3.62
20	50	6.03	3.02	4.56	124.02

layers), measured in selectively doped AlGaAs/GaAs heterojunctions [7.50]. For state-of-the-art selectively doped AlGaAs/GaAs heterojunctions, the electron mobility at 300 K is $\sim 7000 \ \mathrm{cm^2/sV}$. From this value, we can infer an average scattering time $\cong 3 \times 10^{-3}$ s which corresponds to a broadening of $\cong 2$ meV. In Table 7.1, the ratios of the resonance width Γ_r to the collision broadening Γ_c are also shown. For the 50 and 70 Å barrier case, the resonance width is much smaller than the collision broadening so that, by the previously discussed criterion, there is very little resonant enhancement of the transmission via the Fabry–Pérot mechanism at 300 K. However, the latter effect should become visible in structures with thinner barriers (< 30 Å), as seen from Table 7.1. Consider now a temperature of 200 K; from the value of the mobility ($\approx 2 \times 10^4 \ \mathrm{cm^2/sV}$) [7.50], one deduces $\tau \simeq 1$ ps, which corresponds to a broadening of $\simeq 0.67$ meV. This value is comparable to the resonance width for a barrier width of 50 Å. This implies that in *Sollner*'s microwave oscillators [7.22] (which operated at 200 K), coherent RT effects were probably present. This is definitely not the case for the mixing and detection experiments performed up to terahertz frequencies [7.21] in RTDB structures with $L_W = L_B = 50$ Å, $x = 0.25 - 0.30$ at a temperature of 25 K. In this case, the well was intentionally doped to $\simeq 10^{17}/\mathrm{cm^3}$ which would correspond to a mobility of $\simeq 3000 \ \mathrm{cm^2/Vs}$ which gives a collision broadening of 4 meV, significantly larger than the resonant width. Thus, in this case, electrons are tunnelling incoherently (i.e., sequentially) through the DB's.

Finally, we have estimated Γ_r/Γ_c for a temperature of 77 K. State-of-the-art mobilities in selectively doped interfaces exceed $10^5 \ \mathrm{cm^2/Vs}$ so that scattering times are typically longer than 1 ps and the broadenings are less than 0.5 meV. Thus coherent RT will significantly contribute to the current for barrier widths $\lesssim 70$ Å and dominate for $L_B \lesssim 30$ Å. The values of Γ_r/Γ_c at 70 K in Table 7.1 were obtained using a mobility of $3 \times 10^5 \ \mathrm{cm^2/Vs}$ [7.50].

The situation appears to be different in the case of an AlAs/GaAs DB with a well width of 50 Å. The confining barriers in this cases are much higher (≈ 1.00 eV) [7.2], and for barrier thicknesses in the 30–70 Å range, the resonance widths are $\lesssim 10^{-2}$ meV. Thus coherent RT is negligible at room temperature, but is expected to become dominant at 70 K for $L_B \lesssim 70$ Å in high-quality DB's.

Capasso et al. [7.51] have demonstrated sequential RT through a superlattice under strong electric fields. In a strong electric field, the miniband picture in a superlattice breaks down when the potential drop across the superlattice period exceeds the miniband width. When this condition is satisfied the quantum states become localized in the individual wells. In this limit an enhanced electron current will flow at well-defined values of the external field, when the ground state in the nth well is degenerate with one of the excited states in the $(n + 1)$th well, as illustrated in Fig. 7.5a. Under such conditions, the current is due to electron tunnelling between the adjacent wells with a subsequent de-excitation in the $(n + 1)$th well, by emission of phonons. In other words, electron propagation through the entire superlattice involves sequential RT.

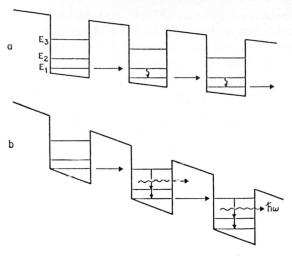

Fig. 7.5. (a) Band diagram of sequential resonant tunnelling. **(b)** Band diagram of new far infrared laser using sequential resonant tunnelling

Experimental difficulties in studying this phenomenon are usually associated with the nonuniformity of the electric field across the superlattice and the instabilities generated by negative differential conductivity. To ensure a strictly controlled and spatially uniform electric field, *Capasso* et al. [7.51] placed the superlattice in the n^- ($\lesssim 10^{14}$ cm^{-3}) region of a reverse-bias $p^+ - n^- - n^+$ junction. This structure allowed for the first time observation of sequential RT. Two NDR peaks observed in the photocurrent characteristics (Fig. 7.6) correspond to the resonances shown schematically in Fig. 7.5. For the sequential RT regime, there is the possibility of a laser action at the intersubband transition frequency – an effect not yet observed experimentally in a superlattice (Fig. 7.5b).

Capasso et al. [7.52] also reported the observation of new extremely large photocurrent amplification phenomenon at very low voltage in a superlattice of $Al_{0.48}In_{0.52}As/Ga_{0.47}In_{0.53}As$ in the quantum coupling regime (35 Å wells, 35 Å

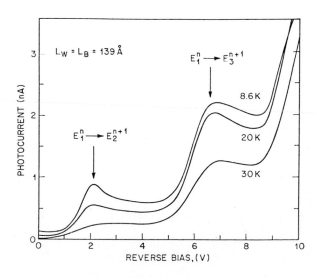

Fig. 7.6. Photocurrent-voltage characteristic at $\lambda = 0.6328$ μm (pure electron injection) for a superlattice of $Al_{48}In_{52}As/Ga_{47}In_{53}As$ with 138 Å thick wells and barriers and 35 periods. The arrows indicate that the peaks correspond to resonant tunnelling between the ground state of the nth well and the first two excited states of the $(n + 1)$th well

barriers). Room-temperature responsivities at $\lambda = 1.3\ \mu m$ are typically 2×10^3 and 300 A/W, at 0.3 V and 0.08 V bias, respectively, while the highest measured value is 4×10^3 A/W, corresponding to a current gain of 2×10^4. This effect, which represents a new quantum-type photoconductivity, is caused by the extremely large difference in the tunnelling rates of electrons and heavy holes through the superlattice layers (*effective mass filtering*; [7.52]). When thickness and compositional fluctuations cause fluctuations in the subband energies of the order of or greater than the miniband width ΔE, miniband conduction cannot be sustained and hence conduction will proceed by phonon-assisted tunnelling between adjacent wells (hopping conduction). Since electrons have a much smaller mass than heavy holes, their tunnelling rate between adjacent wells is much larger (*effective mass filtering*). Photogenerated holes therefore remain relatively localized in the wells (their hopping probability is negligible), while electrons propagate through the superlattice. This effective mass filtering effect produces a photocurrent gain, given by the ratio of the lifetime to the electron transit time. The gain strongly decreases with increasing $Al_{0.48}In_{0.52}As$ barrier layer thickness and becomes unity when this exceeds 100 Å. This confirms effective mass filtering as the origin of the large gain, since, as the barriers are made thicker, electrons also eventually tend to become localized, thus decreasing the tunnelling probability and increasing the recombination rate. The temperature dependence of the responsivity conclusively confirmed hopping conduction.

For superlattices made of the same two materials with wider electron minibands (achieved by using thinner barriers), the electron transport is by miniband conduction, while holes are still localized (Fig. 7.7). Such superlattice effective mass filters will have a much greater gain-bandwidth product than the one described above due to the much shorter electron transit time.

7.1.4 $Ga_{0.47}In_{0.53}As/Al_{0.48}In_{0.52}As$ Resonant Tunnelling Diodes

Many efforts have been directed towards achieving better performance, such as room temperature operation and improved peak-to-valley ratio. So far, RT structures composed of the GaAs/AlGaAs material system have received major

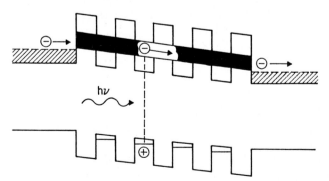

Fig. 7.7. Band diagram showing effective mass filtering effect in the case of miniband conduction of electrons

attention. The highest peak-to-valley current ratio at room temperature obtained so far in this material system is 3.9:1 [7.11]. Recently, *Muto* et al. have reported a systematic study of $Ga_{0.47}In_{0.53}As/Al_{0.48}In_{0.52}As$ RT diodes at low temperature (77 K) [7.9]. The same material system has been used by *Yokoyama* et al. in their resonant tunnelling hot electron transistor (RHET) [7.53] to obtain improved performance at 77 K. *Sen* et al. have presented data on the room temperature operation [7.12] of a $Ga_{0.47}In_{0.53}As/Al_{0.48}In_{0.52}As$ RT diode grown lattice matched to InP substrate by MBE. The current-voltage characteristics of these diodes exhibit peak-to-valley ratios of 4:1 at room temperature and 15:1 at 80 K. The larger peak-to-valley ratio with respect to AlGaAs/GaAs RT diodes is due to the lower electron effective mass in the barriers ($0.075\,m_0$ for $Al_xIn_{1-x}As$ at $x = 0.48$ compared to $0.092\,m_0$ for $Al_xGa_{1-x}As$ at $x = 0.3$) resulting in higher tunnelling current density and to the larger conduction band discontinuity which strongly reduces the thermionic emission current across the barrier.

The structure in [7.12] consisted of 1 μm thick n^+-$Ga_{0.47}In_{0.53}As$ ($n \sim 3 \times 10^{17}$ cm^{-3}) buffer layer grown on an n^+ InP substrate. On top of the buffer layer is grown the RTDB consisting of an undoped 50 Å wide $Ga_{0.47}In_{0.53}As$ quantum well sandwiched between two 50 Å wide undoped $Al_{0.48}In_{0.52}As$ barriers. The growth ends with a 1 μm thick $Ga_{0.47}In_{0.53}As$ cap layer doped to $n^+ \sim 3 \times 10^{17}$ cm^{-3}.

The structures were etched into 50 μm diameter mesas using 1 H_2O_2 + 3 H_3PO_4 + 50 H_2O etchant at room temperature. Ge(60 Å)/Au (135 Å)/ Ag (500 Å)/Au (750 Å) deposited in sequence and alloyed at 420 °C for 30 s were used for 30 μm diameter ohmic contacts. For the bottom contact, Ni (50 Å)/Au (385 Å)/Ge (215 Å)/Au (750 Å) were deposited on the etched surface of the buffer layer and alloyed at 420°C for 30 s.

The samples were tested at different temperatures in a Helitran dewar equipped with microprobes. Figure 7.8 shows the current voltage (I–V) characteristics of the diodes in both polarities measured at room temperature (top) and at 80 K (bottom). Positive polarity refers to the top contact being positively biased with respect to the bottom. The room temperature characteristics indicate a peak-to-valley ratio of 4:1 in one polarity and 3.5:1 in the other. Figure 7.9 shows the room temperature I–V in one polarity on an expanded scale. At low temperature (80 K) the peak-to-valley ratio increases to 15:1. It should be noted that though the peak-to-valley ratio increases dramatically on cooling down, the peak current remains the same. The peak in the I–V occurs at $\sim$ 600 mV and does not shift with temperature. An electron tunnelling transmission calculation shows that the first resonance is at $E_1 = 126$ meV from the bottom of the quantum well. Note that the peak in the I–V appears at a voltage greater than $2\,E_1/e = 252$ mV. This can be explained by considering the voltage drop in the depletion and accumulation regions in the collector and emitter layers adjacent to the DB. Thus, a larger voltage must be applied across the entire structure to line up the first sub-band in the well with the bottom of the conduction band in the emitter, to quench RT. A simple

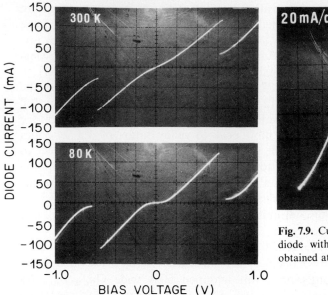

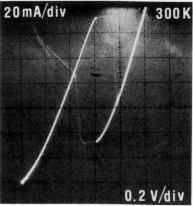

Fig. 7.9. Current-voltage characteristics of diode with highest peak-to-valley ratio obtained at room temperature

Fig. 7.8. Typical current-voltage characteristics of the $Al_{0.48}In_{0.52}As/Ga_{0.47}In_{0.53}As$ resonant tunnelling diode at 300 K (*top*) and 80 K (*bottom*). Positive polarity refer to the top contact being positively biased with respect to the bottom

calculation, taking the above effects into account, indicates that the peak should occur at $\simeq 580$ mV applied bias, which is in reasonable agreement with the measured value.

The large peak-to-valley ratio observed at room temperature makes this device suitable for many circuit applications. A circuit with a 30 Ω load resistance in series with the device and a 3.0 volt supply has two stable operating points which are measured to be 0.47 V and 0.85 V respectively at room temperature. The corresponding load line drawn on the room temperature $I-V$ characteristics indicates the stable operating points at 0.46 V and 0.84 V respectively, in close agreement with the measured values. The circuit can thus be used as a static RAM cell involving only one device. Such a RAM cell is also suitable for integration in a large memory array, as discussed in Sect. 7.2.1, in connection with multi-state memory.

7.1.5 Resonant Tunnelling Through Parabolic Quantum Wells

Parabolic QW have interesting possibilities for device applications [7.25], because the levels in such a well are equally spaced unlike rectangular wells. The $I-V$ characteristics of RT structures with parabolic wells therefore are expected to produce equally spaced peaks in voltage. The first experimental observation of such resonances was reported by *Sen* et al. [7.20].

The samples in [7.20] were grown by MBE on silicon-doped (100) GaAs substrates at a substrate temperature of 680°C. The growth was computer controlled and calibrated by ion-gauge flux measurement at the position of the substrate. Parabolically graded well compositions were produced by growth of short-period ($\sim$ 15 Å), variable duty cycle, GaAs/Al$_x$Ga$_{1-x}$As superlattices in which the Al content within each period of all superlattice corresponded to the Al content at the same point in a smooth parabolic well [7.54]. A cross-sectional transmission electron micrograph (TEM) of one such structure is shown in Fig. 7.10. The structure consists of a 439 Å parabolic QW of Al$_x$Ga$_{1-x}$As, with x varying from 0.3 at the edges to 0 at the center, sandwiched between two 35 Å AlAs barriers. The parabolic part of the structure is composed of variable gap superlattice with a period of nearly 10 Å as discussed above. The brighter lines in the well part of the TEM picture represent Al$_{0.3}$Ga$_{0.7}$As layers while the darker lines represent GaAs layers. Notice how the relative widths of the bright and the dark lines change from the edges of the well to its center. The electrons of course "sense" the local average composition since their de Broglie wavelength is much greater than the superlattice period.

Two types of structures were grown. In one, sample A, the 300 Å undoped well is sandwiched between two 20 Å AlAs undoped barriers. The parabolic well composition is effectively graded from $x = 1$ at the edges to $x = 0$ at the center.

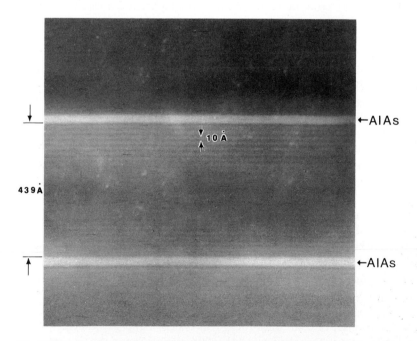

Fig. 7.10. A cross-sectional transmission electron micrograph (TEM) of a 439 Å wide parabolic quantum well composed of Al$_x$Ga$_{1-x}$As, with x varying from 0.3 at the edges to 0 at the center, sandwiched between two 35 Å AlAs barriers

The portion of the well from $x = 0.49$ to $x = 0$ is achieved by means of an $Al_{0.50}Ga_{0.50}As/GaAs$ superlattice, while the rest (from $x = 0.49$ to $x = 1$) using an $AlAs/GaAs$ superlattice. Undoped 20 Å thick GaAs spacer layers were used between the barriers and the Si-doped ($n = 10^{18}$ cm^{-3}) 5000 Å thick GaAs contact layers. Systematic studies have shown that offsetting the doping in the regions adjacent to the barriers improves significantly the I–V of RT diodes [7.5]. In the other, sample B, the 439 Å undoped well is bound by 35 Å AlAs undoped barriers and the composition of the well is graded from $x = 0.30$ at the edges to $x = 0$ at the center using an $Al_{0.325}Ga_{0.675}As/GaAs$ superlattice. $Al_{0.02}Ga_{0.98}As$ 1000 Å thick layers Si-doped to 5×10^{17} cm^{-3} (with a doping offset of 50 Å from the barriers) were used as contact regions to the RTDB. The composition of these layers was chosen in such a way that the bottom of the conduction band in the emitter is nearly lined up with (but always below) the first energy level of the well, a technique successfully used in improving the peak-to-valley ratio of RT transistors and diodes [7.6, 8, 32]. These layers are followed by 1000 Å regions compositionally graded from $x = 0.02$ to $x = 0$ Si-doped to $n = 5 \times 10^{17}$ cm^3 and by 4000 Å thick Si-doped ($n = 1 \times 10^{18}$ cm^{-3}) GaAs. The thicknesses of the layers were verified by cross-sectional TEM.

The energy band diagrams at the Γ point [7.55] for samples A and B are shown in Fig. 7.11.

The structures were processed into 50 μm diameter mesa diodes as described in Sect. 7.1.4. The diodes were tested at temperatures in the range from 7 to 300 K. The I–V and the differential conductance were measured with an HP4145 parameter analyzer.

Figure 7.12 shows the I–V and the corresponding differential conductance dI/dV for a representative diode from sample A measured at 7.5 K. Positive and negative polarity refer to the top contact being positively and negatively biased with respect to the bottom contact.

Consider first the positive polarity data. These display five equally spaced inflections in I–V and five corresponding minima in the conductance. For negative polarity four of the conductance minima occur at practically identical voltages as the corresponding minima for positive polarity with the exception of the resonance at $+0.3$ V, which is not observed experimentally for negative polarity. The resonances for negative polarity are more pronounced and the one at $\simeq 0.72$ V actually exhibits negative differential resistance.

Energy levels in the wells under bias were determined by electron tunnelling transmission calculations for the grown layer sequence; thus the effect of the superlattice grading was directly included. The effects of depletion and accumulation in the emitter and collector layers together with the electron effective mass dispersion with Al content were also taken into account. A conduction band offset of 0.60 times the direct energy band gap difference was assumed [7.54]. From these calculations the voltage position of the transmission peaks was directly obtained. These voltages are indicated by the vertical segments at the bottom of Fig. 7.12 and correspond, respectively, to the first six

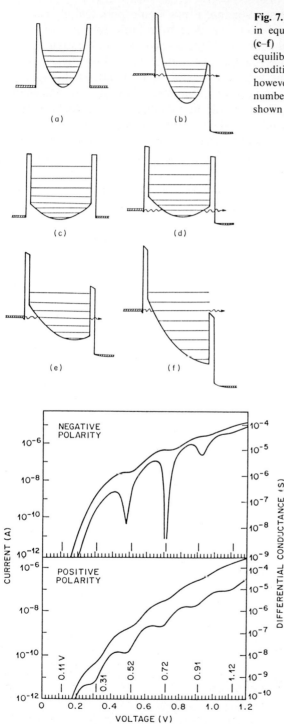

Fig. 7.11. (a–b) Band diagram of sample *A* in equilibrium and under RT conditions. **(c–f)** Band diagram of sample *B* in equilibrium and under different bias conditions. The wells are drawn to scale; however, for sake of clarity only half the number of levels in an energy interval are shown

Fig. 7.12. Current-voltage characteristic at 7.4 K and corresponding conductance for a representative diode of sample *A* under opposite bias polarity conditions. The vertical segments near the horizontal axis indicate the calculated positions of the resonances

energy levels of the well. The first resonance is not seen experimentally because the corresponding current is below the detection limit of the apparatus (~ 1 pA). The other calculated positions of the resonances (E_2 through E_6) are in good agreement with the observed ones. The calculations show that not only the energy levels, for a given bias, are nearly equally spaced, but also the spacing ΔE between the quasi-bound states is little dependent on the electric field as the voltage is varied from 0 to 1 V. For example, at zero bias $\Delta E \simeq 90$ meV while at 1 V, $\Delta E \simeq 80$ meV. The latter effect is easily understood if one considers that the application of a uniform electric field to a parabolic well (Fig. 7.11a) preserves the curvature of the parabola and therefore the spacing ΔE, while shifting its origin to the right (Fig. 7.11b).

Figure 7.13 shows the I–V and corresponding conductance for sample B for opposite bias polarities. The band diagrams at different voltages are shown in Fig. 7.11c–f.

It is interesting to note that the group of resonances from the 5th to the 11th are the most pronounced ones and actually display negative differential resistance. A total of fourteen resonances is observed in the sample of Fig. 7.13, for positive polarity. In a few diodes two additional resonances were also

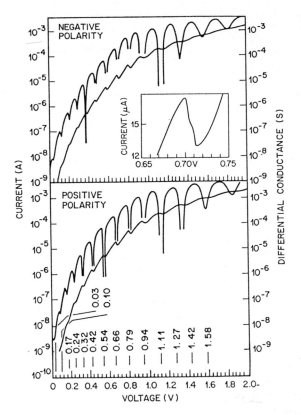

Fig. 7.13. Current-voltage characteristic at 7.1 K and conductance for a representative diode of sample B under opposite bias polarity conditions. The inset shows the eighth resonance on a linear scale. The vertical segments near the horizontal axis indicate the calculated positions of the resonances

observed. The resonances were observed up to temperatures $\simeq 100$ K, but were considerably less pronounced. The vertical segments near the horizontal axis indicate the calculated positions of the transmission peaks. Overall good agreement with the observed minima in the conductance is found.

The overall features of the $I-V$ can be interpreted physically by means of the band diagrams of Fig. 7.11c–f and of the calculations described above. At zero bias the first six energy levels of the well are confined by a parabolic well 225 meV deep, corresponding to the grading from $x = 0$ to $x = 0.30$ and their spacing is $\simeq 35$ meV. When the bias is increased from 0 to 0.3 V the first four energy levels probed by RT (Fig. 7.11d) remain confined by the parabolic portions of the well and their spacing is practically independent of bias, for reasons identical to those discussed in the context of sample Λ. This gives rise to the calculated and observed equal spacing of the first four resonances in the $I-V$ characteristic (Fig. 7.13). Consider now the higher energy levels confined by the rectangular part of the well (> 230 meV) at zero bias. When the voltage is raised above 0.3 V these levels become increasingly confined on the emitter side by the parabolic portion of the well and on the collector side by a rectangular barrier, thus becoming progressively more separated, although retaining the nearly equal spacing (Fig. 7.11e). This leads to the observed gradual increase in the voltage separation of the resonances as the bias is increased from 0.3 to 1.0 V. Above 1 V the electrons injected from the emitter probe the virtual levels in the quasi continuum above the collector barrier (Fig. 7.11f). These resonances result from electron interference effects [7.56] associated with multiple quantum mechanical reflections at the well-barrier interface for energies above the barrier height. It should be noted that these reflections give rise to the existence of 2-D quasi-eigenstates in the well region. The observed NDR is due to the four resonances observed above 1 V and must be clearly distinguished from the ones occurring at lower voltages which are due to RT through the DB.

A simple physical explanation of why the resonances above the fourth (5th to 12th) are the most pronounced ones leading to negative differential resistance, can be easily given in terms of the calculated voltage dependence of the transmission. Up to 0.3 V, tunnelling out of the well (Fig. 7.11d) occurs through the thick parabolic part of the collector barrier and the resulting widths of the transmission resonances are very small (< 1 μeV). As the bias is increased above 0.3 V not only is the barrier height further reduced but now electrons tunnel out of the well through the thin (20 Å) rectangular part of the barriers. This greatly enhances the barrier transmission and the resonance widths (Fig. 7.11c). This behavior is clearly observed in the calculation of the total transmission versus bias. For example the calculated energy width of the level corresponding to the 10th resonance (0.9 V) is 1 meV, which is not negligible compared to the width of the incident energy distribution in the emitter. As the bias voltage is further increased, the competing effect of the decrease of the peak-to-valley ratio becomes dominant, as shown by the calculations. This explains why the highest resonances (above 1 V) become less pronounced.

7.1.6 Resonant Tunnelling Electron Spectroscopy

In this section we discuss an interesting application of RT through DB's. A RTDB can be used to analyze the energy distribution of hot electrons [7.57–59]. Compared to conventional hot electron spectroscopy, this resonant tunnelling spectroscopy technique has the advantage of not requiring derivative methods [7.60, 61].

Figure 7.14a illustrates the energy band diagram of the structure used for resonant tunnelling electron spectroscopy. It consists of a reverse biased p-i-n heterojunction and can be used to investigate hot minority carrier transport. Low intensity incident light is strongly absorbed in the wide-gap p^+ layer. Photo-generated minority carrier electrons diffuse to an adjacent low-gap layer. Upon entering this region, electrons are ballistically accelerated by the abrupt potential step and gain a kinetic energy $\cong \Delta E_c$ and a forward momentum $p_\perp \simeq \sqrt{2m_e^* \Delta E_c}$. Collisions in the low gap layer tend to randomize the injected, nearly mono-energetic distribution. Hot electrons subsequently impinge on the DB in the collector. From simple considerations of energy and lateral momentum $p_\parallel$ conservation in the tunnelling process it can be shown that only those electrons with a perpendicular energy $E_\perp$ ($p_\perp^2/2m_e^*$ for a parabolic band) equal (within the resonance width) to the energy of the bottom of one of the subbands of the quantum well resonantly tunnel through the quantum well and give rise to a current [7.43]. Thus by varying the applied bias (i.e., changing the energy difference between the resonance of the quantum well and the bottom of the conduction band in the low gap p^+ layer) and measuring the current, one directly probes the electron energy distribution $n(E_\perp)$ or equivalently, the

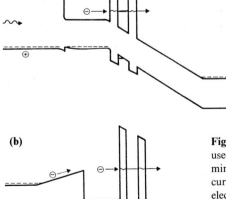

(a)

(b)

E   B   C

Fig. 7.14. (a) Band diagram of heterojunction diode used for resonant tunnelling spectroscopy of hot minority-carrier electrons. By measuring the photo-current as a function of the reverse bias the hot electron energy distribution $n(E_\perp)$ can be directly probled. (b) Unipolar transistor structure for resonant tunnelling spectroscopy of hot majority-carrier electrons in the n^+ base layer

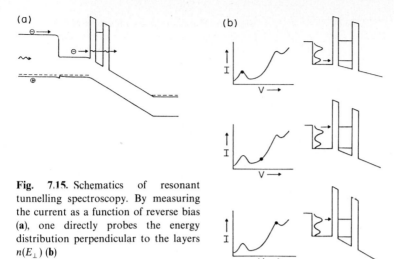

Fig. 7.15. Schematics of resonant tunnelling spectroscopy. By measuring the current as a function of reverse bias (**a**), one directly probes the energy distribution perpendicular to the layers $n(E_\perp)$ (**b**)

momentum distribution $n(p_\perp)$ (Fig. 7.15). One has therefore

$$E_\perp = E_n = \frac{e(V + V_{bi})(L_B + L_W/2 + L_{sp})}{L_C} \qquad (7.4)$$

where V is the reverse bias voltage, V_{bi} the built-in potential of the p-i-n diode, L_C the total collector layer thickness, L_B and L_W the barrier and well layer thickness respectively, and L_{sp} the thickness of the undoped spacer layer (20 Å) between the p-type region and the DB (see later in text). E_n is the energy of the bottom of the nth subband measured with respect to the bottom of the center of the well. (Note that E_n is assumed to be independent of the electric field F, which is a good approximation as long as E_n is significantly greater than eFL_W.) Identical arguments apply to the case of the unipolar transistor structure of Fig. 7.14b which can be used to analyze the electron distribution in the base layer by measuring the collector current as a function of the collector-base voltage. In the above arguments we have assumed that thermionic currents over the DB can be minimized. This can be done by operating the structure at sufficiently low temperature and by suitably designing the DB [7.2]. To obtain the actual energy distribution $n(E_\perp)$ from the current, the latter must be properly normalized by taking into account the field dependence of the resonant tunnelling probability (integrated over the resonance width). This procedure does not alter, of course, the position of the peaks in the current voltage characteristic (see Fig. 7.16) since the above probability varies monotonically with the electric field, irrespective of whether electrons resonantly tunnel sequentially or coherently through the DB [7.43]. Thus the main features of the electronic transport can still be obtained directly from the current, without normalization.

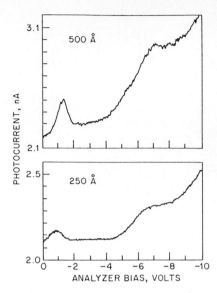

Fig. 7.16. Photocurrent as a function of reverse bias for the structure of Fig. 7.14a, with GaAs p^+ layer thickness of, 500 Å (*top*) and 250 Å (*bottom*)

The structures were grown by molecular beam epitaxy on a $\langle 100 \rangle$ p^+ GaAs substrate and consist of pin heterojunction diodes. Their band diagram is shown in Fig. 7.14a at a given reverse bias. The growth starts with a 2000 Å thick $n^+ = 2 \times 10^{17}$ cm^{-3} buffer layer followed by an undoped ($|N_D - N_A| \simeq 10^{14}$ cm^{-3}) 5000 Å GaAs layer and an AlAs/GaAs/AlAs DB, with barrier and well thicknesses of 20 Å and 80 Å respectively. A 20 Å undoped GaAs spacer layer separates the DB from the p^+ ($= 3 \times 10^{18}$ cm^{-3}) GaAs layer, in which electrons are launched. Different thicknesses were used for this region (250 Å, 500 Å, 1800 Å) while keeping everything else the same. The last layer consists of 2 µm thick Al$_{0.3}$Ga$_{0.7}$As doped to $p = 3 \times 10^{18}$ cm^{-3}. This provides a launching energy $\simeq 225$ meV, i.e., the conduction band discontinuity between GaAs and Al$_{0.3}$Ga$_{0.70}$As (obtained from $\Delta E_c = 0.6 \Delta E_g$). The depletion width on the p^+ side of the junction, is negligible with respect to the p^+ GaAs well thickness, up to the highest applied bias (10 V), due to the high doping. The parameters of the DB were chosen in such a way that over the applied voltage range (0–10 V) the electron energy distribution is probed essentially by one resonance at a time. For this DB the first resonance is at $E_1 = 60$ meV from the well bottom and the second at $E_2 = 260$ meV with full widths at half maximum of ≈ 0.1 meV and ≈ 1 meV respectively [7.2]. It is easily shown from (7.4) that over the range of applied bias (Fig. 7.16) the first resonance samples the $E_\perp$ energy range from 37 meV to 0 meV, while the second resonance samples the energy range from 225 meV to 80 meV. The thickness of the collector layer L_c was made much greater than that of the DB to enhance the energy resolution of the spectrometer.

The samples were processed into mesa devices, using standard photo-lithographic, wet etching and metallization techniques. The photosensitive area of these detectors is 10^{-4} cm^2. Light from a He-Ne laser ($\lambda = 6328$ Å) heavily absorbed in the Al$_{0.3}$Ga$_{0.7}$As region (absorption length $\simeq 5000$ Å) was used to achieve pure electron (minority carrier) injection and the dc photocurrent was measured as a function of reverse bias at low temperature. Figure 7.16 illustrates the measured photocurrent at 9.2 K for the structure with a 500 Å thick GaAs p^+ layer. At these current levels and higher (up to 10 μA) space charge effects are negligible, as shown by varying the light intensity and monitoring the photocurrent-voltage characteristic. The dark current was completely negligible ($\leq 10^{-12}$ A) in the same voltage range. Two distinct features are present at 1.3 V and 7 V respectively. Using (7.4) one can easily see that the first peak corresponds to electrons with perpendicular energy of a few tens of meV ($\simeq 17$ meV) that have resonantly tunnelled through the first resonance of the quantum well. The second peak is much broader and corresponds to incident electrons with energy $E_\perp \simeq 130$ meV which have resonantly tunnelled through the second resonance of the well. It is therefore clear that the energy distribution of the electrons in the p^+ GaAs layer, following high energy injection, consists of two parts. One has relaxed close to bottom of the conduction band, while the other has considerably higher perpendicular kinetic energy $E_\perp$. Thus the distribution is strongly non-Maxwellian similar to what has been found in the case of majority carrier electrons in the base of hot electron planar-doped barrier transistors [7.62]. Note that the peaks in the photocurrent were observed at temperatures as high as 70 K and did not appreciably shift with temperature.

Similar results are found by decreasing the GaAs p^+ layer thickness from 500 Å to 250 Å (Fig. 7.16) The peaks are located at somewhat lower voltages (corresponding to 10%–20% higher energies) implying that the relaxation of carriers is somewhat less, due to the thinner layer, as expected. Overall, however, the shape of the energy distribution has not changed significantly, which implies that already over a length of a few hundred Å the near ballistic injected distribution has strongly relaxed. Recent electron spectroscopy measurements in heterojunction bipolar transistors with base thicknesses as short as 400 Å have also demonstrated that electrons undergo strong relaxation in the p^+ ($= 2 \times 10^{18}$ cm^{-3}) base [7.63].

On the other hand, it is worth noting that *Berthold* et al. [7.64] have recently demonstrated the existance of quasi-ballistic electron transport in the base of a heterojunction bipolar transistor having a thickness of 260 Å and doping $p = 3 \times 10^{18}$ cm^{-3}. They also showed that one must minimize quantum reflections from the analyzer barrier by optimizing the design of the latter in the order to maximize the number of electrons in the high energy peak of the distribution. Thus we tentatively ascribe the lack of minority ballistic electrons observed in [7.62, 63] to quantum reflection from the spectrometer barrier.

7.2 Application of Resonant Tunnelling: Transistors and Circuits

In this section we discuss the various interesting applications of RT through DB's. These include RT transistors and circuits utilizing RT devices.

A variety of RT transistors, based on different operating principles, have been proposed and demonstrated [7.25–40]. It has been shown that RTDB's can be easily incorporated in bipolar, field-effect and hot electron transistors. In addition, novel structures where transistor action is based on the gating of the QW subbands have been demonstrated [7.40]. In all of these transistors, the purpose of the RTDB is to control the collector or drain current via modulation of the base or gate terminal. Thus peaks are obtained in the direct and transfer characteristics. It is this feature that is very useful for the implementation of many circuits with reduced complexity. These include exclusive OR's, parity checkers, analog-to-digital converters, frequency multipliers and multiple valued logic. Some of these circuits are discussed in the following section.

7.2.1 Integration of Resonant Tunnelling Diodes and Their Circuit Applications

A variety of potential applications can be realized with devices exhibiting multiple peaks in the $I–V$. These include ultrahigh-speed analog-to-digital converters, parity bit generators and multiple valued logic [7.24, 25]. RT devices offer interesting possibilities towards realizing this characteristic. One way of obtaining multiple peaks in the $I–V$ of course is by using the multiple resonances of a quantum well. This approach however, suffers from the difficulty that the peaks corresponding to the excited states in general carry significantly higher current than that associated with the ground state for a variety of structural and material reasons. On the other hand the above mentioned circuit applications require nearly equal peak currents. A novel approach for obtaining multiple peaks in the $I–V$ of RT devices is the integration of a number of RT diodes. In this method, a single resonance of the quantum well is used to generate the multiple peaks. Hence, they occur at almost the same current level and exhibit similar peak to valley ratios. There are two possible methods of integrating RT diodes to achieve this characteristic. One is to horizontally integrate them so that the diodes come in parallel in the equivalent circuit [7.42, 65] and the other is to vertically integrate them in a series combination [7.66–68].

a) Horizontal Integration of RT Diodes

The device structure, grown on a $\langle 100 \rangle$ n^+ Si-doped GaAs substrate is shown in Fig. 7.17a. An undoped GaAs layer 2500 Å thick is grown on a 1 μm thick $n^+ = 5 \times 10^{17}/cm^3$ GaAs buffer layer and is followed by the RTDB. The latter consists of a 70 Å GaAs quantum well sandwiched between two 20 Å AlAs barriers. A modulation doped $Al_{0.35}Ga_{0.65}As/GaAs$ heterojunction is then grown on top of the DB; the 200 Å thick GaAs is undoped, while the 480 Å thick $Al_{0.35}Ga_{0.65}As$ layer is doped with Si to $2 \times 10^{18}/cm^3$ except for an 80 Å spacer region adjacent to the GaAs channel. The channel contains a high density $\simeq 10^{18}/cm^3$ high mobility electron gas, spatially separated from the parent donors in the AlGaAs layer. As a result, the AlGaAs layer is completely

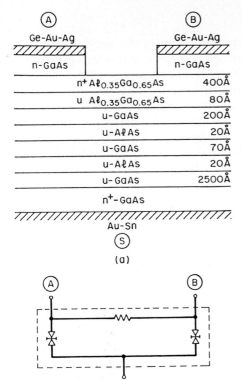

Fig. 7.17. (a) Schematics of the integrated RT diode structure. (b) Equivalent circuit: Two RT diodes in parallel connected by the resistance R of the 200 A GaAs channel between A and B. The resistance of the $Al_{0.35}Ga_{0.65}As$ layer between A and B is much higher than R due to carrier depletion by electron transfer into the GaAs channel. The choice of the circuit symbol for the RT diode (two back-to-back tunnel diodes) is motivated by the symmetry of the current voltage characteristic of the RT diode

depleted. The growth ends with an n^+ GaAs 1400 Å contact layer doped to $n \simeq 2 \times 10^{17}/cm^3$.

The prototype device fabricated has two rectangular (240 μm × 80 μm) contact pads separated by a distance of 6.5 μm along the long side, defined by evaporating in succession Ge (120 Å), Au (270 Å), Ag (1000 Å), Au (1500 Å) and using lift-off techniques. The metallizations were then alloyed at 380°C for 10 s and used as a mask for wet chemical etching. A selective stop etch (H_2O_2 and NH_4OH, pH = 7.2) was used to reveal the $Al_{0.35}Ga_{0.65}As$ barrier. Note that the thickness of the cap layer and the composition of the two top contacts and the alloying temperature and time were the same used for the fabrication of the charge injection transistor which is structurally similar to this device [7.69]. This ensures that the contacts to the electron gas in the GaAs layer beneath the AlGaAs barrier do not penetrate through the RTDB.

This is thus an integration of two RT diodes in parallel (Fig. 7.17b) that exhibits two peaks of nearly equal current at 100 K. The device has been used to demonstrate for the first time a number of practical circuits using devices with multiple peaks in the I–V. The scheme may however be extended to the integration of more than two RT diodes, as discussed in the following section.

i) Device Operation

The operation of the device can be understood from the equivalent circuit shown in Fig. 7.17b. The resistance shown in Fig. 7.17b is that of the GaAs 200 Å channel connecting the two diodes and its measured value is $\approx 12\,\Omega$. In the two diode case discussed in this section, this resistance is not essential for the operation of the device. But the scheme can be obviously extended to more than two RT diodes; in the latter case the resistance of the channel linking the devices provides the useful function of a monolithically integrated voltage divider. For proper biasing of this voltage divider, the structure should be suitably designed so that the current in the divider network is sufficiently large compared to that through the RT diodes.

The use of the modulation doped heterojunction allows the formation of a low resistance ohmic contact to the RT diodes, while keeping the dopants away from the DB. In addition, the AlGaAs passivates the GaAs channel between the two metallizations.

The substrate current (i.e., the one through terminal S) is measured as a function of positive bias applied between terminals S and A (which is grounded) for different values of the potential difference V_{BA} applied between B and A. The substrate current consists primarily of the sum of the two RT currents flowing through the two RT diodes. For zero potential difference V_{BA}, the structure behaves like a conventional RT diode and the I–V displays one peak (Fig. 7.18a and b). The negative conductance region is of course due to the quenching of RT through the two DB's under terminals A and B respectively. When terminal B is biased negatively with respect to terminal A (which is grounded) the I–V characteristic (see Fig. 7.18a) develops an additional peak at lower voltages; the position of one peak remains unchanged while that of the other moves to lower bias as the potential difference V_{BA} between B and A is made more negative. Note that by appropriate choice of the bias between B and A the two peak currents can be made nearly equal.

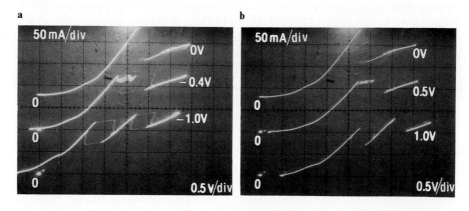

Fig. 7.18. Substrate current versus positive substrate bias at 100 K with (**a**) negative and (**b**) positive potential difference (V_{BA}) between terminals B and A as the parameter. Terminal A is grounded

This effect is explained as follows. As a result of the bias applied between A and B, the potential differences across the two DB's are different and for B negatively biased with respect to A, RT through the DB under B is obviously quenched at a lower substrate bias than in the DB under terminal A, leading to two peaks in the $I–V$.

The peak that does not shift with varying V_{BA} is of course associated with suppression of RT through diode A. Note also that, as expected, the separation between the peaks is nearly equal to the bias applied between A and B. Finally, if terminal B is positively biased with respect to A, a higher voltage is required to quench RT through the DB B, leading to a second peak which shifts to higher voltages as B_{BA} is increased (Fig. 7.18b). Similar results are obtained with negative bias applied to S.

The characteristics of Fig. 7.18 were obtained for an operating temperature of 100 K. With improved processing and material quality it should be possible to operate the device at room temperature. This has already been achieved in RT diodes and transistors.

ii) Circuit Applications

A variety of circuit applications ranging from frequency multipliers to multiple valued logic elements [7.42, 65] have been realized using this structure. Such applications for devices with multiple peaks in the $I–V$ had been predicted before [7.24, 25] but could not be implemented for the lack of a practical device exhibiting such characteristics. The circuits constructed using the new device are discussed and the experimental results are presented in this section.

Frequency Multiplier. The $I–V$ characteristic with two peaks is used to design a frequency multiplier. Its operation is understood from the diagrams of Fig. 7.21, which show the $I–V$ for a typical bias voltage V_{BA} between the terminals A and B of the device. Figure 7.19a and b show the operation with a sawtooth and a sinewave input respectively. Let us consider the operation with a sawtooth input first (Fig. 7.19a). The substrate bias V_{SS} is adjusted to select the quiescent operating point at A_2 of the $I–V$. As the sawtooth input voltage increases from A_1 to B_1, the operating point shifts from A_2 to B_2 along the $I–V$, with the substrate current I_s increasing almost linearly. The output voltage across a resistance in series with the structure is proportional to I_s and hence also increases from A_3 to B_3 linearly. As the input increases beyond B_1, the current I_s suddenly drops to the valley point B'_2 resulting in a sudden drop in the output voltage from B_3 to B'_3. Between B_3 and C_3, the output continues to rise again followed by a second drop at C_2 and rise thereafter as the input continues to rise up to D_1. At D_1, the input returns to zero to start a new cycle and the operating point also shifts back to A_2 with a drop in the output as well. Thus the frequency of the sawtooth input signal has been multiplied by a factor of 3. It should be noted here that the multiplier circuit described is independent of the input signal frequency. Conventionally, a phase-lock loop in conjunction with digital frequency divider is used to construct a frequency independent multiplier.

The operation of the circuit with a sinewave input is shown in Fig. 7.19b. The output waveform in this case can also be explained following similar arguments and is found to be rich in the fifth harmonic of the input. Figure 7.20a and b show the experimental results for a sawtooth and a sinewave input respectively, with the device biased at $V_{BA} = 1V$ and $V_{SS} = 2.3$ V. The efficiency of this device in generating the fifth harmonic is thus found to be much better than conventional devices, like a step recovery diode, used in frequency multiplier circuits. It should also be noted here that if V_{BA} is adjusted to produce a single peak in the I–V instead of two, the sawtooth will be multiplied by a factor of 2 instead of 3 and the output for sinewave will be rich in the third harmonic. Sinewave multiplication by a factor of 2 using a single peak in the I–V of a RT hot electron transistor had been demonstrated before [7.26].

Multiple Valued Logic.   The circuit shown in the inset of Fig. 7.21 can be used as a memory element in a 3-state logic system. The bias voltage V_{BA} between the terminals A and B is again adjusted to produce the I–V as in Fig. 7.21 with two

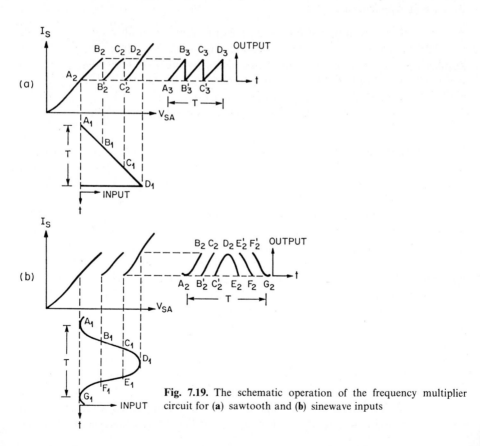

Fig. 7.19. The schematic operation of the frequency multiplier circuit for (a) sawtooth and (b) sinewave inputs

a   b

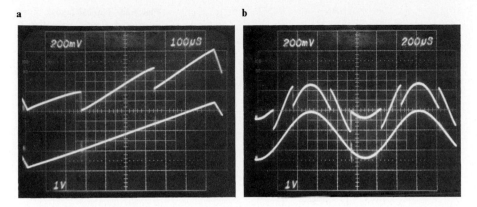

Fig. 7.20a, b. Experimental results of frequency multiplication. (**a**) Sawtooth input. (**b**) Sinewave input

nearly equal peaks at the same current level. For a suitable supply voltage V_{SS} and load resistance R_L, the load line intersects the I–V at five different points of which three (Q_1, Q_2 and Q_3) are in the positive slope parts of the curve and are hence stable operating points. The output voltage of the circuit corresponding to the three operating points Q_1, Q_2 and Q_3 are respectively V_1, V_2 and V_3 as shown in Fig. 7.21. The circuit can stay indefinitely on any one of the three points, thus retaining the last voltage information impressed on it. It can therefore be used as a memory element in a three-state logic circuit, with V_1, V_2 and V_3 being the voltages corresponding to the three logic states. This is a significant component reduction over the existing three-state logic circuits which require 4 conventional transistors and 6 resistors to construct a memory cell [7.70]. The circuit can be switched from one stable state to another by applying a short voltage pulse. In the experimental studies [7.42, 65], the

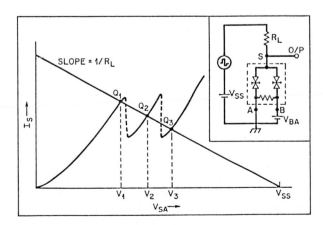

Fig. 7.21. The current-voltage characteristic and schematic of a 3-state memory cell using the integrated RT diodes. The associated load line shows three stable operating points Q_1, Q_2 and Q_3

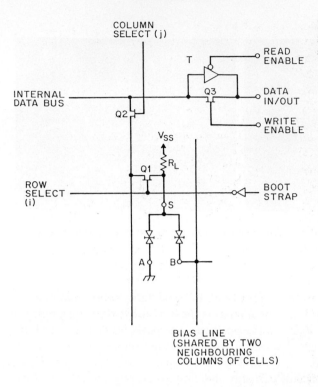

Fig. 7.22. Typical layout of an integrated circuit using the 3-state memory cells of Fig. 7.21

operating point was shifted from one state to another by momentarily changing the supply voltage V_{SS}, which has the same effect as applying a short voltage pulse. With a supply voltage $V_{SS} = 16$ V, load resistance $R_L = 215\ \Omega$ and the device biased to $V_{BA} = 0.7$ V, the three stable states were measured to be at 3.0 V, 3.6 V and 4.3 V. The corresponding load line drawn on the measured I–V characteristic of the device at $V_{BA} = 0.7$ V, intersects at 2.8 V, 3.4 V and 4.1 V respectively, which are in close agreement with the measured values of the three stable operating points.

The three-state memory cell discussed above is also suitable for integration in memory IC's with Read/Write and Decoding network laid out as shown in Fig. 7.22. The memory cells are placed in a matrix array and a particular element in the array is addressed by activating the corresponding row and column select lines. A row select connects each device in that row to the corresponding column lines. The column select finally connects the selected column to the data bus. Consider the element (i, j) of the memory matrix shown in Fig. 7.22. When the row select line is activated, it turns the driving switch $Q1$ on. It also turns on the switches for every element in the ith row. The column select logic now connects the jth column only to the data bus. The ternary identity cell [7.71] T acts as the buffer between the memory element and the external circuit for reading data. For reading data from the memory, the identity cell is activated with the Read Enable line and data from the element no. (i, j) in the matrix goes, via the data bus, to the In/Out pin of the IC. When the write enable line is activated, data from the external circuit is connected to the data bus and is subsequently forced on the $(i, j)^{th}$ element in the array and is written there.

Parity Generator. A 4-bit parity generator circuit using the new device is shown in Fig. 7.23a. The operation of the circuit can be understood from Fig. 7.23b which shows the $I–V$ of the device with the bias voltage V_{BA} properly adjusted and the resultant voltage waveforms at various points in the circuit for different input conditions. The four digital inputs are added in the inverting summing amplifier A_1 to produce five distinct voltage steps at its output corresponding to the number of digital bits being in the high state. Normally, the output of A_1 would be negative for positive input voltages. The addition of a suitable negative offset voltage V_{OFF} at the input shifts the whole waveform up, to produce the A_1 output as shown at the bottom of Fig. 7.23b. The substrate bias voltage V_{SS} is adjusted to select the operating points of the device at the five dots shown in the $I–V$ curve, corresponding respectively to the five different voltage levels at A_1 output. The substrate current of the device generates a voltage across the 7.5 Ω resistor, which is picked up by the buffer amplifier A_2.

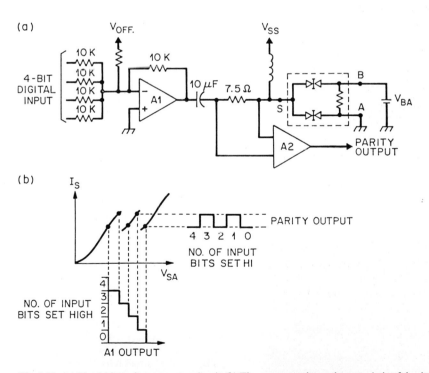

Fig. 7.23. (a) The 4-bit parity generator circuit. (b) The current-voltage characteristic of the device and the waveform at various points in the circuit for different input conditions

Note that the output is high when the number of input bits set high is odd and vice versa. The circuit can thus be used as a 4-bit parity generator. The two difference amplifiers in the circuit can be constructed using three transistors each. We thus find that there is considerable reduction in the number of components compared to a conventional circuit which needs 3 exclusive-OR gates, each requiring 8 transistors.

Typical experimental output from the circuit of Fig. 7.23a is shown in Fig. 7.24. The 4 digital inputs are driven by the outputs of a 4-bit binary counter. The top trace of Fig. 7.24 shows the output of amplifier A_1 and the bottom trace, that of A_2. Considering the dotted line as the reference level of a logic circuit, we find that the output is high for the second and the fourth voltage levels of A_1, while it is low at the first, third and the fifth levels. It should be noted however, that there are considerable decoding spikes in the output, whenever the operating point of the device is shifted across a negative resistance region. This is believed to be due to the inherent oscillations of a circuit involving a negative resistance device, and may be taken care of by proper choice of the resistance R (7.5 Ω in the present experiments). The oscillations can be suppressed if this resistance is made larger than the magnitude of the negative resistance in the I–V. However, the choice of this resistance is very important for the operation of the parity generator circuit. Too large a resistance will lead to a much flatter load line, producing hysteresis [7.72] in the circuit operation whenever the operating point is moved across a peak. This is the case of the memory circuit described before where multiple stable points are obtained at a given bias. For the successful operation of the parity checker on the other hand, there must be only one stable operating point at a given bias voltage. This is obtained with a nearly vertical load line, which can be freely shifted back and forth between any of the peaks and the following valley, without encountering any hysteresis.

iii) Summary

The structure also lends itself to the realization of multiple (≥ 3) peaks, using the same operating principle and a series of metallizations. Multiple peaks in the I–V characteristic could of course also be realized by connecting in parallel a

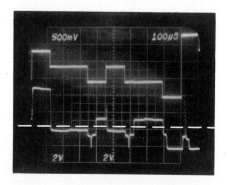

Fig. 7.24. Experimental results of the parity generator circuit. The top trace shows the output of the amplifier A_1, the bottom trace the parity output. The dotted line is the threshold voltage level of the output logic

series of tunnel diodes with resistors in between, which amounts basically to the circuit of Fig. 7.17b in the case of two diodes. The approach presented here has however two clear potential advantages: (a) it is a monolithic integration of RT devices and the voltage divider with resulting reduced parasitic resistances and capacitances; note that the monolithic integration of tunnel diodes would be a much more demanding task; (b) reproducibility of the $I-V$'s as discussed at the beginning of this chapter.

Following the above demonstration, *Söderström* and *Andersson* [7.73] have demonstrated a new way of combining RT diodes in parallel having different series resistances with each of them to separate the peaks in voltage, instead of the external bias. This has the advantage that the external bias source is not required. However, the integration of different series resistances is a more demanding task, making the fabrication of the device difficult.

b) Vertical Integration of RT Diodes

Another way of obtaining multiple peaks in the $I-V$ using only the ground state resonance of quantum wells is the vertical integration of RT diodes [7.68]. The structure consists of a number (n) of RTDB's, each composed of 50 Å undoped $Ga_{0.47}In_{0.53}As$ QW's sandwiched between two undoped 50 Å $Al_{0.48}In_{0.52}As$ barriers, connected in series through 1000 Å thick heavily doped ($\sim 5 \times 10^{17}/cm^3$) n-type $Ga_{0.47}In_{0.53}As$ cladding layers. The individual RTDB's were separated from the cladding layers on the two sides by 50 Å thick undoped $Ga_{0.47}In_{0.53}As$ layers to offset the effect of dopant diffusion during the high temperature growth process. The entire structure was grown lattice matched to an n^+ InP substrate, on which first a 5000 Å n^+ ($1 \times 10^{18}/cm^3$) $Ga_{0.47}In_{0.53}As$ buffer layer was deposited. The growth ended with another 5000 Å thick n^+ ($1 \times 10^{18}/cm^3$) $Ga_{0.47}In_{0.53}As$ contact layer. The devices were processed into 50 μm diameter mesas.

It has been previously shown that the GaInAs/AlInAs material system is suitable for the room temperature operation of RT diodes with high peak-to-valley ratios [7.12]. The present device is equivalent to a series combination of n such RT diodes. The DB's are designed so that the ground state in the QW is substantially above the Fermi Level in the adjacent cladding layers. When a voltage is applied, the electric field is higher at the anode end of the device (Fig. 7.25a), because of the screening of the applied field by the charge accumulated in the QW's under bias. Quenching of RT is thus initiated across the DB adjacent to the anode and then sequentially propagates to the other end, as the high field region widens with increasing applied voltage, as shown in Fig. 7.25a and b. Once RT has been quenched across a DB, the voltage drop across it quickly increases with bias because of increased resistance. The non-resonant tunnelling component through this DB is large enough to provide continuity for the RT current through the other DB's closer to the cathode. An NDR region is obtained in the $I-V$, corresponding to the quenching of RT through each diode. Thus with n diodes, we observe n peaks in the $I-V$. This

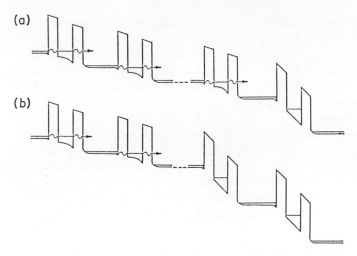

Fig. 7.25. Band-diagram under applied bias (**a**) with RT suppressed through the DB adjacent to the anode and (**b**) after expansion of the high-field region to the adjacent DB with increasing bias. The arrows indicate the RT component of the current

expansion of the high field region from one DB to the next is somewhat similar to the phenomenon observed by *Choi* et al. [7.74] in sequential tunnelling through a superlattice. Note however, that the later effect gives rise to much smaller peak-to-valley ratios and is observed only at cryogenic temperatures. Generating multiple peaks by combining tunnel diodes in series is well known [7.75]. However, the mechanism in that arrangement is completely different. The tunnel diodes used in such a combination must have different characteristics with successively increasing peak currents, so that each of them can go into the NDR region only when the corresponding current level is reached [7.75]. Besides, the present structure has the usual advantages over tunnel diodes discussed before.

Devices consisting of three and five RT structures in series were tested by *Sen* et al. [7.68]. The resulting *I–V* characteristics taken in both polarities of the applied bias are shown respectively in Figs. 7.26 and 7.27. Positive polarity here refers to the top of the mesa being biased positive with respect to the bottom and vice versa. A systematic study of the *I–V*'s at various temperatures from 300 K down to 7 K was made. The results presented in Figs. 7.26 and 7.27 are for room temperature (left) and 77 K (right). At 77 K, the devices with three RTDB's indicate three peaks (Fig. 7.26, right) and the one with five indicates five peaks (Fig. 7.27, right) in both polarities, as expected. Note that the respective peaks in both polarities occur at nearly the same voltages. At 300 K, Fig. 7.26 shows three distinct peaks in the positive polarity while in the negative polarity the third peak is not observed because of the rapidly increasing background current. The difference in the observed characteristics in the two polarities may be due to structural asymmetry, unintentionally introduced during growth and processing. The device with five DB's shows five clear peaks in both polarities

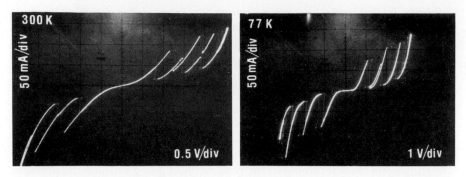

Fig. 7.26. Current-voltage characteristics of the device with three vertically integrated RT double barriers taken for both bias polarities at 300 K (*left*) and 77 K (*right*)

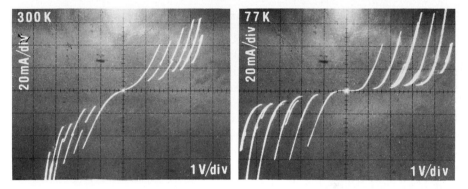

Fig. 7.27. Current voltage characteristics of the device with five vertically integrated RT double barriers taken for both bias polarities at 300 K (*left*) and 77 K (*right*)

also at 300 K (Fig. 7.27, left). The best peak-to-valley ratio observed at room temperature is 5:1 in both structures. At 77 K, the highest peak-to-valley ratios are respectively 9:1 and 18:1 in the structures with three and five peaks.

Note that there is considerable hysteresis associated with nearly all the peaks in the I–V's. This occurs whenever there is a significantly large parasitic resistance in series with the devices. In the present devices, when one of the RT diodes is active, all the other diodes contribute to this parasitic resistance. This hysteresis is different in nature from the load line effect discussed previously. In the present case, hysteresis effect cannot be avoided even with an absolutely vertical load line ($R_\mathrm{L} = 0\,\Omega$) because of the multiple-valued-current nature of the device characteristic around the peak. The effect may however be reduced with proper optimization of the device design. The series resistance also pushes the peaks in the I–V's towards higher voltages. The systematic studies at different temperatures indicate that the positions of the peaks gradually shift towards lower voltages with increasing temperature. This is due to reduction in the parasitic resistance with increasing temperature.

In conclusion, *vertical integration* is another technique for obtaining multiple peaks in the $I-V$ of RT devices, which combines *growth and processing simplicity and does not require an auxiliary bias source* to generate the peaks. The prototype devices demonstrated so far exhibit three and five peaks with high peak-to-valley current ratios at room temperature. These devices can be used in most of the applications involving devices with multiple peaks, demonstrated in the previous section. However, the hysteresis in the characteristics makes it difficult to use it for parity bit generation, since in that application, a nearly vertical load line has to be moved back and forth between any of the peaks and the following valley by changing the bias voltage. The hysteresis will prevent the operating point from returning to the peak without going through the previous valley. The multiple-valued-current nature of the characteristic on the other hand, can be utilized in other applications, such as a Schmitt trigger circuit.

7.2.2 Resonant Tunnelling Bipolar Transistors

The negative differential resistance of RTDB's showed enough potential to be included in three terminal devices, to take advantage of the NDR as well as the transistor action. The first of these kind of structures was the RT bipolar transistor (RTBT), proposed by *Capasso* and *Kiehl* in 1985 [7.25]. The structures initially proposed are shown in Figs. 7.28 and 7.29. They consisted of heterojunction bipolar transistors with a quantum well in the p-type base layer. In order to always satisfy the condition of tunnelling through symmetric DB's, discussed in Sect. 7.1.1, these structures employed high energy or ballistic injection of minority carriers into the base to achieve RT through the DB, rather than applying a field across the latter.

Figure 7.28 shows the band diagram of one of these devices. The structure is a heterojunction bipolar transistor with a degenerately doped tunnelling emitter and a symmetric DB in the base. The collector current as a function of base-emitter voltage V_{BE} should exhibit a series of peaks corresponding to RT through the various quasi-stationary states of the well. Multiple negative conductance in the collector circuit can therefore be expected.

An alternative injection method is the abrupt or nearly abrupt emitter which can be used to ballistically launch electrons into the quasi eigenstates with high momentum coherence. As V_{BE} is increased, the top of the launching ramp eventually reaches the energy of the quasi eigenstates so that electrons can be balistically launched into the resonant states (Fig. 7.29a).

To achieve equally spaced resonances in the collector current, the rectangular quantum well in the base should be replaced by a parabolic one (Fig. 29b). RT through parabolic quantum wells was discussed in Sect. 7.1.3. Assuming the depth of the parabolic well in the conduction band to be 0.34 eV (corresponding to grading from $Al_{0.45}Ga_{0.55}As$ to GaAs) and its width to be 200 Å, one finds that the first state is at an energy of 32 meV from the bottom of the well and that the resonant states are separated by $\simeq 64$ meV. This gives a

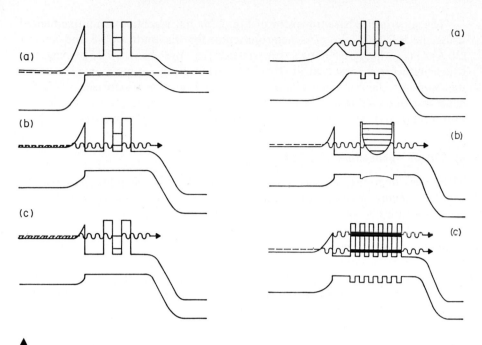

▲

Fig. 7.28a–c. Band diagram of RTBT with tunnelling emitter under different bias conditions: **(a)** In equilibrium; **(b)** RT through the first level in the well; **(c)** RT through the second level. (Not to scale)

Fig. 7.29. (a) Band diagram of RTBT with graded emitter (at resonance). Electrons are ballistically launched into the first quasi eigenstate of the well. **(b)** RTBT with a parabolic quantum well in the base and tunnelling emitter. A ballistic emitter can also be used. **(c)** RTBT with superlattice base. (Not to scale)

total of five states in the well. In a recent experiment, as many as 16 resonances through a parabolic quantum well were observed [7.20].

Finally, in Fig. 7.29c, we illustrate another method, that of high-energy injection and transport in the minibands of a superlattice, using ballistic launching or tunnel injection.

A structure similar to that of Fig. 7.28 with a rectangular tunnel barrier in the emitter has recently been demonstrated in the $Al_{0.48}In_{0.52}As/Ga_{0.47}In_{0.53}As$ system [7.76]. Negative trans-conductance with a small peak-to-valley ratio was observed only at cryogenic temperatures. These results also highlight the inherent difficulty of achieving good $I-V$ characteristics with devices utilizing RT of nonequilibrium electrons. Greatly improved performance can be obtained with the structures described in parts b) and d) of this section. The circuit applications described in a) do not necessarily rely on the devices of Figs. 7.28 and 7.29 and can be implemented, at least in principle, with all multistate RT transistors.

The superlattice base transistor of Fig. 7.29c has recently been implemented using the $InP/Ga_{0.47}In_{0.53}As$ heterojunction for the emitter/base and an InP (20 Å)/$Ga_{0.47}/In_{0.53}As$ (70 Å) superlattice in the base [7.77]. Negative transconductance, observed at $T \leq 77$ V, arises from suppression of electron injection into the first miniband as the base-emitter bias is increased. A similar effect was observed in a unipolar transistor with superlattice base and injection into a miniband lying in the classical continuum above the barriers [7.78].

a) Circuit Applications of RTBTs

These new functional devices, because of their multiple resonant characteristic, can have many potential applications, leading to tremendous reduction in circuit complexity and size. These are discussed in this section.

Multiple Valued Logic. Consider the common emitter circuit shown in Fig. 7.30. For an input voltage V_i in the base for which the electrons undergo RT, the transistor strongly conducts and the output voltage V_o is low. Off resonance, instead, the device basically does not conduct and the output voltage is high. This results in the multiple-valued voltage transfer characteristic of Fig. 7.30, having as many peaks at the number of resonances in the well. The output voltage V_o takes on one of the two values in accordance with the level of the input voltage V_i. Thus the device provides a binary digital output for an analog input, or a multiple-valued digital input.

Parity Generator. The multiple valued characteristics of Fig. 7.30 can be used to design the parity generator circuit shown in Fig. 7.31. In this circuit, the binary bits of a digital word are added in the resistive network at the input of the RTBT. With proper weighting of the resistors R_o and R_B, the operating point would be placed either on a peak or a valley of the I–V depending on whether the total number of 1's at the input is even or odd respectively. The advantage of this approach over conventional circuits is that the RTBT implementation, apart from being smaller in size and simpler, should also be extremely fast since it uses a single high speed switching device. Conventional transistor implementation requires complex circuitry involving many logic gates with a consequent reduction in speed.

Compare this implementation of the parity generator with that discussed in Sect. 7.2.1. The advantage of using a transistor structure, as shown in this

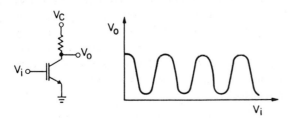

Fig. 7.30. Common emitter amplifier circuit using the RTBT and the corresponding multiple-valued voltage transfer characteristics

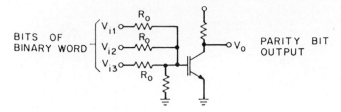

Fig. 7.31. The parity generator circuit using RTBT

section, is further simplification of the circuit. The function of adding the voltages corresponding to the digital input bits, as performed by the amplifier A_1 in Fig. 7.23, is performed by the transistor in this case. Also, since the input and the output in the transistor are isolated, the amplifier A_2 is not necessary, as the output automatically comes as ground referenced.

Analog to Digital Converter.   The circuit shown in Fig. 7.32 can be used as an analog to digital converter. In this application, the analog input is simultaneously applied to an array of RTBT circuits having different voltage scaling networks. To understand the operation of the circuit, consider the simplest system comprising of only the two transistors Q_1 and Q_2. The voltages at different points of this circuit are shown in Fig. 7.33a, for various input voltages V_i. Consider that the resistances R_0, R_1 and R_2 are so chosen that the base voltages of the transistors Q_1 and Q_2 vary according to the curves V_{B1} and V_{B2} respectively with V_i. With the input voltage at V_1, the output of both the transistors will be at the operating point P_1 (Hi-state). With the input changing to V_2, the output of Q_1 will become low (P_2), while that of Q_2 will still remain high (closer to P_1). Applying this logic to the input voltages V_3 and V_4, it can be easily shown that circuit indeed follows the Truth Table of Fig. 7.33b. The outputs of the RTBT array thus constitute a binary code representing the quantized analog input level. The system can be extended to more bits with a larger number of peaks in the I–V. Again, the circuitry involved in this approach is simple and should be very fast.

Multiple State Memory.   This application takes advantage of the ability to achieve a multiple valued negative differential resistance characteristic. This type of characteristic is achieved at the emitter-collector terminals by holding the base collector junction at fixed bias V_{BC}, as shown in the inset of Fig. 7.34. With V_{BC} fixed, variations in V_{CE} produce variations in V_{EB} which cause the collector current to peak as V_{EB} crosses a tunnelling resonance Fig. 7.34. When connected to a resistive load R_L and voltage supply V_{CC}, as shown in the circuit of Fig. 7.34 the resulting load line intersects the I–V at N stable points where N is the number of resonant peaks. The circuit thus acts as an N state memory element, providing the possibility of extremely high density data storage. Such

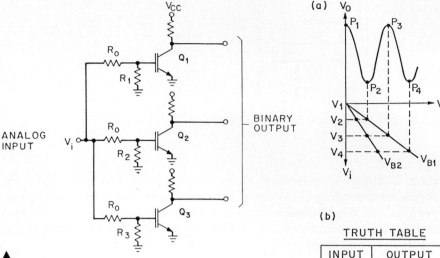

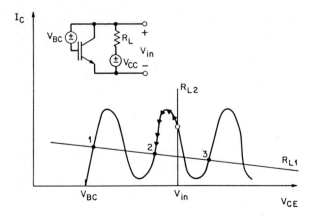

Fig. 7.32. The analog to digital converter circuit using RTBT's

(b)

TRUTH TABLE

INPUT	OUTPUT	
V_i	Q_2	Q_1
V_1	1	1
V_2	1	0
V_3	0	1
V_4	0	0

Fig. 7.33a,b. The schematic operation of the analog to digital converter circuit of Fig. 7.32, involving only 2 bits: (a) The voltages at different points of the circuit at various input voltages; (b) The truth table

Fig. 7.34. The current voltage characteristics with multiple-valued negative differential resistance when the base-collector voltage of the RTBT is held fixed, as shown in the circuit in the inset of the figure. The load line corresponding to R_{L1} demonstrates its operation as a multiple valued memory element. The solid circles denote stable states. The load line R_{L2} and the path indicated by the arrows show how such a memory can be pulsed from one stable state to another

an element can be latched onto any one of the stable states by momentarily applying a voltage close to the desired state. It can therefore be integrated in a large memory array as discussed in Sect. 7.1.4.

An N-state latch such as this can also be used to build a counter in the N-state logic system, as the circuit can be switched from one stable state to the immediately adjacent one by a voltage pulse of height V_{LS} to the circuit, forcing the operating point to that of the open circle on the unstable part of the characteristics in Fig. 7.34. It can be easily shown that, as the input pulse is removed, the operating point will move along the indicated trajectory, finally latching on to the State 2. Circuits like these and others, such as multipliers and dividers in the N-state logic system had been of considerable interest for some time [7.70]. However, since no physical device indicating multiple valued negative resistance previously existed, such circuits were possible only with combinations of binary devices. In order to achieve N states, N two-state devices were connected, resulting in a complex configuration with reduced density and speed.

b) Resonant Tunnelling Bipolar Transistors Operating at Room Temperature

The experiments described in [7.76] indicate that it is difficult to operate the RTBT with ballistic or high-energy electron injection into the heavily doped p^+-type base region. The first operating resonant tunnelling bipolar transistor (RTBT), demonstrated by *Capasso* et al. [7.32] in 1986, was designed to have the minority electrons *thermally* injected into and transported through the base, rather than *hot-electron* or *quasi-ballistic* transport. This made the operation of the device much less critical and the structure implemented in the AlGaAs/GaAs material system showed resonance peaks even at room temperature.

The band diagram of this transistor is shown in Fig. 7.35. Thermal injection is achieved by adjusting the alloy composition of the portion of the base adjacent to the emitter in such a way that the conduction band in this region lines up with or is slightly below the bottom of the ground-state sub-band of the quantum well (Fig. 7.35a). For a 74 Å well and 21.5 Å AlAs barriers the first quantized energy level is $E_1 = 65$ meV. Thus the Al mole fraction was chosen to be $x = 0.07$ (corresponding to $E_g = 1.521$ eV) so that $\Delta E_c \simeq E_1$. This equality need not be rigorously satisfied for the device to operate in the desired mode, as long as E_1 does not exceed ΔE_c by more than a few kT. The quantum well is undoped; nevertheless it is easy to show that there is a high concentration ($\cong 7 \times 10^{11}$ cm^{-2}) two-dimensional hole gas in the well. These holes have transferred from the nearby Al$_{0.07}$Ga$_{0.93}$As region, by tunnelling through the AlAs barrier, in order to achieve Fermi level line-up in the base.

The structures were grown by MBE on an n^+ Si-doped GaAs substrate. A 2100 Å $n = 3 \times 10^{17}$ cm^{-3} GaAs buffer layer is followed by a 1.6 μm thick GaAs n-type ($= 1 \times 10^{16}$ cm^{-3}) collector. The base layer starts with a Be-doped p^+ ($= 1 \times 10^{18}$ cm^{-3}) 1900 Å GaAs region adjacent to the collector,

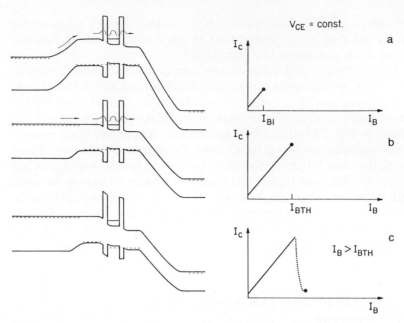

Fig. 7.35a–c. Energy band diagrams of the RTBT with thermal injection and corresponding schematics of collector current I_C for different base currents I_B at a fixed collector emitter voltage V_{CE} (not to scale). As I_B is increased the device first behaves as a conventional bipolar transistor with current gain (**a**), until near flat-band conditions in the emitter are achieved (**b**). For $I_B > I_{Bth}$ a potential difference develops across the AlAs barrier between the contacted and uncontacted regions of the base. This raises the conduction band edge in the emitter above the first resonance of the well, thus quenching resonant tunnelling and the collector current (**c**)

followed by a 210 Å undoped GaAs set-back layer. The DB is then grown. It consists of a 74 Å undoped GaAs quantum well sandwiched between two undoped 21.5 Å AlAs barriers. The last portion of the base is 530 Å thick $Al_{0.07}Ga_{0.93}As$ of which 105 Å adjacent to the DB is undoped and the rest is p-type doped to $\simeq 1 \times 10^{18}$ cm^{-3}. The purpose of the two set-back layers is to offset Be diffusion into the DB during the high temperature growth ($T = 680°$ C) of the AlGaAs graded emitter [7.79]. The latter consists of a 530 Å $n^+ \approx 3 \times 10^{17}$ cm^{-3} region linearly graded between $x = 0.07$ and $x = 0.24$, adjacent to the base, and of 3200 Å thick $Al_{0.25}Ga_{0.75}As$ doped to $\cong 3 \times 10^{17}$ cm^{-3}. The growth ends with a 1000 Å $n^+ = 3 \times 10^{18}$ cm^{-3} GaAs contact layer separated from the emitter by a 530 Å $n^+ = 3 \times 10^{18}$ cm^{-3} region linearly graded from $x = 0.24$ to $x = 0$.

Test structures with 7.5×10^{-5} cm^2 emitter area were fabricated using photolithography, wet and anodic etching techniques. The base layer was revealed by anodic etching in H_3PO_4/H_2O. The portion of the base ($Al_{0.07}Ga_{0.93}As$) adjacent to the emitter was also anodically etched-off at 12 Å/volt, while continuously monitoring the mesa height with a Dektak depth profiler. The rest of the base was contacted using AuBe (1% Be by weight,

400 Å)/Au (1100 Å) alloyed at 400°C in a H_2 flow for 2 sec. Au (500 Å)/ Sn(250 Å/Au(2000 Å) alloyed at 450°C for 1 sec was used as the n-type contact to the emitter and collector.

The present structure consists therefore of a HBT with a DB *in the base region*.

In order to understand the operation of this device, consider a common emitter bias configuration. Initially the collector-emitter voltage V_{CE} and the base current I_B, are chosen in such a way that the base-emitter and the base-collector junctions are respectively forward and reverse-biased. If V_{CE} is kept constant and the base current I_B is increased, the base-emitter potential also increases until flat-band condition in the emitter region is reached (Fig. 7.35b, left). In going from the band configuration of Fig. 7.35a to that of Fig. 7.35b the device behaves like a conventional transistor with the collector current linearly increasing with the base current (Figs. 7.35a, b, right). The slope of this curve is, of course, the current gain β of the device. In this region of operation, electrons in the emitter overcome, by thermionic injection, the barrier of the base-emitter junction and undergo RT through the DB. If now the base current is further increased above the value I_{Bth} corresponding to the flat band condition, the additional potential difference drops primarily across the first semi-insulating AlAs barrier (Fig. 7.35c), between the contacted and uncontacted portions of the base, since the highly doped emitter is now fully conducting. This pushes the conduction band edge in the $Al_{0.07}Ga_{0.93}As$ above the first energy level of the well, thus quenching the RT. The net effect is that the base transport factor and the current gain are greatly reduced. This causes an abrupt drop of the collector current as the base current exceeds a certain threshold value I_{Bth} (Fig. 7.35c, right). This is the most important manifestation of the inherent negative transconductance of this device. It should be noted that although the base metallization penetrates into the AlAs barrier, the latter can still sustain the potential drop in the region under the emitter, as discussed above, since the base contact is placed away from the emitter mesa and the barrier is undoped (semi-insulating).

The devices were biased in a common emitter configuration at 300 K and the I–V characteristics were displayed on a curve tracer. For base currents ≤ 2.5 mA the transistor exhibits normal characteristics, while for $I_B \geq 2.5$ mA the behavior previously discussed was observed. Figure 7.36 shows the collector current versus base current at $V_{CE} = 12$ V, as obtained from the common emitter characteristics. The collector current increases with the base current and there is clear evidence of current gain ($\beta = 7$ for $I_c > 4$ mA). As the base current exceeds 2.5 mA, there is a drop in I_c because the current gain mechanism is quenched by the suppression of RT. The transistor characteristics were also measured in a pulsed mode using 300 μs pulses. No changes were detected and a behavior identical to that of Fig. 7.36 was observed, thus ruling out heating effects.

The devices exhibited similar behavior in all the investigated temperature range from 100 K to 300 K, although the negative conductance effects are more

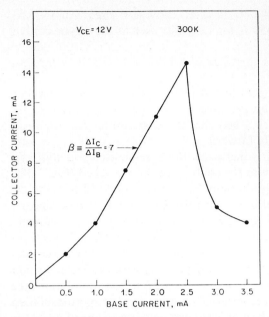

Fig. 7.36. Collector current versus base current in the common emitter configuration of the RTBT of Fig. 7.35, at room temperature with the collector-emitter voltage held constant. The line connecting the data points is drawn only to guide the eye

pronounced at lower temperatures, because the quenching of RT is more abrupt than at higher temperatures. Figure 7.37 illustrates the common emitter characteristics at 100 K. At relatively low V_{CE} both the emitter-base and the collector-base junctions are forward biased (saturation region) and the collector current is negative corresponding to a net flow of electrons from the collector contact into the collector layer. This gives rise to a collector-emitter offset voltage, which is typical of asymmetric heterojunction bipolar transistor [7.80]. In the present case this offset is large due to the relatively small α of this structure at low temperatures and to the relatively large emitter resistance and ideality factor ($n \approx 2$) of the base-emitter pn junction [7.80]. This offset is greatly reduced at room temperature. As V_{CE} is further increased, the collector-base junction becomes sufficiently reverse biased and for base currents $I_B \leq 4$ mA the characteristics are similar to that of a conventional bipolar (Fig. 7.37). For $I_B > 4$ mA, at sufficiently high V_{CE}, the collector current instead decreases with increasing base current. It is apparent from Fig. 7.37 that in addition to this behavior previously discussed (see Fig. 7.37) there is also a large negative conductance in the I_C versus V_{CE} curve for base currents in excess of the threshold value ($= 4$ mA). This is easy to understand by noting that in order to reach the band configuration of Fig. 7.37c and quench RT (at a fixed $I_B > I_{Bth}$) the collector-emitter voltage V_{CE} should be large enough for the collector-base junction to be reverse biased and draw a significant collector current. In the present structure, the higher I_{Bth} at lower temperatures (4 mA at 100 K compared to 2.5 mA at 300 K), is a consequence of the larger collector-emitter offset voltage.

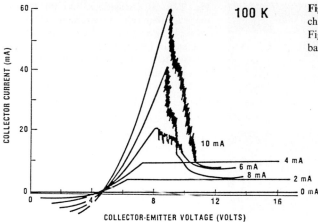

Fig. 7.37. Common emitter characteristics of the RTBT of Fig. 7.35 at 100 K, for various base currents

These bipolars in the common emitter configuration act as oscillators, when biased in the negative conductance region of the characteristic. The current oscillation in the collector circuit was picked up by a loop and displayed. Figure 7.38 shows the oscillation in the time domain at room temperature and in the frequency domain at both 300 K and 100 K, at an operating point $V_{CE} = 12$ V, $I_B = 6$ mA. Note the high spectral purity (near single frequency response), particularly at low temperature. The oscillation frequency ($\simeq 20$ MHz) is limited at present by the probe stage used, and the collector bias circuit. Much higher oscillation frequencies (> 10 GHz) may be ultimately expected.

By changing the bias conditions (I_B, V_{CE}) the oscillation frequency can be tuned over a few MHz range. At room temperature the device ceases to oscillate for base currents $\lesssim 2.5$ mA since at such base currents the device is out of the negative conductance region (RT is not quenched, see Fig. 7.36). A simple, physical picture of the oscillations can be given. As the dc base bias current is increased above the threshold value RT is suppressed. Thus the collector current is reduced, which implies a reduction of the emitter current since the bias current I_B is kept fixed. This in turn implies a decrease of the voltage applied across the emitter, followed by a restoration of the flat band conditions (since $I_B > I_{Bth}$) and the cycle is repeated.

c) Alternative Designs of RTBTs

An alternative RTBT design, with the DB in the base-emitter junction rather than in the base region, was reported shortly after by *Futatsugi* et al. [7.33] of Fujitsu Laboratories. The operation of this device is very similar to the one discussed in the previous section. With the emitter-base junction forward biased, a resonance peak could be observed at 77 K in the emitter and hence in the collector current also as a function of base-emitter voltage V_{BE}, at a fixed collector-emitter voltage V_{CE}. However, in this design, the tunnelling probability

a

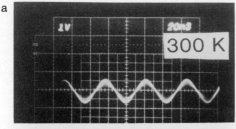
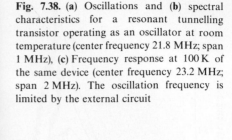

Fig. 7.38. (a) Oscillations and (b) spectral characteristics for a resonant tunnelling transistor operating as an oscillator at room temperature (center frequency 21.8 MHz; span 1 MHz), (c) Frequency response at 100 K of the same device (center frequency 23.2 MHz; span 2 MHz). The oscillation frequency is limited by the external circuit

b

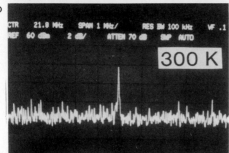

c

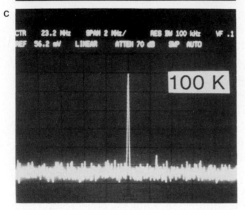

becomes a strong function of the base-emitter voltage V_{BE}. This makes it difficult to observe NDR at room temperature. Recently, the Fujitsu group has implemented an RTBT in the AlInAs/GaInAs material system, grown lattice matched to an InP substrate, with the DB in the emitter layer [7.81]. The parameter advantages of this material system discussed earlier, made it possible to observe NDR at room temperature [7.81].

d) RTBT with Multiple Peak Characteristics

The results of vertical integration of RT diodes, discussed in part b) of Sect. 7.2.1, made it possible to design an RTBT exhibiting multiple NDR regions in the characteristics, with nearly equal peak currents and peak-to-valley ratios

[7.82–84]. The structure and the band diagram, under zero bias, of the $Ga_{0.47}In_{0.53}As/Al_{0.48}In_{0.52}As$ RTBT, grown lattice matched to an n^+ InP substrate by MBE, is shown in Fig. 7.39. The structure essentially consists of an npn bipolar transistor with two RTDB's in series included in the emitter. The design of the RTDB's and the cladding layer connecting them are identical to that discussed in part b) of Sect. 7.2.1. The DB's are also separated from the adjacent heavily doped regions on both sides by 50 Å wide undoped $Ga_{0.47}In_{0.53}As$ offset layers to prevent dopant diffusion into the barriers during the high temperature growth process. These doping offset layers are not shown in Fig. 7.39, to keep the diagram simple. The collector, base and the part of the emitter adjacent to the base are respectively doped to $2 \times 10^{16}/cm^3$, $2 \times 10^{18}/cm^3$ and $1 \times 10^{18}/cm^3$. The devices were processed into 50 µm diameter emitter and 125 µm diameter base mesas using photolithography and wet chemical etch ($50H_2O + 3H_3PO_4 + 1H_2O_2$). Ge/Au/Ag/Au were evaporated in succession for the emitter and collector and Au-Be/Au for the base contact metallizations. The contacts were alloyed together at 375° C for 10 sec in a hydrogen atmosphere. The devices were tested in the temperature range from 10 K to 30 K using a Helitran dewar equipped with microprobes.

The physics of this transistor is best understood in the common base configuration, using the band diagrams of Fig. 7.40. The collector bias is kept fixed and the emitter-base voltage (V_{EB}) is increased. For V_{EB} smaller than the built-in voltage ($V_{bi} \simeq 0.7$ eV at 300 K) of the $Ga_{0.47}In_{0.53}As$ p–n junction, most of the bias voltage falls across this junction (Fig. 7.40a, not in scale) since its impedance is much greater than that of the two DB's in series, both of which are

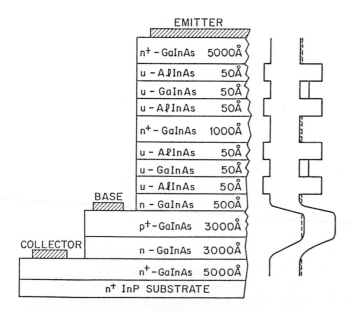

Fig. 7.39. Structure and band diagram under zero bias of the multiple peak RTBT

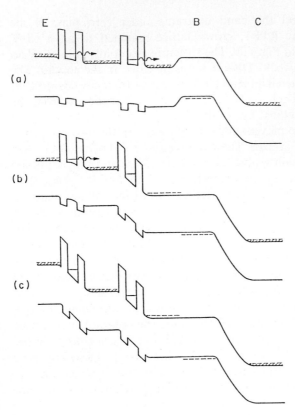

Fig. 7.40a–c. Band diagram of the RTBT of Fig. 7.39 in the common base configuration for different emitter-base bias conditions. **(a)** Electrons resonantly tunnel through both DB's; in this regime the transistor operates as a conventional bipolar. **(b)** Quenching of RT through the DB adjacent to the *pn* junction, gives rise to a negative transconductance region in the collector current. **(c)** Quenching of RT through the other DB produces a second peak in the *I–V*

conducting via RT. As V_{EB} further increases and equals V_{bi} the junction reaches a flat band configuration and strongly conducts. Any additional increase in V_{EB} will then fall primarily across the DB's (Fig. 7.40b). These are designed so that the ground state in the quantum well ($E_1 \simeq 126$ meV) is substantially above the Fermi level in the adjacent cladding layers. The electric field distribution across the DB's is nonuniform. As V_{EB} is then further increased, quenching of RT is initiated across the DB adjacent to the GaInAs *p–n* junction and then sequentially extends to the next one, as the high field region widens with increasing emitter-base bias (Fig. 7.40b, c). Once RT has been quenched across a DB, the voltage drop across it quickly increases with bias because of the increased resistance. The nonresonant tunnelling component through this DB is large enough to provide continuity for the RT current through the other DB. A negative transconductance region is thus obtained in the collector current versus emitter-base voltage, corresponding to the quenching of RT through each DB. With *n* DB's there will be therefore *n* peaks in the transfer characteristics. This is precisely what occurs in this device where two peaks are observed in the *I–V*. Figure 7.41 shows the collector current versus V_{EB} at a collector-base bias $V_{CB} = 0.1$ V, at 300 K and 77 K. Note that for V_{EB} greater than the V_{bi} (≈ 0.7

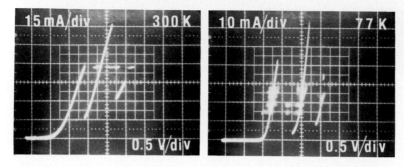

Fig. 7.41. Collector current versus emitter-base voltage, in the common base configuration for $V_{CB} = -0.1$ V at 300 K (*left*) and 77 K (*right*)

-0.8 V), the p–n junction starts to strongly conduct and the collector current I_C rapidly increases until RT through the first DB is suppressed and I_C exhibits a sharp drop. The effect repeats itself for the second DB, thus giving rise to two peaks in the I–V. The peak-to-valley ratio is 4:1 at 300 K for the first peak and 3:1 for the second peak. At liquid nitrogen temperature the corresponding ratios are 22:1 and 8:1 for the first and second peak respectively. The I–V's were virtually identical for different values of V_{CB} up to $\simeq 2.5$ V. Above this value onset of breakdown in the base collector junction, possibly due to Zener tunnelling in the small band-gap, small effective mass $Ga_{0.47}In_{0.53}As$ collector layer [7.85], was observed.

The most commonly used mode of transistor operation in a circuit is the common emitter. Figure 7.42 shows the common emitter output characteristics of the transistor. These can easily be understood in terms of the physical picture developed above. For base currents smaller than a critical value ($I_{Bth1} \simeq 1.2$ mA, corresponding to $V_{BE} = V_{bi}$) the device behaves like a regular transistor. Values of dc current gain ($ = I_C/I_B$) of up to 60 at 300 K and up to 150 at 77 K are observed. The differential current gains are respectively as high as 80 at 300 K and 200 at 77 K. For base currents higher than I_{Bth1}, the collector current I_C displays an NDR region corresponding to quenching of RT through the DB adjacent to the p–n junction. The current then rises again with increasing V_{CE} due to inelastic processes and finally saturates. At even higher base current ($\lesssim I_{Bth2} = 1.6$ mA) and hence base-emitter voltage V_{BE}, a second NDR region is caused by suppression of RT through the second DB. Note that at 300 K, after the second peak, the collector current does not steeply rise with V_{CE} and saturates at a much lower value than after the first peak. This effect can be easily explained in terms of the loss of injection efficiency at high V_{BE}. When the p–n junction is in flat-band conditions there is a relatively large nonequilibrium concentration of holes in the emitter region adjacent to the base. These holes give rise to a base-emitter current over the AlInAs/GaInAs valence band barriers ($\simeq 0.2$ eV), which is small at moderate V_{CE}. At sufficiently high V_{CE}, however, this current is strongly increased by the high electric field in the DB

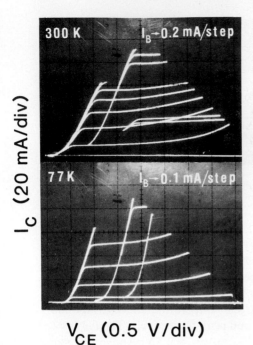

I_C (20 mA/div)

V_{CE} (0.5 V/div)

Fig. 7.42. Common emitter characteristics. Collector current versus collector emitter voltage for different base currents, at 300 K (*top*) and 77 K (*bottom*)

emitter region. This leads to the observed loss of injection efficiency and low saturation value of I_C after the second peak. At 77 K, however, the thermionic emission of holes over the barrier is strongly suppressed by the small Boltzmann factor and this large reduction in the injection efficiency following the second peak is not observed (Fig. 7.42, bottom).

Figure 7.43 shows the common emitter transfer characteristics (I_C vs V_{BE} at a constant $V_{CE} = 2.5$ V) at 300 K and 77 K. At a constant V_{CE}, as V_{BE} is increased, the emitter current and hence the collector current increases until the emitter-base junction reaches flat band condition. Beyond that, as RT through the two DB's quenches sequentially, abrupt drops in the emitter and hence the collector current are observed. The highest peak-to-valley ratio in the transfer characteristics at room temperature is 4:1 while it increases to about 20:1 at 77 K.

The transfer characteristics of Fig. 7.43 are used to design the frequency multiplier circuit shown in Fig. 7.44a. As the input voltage is increased, the collector current increases, resulting in a decrease in the collector voltage until the device reaches the negative transconductance regions, where a sudden decrease in the collector current and hence increase in the output voltage is observed. Thus under suitable bias (V_{BB}), triangular input waves will be multiplied by a factor of three and sinewaves by a factor of five. It should be noted that this multiplier circuit has all the advantages of the one discussed in part a) of Sect. 7.2.1. In addition, the output signal in this case is ground

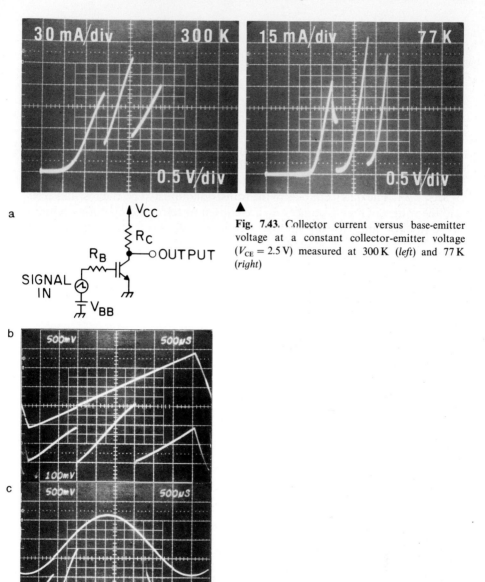

a

Fig. 7.43. Collector current versus base-emitter voltage at a constant collector-emitter voltage ($V_{CE} = 2.5$ V) measured at 300 K (*left*) and 77 K (*right*)

◀**Fig. 7.44.** (a) Frequency multiplier circuit using the RTBT and the experimental results of multiplying (**b**) sawtooth and (**c**) sinewave input signals, at room temperature

referenced and is also isolated from the input. These advantages are obtained in this circuit because the multiple peaks are present in the transfer characteristic of a transistor rather than the $I-V$ curve of a two terminal device. The gain of the circuit is determined by the transconductance of the transistor and the collector resistance R_C. However, too large a value for R_C will lead to saturation of the device at large input voltages. The saturation can of course be avoided by the choice of a larger supply voltage V_{CC}, but the maximum usable V_{CC} is limited by the collector-emitter breakdown of the device. In our circuits we had $V_{CC} = 3.0$ V, $V_{BB} = 1.8$ V, $R_C = 5\,\Omega$ and $R_B = 50\,\Omega$. Figure 7.44b and c show the experimental results of multiplying the frequency of triangular and sinewave inputs respectively. The polarity of the output signals (bottom traces) are inverted in the display for clarity of presentation.

Figure 7.45a shows a four-bit parity generator circuit. The voltages of the four input bits of the digital word are added up at the base node of the transistor by the resistive network, to generate a step-like waveform as discussed in part a) of Sect. 7.2.1. The quiescent bias of the transistor, adjusted by the resistance R_{B1}, and the values of the resistances R_0 are chosen to select the operating points of the transistor alternatively at low and high collector current levels at the

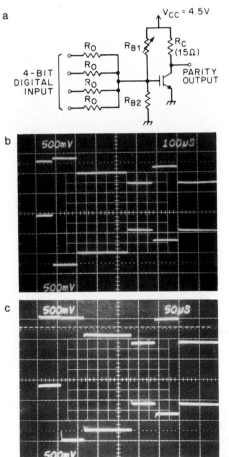

Fig. 7.45. (a) Four-bit parity generator circuit using the RTBT and the collector (*top traces*) and base (*bottom traces*) waveforms in the circuit at (b) 77 K and (c) 300 K

successive steps of the summed up voltage. In our circuit, we had $R_o = 15$ kΩ, $R_{B1} \sim 6.9$ kΩ, $R_{B2} = 2.4$ kΩ, $R_C = 15$ Ω and $V_{CC} = 4.5$ V. The output voltage at the collector would thus be high or low depending on the number of input bits set high being even or odd respectively. Thus we obtain a 4-bit parity generator using only one transistor as compared to 24 needed in an optimized conventional circuit using three exclusive OR's. The advantage of the present circuit over parity generators using RT diodes (Fig. 7.23a) is that a separate summing amplifier is not required, resulting in further reduction in complexity.

To test the circuit, a pseudo-random sequence of 4-bit binary words was used [7.86]. Experimental results at 77 K and 300 K are shown in Fig. 7. 45b and c respectively, where the top traces show the output waveforms and the bottom traces, the base waveforms of the transistor. Considering the dotted line in the upper trace (Fig. 7.45b) as logic threshold level, we find that the output is low for the second and the fourth voltage levels at the base while it is high for the others.

7.2.3 Resonant Tunnelling Unipolar Transistors

Following the announcement of the RTBT from Bell Laboratories in 1984, several unipolar three-terminal devices were proposed and implemented that utilized the RT structure as electron injectors to generate voltage tunable NDR and negative transconductance characteristics. The first of these unipolar structures was the resonant tunnelling hot electron transistor (RHET) [7.26] developed at the Fujitsu Laboratories in 1985. This device is discussed in a separate chapter of this book. The same year, *Luryi* and *Capasso* proposed the quantum wire transistor [7.29]; a novel device in which the quantum well is linear rather than planar and the tunnelling is of two-dimensional electrons into a one-dimensional density of states. In 1987, the resonant tunnelling gate field effect transistor (RT-FET) [7.34, 36, 37] was developed at the Bell Laboratories. Recently, a device exhibiting the generalized Stark effect [7.87] and the quantum capacitance effect [7.88] has been demonstrated at the Bell Laboratories [7.40]. Among other proposals of unipolar three terminal devices, the one involving integration of RT diodes and FETs, developed by Caltech and Xerox PARC [7.28, 35, 89] and their circuit applications [7.90] deserve mention. These devices are discussed in this section.

a) Resonant Tunnelling Gate Field Effect Transistor

i) Structure and Processing

Figure 7.46a shows the schematics of the device grown by MBE on an LEC semi-insulating substrate. The structure consists of an *n*-type GaAs channel, 1 μm thick, and doped to 4×10^{17} cm^{-3}. The DB, consisting of a 70 Å undoped GaAs well layer sandwiched between two 25 Å undoped AlAs barriers, was grown on top of the channel. The gate contact layer is 0.4 μm thick GaAs and

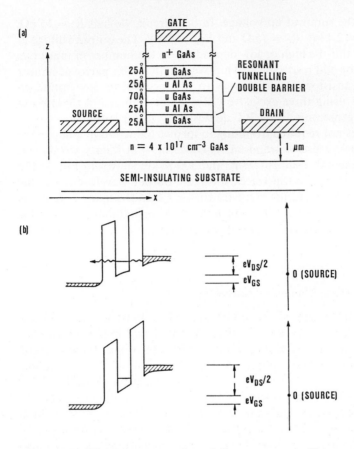

Fig. 7.46. (a) Schematic cross section of the resonant tunnelling gate FET. **(b)** Band diagram showing RT through double barrier in the gate of electrons injected from the channel and quenching of RT. Note the combined action of the gate and drain voltages in biasing the double barrier

doped to 5×10^{17} cm^{-3}. The undoped GaAs spacer layers (~ 25 Å) are left on the two sides of the undoped DB to offset the effect of Si diffusion from the adjacent n-type layers, during the high temperature growth process.

The devices have a 4.65 µm gate length, 308 µm gate width, 2.15 µm source-gate spacing and 9.8 µm source-drain spacing. The asymmetry between the source-gate and drain-gate spacing was unintentionally introduced during processing.

The devices were processed by evaporating the gate electrode followed by mesa etching. The gate mesa was formed by wet etching using the stop etches $H_2O_2 + NH_4OH$ (7.2 pH) for the GaAs and 1:1 $HCl + H_2O$ for the AlAs layers alternatively. The height of the gate mesa is 5500 Å. The source and drain electrodes were then deposited on the exposed channel. The gate contact was composed of Ge (60 Å)/Au (135 Å)/Ag (500 Å)/Au (750 Å) alloy. Ni (50 Å)/Au

(385 Å)/Ge (215 Å)/Au (750 Å) alloy was used as the source and drain contacts. All the contacts were alloyed together at 400°C for 10 s in a hydrogen flow.

ii) Principle of Operation

The operation of the device is based on the quenching of RT through the DB between the gate electrode and the channel. The biasing of the DB, when a gate-to-source (V_{GS}) as well as a drain-to-source (V_{DS}) voltage is applied, is shown in Fig. 7.46b. Note the combined action of the gate voltage and half the drain voltage in controlling RT. The voltage appearing across the DB is, a first approximation, given by

$$V_{DB} = V_{GS} - r V_{DS}, \tag{7.5}$$

where r is a factor determined by the ratio of the gate-to-source and the drain-to-gate spacings. Ideally, r should be 0.5. In the devices tested, however, this factor was 0.42, due to the structural asymmetry unintentionally introduced during processing. Thus RT through the DB may be controlled by either the gate or the drain voltage to produce peaks in the gate current characteristics. This in turn generates structures in the drain current as well, since the gate current adds to the drain-to-source current in the channel. Thus, in addition to negative differential resistance, negative transconductance was obtained as well, by controlling structures in the drain current with the variation of the gate voltage.

I_D **and** I_G **Versus** V_{GS}. To understand quantitatively the current voltage characteristics, it is necessary to discuss the potential distribution inside the device. Let us first consider the gate (I_G) and the drain (I_D) current variation with V_{GS} when $V_{DS} = 0$. Under this condition, the electrons tunnelling from the gate to the channel and vice versa form two equal (in the ideal case when $r = 0.5$) and opposite current flows in the channel, between its center and the source and drain electrodes. Half the gate current thus forms the drain current. The resulting potential distribution is shown in Fig. 7.47a and b respectively for positive and negative gate voltages. The conduction band energy diagram across the DB is shown on the left of Fig. 7.47 while the electron potential energy distribution due to ohmic drop along the channel in the region immediately adjacent to the DB is shown on the right. The interesting points to note from these diagrams are the following:

a) For positive gate bias, an electron accumulation layer is formed at the heterointerface between the channel and the bottom AlAs barrier while the gate side of the DB is depleted of carriers. The density of electrons in the thin (100–200 Å) accumulation layer substantially exceeds the average carrier concentration in the channel, thus strongly reducing, by screening, the source-to-drain electric field in the immediate vicinity of the DB channel interface, compared to the rest of the channel, as shown at the right of Fig. 7.47a. The near

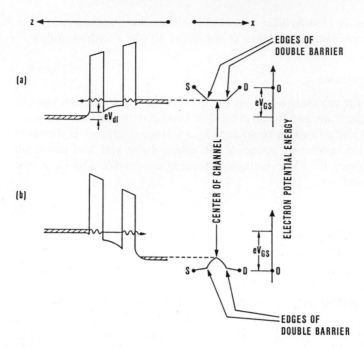

Fig. 7.47. Conduction band energy diagram across the double barrier (*left*) and electron potential energy distribution along the channel in the region immediately adjacent to the double barrier (*right*) at $V_{DS} = 0$ for (**a**) $V_{GS} > 0$ and (**b**) $V_{GS} < 0$

equipotential at the DB channel interface allows RT to be quenched everywhere at the same gate bias, resulting in an abrupt drop of the current with voltage, as observed in the experimental data (Fig. 7.48a). The important role of the accumulation and depletion layers adjacent to the DB on the I–V characteristics of RT diodes has been discussed by *Goldman* et al. [7.91] previously. These data provide the first direct evidence of such an effect.

b) For negative gate bias, on the other hand, the accumulation layer is formed on the gate side while the region of the channel adjacent to the DB is depleted of carriers. As a result, the flow of electrons causes a potential variation in the channel with the center being at the highest energy, while the edges of the DB being at the lowest (Fig. 7.47b). Thus, quenching of RT is initiated at the edges of the DB and gradually proceeds to the center with increasing magnitude of negative gate voltage. The I–V thus exhibits a gradual drop, as opposed to the abrupt drop with positive gate bias (Fig. 7.48a). The same effect is also observed for finite voltages applied externally between the drain and the source (Fig. 7.48b and c), since the accumulation layer in the channel also screens the applied drain-to-source field in the immediate vicinity of the DB, rendering it near equipotential. For negative gate bias in this latter case, the electron potential energy diagram in the channel (which is left to the reader as an exercise) implies

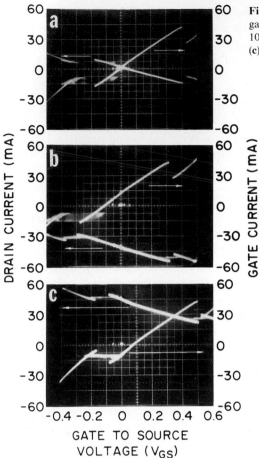

Fig. 7.48. Drain and gate currents versus gate-to-source voltage (V_{GS}) measured at 100 K for (**a**) $V_{DS} = 0$, (**b**) $V_{DS} = -0.2$ V, and (**c**) $V_{DS} = 0.2$ V

DRAIN CURRENT (mA)

GATE CURRENT (mA)

GATE TO SOURCE
VOLTAGE (V_{GS})

that RT is quenched initially at either the drain or the source end (depending on the polarity of V_{DS}) of the DB and gradually proceeds to the other end with increasing magnitude of gate voltage.

c) For positive gate voltage (Fig. 7.47a), there is a significant potential difference between the equipotential region under the DB and the source and drain electrodes (which are at the same potential since $V_{DS} = 0$). This is due to the flow of electrons in the channel that come from the gate by RT. Because of this ohmic drop, only a part of the applied V_{GS} appears across the DB. Also, there is a potential drop V_{dl} (~ 0.1 V) in the depletion layer adjacent to the DB on the gate side (Fig. 7.47a, left). Thus the voltage appearing across the DB is substantially less than that applied between the gate and source electrodes externally. Therefore a larger V_{GS} (0.4 V) is required to quench RT than what is expected from a simple tunnelling calculation ($2E_1 \simeq 0.2$ V).

For negative V_{GS} on the other hand, the portion of the channel under the gate immediately adjacent to the DB is depleted. Hence, the ohmic potential drop is larger in this part of the channel than in the rest, bringing the center of the channel at the highest energy point (Fig. 7.47b, right). Also, as there is no depletion layer in the gate side of the barrier, the potential drop V_{dl} is absent. The voltage appearing across the DB at its edges and almost equal to the applied voltage V_{GS}. Quenching of RT therefore is initiated at the edges of the DB and at a much lower $|V_{GS}|$ ($\simeq 0.2$ V, as expected from tunnelling calculations), than with positive gate bias. With increasing negative V_{GS}, this propagates inward until RT is finally suppressed at the center. The absence of the drop V_{dl} also helps it to totally suppress RT at a lower V_{GS} (0.3 V) as opposed to 0.4 V required in the case of positive V_{GS}.

When the drain is negatively biased with respect to the source, the negative conductance region and the overall I–V characteristics shift to a lower V_{GS} (Fig. 7.48b). This is a result of the increase of the electron potential energy in the region of the channel under the gate, so that less positive bias is required on the gate to quench RT. For negative gate bias, however, a larger voltage is necessary to obtain the same effect. Note that, as RT is quenched, there is a change not only in I_G but also in I_D as in the case with $V_{DS} = 0$. This can be explained as follows. With $V_{DS} < 0$ and $V_{GS} > 0$, the drain current consists of electrons flowing from the drain to the source and the drain to the gate. When RT is suppressed, the latter flow is reduced and I_D drops.

For $V_{DS} < 0$ and $V_{GS} < 0$, however, the picture is somewhat different. With $V_{GS} \simeq 0$, the electron potential energy in the center of the channel is higher than that in the gate due to the drain-to-source current flow. Electrons thus flow from the channel to the gate by RT resulting in a positive gate current for small negative gate voltages. With increasing negative bias on the gate, this flow decreases and finally changes direction, giving rise to a negative gate current at a sufficiently large V_{GS}. Before RT is quenched, electrons flowing from the gate to the channel by RT add up to those coming from the drain by ohmic conduction, and flow out in the source electrode, causing an ohmic potential drop in the source-gate part of the channel. The electron potential energy in the region under the gate is thus higher than what would have been expected in the absence of the gate current. When RT is suppressed, the potential drop in the source-gate part, therefore, is decreased. But as the drain-to-source voltage is fixed, the potential drop in the drain-gate part of the channel has to increase resulting in an increase in the drain current flow. This is observed as a sudden increase in the magnitude of the negative drain current.

For $V_{DS} > 0$ (Fig. 7.48c), a negative gate current is produced even at $V_{GS} = 0$ by the electrons resonantly tunnelling from the gate to the channel, since the positive V_{DS} has brought the electron potential energy in the middle of the channel below that in the gate. These electrons also add to the drain current. With V_{GS} going positive, the RT gate current is first reduced to zero and then changes direction with a corresponding reduction in the drain current, as some of the electrons coming from the source are directed to the gate. When RT is finally quenched with a drop in the gate current, there is a corresponding abrupt rise in the drain current, because all the electrons coming from the source are now directed to the drain. For negative V_{GS}, the resonantly tunnelling electrons from the gate always add to the drain current and hence the latter increases with increasing $|V_{GS}|$. A drop in the gate as well as the drain current is observed when RT is quenched.

I_D **and** I_G **Versus** V_{DS} **for Different** V_{GS}. From the foregoing discussions, we find that a negative drain bias has the same effect as a positive gate bias and vice versa. It therefore is easy to understand that the drain (I_D) and the gate (I_G) current variation with V_{DS} at different V_{GS} will show similar NDR characteristics, with the suppression of RT being abrupt at negative V_{DS} and gradual with positive V_{DS}. Also, for a change ΔV_{GS} in the gate bias, the NDR region will shift by $\Delta V_{DS} \simeq 2\Delta V_{GS}$.

Figure 7.49 shows I_G and I_D as a function of the drain-to-source bias V_{DS}, for $V_{GS} = 0$ (top) and $V_{GS} = +0.2$ V (bottom). Let us consider the curves for $V_{GS} = 0$ (top) first. Note that for positive V_{DS}, the region of the channel adjacent to the DB is depleted and electrons resonantly tunnel from the gate contact layer into the channel. For negative V_{DS}, on the other hand, electrons resonantly tunnel from the accumulation layer at the DB channel interface into the gate contact layer. In fact from Fig. 7.46b, we find that the application of a positive gate voltage has the same effect, as far as biasing the DB and controlling RT, as of a negative drain bias. It is therefore easy to explain the differences in the

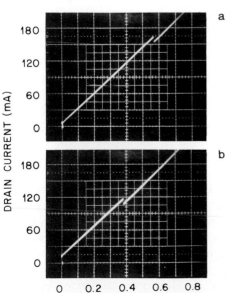

Fig. 7.49. Drain and gate currents versus drain-to-source voltage (V_{DS}) measured at 100 K for (a) $V_{GS} = 0$ and (b) $V_{GS} = 0.2$ V

steepness of the I–V (Fig. 7.49) in the NDR regions for different bias polarities, in a manner similar to those in Fig. 7.48. Following similar arguments it is also understood why the NDR region occurs at a significantly lower $|V_{DS}|$ when the drain is positively biased than when it is negatively biased. Application of a positive gate bias ($V_{GS} = +0.2$ V, Fig. 7.49, bottom) shifts the NDR region to higher V_{DS} by nearly 0.4 V, as expected. Also, at $V_{DS} = 0$, electrons now tunnel from the channel into the gate, giving rise to positive gate current. A positive V_{DS} is then required to suppress this tunnelling first ($I_G = 0$ at $V_{DS} \simeq 0.4$ V for $V_{GS} = 0.2$ V) and then reverse the direction of RT electrons.

An even more interesting situation occurs when the applied gate bias is large enough to quench RT even at $V_{DS} = 0$. The conduction band energy diagram across the DB under this condition is shown in Fig. 7.50a (left). Even if RT is suppressed, there will be some flow of electrons from the channel to the gate by thermionic emission over the barrier and inelastic tunnelling, resulting in a positive gate current (Fig. 7.51). These electrons are supplied by the drain and the source contacts. The resulting ohmic drop will place the drain and the source points at a higher energy than the region under the DB, as shown in the right half of Fig. 7.50a. As a positive drain voltage is applied, the electron flow from the drain end is reduced, resulting in a reduction in the negative drain and positive gate currents until a condition is reached when the drain is at the same potential as the middle of the channel and the drain current is reduced to zero. As the drain voltage is further increased, a positive drain current starts flowing. The positive drain voltage also pulls down the middle of the channel in the energy diagram, and the gate current continues to decrease until RT is restored at some V_{DS} (Fig. 7.50b). At this point, a large fraction of the electrons are again transferred to the gate by RT, resulting in a sudden increase in the gate current and corresponding decrease in the drain current, as observed experimentally (Fig. 7.51). Note that the onset of RT is quite abrupt in this case, because of the accumulation layer in the channel (Fig. 7.50b). Beyond this point, the gate current continues to decrease with a decreasing RT flow of electrons and the drain current increases.

At larger V_{DS}, the drain current is large compared to the gate current, and hence the potential in the channel can be solely determined by V_{DS}. So, at $V_{DS} \simeq 2V_{GS}$, the gate is at the same potential as the center of the channel (Fig. 7.50c) and no gate current flows. The experimental data taken at $V_{GS} = 0.5$ V (Fig. 7.51) in fact indicate that $I_G = 0$ at $V_{DS} \simeq 1.0$ V. In this situation, the region of the channel adjacent to the DB cannot be considered equipotential as there cannot be any accumulation of electrons. The part of the region nearer the source is at a higher energy than the gate while the other half is at a lower energy. Electrons therefore transfer from the channel to the gate at the source end while in the opposite direction at the other end. When these two flows are equal, the gate current is zero.

With a further increase in the drain voltage, electrons start flowing from the gate to the channel by RT, giving rise to a negative gate current. These electrons also add up in the channel with those coming from the source, to further increase

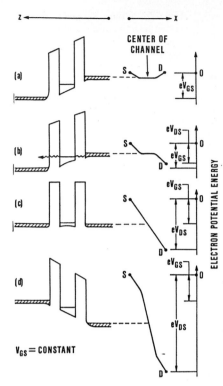

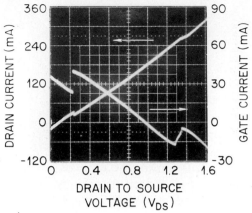

Fig. 7.51. Drain and gate currents versus positive drain-to-source voltage at $V_{GS} = 0.5$ V, exhibiting two peaks as illustrated in Fig. 7.50

◀ **Fig. 7.50a–d.** Conduction band energy diagram across the double barrier (left) and electron potential energy distribution along the channel in the region immediately adjacent to the double barrier (right) at a large positive V_{GS} (constant): (a) $V_{DS} = 0$, RT quenched; (b) small positive V_{DS}, RT established; (c) larger V_{DS}, gate current is zero; and (d) large positive V_{DS}, RT quenched again

the positive drain current (Fig. 7.51). When RT is quenched again at a sufficiently large V_{DS} (Fig. 7.50d), there is a drop in the gate as well as the drain currents (Fig. 7.51). It should be noted that the quenching of RT is gradual in this case, as is expected, because of the depletion of the channel adjacent to the gate (Fig. 7.50d).

A similar situation can also be obtained with large negative bias applied to the gate and the characteristics taken against negative V_{DS}. Figure 7.52 shows the experimental data taken against $-V_{DS}$ at $V_{GS} = -0.3$ V. These curves can be explained quantitatively, following similar arguments as before. It may also be noted that, unlike the previous one, the first NDR region ($V_{DS} = -0.2$ V) in this case is broad while the second one ($V_{DS} = -1.3$ V) is abrupt. With $V_{GS} = -0.3$ V, the channel is at a lower energy than the gate when $V_{DS} = -0.2$ V, and hence its depletion region adjacent to the DB leads to a gradual suppression of RT. For $V_{DS} = -1.3$ V on the other hand, an accumulation layer is formed in the channel, and thus the quenching is abrupt.

All these qualitative and quantitative agreements of the experimental data for various bias configurations verify the proposed model of the device.

In another attempt to integrate RTDB's with field effect transistors (FET), developed jointly by Caltech and Xerox PARC [7.28, 35, 89], the DB is placed in

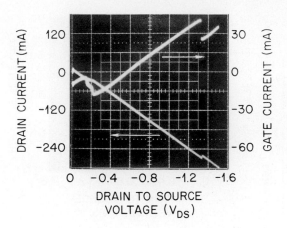

Fig. 7.52. Drain and gate currents versus negative drain-to-source voltage at $V_{GS} = -0.3$ V, exhibiting two peaks

the channel, adjacent to the source electrode. The operation of this class of structures, called DB/FET by its developers, is quite different from the resonant tunnelling gate field effect transistor (RT-FET) discussed above. In principle, the DB/FET is electrically equivalent to a RT diode with a resistance (that of the channel) in series with it. The role of the resistance is to push the NDR region in the I–V characteristics to higher voltages since a significant fraction of the applied voltage drops across the same. In the DB/FET, since the gate voltage changes the channel resistance, it effectively controls the position of the peak. Thus, a voltage controllable negative resistance characteristics is obtained [7.28]. The DB/FETs have been implemented both in the Vertical FET [7.35] and the MESFET [7.89] geometry. The I–V characteristics in both the geometries illustrate the same basic nature, viz., gate controllable negative resistance, although there are differences in details arising out of the differences in the field distributions in the two geometries. The DB/FETs have been used to construct frequency multipliers and flip-flops [7.90].

b) Quantum Wire Transistor

This novel device, proposed by *Luryi* and *Capasso* [7.29], uses a linear rather than a planar quantum well as the active region. In this device electrons resonantly tunnel from 2-D to 1-D (Quantum Wire) states. The properties of 0 and 1 dimensional systems are receiving increasing attention as new techniques are developed to realize them. *Sakaki* [7.92] discussed the possibility of obtaining an enhanced mobility along quantum wires, because of the suppression of the ionized-impurity scattering. He proposed a V-groove etch of a planar heterojunction quantum well as a means of achieving the one-dimensional confinement. *Chang* et al. [7.93] proposed a technique involving epitaxial overgrowth on a vertical ⟨110⟩ edge of a pre-grown ⟨100⟩ heterostructure as a means of obtaining the quantum wire. *Petroff* et al. [7.94] reported experimental attempts of implementing one-dimensional confinement by etching techniques. *Cibert* et al. [7.95] experimentally demonstrated carrier confinement in 1 and 0 dimensions. They used a novel technique involving electron-beam lithography and laterally confined inter-diffusion of aluminum in a GaAs/AlGaAs heterostructure grown by MBE. Recently, *Reed* et al. [7.96] reported dimensional quantization effects in GaAs/AlGaAs "quantum dots".

The idea of the quantum wire transistor is illustrated in Fig. 7.53, assuming a GaAs/AlGaAs heterostructure implementation. The device consists of an epitaxially grown undoped planar quantum well and a double AlGaAs barrier sandwiched between two undoped GaAs layers and heavily doped GaAs contact layers. The working surface defined by a *V*-groove etching is subsequently overgrown epitaxially with a thin AlGaAs layer and gated. The thickness of the gate barrier layer ($d \gtrsim 100$ Å) and the Al content in this layer ($x \gtrsim 0.5$) should be chosen so as to minimize gate leakage. The thicknesses of the quantum well barrier layers are chosen so that their projection on the slanted surface should be $\lesssim 50$ Å each. The Al content in these layers should be typically $x \lesssim 0.45$. Application of a positive gate voltage V_G induces 2-D electron gases at the two interfaces with the edges of undoped GaAs layers outside the quantum well. These gases will act as the source (S) and drain (D) electrodes. At the same time, there is a range of V_G in which electrons are not yet induced in the

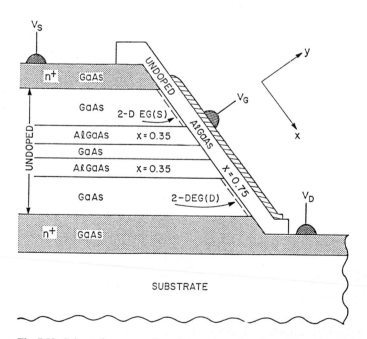

Fig. 7.53. Schematic cross section of the proposed surface resonant tunnelling device, the quantum wire transistor structure. A "*V*-groove" implementation of the quantum wire is assumed. Thicknesses of the two undoped GaAs layers outside the double barrier region should be sufficiently large ($\gtrsim 1000$ Å) to prevent the creation of a parallel conduction path by the conventional (bulk) RT

quantum wire region (which is the edge of the quantum well layer) because of the additional dimensional quantization.

To understand the operation of the device, consider first the band diagram in the absence of a source to drain voltage, $V_{DS} = 0$ (Fig. 7.54a). The diagram is drawn along the x-direction (from S to D parallel to the surface channel). The y-direction is defined as the one normal to the gate and z, that along the quantum wire. Dimensional quantization induced by the gate results in a zero-point energy of electronic motion in the y-direction, represented by the bottom E_0 of a 2-D subband corresponding to the free motion in the x and z directions. The thicknesses of the undoped S and D layers are assumed to be large enough ($\gtrsim 1000$ Å), so that the electronic motion in x-direction in these layers can be considered free. On the other hand, in the quantum well region of the surface channel, there is an additional dimensional quantization – along the x-direction – which defines the quantum wire [7.92]. Let t be the x-projection of the quantum well layer thickness, then the additional zero-point energy is approximately given by

$$E'_0 - E_0 = \pi^2\hbar^2/2m^*t^2 .$$ (7.6)

This approximation is of course good only when the barrier height substantially exceeds E'_0.

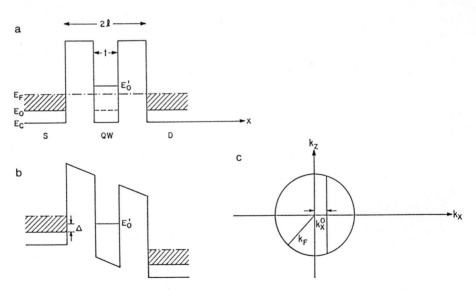

Fig. 7.54a–c. Illustration of the quantum wire transistor operation. (a) Band diagram along the channel in "equilibrium", i.e., in the absence of a drain bias. (b) Band diagram for an applied bias V_{DS}, when the energy of certain electrons in the source (S) matches unoccupied levels of the lowest 1-D subband E'_0 in the quantum wire. (c) Fermi disk corresponding to the 2-D degenerate electron gas in the source electrode. Vertical chord at $k_x = k_x^0$ indicates the momenta of electrons which can tunnel into the quantum wire while conserving their momentum k_z along the wire

Application of a gate voltage V_{GS} moves the 2-D subband E_0 with respect to the (classical) bottom of the conduction band E_C and the Fermi level E_F. The resonant tunnelling condition is set in by the application of a positive V_{DS}, as illustrated in Fig. 7.54b. In this situation, the energy of certain electrons in S matches unoccupied levels in the quantum wire (Fig. 7.54c). Compare this with the tunnelling of 3-D electrons into 2-D density of states discussed in Sect. 7.1.1. In the present case, the dimensionality of both the emitter and the base is reduced by one. Hence the emitter Fermi sea of Fig. 7.1 has become a disk in this case and the Fermi disk of the previous case is replaced by a resonant segment, as shown in Fig. 7.54c. Since both k_x and k_y are quantized in the quantum wire, RT requires conservation of energy and the lateral momentum k_z. This is satisfied only for those electrons whose momenta lie in the segment $k_x = k_x^0$ (Fig. 7.54), where

$$\hbar^2(k_x)/2m^* = \Delta .\tag{7.7}$$

It should be noted that the energies of all electrons in this segment ($k_x = k_x^0$) lie in the band $E_0 + \Delta \le E \le E_F$. However, only those electrons in this energy band that satisfy the momentum conservation condition are resonant. As V_{DS} is increased, the resonant segment moves to the left (Fig. 7.54c), towards the vertical diameter $k_x = 0$ of the Fermi disk, and the number of tunnelling electrons grows, reaching a maximum $[2m^*(E_F - E_0)]^{1/2}/\pi\hbar$ per unit length in the z-direction when $\Delta = 0$. At higher V_{DS}, when $\Delta < 0$, there are no electrons in the source which can tunnel into the quantum wire while conserving their lateral momentum. This gives rise to the NDR in the drain circuit.

In the present device, apart from obtaining high electron mobility as discussed by *Sakaki* [7.92], additional flexibility is achieved through the gate electrode. The gate voltage in this structure not only determines the number of electrons available for conduction but also controls the position of the E_0' level in the quantum wire with respect to E_0 in the source. This latter control is effected by the fringing electric fields and gives rise to the interesting possibility of negative transconductance, as in the RT-FET. *Luryi* and *Capasso* [7.29] have solved the corresponding electrostatic problem by suitable conformal mappings and have shown that in the operating regime of the device, an increasing $V_{GS} > 0$ *lowers* the electrostatic potential energy in the base (quantum wire) with respect to the emitter (source), nearly as effectively as does an increasing V_{DS}.

c) The Gated Quantum Well Resonant Tunnelling Transistor

This unipolar RT transistor was demonstrated by *Beltram* et al. [7.40] in 1988. Although the structure of the device looks similar to the one proposed by *Bonnefoi* et al. [7.27] under the name of Stark effect transistor (SET), the authors in [7.40] have shown its additional possibilities, in particular the existence of NDR at a fixed gate bias and negative transconductance at a fixed emitter-collector bias. The key idea of this transistor is the use of a quantum-well collector and the inverted sequence of layers in which the controlling electrode was placed "behind" the collector layer. The controlling electrode was called "gate". The nomenclature "emitter, collector and *gate*" is, in fact, best suited for a transistor of this kind. Like all potential-effect transistors, this one has an emitter, a collector and a controlled injection process – but the control is effected by an insulated gate through which no dc current is flowing.

Figure 7.55 shows the schematics of the device grown by MBE in the AlGaAs material system. It consisted of an undoped quantum well collector separated from a n^+-doped emitter layer by a thin undoped barrier. A thicker undoped barrier on the other side of the well is followed by a n^+-doped gate. The layer thicknesses indicated were measured by transmission electron microscopy; the doping level in the n^+-GaAs layers was nominally 2×10^{18} cm^{-3}. The devices were defined by standard photolithographic techniques and wet-etched with a $H_3PO_4:H_2O_2:H_2O$ solution. The evaporated contacts were provided by Ge/Au/Ag/Au for the emitter and the collector and by Ni/Au/Ge/Au for the gate.

The emitter-collector $I-V$ characteristics of the device are expected to peak at biases which maximize the RT of the emitter electrons into the 2-D collector subbands. The expected NDR is similar to that in RTDB structures, and results solely from the tunnelling from a 3-D into a 2-D system. The presence of two tunnel barriers is not essential as discussed in Sect. 7.1.1. Transistor action in the structure is obtained via the influence of the gate field on the alignment of the 2-D electron gas (2DEG) energy levels relative to the emitter Fermi level. This occurs for two distinct reasons. One – which in accordance with [7.87] can be called a generalized Stark effect – is associated with the field penetration into the QW. The other effect is the *quantum capacitance* of a 2DEG [7.88]; because of it the gate field partially penetrates beyond the 2-D metal in the QW and induces charges on the emitter electrode.

In Fig. 7.56, the band diagram of our device is shown in the common-collector configuration with applied biases $V_G > 0$ and $V_E < 0$ such that the

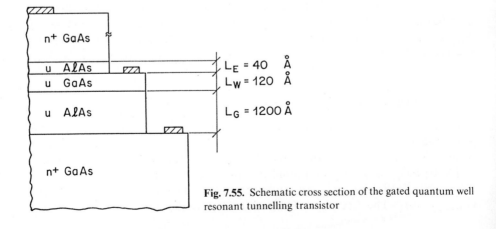

Fig. 7.55. Schematic cross section of the gated quantum well resonant tunnelling transistor

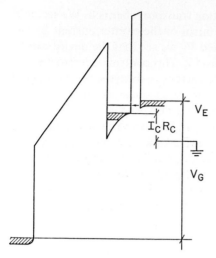

Fig. 7.56. Band diagram with the collector at reference and the biases $V_G > 0$ and $V_E < 0$ corresponding to peak resonant tunnelling of emitter electrons into the second subband of the well

bottom of the conduction band in the emitter is in resonance with the second collector subband; this corresponds to a peak in the current. The RT current can be subsequently quenched by increasing V_G: this leads to negative trans-conductance. As will become clear later, we can be certain that the observed peaks correspond to the RT into the second subband rather than the first, because at the experimental bias conditions corresponding to the peaks, the ground-subband bottom is pushed below the conduction band edge in the emitter. Moreover, the ground subband wavefunction in the triangular part of the well is displaced away from the emitter barrier, which further suppresses tunnelling into it.

Figure 7.57 shows experimental data at 7 K. The expected features present in the I–V were observed up to liquid nitrogen temperature – not as pronounced

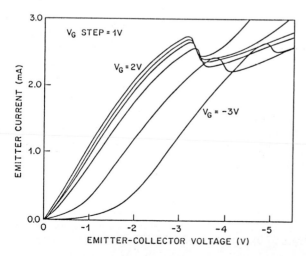

Fig. 7.57. Common-collector characteristics of the resonant tunnelling transistor at various V_G (2, 1, 0, −1, −2, −3 V). The measurements were performed at 7 K

because of the increased influence of competing transport channels. We see both the NDR in the emitter current and the control of the emitter current by the gate. In particular, if we examine I_E at a fixed V_E we see that the device can be brought into and out of resonance by varying V_G. This control is electrostatic in nature as evidenced by the fact that the gate current is always several orders of magnitude smaller than the emitter current. At the resonances, for instance, I_G varies from ~ 1 pA with $V_G = -3$ V up to ~ 10 nA with $V_G = 2$ V.

In order to understand quantitatively the operation of the device in the range $V_G > 0$, let us first analyze the shift of the I–V peaks with varying positive V_G. As discussed above, to estimate these shifts $(\Delta V_E)_p$ one has to calculate the shift of the second subband relative to $E_{F,E}$. We shall perform this in two steps, first by calculating with first-order perturbation theory the "Stark" shift due to the penetration of the gate field into the well, and then by taking into account the quantum capacitance effect and the corresponding additional shift due to the gate field penetration into the emitter barrier.

Neglecting the quantum capacitance effect, the first-order variation in E_2 in response to a variation in the gate field is given by $\delta E_2 = \langle \psi_2 | e\delta\phi | \psi_2 \rangle$, where $\delta\phi(z)$ is the variation in the electrostatic potential in the well, which can be calculated from the Poisson equation

$$\frac{d^2\delta\phi}{dz^2} = \frac{e\delta n}{\varepsilon} |\psi_1|^2 .$$ (7.8)

Here δn is the variation in surface electron concentration and ε is the dielectric constant of the well layer. If we take for the ground subband the variational function of Stern and Howard [7.97] $|\psi_1|^2 = (b^3/2)z^2 e^{-bz}$, where $b = 3/\langle z \rangle_1$ and

$$\langle z \rangle_1 = \left[\frac{72\varepsilon\hbar^2}{11me^2n} \right]^{1/3} = 81\text{A} \times (10^{12}/n)^{1/3} ,$$ (7.9)

then (7.8) can be integrated analytically. For the second state, which is in the rectangular part of the energy diagram, we use the second sine solution of the corresponding square well, i.e. $\psi_2 = (2/L_W)^{1/2} \sin(2\pi z/L_W)$. We obtain then

$$\delta E_2 = \frac{6e^2\delta n}{\varepsilon b^2 L_W} \left[1 - \frac{\alpha^4 + 3\alpha^2 + 6}{6(1 + \alpha^2)^3} \right] ,$$ (7.10)

where $\alpha \equiv 4\pi/bL_W$. In our case of a rather thin well, the second term in the brackets in (7.10) is small. Defining the gate leverage factor λ as the variation in E_2 per unit variation in the gate voltage, $\lambda \equiv \delta E_2/e\delta V_G$, we obtain the Stark-effect contribution to this factor in the form

$$\lambda_s = \frac{2\langle z \rangle_1^2}{3L_G L_W} \approx \frac{1}{51} ,$$ (7.11)

where $\langle z \rangle_1$ was evaluated from (7.9) with $n \approx 2 \times 10^{12}$ cm^{-2}.

The second contribution to λ results from the gate field penetration into the emitter barrier. We can easily estimate the additional shift from the expression [7.88] for the quantum-capacitance ideality factor ($\equiv \lambda^{-1}$), which gives

$$\lambda_Q = \frac{C_1}{C_1 + C_2 + C_Q} \approx \frac{1}{58}, \tag{7.12}$$

where $C_1 \approx \varepsilon/L_G$ and $C_2 \approx \varepsilon(L_E + L_W)$ are the gate-collector and emitter-collector geometric capacitances per unit area, and C_Q is the quantum capacitance of a GaAs 2DEG, $C_Q = me/\pi\hbar \approx 4.5\,\mu\text{F/cm}^2$. The total leverage factor $\lambda = \lambda_S + \lambda_Q = 1/27$ is directly measured in the $I{-}V$ as a shift $(\Delta V_E/\Delta V_G)_p$. The predicted value of λ (≈ 37 mV per 1 V variation in V_G) is in good agreement with the experimentally measured ~ 40 mV per 1 V variation in V_G.

The second question to be considered is why the peaks in the $I{-}V$ occur at such a high applied bias V_E. This is associated with the series resistance introduced by the exposed part of the collector layer between the ring contact and the emitter mesa (in our devices this separation is $\approx 10\,\mu\text{m}$). The Fermi-level pinning at the surface depletes the exposed collector channel much like the gate of a field effect transistor [7.98]. It is easily shown that, for the whole range of V_G examined, the portion of the collector layer between the mesa and the ring contact is always pinched off by the surface potential (≈ 0.8 V). It will then present a constant resistance R_C characteristic of a space-charge-limited conduction with a constant saturation velocity. The potential drop across this resistance is in series with the internal emitter to collector bias. Referring to Fig. 7.56 we can write (at resonance)

$$eI_E R_C + (E_2 - E_1) - E_{F,W} = eV_E - E_{F,E} \tag{7.13}$$

where $E_{F,E}$ and $E_{F,W} = \pi\hbar^2 n/m$ are the quasi Fermi levels in the emitter and collector respectively, and E_1 and E_2 are the bottoms of the first and the second subbands in the quantum well. Taking variation of (7.13), using (7.10) and a similar relation easily derived for δE_1, and substituting the experimental variations of V_E and I_E at resonance, we obtain a constant $R_C \cong 1$ kΩ in wide range of accumulation of V_G. This constancy of R_C for the different characteristics indicates that the operation of our structure cannot be understood as resulting from the series combination of the RT emitter-to-collector diode and a parasitic field effect transistor [7.35]

The operation of the device for negative V_G – at least for large magnitudes – is very different because in that limit no charge is induced in the collector layer. The field is then constant across the structure and can be calculated simply as $(V_G - V_E)/(L_G + L_E + L_W)$. In order to re-establish the resonant condition after a variation of V_G, one has to vary V_E by the same amount. This is observed experimentally for V_G varying from -2 V to -3 V. For small negative V_G it is difficult to estimate the amount of charge induced in the well, but, qualitatively, a smooth transition to the "dry-collector" regime can be expected. This is experimentally observed for V_G ranging from 0 V to -2 V where steps of 1 V in V_G determine (at resonance) increasing steps in V_E from the 40 mV to the 1 V limits modeled above.

References

7.1 L. L. Chang, L. Esaki, R. Tsu: "Resonant Tunnelling in Semiconductor Double Barriers", Appl. Phys. Lett. 593, **24** (1974)

7.2 M. Tsuchiya, H. Sakaki, J. Yoshino: " Room Temperature Observation of Differential Negative Resistance in an AlAs/GaAs/AlAs Resonant Tunnelling Diode", Jpn. J. Appl. Phys., L-466, **24** (1985)

7.3 M. Tsuchiya, H. Sakaki: "Precise Control of Resonant Tunnelling Current in AlAs/GaAs/AlAs Double Barrier Diodes with Atomically-Controlled Barrier Widths", Jpn. J. Appl. Phys., L-185, **25** (1986)

7.4 M. Tsuchiya, H. Sakaki: "Dependence of Resonant Tunnelling Current on Well Widths in AlAs/GaAs/AlAs Double Barrier Diode Structures", Appl. Phys. Lett. 88, **49** (1986)

7.5 S. Muto, T. Inata, H. Ohnishi, N. Yokoyama, S. Hiyamizu: "Effect of Silicon Doping Profile on $I-V$ Characteristics of an AlGaAs/GaAs Resonant Tunnelling Barrier Structure Grown by MBE", Jpn. J. Appl. Phys., L-577, **25** (1986)

7.6 H. Toyoshima, Y. Ando, A. Okamoto, T. Itoh: "New Resonant Tunnelling Diode with a Deep Quantum Well", Jpn. J. Appl. Phys., L-786, **25** (1986)

7.7 M. A. Reed, R. J. Koestner, M. W. Goodwin: "Resonant Tunnelling Through HgTe/ $Hg_{1-x}Cd_xTe$ Double Barrier, Single Quantum Well Heterostructure", Appl. Phys. Lett., 1293, **49** (1986)

7.8 M. A. Reed, J. W. Lee: "Resonant Tunnelling in a GaAs/AlGaAs Barrier/InGaAs Quantum Well Heterostructure", Appl. Phys. Lett., 845, **50** (1987)

7.9 S. Muto, T. Inata, Y. Sugiyama, Y. Nakata, T. Fujii, H. Ohnishi, S. Hiyamizu: "Quantum Well Width Dependence of Negative Differential Resistance of $In_{0.52}Al_{0.48}As/In_{0.53}Ga_{0.47}As$ Resonant Tunnelling Barriers Grown by MBE", Jpn. J. Appl. Phys., L-220, **26** (1987)

7.10 M. Tsuchiya, H. Sakaki: "Dependence of Resonant Tunnelling Current on Al Mole Fractions in $Al_xGa_{1-x}As$-GaAs-$Al_xGa_{1-x}As$ Double Barrier Structures", Appl. Phys. Lett., 1503, **50** (1987)

7.11 C. I. Huang, M. J. Paulus, C. A. Bozada, S. C. Dudley, K. R. Evans, C. E. Stutz, R. L. Jones, M. E. Cheney: "AlGaAs/GaAs Double Barrier Diodes with High Peak-to-Valley Current Ratio", Appl. Phys. Lett., 121, **51** (1987)

7.12 S. Sen, F. Capasso, A. L. Hutchinson, A. Y. Cho: "Room Temperature Operation of $Ga_{0.47}In_{0.53}As/Al_{0.48}In_{0.52}As$ Resonant Tunnelling Diodes", Electron. Lett., 1229, **23** (1987)

7.13 T. Inata, S. Muto, Y. Nakata, S. Sasa, T. Fujii, S. Hiyamizu: "A Pseudomorphic $In_{0.53}Ga_{0.47}As$/AlAs Resonant Tunnelling Barrier with a Peak-to-Valley Current Ratio of 14 at Room Temperature", Jpn. J. Appl. Phys., L-1332, **26** (1987)

7.14 P. D. Hodson, D. J. Robbins, R. H. Wallis, J. I. Davies, A. C. Marshall: "Resonant Tunnelling in AlInAs/GaInAs Double Barrier Diodes Grown by MOCVD", Electron. Lett., 187, **24** (1988)

7.15 E. E. Mendez, W. I. Wang, B. Ricco, L. Esaki: "Resonant Tunnelling of Holes in AlAs-GaAs-AlAs Heterostructures", Appl. Phys. Lett., 415, **47** (1985)

7.16 M. A. Reed, J. W. Lee, H.-L. Tsai: "Resonant Tunnelling through a Double GaAs/AlAs Superlattice Barrier, Single Quantum Well Heterosturcture", Appl. Phys. Lett., 158, **49** (1986)

7.17 T. Nakagawa, H. Imamoto, T. Kojima, K. Ohta: "Observation of Resonant Tunnelling in AlGaAs/GaAs Triple Barrier Diodes", Appl. Phys. Lett., 73 **49** (1986)

7.18 T. Nakagawa, T. Fujita, Y. Matsumoto, T. Kojima, K. Ohta: "Resonant Tunnelling of Holes in AlAs/GaAs Triple Barrier Diodes", Appl. Phys. Lett., 974, **50** (1987)

7.19 J. Allam, F. Beltram, F. Capasso, A. Y. Cho: "Resonant Zener Tunnelling of Electrons Between Valence-Band and Conduction-Band Quantum Wells", Appl. Phys. Lett., 575, **51** (1987)

7.20 S. Sen, F. Capasso, A. C. Gossard, R. A. Spah, A. L. Hutchinson, S. N. G. Chu: "Observation of Resonant Tunnelling through a Compositionally Graded Parabolic Quantum Well", Appl. Phys. Lett., 1428, **51** (1987)

7.21 T. C. L. G. Sollner, W. D. Goodhue, P. E. Tannenwald, C. D. Parker, D. D. Peck: "Resonant Tunnelling through Quantum Wells at Frequencies up to 2.5 THz.", Appl. Phys. Lett., 588, **43** (1983)

7.22 T. C. L. G. Sollner, P. E. Tannenwald, D. D. Peck, W. D. Goodhue: "Quantum Well Oscillators", Appl. Phys. Lett., 1319, **45** (1984)

7.23 E. R. Brown, T. C. L. G. Sollner, W. D. Goodhue, C. L. Chen: "High-Speed Resonant-Tunnelling Diodes", to be published in the SPIE Proc. (1988)

7.24 F. Capasso: "New High Speed Quantum Well and Variable Gap Superlattice Devices", in *Picosecond Electronics and Optoelectronics*, G. A. Mourou, D. M. Bloom, C. H. Lee, Eds. Berlin: Springer, 112 (1985)

7.25 F. Capasso, R. A. Kiehl: "Resonant Tunnelling Transistor with Quantum Well Base and High-Energy Injection: A New Negative Differential Resistance Device", J. Appl. Phys., 1366, **58** (1985)

7.26 N. Yokoyama, K. Imamura, S. Muto, S. Hiyamizu, H. Nishi: "A New Functional Resonant Tunnelling Hot Electron Transistor (RHET)", Jpn. J. Appl. Phys., L-853, **24** (1985)

7.27 A. R. Bonnefoi, D. H. Chow, T. C. McGill: "Inverted Base-Collector Tunnel Transistors", Appl. Phys. Lett., 888, **47** (1985)

7.28 A. R. Bonnefoi, T. C. McGill, R. D. Burnham: "Resonant Tunnelling Transistors with Controllable Negative Differential Resistance", IEEE Electron Dev. Lett., 636, **EDL-6** (1985)

7.29 S. Luryi, F. Capasso: "Resonant Tunnelling of Two Dimensional Electrons through a Quantum Wire: A Negative Transconductance Device", Appl. Phys. Lett., 1347, **47** (1985); also Erratum, Appl. Phys. Lett., 1693, **48** (1986)

7.30 Y. Nakata, M. Asada, Y. Suematsu: "Novel Triode Device using Metal Insulator Superlattice Proposed for High Speed Response", Electron. Lett., 58, **22** (1986)

7.31 F. Capasso, K. Mohammed, A. Y. Cho: "Resonant Tunnelling Through Double Barriers, Perpendicular Quantum Transport Phenomena in Superlattices, and their Device Applications", IEEE J. Quant. Electron., 1853, **QE-22** (1986)

7.32 F. Capasso, S. Sen, A. C. Gossard, A. L. Hutchinson, J. H. English: "Quantum Well Resonant Tunnelling Bipolar Transistor Operating at Room Temperature", IEEE Electron Dev. Lett., 573, **EDL-7** (1986)

7.33 T. Futatsugi, Y. Yamaguchi, K. Ishii, K. Imamura, S. Muto, N. Yokovama, A. Shibatomi: "A Resonant Tunnelling Bipolar Transistor (RBT): A New Functional Device with High Current Gain", Jpn. J. Appl. Phys., L-131, **26** (1987)

7.34 F. Capasso, S. Sen, F. Beltram, A. Y. Cho: "Resonant Tunnelling Gate Field-Effect Transistor", Electron. Lett., 225, **23** (1987)

7.35 T. K. Woodward, T. C. McGill, R. D. Burnham: "Experimental Realization of a Resonant Tunnelling Transistor", Appl. Phys. Lett., 451, **50** (1987)

7.36 S. Sen, F. Capasso, F. Beltram, A. Y. Cho: "The Resonant Tunnelling Field-Effect Transistor: A New Negative Transconductance Device", IEEE Trans. Electron Dev., 1768, **ED-34** (1987)

7.37 F. Capasso, S. Sen, A. Y. Cho: "Negative Transconductance Resonant Tunnelling Field Effect Transistor", Appl. Phys. Lett., 526, **51** (1987)

7.38 F. Capasso, S. Sen, A. Y. Cho: "Resonant Tunnelling: Physics, New Transistors and Superlattice Devices", in *Quantum Well and Superlattice Physics*, 10, **SPIE-792** (1987)

7.39 F. Capasso, S. Sen, A. Y. Cho: "Physics and New Device Applications of Resonant Tunnelling in Quantum Well Heterostructures", Physica Scripta, 199, **T19** (1987)

7.40 F. Beltram, F. Capasso, S. Luryi, S. N. G. Chu, A. Y. Cho: "Negative Transconductance Via Gating of the Quantum Well Subbands in a Resonant Tunnelling Transistor", Appl. Phys. Lett., 219, **53** (1988)

7.41 G. H. Heilmeier: "Microelectronics: End of the Beginning or Beginning of the End?", In IEEE *International Electron Device Meeting Technical Digest*, 2, **IEDM-84**, San Francisco, CA

7.42 S. Sen, F. Capasso, A. Y. Cho, D. Sivco: "Resonant Tunnelling Device with Multiple Negative Differential Resistance: Digital and Signal Processing Applications with Reduced Circuit Complexity", IEEE Trans. Electron Dev., 2185, **ED-34** (1987)

7.43 S. Luryi: "Frequency Limit of Double-Barrier Resonant-Tunnelling Oscillators", Appl. Phys. Lett., 490, **47** (1985)

7.44 B. Ricco, M. Ya Azbel: "Physics of Resonant Tunnelling. The One Dimensional Double-Barrier Case", Phys. Rev. B, 1970, **29** (1984)

7.45 T. Weil, B. Vinter: "Equivalence Between Resonant Tunnelling and Sequential Tunnelling in Double-Barrier Diodes", Appl. Phys. Lett., 1281, **50** (1987)

7.46 M. Jonson, A. Grincwajg: "Effect of Inelastic Scattering on Resonant and Sequential Tunnelling in Double Barrier Heterostructures", Appl. Phys. Lett., 1729, **51** (1987)

7.47 S. Luryi: "Coherent Versus Incoherent Resonant Tunnelling and Implications for Fast Devices", to appear in Superlattices and Microstructures (1988)

7.48 K. K. Choi, B. F. Levine, C. G. Bethea, J. Walker, R. J. Malik: "Photoexcited Coherent Tunnelling in a Double-Barrier Superlattice", Phys. Rev. Lett., 2459, **59** (1987)

7.49 A. D Stone, P. A. Lee: "Effect of Inelastic Processes on Resonant Tunnelling in One Dimension", Phys. Rev. Lett., 1196, **54** (1985)

7.50 C. W. Tu, R. Hendel, R. Dingle: "Molecular Beam Epitaxy and the Technology of Selectively Doped Heterostructure Transistors", in *Gallium Arsenide Technology*, D. K. Ferry Ed. Indianapolis, IN: Howard & Sams, 107 (1985)

7.51 F. Capasso, K. Mohammed, A. Y. Cho: "Sequential Resonant Tunnelling through a Multiquantum Well Superlattice", Appl. Phys. Lett., 478, **48** (1986)

7.52 F. Capasso, K. Mohammed, A. Y. Cho, R. Hull, A. L. Hutchinson: "Effective Mass Filtering: Giant Quantum Amplification of the Photocurrent in a Semiconductor Superlattice", Appl. Phys. Lett, 420, **47** (1985)

7.53 N. Yokoyama, K. Imamura, H. Ohnishi, T. Mori, S. Muto, A. Shibatomi: "Resonant Tunnelling Hot Electron Transistor (RHET)", 5th *Int. Conf. on Hot Carriers in Semiconductors*, Boston, MA (20–24 July, 1987)

7.54 A. C. Gossard, R. C. Miller, W. Wiegmann: "MBE Growth and Energy Levels of Quantum Wells with Special Shapes", Surf. Sci., 131, **174** (1986)

7.55 Recent systematic studies in [7.10] have shown that electron RT through $GaAs/Al_xGa_{1-x}As$ diodes with thin barriers (30 Å) is dominated by the barrier height at the Γ point also in the indirect gap region ($0.45 \leq x \leq 1$)

7.56 M. Heiblum, M. V. Fischetti, W. P. Dumke, D. J. Frank, I. M. Anderson, C. M. Knoedler, L. Osterling: "Electron Interference Effects in Quantum Wells: Observation of Bound and Resonant States", Phys. Rev. Lett., 816, **58** (1987)

7.57 F. Capasso, S. Sen, A. Y. Cho, A. L. Hutchinson: "Hot Electron Resonant Tunnelling Through a Quantum Well: A New Electron Spectroscopy", in *Gallium Arsenide and Related Compounds 1986*, 539 (1986)

7.58 F. Capasso, S. Sen, A. Y. Cho, A. L. Hutchinson: "Resonant Tunnelling Electron Spectroscopy", Electron. Lett., 28, **23** (1987)

7.59 F. Capasso, S. Sen, A. Y. Cho, A. L. Hutchinson: "Resonant Tunnelling Spectroscopy of Hot Minority Electrons Injected in Gallium Arsenide Quantum Wells", Appl. Phys. Lett., 930, **50** (1987)

7.60 J. R. Hayes, A. F. J. Levi, W. Wiegmann: "Hot Electron Spectroscopy", Electron. Lett., 851, **20** (1984)

7.61 N. Yokoyama, K. Imamura, T. Oshima, H. Nishi, S. Muto, K. Kondo, S. Hiyamizu: "Characterization of Double Heterojunction GaAs/AlGaAs Hot Electron Transistor" in IEEE *International Electron Device Meeting Technical Digest*, 532, **IEDM-84**, San Francisco, CA (Dec. 9–12, 1984)

7.62 J. R. Hayes, A. F. J. Levi: "Dynamics of Extreme Nonequilibrium Electron Transport in GaAs", IEEE J. of Quantum Electron., 1744, **QE-22** (1986)

7.63 J. R. Hayes, A. F. J. Levi, A. C. Gossard, J. H. English: "Base Transport Dynamics in a Heterojunction Bipolar Transistor", Appl. Phys. Lett., 1481, **49** (1986)

7.64 K. Berthold, A. F. J. Levi, J. Walker, R. J. Malik: "Extreme Nonequilibrium Transport in Heterojunction Bipolar Transistors", Appl. Phys. Lett., 2247, **52** (1988)

7.65 F. Capasso, S. Sen, A. Y. Cho, D. Sivco: "Resonant Tunnelling Devices with Multiple Negative Differential Resistance and Demonstration of a Three-State Memory Cell for Multiple-Valued Logic Applications", IEEE Electron Dev. Lett., 297, **EDL-8** (1987)

7.66 R. C. Potter, A. A. Lakhani, D. Beyea, H. Hier, E. Hempfling A. Fathimulla: "Three-Dimensional Integration of Resonant Tunnelling Structures for Signal Processing and Three-State Logic", Appl. Phys. Lett., 2163, **52** (1988)

7.67 A. A. Lakhani, R. C. Potter, H. S. Hier: "Eleven-Bit Parity Generator with a Single, Vertically Integrated Resonant Tunnelling Device", Electron. Lett., 681, **24** (1988)

7.68 S. Sen, F. Capasso, D. Sivco, A. Y. Cho: "New Resonant Tunnelling Devices with Multiple Negative Resistance Regions and High Room Temperature Peak to Valley Ratio", IEEE Electron Dev. Lett., 402, **9** (1988)

7.69 S. Luryi, A. Kastalsky, A. C. Gossard, R. H. Hendel: "Charge Injection Transistor Based on Real-Space Hot-Electron Transfer", IEEE Trans. Electron Dev., 832, **ED-31** (1984)

7.70 C. Rine, Ed.: *Computer Science and Multiple Valued Logic.* Amsterdam: North-Holland (1977)

7.71 A. Heung, H. T. Mouftah: "An All-CMOS Ternary Identity Cell for VLSI Implementation", Electron. Lett., 221, **20** (1984)

7.72 *General Electric Tunnel Diode Manual*, First Ed., 66 (1961)

7.73 J. Söderström, T. G. Andersson: "A Multiple-State Memory Cell Based on the Resonant Tunnelling Diode", to be published in IEEE Electron Dev. Lett., (May, 1988)

7.74 K. K. Choi, B. F. Levine, R. J. Malik, J. Walker, C. G. Bethea: "Periodic Negative Conductance by Sequential Resonant Tunnelling Through an Expanding High-Field Superlattice Domain", Phys. Rev. B, 4172, **35** (1987)

7.75 S. P. Gentile: *Basic Theory and Application of Tunnel Diodes*, Princeton: Van Nostrand, 156 (1962)

7.76 A. S. Vengurlekar, F. Capasso, S. Sen, A. L. Hutchinson, S. N. G. Chu, D. Sivco, A. Y. Cho: "Quasiballistic Resonant Tunneling of Minority Electrons into the Excited States of a Quantum Well", Appl. Phys. Lett., 2529, **55** (1989)

7.77 F. Capasso, A. S. Vengurlekar, A. Hutchinson, W. T. Tsang: "Negative Transconductance Superlattice Base Bipolar Transistor", Electron. Lett. 1117, **25** (1989)

7.78 F. Beltram, F. Capasso, A. L. Hutchinson, R. J. Malik: "Continuum Mini-band Superlattice Base Transistor with Graded Gap Electron Inject", Electron. Lett. 1219, **25** (1989)

7.79 R. J. Malik, F. Capasso, R. A. Stall, R. A. Kiehl, R. W. Ryan, R. Wunder, C. G. Bethea: High Gain, High Frequency AlGaAs/GaAs Graded Band-Gap Base Bipolar Transistors with a Be Diffusion Setback Layer in the Base", Appl. Phys. Lett., 600, **46** (1985)

7.80 D. Ankri, R. A. Zoulay, E. Caquot, J. Dangal, C. Dubon, J. Palmier: "Analysis of D. C. Characteristics of GaAlAs/GaAs Double Heterojunction Bipolar Transistors", Solid-State Electron., 141, **29** (1986)

7.81 T. Futatsugi, Y. Yamaguchi, S. Muto, N. Yokoyama, A. Shibatomi: "InAlAs/InGaAs Resonant Tunnelling Bipolar Transistor (RBTs) Operating at Room Temperature with High Current Gains", IEEE *International Electron Device Meeting Technical Digest*, 877, **IEDM-87**, Washington, DC (Dec. 6–9, 1987)

7.82 S. Sen, F. Capasso, A. Y. Cho, D. L. Sivco: "Stacked Double Barriers and their Application in Novel Multi-State Resonant Tunnelling Bipolar Transistor", Inst. Phys. Conf. Ser. 605, **96** (1988)

7.83 S. Sen, F. Capasso, A. Y. Cho, D. L. Sivco: "Multiple State Resonant Tunnelling Bipolar Transistor Operating at Room Temperature and its Application as a Frequency Multiplier", IEEE Electron Dev. Lett., 533, **9** (1988)

7.84 F. Capasso, S. Sen, A. Y. Cho, D. L. Sivco: "Multiple Negative Transconductance and Differential Conductance in a Bipolar Transistor by Sequential Quenching of Resonant Tunnelling", Appl. Phys. Lett., 1056, **53** (1988)

7.85 S. R. Forrest, M. DiDomenico, Jr., R. G. Smith, H. J. Stocker: "Evidence for Tunnelling in Reverse-Biased III–V Photodetector Diodes", Appl. Phys. Lett. 580, **36** (1980)

7.86 S. Sen, F. Capasso, A. Y. Cho, D. L. Sivco: "Parity Generator Circuit Using a Multi-State Resonant Tunnelling Bipolar Transistor", Electron. Lett., 1506, **24** (1988)

7.87 D. A. B. Miller, D. S. Chemla, T. C. Damen, A. C. Gossard, W. Wiegmann, T. H. Wood, C. A. Burrus: "Band-Edge Electroabsorption in Quantum Well Structures", Phys. Rev. Lett., 2173, **53** (1984)

7.88 S. Luryi: "Quantum Capacitance Devices", Appl. Phys. Lett., 501, **52** (1988)

7.89 T. K. Woodward, T. C. McGill, H. F. Chung, R. D. Burnham: "Integration of a Resonant-Tunnelling Structure with a Metal-Semiconductor Field-Effect Transistor", Appl. Phys. Lett., 1542, **51** (1987)

7.90 T. K. Woodward, T. C. McGill, H. F. Chung, R. D. Burnham: "Applications of Resonant-Tunnelling Field-Effect Transistors", IEEE Electron Dev. Lett., 122, **EDL-9** (1988)

7.91 V. J. Goldman, D. C. Tsui, J. E. Cunningham: "Resonant Tunnelling in a Magnetic Field: Evidence for Space-Charge Build-Up", Phys. Rev., 9387, **B 35** (1987)

7.92 H. Sakaki: "Scattering Suppression and High-Mobility Effect of Size-Quantized Electrons in Ultrafine Semiconductor Wire Structures", Jpn. J. Appl. Phys., L-735, **19** (1980)

7.93 Yia-Chung Chang, L. L. Chang, L. Esaki: "A New One-Dimensional Quantum Well Structure", Appl. Phys. Lett., 1324, **47** (1985)

7.94 P. M. Petroff, A. C. Gossard, R. A. Logan, W. Wiegmann: "Toward Quantum Well Wires: Fabrication and Optical Properties", Appl. Phys. Lett., 636, **41** (1982)

7.95 J. Cibert, P. M. Petroff, G. J. Dolan, S. J. Pearton, A. C. Gossard, J. H. English: "Optically Detected Carrier Confinement to One and Zero Dimensions in GaAs Quantum Well Wires and Boxes", Appl. Phys. Lett., 1275, **49** (1986)

7.96 M. A. Reed, R. T. Bate, K. Bradshaw, W. M. Duncan, W. R. Frensley, J. W. Lee, H. D. Shih: "Spatial Quantization in GaAs-AlGaAs Multiple Quantum Dots", J. Vac. Sci. Technol., 358, **B 4** (1986)

7.97 F. Stern, W. E. Howard: Phys. Rev. **163**, 816 (1967)

7.98 It should be noted that while the exposed portion of the channel is depleted, the portion under the emitter is not. This follows unambiguously from the identification of the current peaks with resonant tunnelling. At the bias conditions corresponding to the resonances in the range $V_G \gtrsim 0$, the field drop associated with charge in the quantum well is always $\gtrsim 2 \times 10^5$ V/cm corresponding to $n \gtrsim 2 \times 10^{12}$ cm^{-2}.

8. Resonant-Tunnelling Hot Electron Transistors (RHET)

N. Yokoyama, S. Muto, H. Ohnishi, K. Imamura, T. Mori, and T. Inata

With 24 Figures

Heiblum proposed a hot electron transistor, THETA, that [8.1] used semi-conductor heterojunctions. The good lattice match and the single-crystal epitaxial growth with molecular beam epitaxy (MBE) provides superior inter-faces difficult to obtain with metal-oxide or metal-semiconductors. The very short carrier transit time indicates the potential application for very high speed devices. We fabricated hot electron transistors using [8.2, 3] MBE-grown GaAs/AlGaAs heterostructures. The device had a current gain of more than one at 40 K. We were the first to propose hot electron spectroscopy using the hot electron transistor [8.3], and measured the hot electron spectrum. However, we could not observe ballistic transport in this device due to scattering into the upper satellite valley in the AlGaAs collector barrier. We noticed evidence of near-ballistic transport in the base region of this device by measuring the transfer ratio of the hot electron transistor in a magnetic field [8.4]. We found that the transfer ratio decreases as the magnitude of the magnetic field normal to the direction of injection increases. We attribute this to the cyclotron motion of hot electrons. From these observations, the transit time for a 100 nm GaAs base was estimated to range from 0.1 ps to 1.0 ps [8.5], indicating a transit velocity from 1×10^7 to 1×10^8 cm/s suggesting near-ballistic transport in the base region.

Having demonstrated that hot electron transistors have superior per-formance characteristics, our goal is to develop high-speed integrated circuits. At present, the wiring delay limits the operating speed of integrated circuits. RHETs used in integrated circuits could reduce the number of circuit components, thereby reducing wiring delays. This chapter describes the device technology, feasibility, and physics related to RHETs.

8.1 RHET Operation

The RHET we proposed [8.6] is essentially the same as a hot electron transistor, but with one important difference: The RHET uses a resonant tunnelling barrier as a hot electron injector as shown in Fig. 8.1. The conventional hot electron transistor uses a Fowler–Nordheim or direct tunnelling barrier. RHETs are thus an important tool for the investigation of the physics of hot electron transport because resonant tunnelling generates monoenergetic hot electron beam. An-

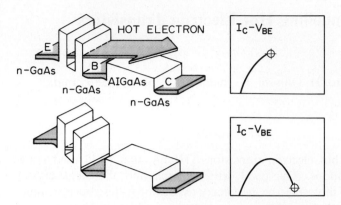

Fig. 8.1. Operating principle of RHET

other important feature of the RHET is its negative transconductance region. With a voltage to the base, electrons are injected into the base by resonant tunnelling and are near-ballistically transported to the collector, causing the collector current to flow. The collector current decreases with further increases in the base voltage, because the resonant-tunnelling current is reduced, generating negative transconductance. Negative transconductance devices may be important for future integrated circuits. The RHET can provide high-speed operation because it uses hot electron and quantum mechanical transport mechanisms.

Figure 8.2 is a schematic band diagram of the RHET, which has a rather wide quantum well barrier and two resonant states in the quantum well. For an increased base-emitter voltage (when the Fermi level of the emitter aligns with the first resonant state), hot electrons are injected into the base through the first resonant state. When the injection energy is designed to be less than the collector barrier height, these electrons cannot surmount the collector barrier. The tunnelling current then flows into the base, causing a base current peak with respect to the base-emitter voltage. With a further increase in the base emitter voltage (when the Fermi level of the emitter aligns with the second resonant state), hot electrons are injected again into the base with higher energies through the

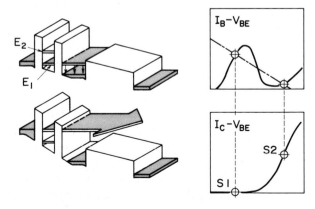

Fig. 8.2. RHET for memory application

second resonant state. These electrons travel through the base and can surmount the collector barrier, resulting in the collector current flow. If we connect a resistor in series to the base of this RHET with a suitable supply voltage, we can draw a load line crossing the base current at three points. The middle point is an unstable state, and other points are stable states. It is clear that the RHET has bistable states [8.7, 8], $S1$ and $S2$. In the $S1$ state the RHET is not conductive, and in the $S2$ state the RHET is conductive.

8.2 RHET Technology Using GaAs/AlGaAs Heterostructures

Figure 8.3 shows a schematic cross section of the RHET fabricated using GaAs/AlGaAs heterostructures [8.9]. This RHET has a 25 nm base layer. The AlAs mole fraction for the collector barrier is 0.16 and is graded to 0 over 5 nm near the base to reduce the quantum mechanical reflection. The RHET has an asymmetric resonant tunnelling barrier structure, enabling us to increase the peak current while simultaneously decreasing the valley current. The quantum well width of 3.68 nm is another important factor in optimizing the injection energy of hot electrons. For this device, the injection energy at the current peak was designed to be 0.30 eV to avoid intervalley scattering in the base. The injection energy is also high enough to surmount the collector barrier. The collector current, indicated by the solid line, and current gain, indicated by the dotted line, are plotted in Fig. 8.4 as functions of the base-emitter voltage for a 25 nm base RHET. These measurements were made at 77 K while the base voltage was increased for a common emitter configuration with a constant 3 V on the collector. Note the pronounced peak in the collector current due to resonant tunnelling, followed by a valley, indicating a negative transconductance region. The peak-to-valley ratio is 2.6. The peak current density reaches 2.7 × 10^4 A/cm². The common emitter current gain is 4 at the peak collector current, and reaches a maximum of 5.

Figure 8.5 shows a RHET application. We built a logic gate using a single RHET (50-nm-base) and resistors. We observed an oscillograph of inputs, A and

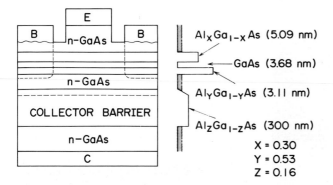

Fig. 8.3. Cross section of RHET fabricated using GaAs-based materials

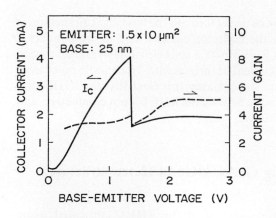

Fig. 8.4. Current-voltage characteristics measured for GaAs-based RHET

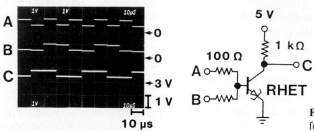

Fig. 8.5. Exclusive-NOR logic function using RHET

B, and output, *C*, using this circuit. Output *C* is high about 4 V, when both *A* and *B* are high at 1 V or both *A* and *B* are low at 0.5 V. Output *C* is low at about 3.5 V when *A* does not equal *B*. This indicates that the circuit can operate as an Exclusive-NOR logic gate. Several MESFETs or bipolar transistors are conventionally required to build an exclusive-NOR logic gate.

Figure 8.6 shows waveforms observed using the circuit shown. The RHET used in this circuit has a 5.6 nm wide quantum well sandwiched between 5-nm thick AlGaAs barriers with a 0.33 AlAs mole fraction. The hot electron injection energy is estimated to be around 0.1 eV, which is comparable to or smaller than the collector barrier height. A positive and negative trigger pulse generator was

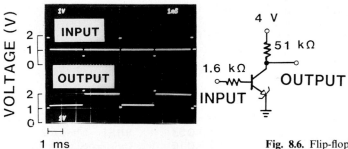

Fig. 8.6. Flip-flop function using RHET

connected to the 1.6 kohm resistor, with a dc offset voltage of 1 V. The upper trace is the input pulses, and lower trace is the output waveform. As shown in the figure, the output voltage goes low with a positive trigger pulse, indicating that the RHET goes to a conductive state. With a negative trigger pulse, the output voltage goes high, indicating that the RHET goes to a poor conductive state. Note that these two states are maintained even after these pulses are removed. Thus. this circuit acts as a bistable multivibrator, or flip-flop [8.7]. This demonstrates that the RHET is useful for memory and/or logic applications.

Thus, the use of RHETs could decrease the number of components in integrated circuits. The RHET's disadvantages are its poor current gain and poor collector current peak-to-valley ratio. These problems have been solved by using InGaAs-based materials instead of GaAs-based materials.

8.3 InGaAs-Based Material Evaluation

Figure 8.7 shows the energy band-gap difference between InGaAs and InAlGaAs determined from the edge emission of photoluminescence spectra of a bulk sample. Also shown is the conduction band-edge discontinuity between them. This was determined from the temperature dependence of thermionic emission current through a single InAlGaAs barrier [8.10]. These parameters are linearly dependent on the Al composition, indicating good design possibilities for band-gap engineering.

Figure 8.8 compares the conduction band structures of GaAs-based materials and InGaAs-based materials. A key to the InGaAs-based RHET is in the conduction bands of the base region. The InGaAs base has a wider separation energy (0.55 eV) between the Γ and L points. This may improve the InGaAs RHET's current gain compared with that of the GaAs-based RHET. The wider separation energy between Γ and L points in the collector barrier helps reduce scattering into the upper satellite valley. Another important point is that the InAlAs used for the resonant tunnelling barrier is a direct-gap semiconductor

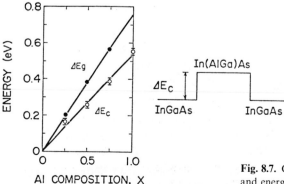

Fig. 8.7. Conduction band edge discontinuity and energy band gap difference

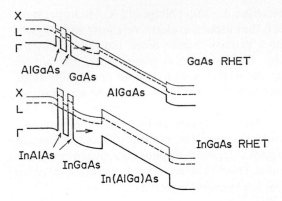

Fig. 8.8. Conduction band comparison

that reduces indirect valley effects for tunnelling transport in the barrier [8.11, 12], thus decreasing excess valley current. The InAlAs barrier has a lighter electron effective mass than AlGaAs barriers – 60 percent of that of AlGaAs barriers (0.123 for an AlAs mole fraction of 0.65). The decreased effective mass increases the electron tunnelling probability and peak current density, thus increasing the peak-to-valley current ratio. This possibly decreases the response time of the barrier because of the decreased dwell time and decreased resonant-tunnelling barrier capacitance charge/discharge time.

To determine the negative-differential-resistance (NDR) properties, we grew resonant-tunnelling barrier (RTB) structures of the form $In_xAl_{1-x}As$ ($x = 0.52$, L_B)/$In_yGa_{1-y}As$ ($y = 0.53$, L_W)/$In_xAl_{1-x}As$ ($x = 0.52$, L_B) sandwiched between thick Si-doped n-$In_yGa_{1-y}As$ layers ($y = 0.53$) on (100) n^+-InP substrate grown by MBE at a temperature of 470°C. The carrier concentration of the Si-doped InGaAs layers was 1×10^{18} cm^{-3} near the InAlAs barrier. After growth, diodes were fabricated by making non-alloyed ohmic contacts on the upper and the lower n InGaAs layers. The carrier concentration of the n-InGaAs layer near the ohmic contacts was 2×10^{19} cm^{-3}. Figure 8.9 shows the schematic cross section of the diode structure.

Figure 8.10 shows the barrier-width (L_B) dependence [8.13] of the peak (I_P) and the valley (I_V) current densities in the NDR region of the diodes at 77 K when

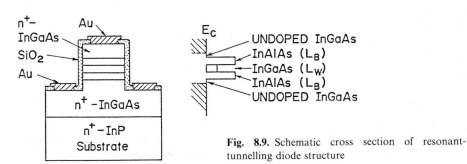

Fig. 8.9. Schematic cross section of resonant-tunnelling diode structure

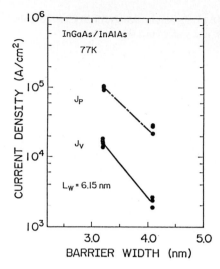

Fig. 8.10. Barrier-width dependence of the peak and valley current density

the well width (L_W) was fixed at 6.15 nm (21 group-III atomic layers). When the barrier width was reduced from 4.10 nm (14 atomic layers) to 3.22 nm (11 atomic layers), I_P increased from 2.2×10^4 A/cm^2 to 1×10^5 A/cm^2. However, I_V increased more drastically than I_P and the resultant peak-to-valley ratio (I_P/I_V) decreased from 11.7 to 6.3. This tendency can be qualitatively understood if we consider I_P as being the resonant current density and I_V as the off-resonant current density. When L_B is reduced, the tunnelling probabilities of single barriers are increased for both the left (injection, or negatively-biased) and the right (positively-biased) barriers. Here, the resonant current density is proportional to the tunnelling probability of the left barrier, or minimum tunnelling probability [8.14], while the off-resonant current density is proportional to the product of the tunnelling probabilities of the left and the right barriers [8.15]. Therefore, it is natural that I_V increases more rapidly than I_P as the L_B decreases.

The peak and the valley current densities at 77 K with a fixed L_B of 4.10 nm are shown in Fig. 8.11 as a function of the quantum well width (L_W) [8.16]. When L_W was reduced from 6.15 nm to 4.40 nm, the peak current density of the NDR region increased monotonically from 2.9×10^4 A/cm^2 to 6.3×10^4 A/cm^2. The valley current density also increased proportionally to the peak current density, and the resultant peak-to-valley ratio remained almost constant (i.e. in the range 10.9–11.7).

In the InGaAs/InAlAs resonant-tunnelling barriers, band nonparabolicity is expected to play an important role in the NDR characteristics, partly due to the small energy band gap of InGaAs (E_g is 0.76 eV at 300 K). Therefore, we performed a simple tunnelling model calculation taking the band nonparabolicity into account. The solid curve in Fig. 8.12 shows the calculated peak current densities (I_P) [8.16]. Excellent agreement with the experimental I_P of Fig. 8.11 was obtained. The dashed curve was produced by assuming a parabolic band. The reason for the increased I_P due to the nonparabolicity is explained by

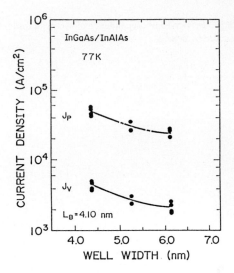

Fig. 8.11. Quantum-well-width dependence of the peak and valley current density

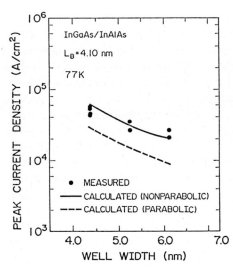

Fig. 8.12. Effect of nonparabolicity on the quantum-well-width dependence of peak current density (I_P) of InGaAs/InAlAs resonant-tunnelling barriers

the behaviour of tunnelling electrons in the InAlAs barrier layer. The tunnelling probability of a single barrier is approximated by

$$T \propto \exp(-2\kappa L_B) . \tag{8.1}$$

Here, κ indicates the imaginary part of the electron wave vector. For InAlAs barriers, within the 2-band kp approximation [8.17], the energy dependence is given by the solid curve on the left side of Fig. 8.13. Here, the energy E, is measured from the conduction band minimum of InGaAs, so the band gap of the InAlAs corresponds to the energy region between 0.53 and -0.93 eV. The dotted curve in Fig. 8.13 indicates the E–κ relation given by the parabolic

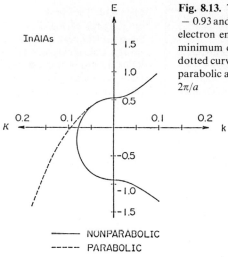

Fig. 8.13. The E–κ relation around the band gap (between -0.93 and $+0.53$ eV) of InAlAs lattice-matched to InP. The electron energy, E, is measured from the conduction band minimum of InGaAs lattice-matched to InP. The solid and dotted curves are results of the 2-band kp approximation and parabolic approximation, respectively. The unit of k and κ is $2\pi/a$

approximation. As seen, the decay rate, κ, becomes smaller and the probability, T, becomes larger by considering the nonparabolicity, especially when the electron energy is far below the conduction band edge. In the resonant tunnelling of the InAlAs/InGaAs barrier, electrons tunnel through the left InAlAs barrier layer with an energy far below the energy of its conduction band edge (0 to 0.2 eV in Fig. 8.13). This is due to the large conduction band discontinuity (ΔE_C is 0.53 eV [8.10]) at the interface. Therefore, nonparabolicity causes a considerably higher tunnelling probability for the left barrier and, as a result, a higher peak current density than that predicted by a parabolic approximation. Thus, the high electron tunnelling probability of InAlAs barrier layer (due to a light electron effective mass) is enhanced by the nonparabolicity of the layer.

The experimental peak-to-valley ratios of the InGaAs/InAlAs RTBs at 77 K are summarized in Fig. 8.14 as a function of I_P, and is contrasted with the data for GaAs/AlGaAs (including GaAs/AlAs) barriers [8.18–23]. The advantages of InGaAs-based material over GaAs-based material is obvious. The NDR, required for an emitter barrier of resonant-tunnelling transistors, is shown by the shaded area. Peak current density over 1×10^5 A/cm^2 is required for high-speed operation, and peak-to-valley ratio over 10 is required for using the resonant-tunnelling transistors as new functional devices. Some InGaAs/InAlAs RTBs nearly meet the required performance area.

The peak-to-valley ratio (I_P/I_V) obtained for InGaAs/InAlAs RTBs at room temperature are not very impressive because of its relatively small barrier height (0.53 eV). As a matter of fact, a peak-to-valley current density ratio of 5.5 [8.24] obtained with an L_B of 4.69 nm and an L_W of 3.22 nm is the best room temperature NDR of InGaAs/InAlAs RTBs. This value is still the highest of any RTB structure, as far as lattice-matched systems are concerned. However, we recently developed a RTB with a larger barrier height by replacing the InAlAs

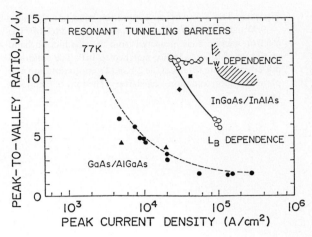

Fig. 8.14. The peak-to-valley ratio (I_P/I_V) of Fig. 8.2 as a function of the peak current density (I_P). Data for GaAs/AlGaAs RTBs are also plotted: ($\bullet$) after [8.19], ($\blacktriangle$) after [8.18, 20, 21], ($\blacksquare$) after [8.22], and ($\blacklozenge$) after [8.23]

barrier with an AlAs barrier. This InGaAs/AlAs pseudomorphic RTB, whose barrier height appears to be as large as 1.4 eV [8.25], shows a pronounced I_P/I_V of 14 at room temperature [8.26].

8.4 RHET Technology Using InGaAs-Based Materials

To improve the current gain and peak-to-valley ratio, we fabricated a RHET using InGaAs-based materials [8.27]. Figure 8.15 shows the schematic cross section for this device. The RHET's resonant-tunnelling barrier consists of a 3.8 nm InGaAs layer sandwiched between 4.4 nm-InAlAs films. These parameters were optimized to increase the resonant-tunnelling current density and peak-to-valley current ratio. The collector barrier is a 200-nm InAlGaAs quaternary alloy layer having an Al mole fraction of 0.5. These were optimized to increase the current gain and to keep base-collector leakage current negligible at 77 K. On the base side of the collector barrier, compositions were changed in three steps, 0.33, 0.25, and 0.2, over 6 nm region to decrease quantum mechanical

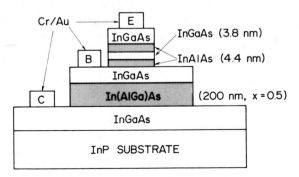

Fig. 8.15. Cross section of RHET fabricated using InGaAs-based materials

reflection. Carrier concentrations were 1×10^{18} cm^{-3} for the emitter and base. InGaAs layers doped to a concentration of 5×10^{19} cm^{-3} were grown at the top to decrease emitter contact resistance. The compositions of these alloys were lattice-matched with the InP substrate using a pulsed molecular beam. The emitter, base, and collector electrodes were formed using nonalloyed Cr/Au ohmic contacts.

In Fig. 8.16, the collector current, indicated by the solid line, and the current gain, indicated by the dashed line, are plotted as functions of the base-emitter voltage. These measurements were made for a common emitter configuration at 77 K with a constant 2.2 V on the collector. The emitter-base junction area was 6 μm × 7 μm. Note that the peak-to-valley ratio in the collector current reaches 19.3, the highest reported so far. This ratio is about eight times greater than that of the GaAs-based RHET. The current gain reaches 17.2 at the peak voltage. These are typical values for this wafer. The current gains are about four times greater than that of the GaAs-based RHET, with the maximum current gain observed at 25. The greatly improved current gain and collector peak-to-valley current ratio are due to the use of InGaAs-based materials.

8.5 Theoretical Analyses of RHET Performance

Figure 8.17 shows the energy-band diagram used for the theoretical analysis of the resonant-tunnelling barrier [8.28] investigate current-voltage characteristics and the hot electron spectrum, we self-consistently solved the Poisson equation together with Schrödinger equation for longitudinal motion. In the Poisson equation, ϕ is the electrostatic potential for electrons and ε is the dielectric constant. We used the ε effective mass Schrödinger equation for longitudinal motion, and determined the wave function ψ in the resonant-tunnelling barrier and the transmission coefficient. For transverse motion, we assumed a plane wave. To solve the equation, the potential is divided into small segments, where we assume the electrical field and effective mass to be constant. This equation for

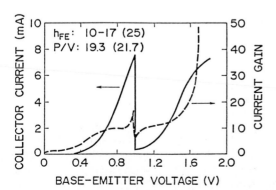

Fig. 8.16. Current-voltage characteristics measured for InGaAs-based RHET

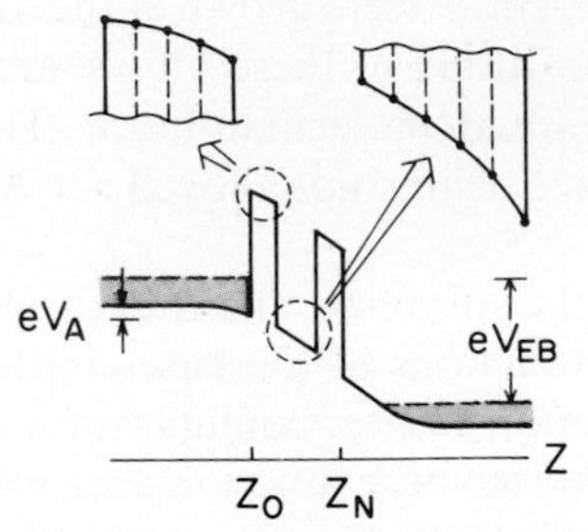

$$\frac{d}{dz}\left(\varepsilon(z)\frac{d\phi}{dz}\right) = e\,[N_D+(Z)-n(z)], \tag{1}$$

$$-\frac{\hbar^2}{2}\frac{d}{dz}\left(\frac{1}{m^*}\frac{d\psi}{dz}\right) + V(Z)\,\psi(k_z,z) = E\psi(k_z,z), \tag{2}$$

$$n(z) = \sum_{lk} f\,[E,E_f(z)] \quad (Z<Z_0)$$

$$n(z) = \sum_{lk} |\psi(k_z,z)|^2 f\,[E,E_f(z_0)] \quad (Z_0<Z<Z_N), \tag{3}$$

$$n(z) = n(z_N) + \sum_{lk} f\,[E,E_f(z)] \quad (Z_N<Z)$$

Fig. 8.17. Conceptual band diagram and equations for resonant-tunnelling barrier

each segment is solved by using Airy functions. Each envelope function is then connected at the boundaries with its two adjacent segments. The carrier distribution is calculated from equations, and is shown in Fig. 8.17. This calculation takes into account the accumulation and depletion regions but not nonparabolicity effects.

The theoretical and experimental $I-V$ characteristics of the InGaAs/InAlAs resonant tunnelling barrier are shown in Fig. 8.18. The solid line shows the emitter current density measured for a common base configuration at 77 K. The collector-base voltage is held constant at 1.8 V. The dashed line is the theoretical curve. We assume the effective masses to be 0.042 for InGaAs and 0.0755 for InAlAs, and the conduction band discontinuity between them to be 0.530 eV [8.10]. The experimental peak voltage is larger than the calculated value. The main reason of the increased peak voltage is emitter and base series resistance. Although the experimental peak current density for the RHET agrees well with the value calculated using our parabolic band model, it is three times smaller than the measured value for InGaAs/InAlAs reference diode having the same double-

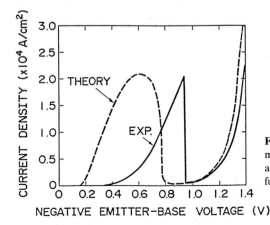

Fig. 8.18. Calculated (*dashed line*) and measured (*solid line*) emitter current density at 77 K for the InGaAs-based RHET as functions of negative emitter-base voltage

barrier structure. The reason for this small experimental peak current density for the RHET is not clear.

We examined the motion of electrons injected into the InGaAs base using a Monte Carlo simulation. Our model took into consideration the energy distribution of injected electrons. Figure 8.19 shows this in the direction of injection (z-direction), calculated for the InGaAs-based RHET with a peak emitter voltage of 0.6 V. The energy spread is very small (0.39 meV) due to injection through the resonant state. The emitter layer, however, is degenerate and, assuming that barriers are free of impurities and inhomogeneities, lateral electron momentum (k_x, k_y) is conserved. This means that tunnelling is possible for electrons whose lateral energy is $0 < h^2 (k_x^2 + k_y^2)/(2m^*) < E_F - E_0$, where $E_F - E_0$ is the difference between the Fermi energy and the energy at the bottom of the quantum level. Figure 8.20 is the total energy distribution. The energy spread is 142 meV, nearly equal to $E_F - E_0$.

For the base region, we accounted for the scattering of polar optical phonons, acoustic phonons, inter-valley phonons, ionized impurities, and plasmons [8.30, 31]. For InGaAs base, we also accounted for alloy scattering [8.32, 33]. For the sake of simplicity, we ignored the coupled plasmon-optical phonon mode [8.34]. This assumption may not be good for GaAs, because the plasmon energy is close to the optical phonon energy. In comparison, for InGaAs the plasmon energy and the optical phonon energy are 53.8 meV and 34.5 meV, respectively. Since they differ rather widely, we assume that the coupling between them is weak. Table 8.1 gives material parameters for the InGaAs base.

As the base width decreases, the effect of the potential profile in the base becomes more important. The voltage drop in the depletion layer at the emitter-base junction decreases the injection energy of hot electrons, and the electrons are accelerated through this layer. The voltage drop in the accumulation layer at the base-collector junction reduces the effective collector barrier height. We calcu-

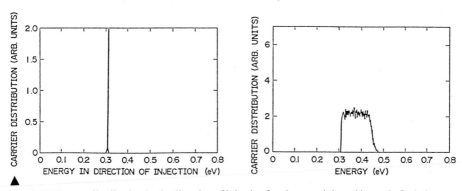

Fig. 8.19. Energy distribution in the direction of injection for electrons injected into a InGaAs base at the peak emitter-base voltage of 0.6 V

Fig. 8.20. Total energy distribution of electrons injected into a InGaAs base at the peak emitter-base voltage of 0.6 V

Table 8.1. In$_{0.53}$Ga$_{0.47}$As parameters

Parameter	Unit	Γ-valley	L-valley	X-valley
Effective mass ratio	—	0.042	0.26	0.62
Nonparabolicity	eV^{-1}	1.167	0.51	0.58
Valley separation from Γ-Valley	eV	—	0.55	0.67
Polar optical phonon energy	eV	0.0345	0.0345	0.0345
Plasmon energy	eV	0.0538	0.0538	0.0538
Acoustic deformation potential	eV	9.2	9.2	9.2
Alloy scattering potential	eV	0.6	0.6	0.6

lated the potential profile of the emitter base junction and that of base-collector junction separately, and then estimated the potential profile in the base region.

To include the effect of the collector barrier tunnelling of hot electrons, we define the transfer ratio as

$$\alpha = \int_0^\infty f(E_z) T(E_z) dE_z \tag{8.2}$$

where $f(E_z)$ is the distribution function after traversing through the base region and $T(E_z)$ is the tunnelling probability of the collector barrier.

The solid line in Fig. 8.21 show the calculated transfer ratio for the InGaAs-based RHET. The base is 25 nm thick and the collector-base voltage is 1 V. Note that the transfer ratio increases with the negative emitter voltage, and then decreases once the negative emitter voltage exceeds 0.55 V. Figure 8.22 shows the potential profile calculated for an emitter-base voltage of -0.6 V and a collector-base voltage of 1 V. It is obvious that the decreased transfer ratio is due to the scattering into the L and/or X valleys. However, we did not observe the transfer ratio peak. One possible reason is that the collector barrier encountered

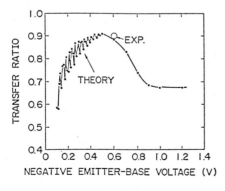

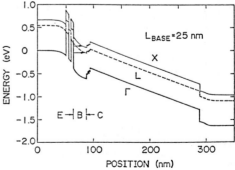

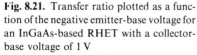

Fig. 8.21. Transfer ratio plotted as a function of the negative emitter-base voltage for an InGaAs-based RHET with a collector-base voltage of 1 V

Fig. 8.22. Energy band distance of the InGaAs-based RHET as a function of distance. The emitter-base voltage is 0.6 V and the base-collector is 1 V. The base is 25 nm thick

for upper-valley electrons are lower than we linearly interpolated from InGaAs, InAs, and AlAs.

Open circle in Fig. 8.21 indicates the transfer ratio measured at the emitter current peak. It is noticed that this value is comparable to the transfer ratio calculated at the emitter current peak voltage of 0.6 V. Figure 8.23 shows the theoretical and measured transfer ratio at the emitter current peak for the InGaAs-based RHET as functions of collector-base voltage. Open circles are measured transfer ratios. The dashed line is the theoretical curve. The measured transfer ratio agrees well theoretical results. The theoretical and experimental transfer ratios both increase with increased collector base voltage. This is due to collector barrier lowering with the increased collector base voltage. Figure 8.24 shows the base width dependence of the transfer ratio for the InGaAs-based RHET at the peak emitter current. The collector-base voltage is 1 V. The solid line shows the calculated result and the open circles the experimental results. The experimental results agree well calculated results.

Thus, the InGaAs-based RHET's transfer ratio at the emitter current peak in resonant conditions can well be explained using our present theory, indicating good design possibilities for RHET circuit applications. However, more realistic and accurate theory will be needed to fully understand the RHET's operation.

8.6 Summary

This chapter has reviewed our research activities in resonant-tunnelling hot-electron transistors, RHETs, discussing advances in RHET technology using InGaAs-based materials. The InGaAs-based RHET's common-emitter current gain is typically 17. This is about four times greater than that of the GaAs-based RHET. The collector current peak-to-valley ratio reaches 19.3, eight times that of the GaAs-based RHET. It is obvious that the material used for the RHET should

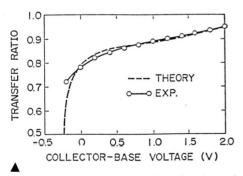

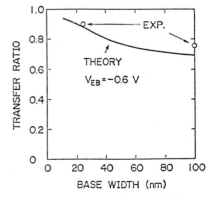

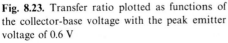

Fig. 8.23. Transfer ratio plotted as functions of the collector-base voltage with the peak emitter voltage of 0.6 V

Fig. 8.24. Transfer ratio plotted as functions of the base width for the InGaAs-based RHET with the peak emitter voltage of 0.6 V and a collector-base voltage of 1 V

be changed from GaAs to InGaAs-based materials, the latter having a higher performance characteristics.

Also described were the theoretical and experimental analyses of the RHET's performance. We calculated the emitter-base current-voltage characteristics for the InGaAs-based RHETs and simulated the transfer ratio using a Monte Carlo simulation, including the effect of the injection energy distribution and the potential profile in the base region and collector barrier tunnelling of hot electrons. The calculated transfer ratio at the emitter current peak agreed well experimental results, indicating good design possibilities for the RHET circuit applications. More accurate and realistic theory will be needed for further investigation.

Acknowledgement: The authors thank T. Fujii, and S. Hiyamizu for their support in the fields of epitaxial growth and evaluation. We also express our gratitude to A. Shibatomi, M. Kobayashi, and T, Misugi for their continuing encouragement. This work was performed under the management of the R & D Association for Future Electron Devices as a part of the R & D Project of Basic Technology for Future Industries sponsored by Agency of Industrial Science and Technology (MITI), Japan.

References

8.1   M. Heiblum: Solid State Electron. **24**, 343–366 (1981)
8.2   N. Yokoyama, K. Imamura, T. Ohshima, H. Nishi, S. Muto, K. Kondo, S. Hiyamizu: Jpn. J. Appl. Phys. **23**, L311–L312 (1984)
8.3   N. Yokoyama, K. Imamura, T. Ohshima, H. Nishi, S. Muto, K. Kondo, S. Hiyamizu: 1984 Technical Digest, 532–535
8.4   S. Muto, K. Imamura, N. Yokoyama, S. Hiyamizu, H. Nishi: Electron. Lett. **21**, 555–556 (1985)
8.5   K. Imamura, S. Muto, N. Yokoyama, M. Sasa, H. Ohnishi, S. Hiyamizu, H. Nishi: Science **174**, 481–486 (1986)
8.6   N. Yokoyama, K. Imamura, S. Muto, S. Hiyamizu, H. Nishi: Jpn. J. Appl. Phys. 24, L853–L854, (1985);
Inst. Phys. Conf. Ser. No. Chap. 3, 739–740 (1985)
8.7   N. Yokoyama, K. Imamura, H. Ohnishi, S. Muto, T. Mori, A. Shibatomi: 44th Annual Device Research Conf., VIB-3 (1986)
8.8   N. Yokoyama: Extended Abstracts of the 1986 International Conference on Solid State Devices and Materials, Tokyo, 347–350 (1986)
8.9   T. Mori, H. Ohnishi, K. Imamura, S. Muto, N. Yokoyama: Appl. Phys. Lett. **49**, 1779 (1986)
8.10 Y. Sugiyama, T. Inata, T. Fujii, Y. Nakata, S. Hiyamizu: Jpn. J. Appl. Phys. **25**, L648 (1986)
8.11 A. R. Bonnefoi, T. C. McGill, R. D. Burnham, G. B. Anderson: Appl. Phys. Lett. **50**, 344 (1987)
8.12 E. E. Mendez, W. I. Wang, E. Callejia, E. T. Silva: Appl. Phys. Lett. **50**, 1263 (1987)
8.13 T. Inata, S. Muto, Y. Nakata, T. Fujii, H. Ohnishi, S. Hiyamizu: Jpn. J. Appl. Phys. **25**, L983 (1986)
8.14 T. Weil, B. Vinter: Appl. Phys. Lett. **50**, 1281 (1987)
8.15 B. Ricco, M. Ya. Azbel: Phys. Rev. **29**, 1970 (1984)
8.16 S. Muto, T. Inata, Y. Sugiyama, Y. Nakata, T. Fujii, H. Ohnishi, S. Hiyamizu: Jpn. J. Appl. Phys. **26**, L220 (1987)
8.17 E. O. Kane: J. Phys. Chem. Solids **1**, 249 (1957)
8.18 M. Tsuchiya, H. Sakaki: Appl. Phys. Lett. **49**, 88 (1986)

8.19 S. Muto, S. Hiyamizu, N. Yokoyama: Proceedings of High-Speed Electronics, Stockholm, 1986 (Springer, Berlin, Heidelberg 1987) pp. 72–78

8.20 M. Tsuchiya, H. Sakaki, J. Yoshino: Jpn. J. Appl. Phys. **24**, L466 (1985)

8.21 M. Tsuchiya, H. Sakaki: Jpn. J. Appl. Phys. **25**, L185 (1986)

8.22 W. D. Goodhue, T. C. L. G. Sollner, H. Q. Le, E. R. Brown, B. A. Vojak: Appl. Phys. Lett. **49**, 1086 (1986)

8.23 H. Morkoc, J. Chen, U. K. Reddy, T. Henderson, S. Luryi: Appl. Phys. Lett. **49**, 70 (1986)

8.24 Y. Sugiyama, T. Inata, S. Muto, Y. Nakata, S. Hiyamizu: Appl. Phys. Lett. **25**, 314 (1988)

8.25 T. Inata, S. Muto, S. Sasa, E. Miyauchi: J. Cryst. Growth **95**, 371 (1989)

8.26 T. Inata, S. Muto, Y. Nakata, S. Sasa, T. Fujii, S. Hiyamizu: Jpn. J. Appl. Phys. **26**, L1332 (1987)

8.27 K. Imamura, S. Muto, H. Ohnishi, T. Fujii, N. Yokoyama: 45th Annual Device Research Conference, June 1987, Santa Barbara USA; Electron. Lett. **23**, 870 (1987)

8.28 H. Ohnishi, T. Inata, S. Muto, N. Yokoyama, A. Shibatomi: Appl. Phys. Lett. **49**, 1248 (1986)

8.29 S. Muto, T. Inata, Y. Sugiyama, Y. Nakata, T. Fujii, H. Ohnishi, S. Hiyamizu: Jpn. J. Appl. Phys. **26**, L220 (1987)

8.30 P. Lugli, D. K. Ferry: IEEE Electron Device Lett. **EDL-6**, 25 (1985)

8.31 S. Imanaga, H. Kawai, K. Kaneko, N. Watanabe: J. Appl. Phys. **59**, 3281 (1986)

8.32 M. A. Littlejohn, J. R. Hauser, T. H. Glisson, D. K. Ferry, J. W. Harrison: Solid State Electron. **21**, 107 (1978)

8.33 Y. Takeda, M. A. Littlejohn, J. R. Hauser: Electron. Lett. **17**, 377 (1981)

8.34 M. A. Hollis, S. C. Polmasteer, L. F. Eastman, N. V. Dandekar, P. M. Smith: IEEE Electron Device Lett. **EDL-4**, 440 (1983)

9. Ballistic Electron Transport in Hot Electron Transistors

M. Heiblum and M. V. Fischetti

With 37 Figures

We review the history and the present impact of hot electron devices. We elaborate in particular on the tunnelling hot electron transfer amplifier (THETA) device. This device generates an almost monoenergetic, variable energy, hot electron beam (by tunnelling), which traverses a thin GaAs region to be eventually collected and energy analyzed. As the hot electrons traverse the device they are used to probe: scattering events, band nonparabolicity, size quantization effects, intervalley transfer, quantum mechanical reflections, and band discontinuities at interfaces.

We describe the experiments that have demonstrated true ballistic transport in GaAs. We show effects due to size quantization – also expected to occur in many devices as their dimensions shrink below 100 nm or so – a direct consequence of the coherency maintained by the ballistic electrons. From these observations we derive basic properties of GaAs. We also speculate on the future attainable performance of the THETA device, i.e. gain and speed. We find the device a promising sub–picosecond amplifier.

9.1 Ballistic Transport

9.1.1 The Search for Ballistic Transport

In a perfectly periodic crystal free electrons are expected to move smoothly and without any collisions with the crystal atoms, having a velocity determined by the crystal structure, the electrons direction and their total energy. In such an ideal case the free electrons will be said to travel ballistically. However, in reality, phonons will be emitted by the electrons, even at 0 K. The phonons will propagate through the lattice, disturb its perfect periodic structure, and cause electron scattering. In a real crystal, at temperatures above 0 K, many additional scattering mechanisms influence the free electron motion. All together they result in a mean free time between collisions and an average group velocity of the electrons (which is related to the applied electric field via the mobility, μ, of the semiconductor in the ohmic regime). If the mean free path (mfp) of the electrons, (the average group velocity times the mean free time), is of the same order of magnitude as the length of the sample, l, it is conceivable to picture the total electron population as composed of two ensembles: ballistic and quasi ballistic, where the quasi ballistic electrons are those that have scattered once or only a few times. For example, if $l \ll$ mfp, one would expect the ballistic fraction of the electrons arriving at the end of the sample to be approximately $\alpha_B = 1 - l/\text{mfp}$.

In 1979 *Shur* and *Eastman* [9.1] proposed that ballistic electron transport could be realized in GaAs due to the long mfp of the electrons (estimated to be on the order of a few hundred nanometers at low temperatures in pure material). Assuming all electrons are ballistic they have predicted an expression for the current in an abrupt $n^+ - n^- - n^+$ structure, which is similar to Child's law (applicable for the current in a vacuum tube), with a modification due to the background of positive charges. However, in actual structures, the boundary conditions between the n^+ and the n^- layers are complicated and difficult to calculate self consistently, particularly on the anode side [9.2], and the contact resistance of the ohmic contacts is a large fraction of the total resistance. Also, because of the two existing populations, the ballistic and quasi ballistic ensembles, each with its own energy distribution, the determination of ballistic transport from the I–V characteristics is impossible. In 1980, *Eastman* et al. published experimental I–V curves for structures in which the n^- layer was 400 nm wide [9.3]. Their resultant current was higher than that expected from velocity saturated transport (Ohm's law) and asymptotically approached the 3/2 power law (Child's law) at higher bias voltages, not contradicting the possibility of some ballistic transport.

A large number of analytical calculations attempting to predict the exact nature of the I–V characteristics of the above mentioned structure appeared later in the literature. They were supplemented by a variety of Monte Carlo based calculations with predictions of overshoot velocities in small structures, resulting from quasi ballistic transport. In 1982 *Hesto* et al. [9.4] proposed to apply an electron spectroscopy technique [9.5] to detect the energy distributions of the electrons after they had traversed an $n^+ - n^- - n^+$ structure. The technique was applied later by *Hayes* et al. [9.6], *Yokoyama* et al. [9.7], and *Heiblum* et al. [9.8], employing hot electron transistors. *Yokoyama* et al. [9.7] and *Levi* et al [9.9] have provided evidence of quasi ballistic transport in heavily doped GaAs layers (100 nm and 65 nm wide, respectively). This was followed by a direct proof of ballistic electron transport and measurements of narrow energy distributions of ballistic electrons in refined GaAs-AlGaAs heterostructure hot electron transistors published by *Heiblum* et al. [9.10]. The observed ballistic fractions collected after traversing 30 nm heavily n doped GaAs layers were about 30% of the total injected currents in these initial experiments. With improved structures, ballistic fractions as high as 75% were measured later [9.11]. These spectroscopic techniques and their results will be described in Sect. 9.4. Similarly, ballistic transport was also observed in InGaAs, lattice matched to InP, by *Reddy* et al. [9.12] and in strained InGaAs layers (15% InAs mole fraction, 30 nm wide layers) by *Seo* et al. [9.76], both using THETA type devices. Recently, ballistic transport of holes had been observed in GaAs [9.77]. This was accomplished via the separation of the light holes from the heavy ones, and injecting them into 31 nm heavily p type doped GaAs layers. Ballistic fractions of about 8% had been observed.

Since this chapter will be devoted to ballistic transport in GaAs layers, it is appropriate to spend some time on the basic properties of GaAs that affect ballistic transport.

9.1.2 Properties of GaAs

An excellent review of the electronic properties of GaAs that are of interest here has been given by *Blakemore* [9.13]. In this short section we would like to review briefly the structure of the Γ-band, since its properties are particularly relevant to ballistic transport. Figure 9.1 shows the structure of the first few conduction bands of GaAs. We have obtained them from the empirical pseudopotential calculation of *Cohen* and *Bergstresser* [9.14].

The narrow Γ-band implies a low density of states below some 0.32 eV energy, as shown in Fig. 9.2, and a very low effective mass, resulting thus in low scattering rates and high electron velocities. Ultimately, the structure of this conduction band is responsible for the high electron mobilities in GaAs. We show in Fig. 9.3 the electron group velocities (we may call them 'ballistic velocities') in the three major crystallographic directions, for electrons in the central valley, calculated from the band structure of Fig. 9.1. We see that velocities in excess of 10^8 cm/sec can be expected for ballistic motion in the $\langle 100 \rangle$ direction (that, by a lucky accident, is also the easiest orientation obtained by epitaxial growth).

If, on one side, the narrow Γ-band is responsible for the high electronic 'speed' of GaAs, on the other side, electrons can easily gain enough energy to reach regions of the Brillouin zone where the conduction band can no longer be approximated by a simple parabolic band (which is true for low energies in the band). Deviations from parabolicity are usually accounted for by using the $\mathbf{k} \cdot \mathbf{p}$ approximation and obtaining a spherical dispersion relation of the form

$$E(\mathbf{k}) = \frac{\hbar^2 k^2}{2m_{C,0}} + \gamma \left(\frac{\hbar^2 k^2}{2m_{C,0}} \right)^2 , \qquad (9.1)$$

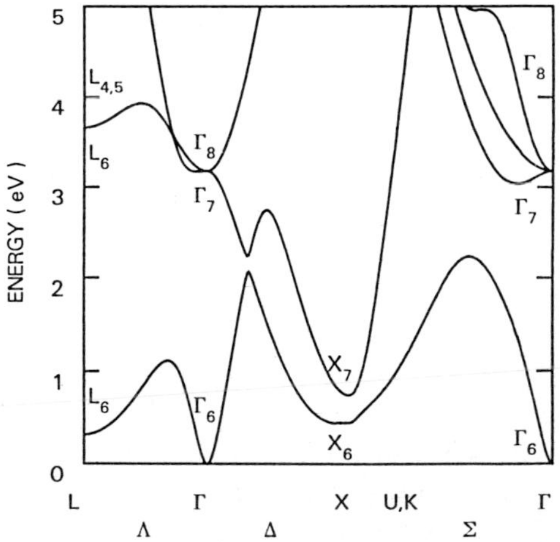

Fig. 9.1. Structure of the conduction bands of GaAs obtained from the local empirical pseudopotentials of Cohen and Bergstresser [9.14]

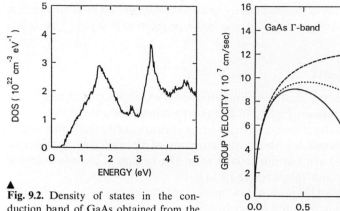

Fig. 9.2. Density of states in the conduction band of GaAs obtained from the band structure of Fig. 9.1 with an algorithm due to Gilat and Raubenheimer [Phys. Rev. **144**, 390 (1966)]

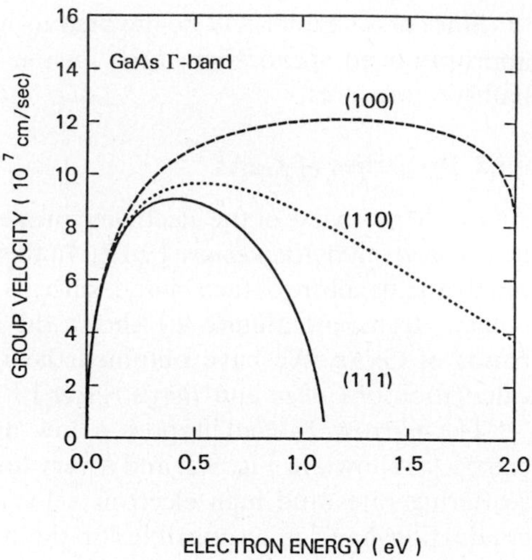

Fig. 9.3. 'Ballistic' group velocity of the electrons in the Γ-band of GaAs in the three major crystallographic directions. The curves are obtained by differentiating the $E(k)$ dispersion relation in the central valley of Fig. 9.1 with respect to k

where $E(k)$ is the electron energy relative to the bottom of the Γ-band, $\hbar$ is the reduced Planck constant, k is the electron wavevector, and $m_{C,0} = 0.067\,m_e$ is the effective mass at the bottom of the band (also called the 'curvature' effective mass). The parameter γ (usually designated by the symbol α in the literature which we here employ for the transfer ratio through devices) has dimensions of inverse energy and 'usually' takes the value of

$$\gamma = (-0.824 + 2 \times 10^{-5}\,T)/E_g, \tag{9.2}$$

where E_g is the GaAs energy gap (a low temperature value of 1.519 eV is given by *Blakemore* [9.13], and T is the lattice absolute temperature.

The 'effective mass' of the electrons is of critical importance. From the dispersion given by (9.1) and (9.2) one can define several 'effective masses':

$$m_{en}(E) = \frac{\hbar^2 k(E)^2}{2E} \simeq m_{C,0}(1 - \gamma E), \tag{9.3a}$$

$$m_{opt}(E) = \hbar k(E)(dE/dk)^{-1}_{k(E)} \simeq m_{C,0}(1 - 2\gamma E), \tag{9.3b}$$

$$m_{curv}(E) = \hbar^2 (d^2 E/dk^2)^{-1}_{k(E)} \simeq m_{C,0}(1 - 6\gamma E), \tag{9.3c}$$

where $k(E) = [(2m_{C,0})^{1/2}/\hbar](1 - \gamma E/2)$ is obtained by inverting (9.1) to first order in γ. We shall refer to m_{en} as to the 'energy' effective mass, to m_{opt} as to the 'optical' effective mass, and to m_{curv} as to the 'curvature' effective mass.

The curvature mass has a defined meaning only at the bottom of the band. The optical mass can be used appropriately when the group velocity $v_g(E)$ of a localized wave-packet around energy E is wanted:

$$v_g(E) = \frac{1}{\hbar}\nabla_k E(k) \simeq \frac{\hbar k(E)}{m_{opt}(E)}. \tag{9.4}$$

Thus, the optical mass will enter the dynamic equations of motion of the electrons under the action of an external field. Finally, *Hiroshima* and *Lang* [9.15] have noted that the use of the optical mass is unjustified when one has to solve the Luttinger-Kohn Schrödinger-like effective mass equation [9.16]:

$$[E(-i\nabla) + eV(x)]\psi(x) = E\psi(x), \tag{9.5}$$

where $E(-i\nabla)$ is the Hamiltonian operator for electrons in the Γ-band, e is the magnitude of the electronic charge, $V(x)$ the external potential, and $\psi(x)$ the envelope (Wannier) wave function associated with the electrons. In tunnelling cases and when electron energies in quantum wells are calculated, one should actually use the rather complicated (9.5) and avoid the use of the optical mass, which provides erroneous results for the eigen-energies. Acting with the LHS of (9.5) on monochromatic waves of energy E, applicable in the above mentioned cases, the eigenvalue of the free Hamiltonian operator becomes simply $\hbar^2 k(E)^2/2m_{en}(E)$. So, the use of the 'energy' effective mass (9.3a) is a sensible approximation for the electron mass when working with plane waves. It should be said that in the presence of heterojunctions, properly matching the wavefunctions at the interfaces of materials with significantly different band-structures on the two sides of the heterojunction, transcends the simple effective-mass approximation. However, within this simple scheme, it is customary to match group velocities ($\hbar k/m_{opt}(E)$) when dispersion is considered to be significant or phase velocities ($\hbar k/m_{en}(E)$) when monochromatic waves are of interest.

In the following sections tunnelling and quantum well situations will be analyzed, thus we shall adopt the second point of view. The integration over the energy distribution of the carriers – which we will perform to obtain the tunnelling current – can be thought of as a way of forming wave packets, and conservation of the 'group' velocity of the dispersive packet at the heterojunction interfaces will be automatically obtained. However, let us stress once more that this effective mass approach is not rigorously correct, despite its widespread use, and more elaborate approaches (such as the use of transfer-matrices or direct tight-binding calculations) would be more appropriate.

A final question concerns the range of validity of a simple first order nonparabolic approximation of the (9.1). We show in Fig. 9.4 the various effective masses we have discussed above as functions of the electron energy in the central valley. The values are obtained from the band structure shown in Fig. 9.1. Once again, the 'technologically significant' $\langle 100 \rangle$ direction is the 'lucky' direction: the energy effective mass increases linearly with k^2; quadratic corrections being negligible even above 0.4 eV. In other crystallographic directions (9.1) becomes

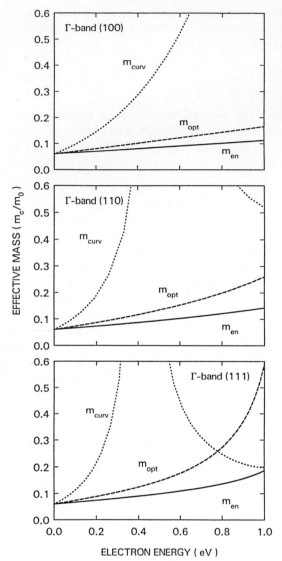

Fig. 9.4. The three different effective masses in the Γ-band defined (9.3a, b, c) of the text are plotted versus the electron energy in the three major crystallographic directions in the Γ-band. Notice the good linearity of the 'energy' effective mass, m_{en}, in the $\langle 100 \rangle$ direction, as a function of energy E up to high energies

inappropriate at much lower energies and the use of the exact band structure becomes necessary.

The value we obtain for the nonparabolicity parameter γ at 0 K in the $\langle 100 \rangle$ direction from the empirical-pseudopotential calculation is $-0.834\,\mathrm{eV}^{-1}$. This value was verified experimentally by us, as we will show later. This is significantly larger than the more commonly used values (ranging from -0.54 to $-0.61\,\mathrm{eV}^{-1}$) [9.13, 17].

The effect of the non-parabolicity of the Γ-band on the electron Fermi energy as a function of electron concentration at various temperatures is shown in

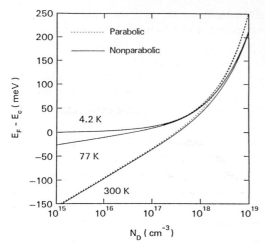

Fig. 9.5. The Fermi energy is plotted as a function of electron concentration at three different temperatures in the parabolic-band (*dotted line*) and nonparabolic band (*solid line*) approximations described in the text (9.6–9)

Fig. 9.5. The Fermi level, E_F, as a function of the carrier concentration, n, is given implicitly by the integral:

$$n(E_F) = \int_0^\infty dE \frac{\rho(E)}{\exp[E - E_F)/(k_B T)] + 1} , \qquad (9.6)$$

where k_B is the Boltzmann constant and the density of states at energy E, $\rho(E)$, is approximated by the spherical, nonparabolic expression

$$\rho(E) \simeq \frac{(2m_{C,0})^{3/2}}{2\hbar^3 \pi^2} E^{1/2}(1 - 5\gamma E/2), \qquad (9.7)$$

(having accounted for the spin degeneracy with a factor 2) so that

$$n(E_F) \simeq 2[(2\pi m_{C,0} k_B T)/(2\pi\hbar)^2]^{3/2} \hat{F}_{1/2}(E_F/(k_B T)) , \qquad (9.8)$$

where the nonparabolic Fermi integral is:

$$\hat{F}_{1/2}(\eta_F) = \frac{2}{\pi^{1/2}} \int_0^\infty d\eta \frac{\eta^{1/2}(1 - 5\beta\eta/2)}{\exp(\eta - \eta_F) + 1} , \qquad (9.9)$$

where $\beta = \gamma k_B T$ and $\eta_F = E_F/k_B T$. It can be shown, by comparison with the exact expression obtained from the complete band structure of Fig. 9.1, that the value of the Fermi energy obtained in this way is minimally affected by the isotropic approximation we have employed.

We conclude this section with a few considerations about the 'dynamics' of electron transport implied by the 'narrow' Γ-band of GaAs. As we have mentioned briefly in previous paragraphs, GaAs is an appealing semiconductor mainly because of the small electron effective mass in the central valley. Ballistic transport can be obtained when the characteristic length scale of the device is comparable to or smaller than the electron mean free path. In a naive parabolic band approximation with effective mass m_{eff} and S being the coupling between an electron and whatever scatterer we wish to consider, the mean free path is given by $v_{\text{g}}\tau \sim v_{\text{g}}/(\Sigma |S_{\text{i,f}}|^2 \rho_{\text{f}})$, where v_{g} is the electron group velocity, the sum extends over the density of final states, ρ_{f}, available to the scattered electron on the energy conserving surface, and $S_{\text{i,f}}$ is the scattering matrix element (function of initial and final state vectors). Since $v_{\text{g}} \sim k/m_{\text{eff}}$ and $\rho_{\text{f}} \sim m_{\text{eff}}^{3/2}$, the mean free path will be proportional to $m_{\text{eff}}^{-5/2} |S|^{-2}$. No matter what the scattering process is, the dependence of the mean free path on the 'narrowness' of the lowest conduction band (i.e. the small value of m_{eff}) is so strong to account for most of the differences between, say, Si and GaAs. For the same coupling constant, S, we would expect electrons in GaAs to have a mean free path some 300 times longer than in Si at the same electric field, assuming $m_{\text{eff}}(\text{Si})/m_{\text{eff}}(\text{GaAs}) = 10$. Of course, the factor S will also have an effect: As an example of a scattering process, the polar coupling between low energy electrons and phonons in GaAs is much stronger than in Si (which, being covalent, lacks the strong polar coupling). So, at low energies, the advantage of GaAs over Si is reduced by an order of magnitude with respect to our estimates above. Note also, at high electron energy the band structure is not forgiving any longer, electrons reaching the satellite L and X valleys which have higher effective masses and lower velocities (this can be seen in the high field drift velocities in GaAs that get closer to the Si velocities as the field grows above 3 kV/cm). Nevertheless, our considerations give a – perhaps oversimplified–justification for the choice of GaAs (or equivalent III–V materials with low m_{eff}) as a semiconductor to employ in the search of ballistic electron transport.

9.2 Hot Electron Transistors

9.2.1 Principles of Operation

Every three terminal device can have gain if a small control signal is used to modulate effectively a relatively large dc current passing through it. In FET type devices a small voltage change on the gate changes the electron concentration in the channel, and thus the current between source and drain. In bipolar transistors, in a common base configuration (CBC), a modulated current is 'forced' to flow from a low input resistance into a high output resistance, achieving thus voltage or power gain. Alternatively, in a common emitter configuration (CEC), a small modulated current into the base modulates the base-emitter injection voltage and, thus exponentially, the large current that is injected into the collector. Hot electron transistors are in principle similar to the bipolar transistors. While the bipolar transistor utilizes holes and electrons, the hot electron transistor takes advantage of 'cold' (in thermal equilibrium with the lattice) and 'hot' electrons. The cold electrons provide the conductivity needed in the various layers of the device, while the hot electrons carry the input information to be amplified.

In the CBC, the emitter (E) injects a hot electron beam that traverses the thin base and is ultimately collected by the collector. The base (B) is separated on both sides, from the emitter and the collector (E), by potential barriers that confine the thermal electrons to their original layers (E, B and C). The injected hot electron beam is energetic to surmount the potential barrier at the collector, almost independently of the output collector voltage, resulting thus in a high output differential resistance. The power gain, G, of the device in a CBC is $\alpha^2 R_o / R_i$, where the differential transfer ratio $\alpha = dI_C / DI_E$, where I_E is the emitter current, I_C is the collector current, and R_o and R_i are the output and input resistances, respectively. Similarly, in a CEC, a differential current gain β is defined $\beta = dI_C / dI_B$, where I_B is the base current, and $\beta = \alpha/(1 - \alpha)$ replaces α in the expression for G.

A hot electron device does not have to be a 'ballistic device' to operate as a fast amplifier. If the hot electrons are injected at sufficiently high energies, they may scatter elastically a few times, change somewhat their forward direction and still be collected. Consequently, the transit time from the emitter to the collector will be somewhat longer, but most probably not the limiting factor in most devices that are normally impeded by charging effects (see Sect. 9.7 for evaluation of potential speed of the devices).

9.2.2 Some History

The first hot electron device was proposed by *Mead* in 1960 [9.18]. Naming it *cold cathode transistor*, *Mead* had proposed a device constructed of two metal-oxide-metal (MOM) structures in an MOMOM configuration. The first MOM had a thin oxide of facilitate tunnelling and the second a thicker oxide to prevent it. The common metal to both MOM structure (base) was made thin enough to allow quasi ballistic transfer; due to the high conductivity of the metal a high base resistance was avoided. Since hot electrons in metals with low energy inherently have a short 'ballistic mfp' (10–20 nm for < 1.0 eV electrons) which gets even smaller as injection energies increase [9.19], the expected current gain in the MOMOM device is small. The transfer ratio, α, is expected to be small also because of the very different wave functions of the electrons in the semi-conductors and the metals. Moreover, the difficult fabrication procedure (achieving pinhole free 10 nm thick metals and 2 nm thick oxides) makes the device difficult to fabricate. In retrospect, it is not surprising that the α's reported by *Mead* were only a few percent, rendering the devices impractical [9.20].

To ease the fabrication procedure and enable the collection of lower energy electrons, by having a lower barrier at the collector, *Spratt* and co-workers had constructed an MOMS (S – stands for a semiconductor collector) device. The initial optimistic report [9.21] were found later to result from a direct contact formed between emitter and collector through pinholes in the 10 nm wide base metal [9.22].

In two consecutive papers *Moll* [9.23] and *Atalla* with *Soshea* [9.24] predicted that the frequency performance of a tunnel emitter based devices will be inferior to bipolar transistors due to the large charging time of the tunnel junction (large capacitance). However, the recent experimental demonstration of the operation of small area MOM diodes ('Point Contact' and 'Edge' type diodes) at infrared frequencies [9.25], contradicted these predictions (that resulted from limiting the current density only to 10^3 A/cm^2). However, it seems, that at that time, these publications were a final blow to the field of tunnelling hot electron devices.

Another hot electron device, the SMS or the *metal base transistor*, was proposed by *Geppert* [9.26] and *Khang* [9.27] in 1961. In the SMS, the tunnel emitter of the MOMS was replaced by another SM-Schottky barrier (Fig. 9.6). All devices fabricated in the sixties and early seventies were plagued with the difficulties encountered by the MOMOM and MOMS devices [9.28]. Recently, an all epitaxial Si-Silicide-Si structure, in situ grown, were fabricated by MBE. They were still suffering from presence of pinholes in the thin base [9.29, 30], and operated effectively as a *permeable base transistor* [9.31].

The recent revivial of the hot electron transistors started with *Shannon*'s *Camel transistor* fabricated in Si [9.32]. The status review and proposal of the *tunnelling hot electron transfer amplifier* (THETA) device [9.19, 33], might have also contributed in part to this revival. In the Camel transistor, the potential barrier in the collector was created by a shallow (a few tens of nm below the

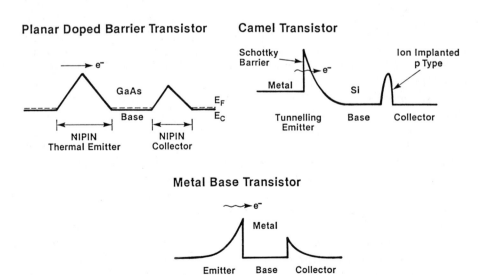

Fig. 9.6. Potential distributions of three hot electron devices. The PDBT, the camel transistor, and the metal base transistor. All have two barriers: One in the emitter for injecting hot electrons and one in the collector to prevent the passage of base electrons into the collector

surface) and narrow (a few nm wide) implantation of a high dose of acceptor ions into *n* type Si. Since all these ions were ionized and their region depleted, a 'potential hump' was created at their location. A heavily doped Schottky barrier at the surface served as a tunnelling emitter when negatively biased (Fig. 9.6). *Shannon* and co-workers had modified the device later by implanting acceptors under the Schottky barrier, thus raising its potential barrier and injecting at higher energies [9.34]. In *Shannon*'s experiment a current gain β of 20 was reported, in an estimated 25 nm base device for high injection energies. However, it was difficult to attribute the operation of the device uniquely to hot electron transfer.

A similar device, the *planar doped barrier transistor* (PDBT) was fabricated by *Malik* et al. [9.35] and later by *Hollis* et al.[9.36]. Similarly to the Camel device, barriers were formed by *p* type planar doping (with MBE), surrounded by *n* type GaAs layers. The emitter barrier was designed to be higher than the collector barrier. Because of the relatively thick emitter barrier, the electrons were injected via thermionic emission above the barrier top (Fig. 9.6). The highest transfer ratio measured at 77 K was 0.75 in a PDBT with a base width of 87 nm [9.36]. In a similar structures with higher emitter barrier heights, *Woodwock* et al. have estimated an α of 0.94 in a 30 nm base device [9.37], deduced from measurements on two terminal devices (emitter to collector current). These structures were adopted by *Hayes* et al. [9.6] to do spectroscopy of hot electrons, a subject that will be discussed in Sect. 9.4.

The tunnelling hot electron transfer amplifier (THETA) device, constructed of abrupt heterojunctions, was proposed by *Heiblum* in 1980 [9.19, 33]. The structure is analogous to *Mead*'s structure, where thin and undoped AlGaAs layers replace the oxides, and heavily doped GaAs layers replace the metals. Here too, a tunnel injector is utilized, producing a fairly monoenergetic, nearly forward moving electron beam, with a variable, controlled injection energy, determined by the applied injection voltage (Fig. 9.7). The first devices of this type fabricated by *Yokoyama* et al. [9.7], with GaAs-AlGaAs heterostructures, operated at low temperature (less than 100 K), with α's as high as 0.56 in devices with 100 nm base width. This was followed with the work of *Heiblum* et al. [9.8, 10, 11] reporting α's as high as 0.9 in devices with 30 nm base width. Similar devices were fabricated later by *Hase* et al. [9.38], who utilized the MOCVD technique to grow the structures, and by *Yokoyama* et al. [9.39] who have incorporated a resonant tunnel emitter in the structure. The same structure, but *p* type doped, was recently fabricated by *Heiblum* et al. [9.77], and has demonstrated directly, for the first time in a solid, ballistic transport of light holes with a maximum transfer ratio of 0.2. The bulk of the discussion later will be devoted to the THETA device, a device which all our experiments were conducted on.

A 'hybrid type device' was fabricated by *Long* et al. [9.40]: a triangular shaped undoped AlGaAs emitter barrier and a planar doped collector barrier. The device was mostly employed for electron spectroscopy. *Reddy* et al. [9.12, 41] reported work on InGaAs-InAlAs lattice matched to InP based devices, with $\alpha = 0.23$ at low temperatures for a 100 nm base device, and *Imamura* et al. [9.42]

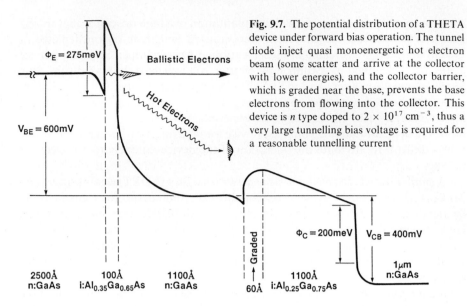

Fig. 9.7. The potential distribution of a THETA device under forward bias operation. The tunnel diode inject quasi monoenergetic hot electron beam (some scatter and arrive at the collector with lower energies), and the collector barrier, which is graded near the base, prevents the base electrons from flowing into the collector. This device is *n* type doped to 2×10^{17} cm^{-3}, thus a very large tunnelling bias voltage is required for a reasonable tunnelling current

reported on InGaAs-InGaAlAs based devices with $\beta = 15$ in 25 nm base devices. Recently, *Chang* et al. had fabricated a GaAs-AlGaAs device with an 'induced base' [9.43], proposed by *Luryi* [9.44] and *Solomon* [9.45]. In this device the base was left undoped and its conductivity was increased due to an induction of electrons in the base via an application of a large positive voltage across the undoped AlGaAs collector barrier. In a device with a 10 nm base width, a maximum α of 0.96 was measured at room temperature. Another induced base device where strong base inversion took place resulting with an accumulation of holes, was demonstrated by *Matsumoto* et al. [9.46]. The resultant device was an induced *p* type base *npn* heterojunction bipolar transistor with an effective base width of about 10 nm. In this induced HBT, a β of 17 was measured at room temperatures for electrons injected at energies higher than the GaAs energy gap.

9.3 Hot Electron Injectors

9.3.1 What is a Hot Electron Injector?

An injector utilizes a potential barrier that prevents electrons from passing from an electron reservoir into an adjacent layer. As the potential energy of the electrons in the reservoir is raised, the effective barrier height for the electrons is lowered and some of them can successfully surmount above or tunnel through its top. If the barrier is fairly abrupt on the electron emergence side, the electrons suddenly accelerate and quickly gain kinetic energy that is equal to their excess potential energy in the reservoir. Since the potential barrier is, by construction, an 'infinite' flat layer, it will select only the electrons that have sufficiently high energy and are moving close to perpendicular to its plane, in other words, the electrons with 'normal' energy, $E_\perp$, greater than its height, Φ. 'Normal' energy is defined as the energy associated with the perpendicular momentum to the planar barriers, $p_\perp$, namely $E_\perp = p_\perp^2/2m_{en}(E)$. (This leads to an injection cone close to the normal direction, as is necessary in hot electron devices.)

9.3.2 The Thermionic Injector

All thermionic type injectors are of the Schottky type and thus are activated by the 'k_BT-tail' of the electron distribution. The $I-V$ characteristic of the thermionic injector has the known form of $I = AT^2\exp[(\Phi - eV)/k_BT]$, where I is the current density, A is the effective Richardson's constant, and e is the electronic charge. Since the effective barrier for electrons is $\Phi - eV$, it can be arbitrarily small or negative, and very large current densities can be injected. Note that all the injected electrons will emerge with kinetic energies approximately equal to the potential barrier height, Φ, independent of the biasing voltage.

A pseudo Schottky barrier can be realized by a heterojunction of heavily doped GaAs and a moderately heavily doped AlGaAs (Fig. 9.8). Under equilibrium conditions, electrons from the AlGaAs will 'spill over' into the GaAs layer, leave behind them ionized donors, and bend the energy bands in both materials. Electrons on either side of the heterojunction will face a potential barrier, similarly to the case of a metal-semiconductor Schottky barrier. At low temperatures $(kT < \Phi - V)$ tunnelling through the top of the barrier will dominate the transport.

Other thermionic type injectors, with barriers formed by doping, had been used recently. In a pn junction, a barrier for electrons and holes with the full

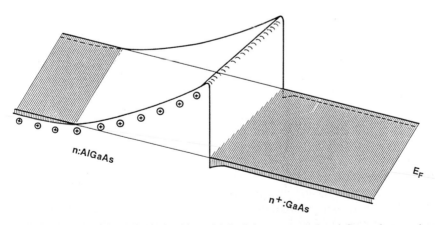

Fig. 9.8. A GaAs-AlGaAs heterojunction with both layers n type doped. Some electrons leave the AlGaAs and reside in the GaAs layer forming a depletion layer in the AlGaAs and a barrier for the rest of the electrons. This heterojunction can be used as a thermionic injector

height of the energy gap exists. If a very thin, heavily doped layer ('doping spike', 'planar doping' or 'delta doping') of say, p type, is introduced in the bulk of an undoped material, bordered on both sides with n type layers, the spike will be completely depleted due to recombination of its holes and the neighboring electrons. Consequently, the unneutralized negative acceptors will form a potential barrier to the surrounding electrons. As the number of impurities in the spike increases, the barrier potential rises, reaching ultimately the value of the energy gap of the material. Since the 'side walls' of these barriers have a considerable slope (about 10 nm, determined by the distance from the center of the spike and the n layers), raising the negative potential of one n layer versus the other will reduce the barrier height for electrons in the negative electrode, and enable the energetic electrons to surmount the barrier. Barriers like this had been realized by *Shannon* [9.32] in his 'Camel' diode by a narrow implantation of boron in n type silicon, and by *Malik* et al. [9.47] in their planar doped barrier diode (Fig. 9.6). By using MBE, thin regions of GaAs were doped with Be and were surrounded by n type regions, in a similar fashion to that in the Camel diodes.

Note that even at doping levels of $1 \times 10^{18} \, \text{cm}^{-3}$, the average distance between impurities is of the order of 10 nm, causing the potential to fluctuate along the barrier. *Arnold* et al. calculated these fluctuations to be on the order of 150 meV at the plane of the barrier [9.48], an effect that might spread considerably the injected electron energy distribution.

Barriers with similar triangular potential shapes were also realized by grading the Al mole fraction linearly in AlGaAs barriers [9.40]. Due to the short order fluctuations of the alloy, potential fluctuations in these barriers are expected to be very small.

Since most ballistic hot electron devices are expected to operate at low temperatures, thermionic type emitters inject a substantial fraction of their current via tunnelling, resulting in an injected energy distribution that is a combination of the two components. The tunnel injector produces a narrow energy distribution with injection energy that can be adjusted by the biasing potential. We utilize this injector in the THETA device, and discuss it next in some more detail.

9.3.3 The Tunnel Injector

The tunnel injector utilizes a thin potential barrier that separates the electrons in the reservoir from the transport region. The barrier is thin enough as to enable substantial tunnelling currents when the effective barrier height for tunnelling is lowered. This can be done for example, by the application of an external voltage across the barrier. Under these conditions, electrons are injected into the positive electrode with an energy that is determined by the applied biasing voltage. In a tunnel injector, where the supply electrode is GaAs and the barrier is AlGaAs, barrier heights are of the order of 0.3 eV and thicknesses in the range of 10 nm are used, leading to an injected normal energy distribution width, associated with the normal momentum to the injector, on the order of 60 meV.

To give a few quantitative examples of the energies and angular distributions of the electrons emerging form a tunnel injector, we need an expression for the tunnelling current through the barrier. The simplest expression among the many employed in the literature can be obtained in the following way: First, we consider the structure of interest (such as the single barrier illustrated in Fig. 9.9 as a way of example) and solve numerically Poisson equation accounting for the charge of the free electrons (in the Thomas–Fermi approximation) and for ionized donors. Shallow donors are usually considered to be fully ionized down to very low temperatures. Notice in Fig. 9.9 the large potential drops in the GaAs regions which, obviously, cannot be ignored. Another serious approximation we make (which will be only partially relaxed in a following section) is to assume a classical charge distribution everywhere in the 'device', even in the accumulated layers. Large differences are expected when the electron quantization is taken into account in the accumulated layers ([9.49] for a Si case). The problem of including quantization effects is quite hard however, and never been addressed in the case of GaAs. We shall simply be cavalier about it and justify the use of the classical approximation only 'a posteriori', after a comparison with experimental data.

We then solve the effective mass equation in the Schrödinger-like form (9.5) by employing the 'energy' effective mass and match phase velocities at the GaAs-AlGaAs interfaces. In the case of graded interfaces (i.e. graded dielectric constants or effective masses) we use an integration scheme proposed by Price [9.50]. At this point we make another approximation: We assume that the tunnelling probability $T(k, V)$ (defined as the ratio between the transmitted and

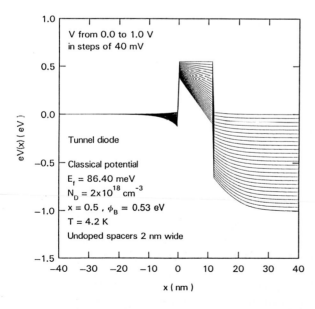

Fig. 9.9. Potential energy distribution for a GaAs-AlGaAs-GaAs tunnel diode obtained from the 'classical' solution of Poisson equation. Notice that undoped spacers 2 nm wide are present at both sides of the AlGaAs 'insulating' barrier. The relevant parameters are either shown in the figure or are taken from the literature [9.13]

incident current of monochromatic electrons) is a function of the normal to the interface k component, or $k_\perp$. This is only approximately correct (as are many other approximations done when dealing with tunnelling!), since the height of the 'insulating' AlGaAs barrier could depend on the parallel component of the wavevector of the tunnelling carrier. To deal with this problem, two-band approximations have been proposed in the past [9.51], but their validity seems to be somewhat questionable [9.52]. Figure 9.10 shows the tunnelling probability for electrons that tunnel from the Fermi energy of the cathode for the structure of Fig. 9.9. A constant (i.e. energy independent) effective mass of $(0.067 + 0.083x)m_{C,0}$ [9.53] has been assumed for the electron effective mass in the AlGaAs layer, x being the Al mole fraction. Notice the peaks in the tunnelling probability resulting from reflections at the anode-AlGaAs interfaces. These peaks – which are not seen when treating tunnelling with the simpler Wenzel–Kramers–Brillouin (WKB) approximation – are due to the phase coherence (therefore, of the ballistic behavior) of the electrons in the barrier. They have been experimentally observed in the past both in Si-SiO$_2$ system [9.54, 55] as well as in GaAs-AlGaAs structures [9.56]. Though indirect, these were indications of ballistic electron transport in these very thin regions. Finally, the tunnelling current density, $I(V)$, as a function of the applied bias, V, can be obtained by integrating the transmission probability, $T(E_\perp, V)$, over the electron flux in the cathode, accounting for the Fermi-Dirac statistics of the electronic states in both electrodes via the Fermi functions and for the spin degeneracy:

$$I(V) \simeq 2e \int \frac{d\mathbf{k}}{(2\pi)^3} f_C(\mathbf{k})[1 - f_A(\mathbf{k})] \, v_\perp(\mathbf{k}) T(k_\perp, V), \tag{9.10}$$

where $f_C(\mathbf{k})$ and $f_A(\mathbf{k})$ are the cathode and anode Fermi functions, and $v_\perp(E)$ is the component of the electron velocity normal to the interface. Using the relations:

$$E(\mathbf{k}) = \frac{\hbar^2 k^2}{2m_{en}(E)}, \tag{9.11a}$$

$$\nabla_{\mathbf{k}} E(\mathbf{k}) = \frac{\hbar^2 \mathbf{k}}{m_{opt}(E)}, \tag{9.11b}$$

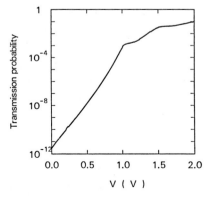

Fig. 9.10. Transmission probability for an electron tunnelling at the cathode Fermi energy across the structure of Fig. 9.9. A direct numerical solution of the Schrödinger eq. – like (9.5) in the text – has been employed. The oscillations at about 1.0 and 1.5 V are due to the reflections the electron wavefunction suffers at the sharp AlGaAs-anode interface and are 'lost' when using the WKB approximation

we can transform the integral over $\mathbf{k}$ to integrals over the normal energy and total electron energies in the case of a spherical band:

$$I(V) \simeq \frac{e}{2} \int_0^\infty dE \frac{\rho(E) f(E)[1 - f(E + eV)]}{[2m_{en}(E)E]^{1/2}} \int_0^\infty dE_\perp T(E_\perp, V), \tag{9.12}$$

where we have used only the cathode Fermi function $f(E)$ and dropped the subscript.

We define the following three distributions: a 'total' energy distribution, $D_{tot}(E, V)$, as the electron distribution as a function of the total electron energy at a bias V; a 'normal' energy distribution, $D_\perp(E_\perp, V)$, as the density of electrons at 'normal' energy, $E_\perp$, at a bias V; and an angular distribution, $D_{ang}(\theta, V)$. These distributions are implicitly defined by

$$I(V) = e \int_0^\infty dE D_{tot}(E, V) = e \int_0^\infty dE_\perp D_\perp(E_\perp, V) = e \int_0^{\pi/2} d\theta D_{ang}(\theta, V), \tag{9.13}$$

and take the forms:

$$D_{tot}(E, V) \simeq \frac{\rho(E) f(E)[1 - f(E + eV)]}{2[2m_{en}(E)E]^{1/2}} \int_0^E dE_\perp T(E_\perp, V), \tag{9.14a}$$

$$D_\perp(E_\perp, V) \simeq T(E_\perp, V) \int_{E_v}^\infty dE \frac{\rho(E) f(E)[1 - f(E + eV)]}{2[2m_{en}(e)E]^{1/2}}, \tag{9.14b}$$

$$D_{ang}(\theta, V) \simeq eh \sin \theta \cos \theta \int_0^\infty dE_\rho(E) f(E)[1 - f(E + eV)]$$

$$\times \frac{k(E)}{m_{en}(E)} T(E \cos^2 \theta, V). \tag{9.14c}$$

In the case of parabolic bands, (14a, b, c) take the form:

$$D_{tot}(E, V) \simeq \frac{m_{C,0}}{\pi^2 \hbar^3} f(E)[1 - f(E + eV)] \int_0^E dE_\perp T(E_\perp, V), \tag{9.15a}$$

$$D_\perp(E_\perp, V) \simeq \frac{m_{C,0}}{\pi^2 \hbar^3} T(E_\perp, V) \int_{E_v}^\infty dE f(E)[1 - f(E + eV)], \tag{9.15b}$$

$$D_{ang}(\theta, V) \simeq \frac{2m_{C,0}}{\pi^2 \hbar^3} \sin \theta \cos \theta \int_0^\infty dEE f(E)[1 - f(E + eV)] T(E \cos^2 \theta, V). \tag{9.15c}$$

As we move along the direction of the electron travel, the energies and angles will change as the potential changes. In Fig. 9.11 we show the total and normal energy distributions of electrons emerging from a 11.5 nm wide hypothetical tunnel barrier, 0.53 eV high. Figure 9.12 illustrates a few angular distributions at

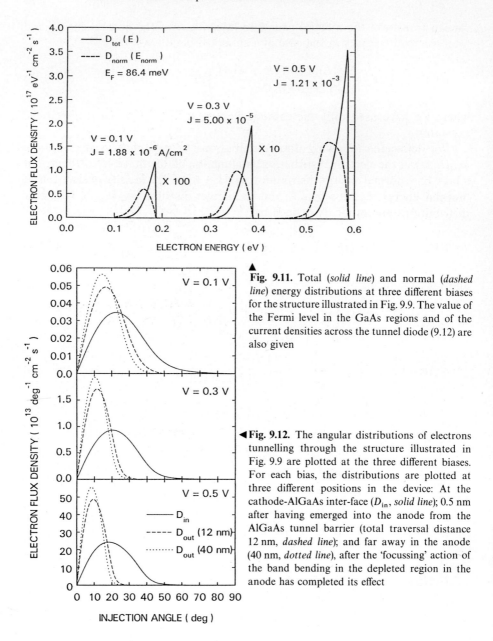

Fig. 9.11. Total (*solid line*) and normal (*dashed line*) energy distributions at three different biases for the structure illustrated in Fig. 9.9. The value of the Fermi level in the GaAs regions and of the current densities across the tunnel diode (9.12) are also given

Fig. 9.12. The angular distributions of electrons tunnelling through the structure illustrated in Fig. 9.9 are plotted at the three different biases. For each bias, the distributions are plotted at three different positions in the device: At the cathode-AlGaAs inter-face (D_{in}, *solid line*); 0.5 nm after having emerged into the anode from the AlGaAs tunnel barrier (total traversal distance 12 nm, *dashed line*); and far away in the anode (40 nm, *dotted line*), after the 'focussing' action of the band bending in the depleted region in the anode has completed its effect

various biases and positions away from the potential barrier. Notice the narrowing of the distributions as the electrons gain more and more 'normal' momentum as they move toward the lower potential in the anode. The fact that most electrons tunnel at a nonzero angle seems surprising but can be easily understood by recalling that while the tunnelling probability favors electrons entering the barrier in the normal direction, a vanishingly small number of electrons will have their velocity oriented in the normal direction. The competitions of these two factors results in a maximum of the distribution at a nonzero angle. This angle is, of course, a function of the barrier parameters, and will decrease with increasing thickness, height, and electron effective mass in the barrier.

Another basic property of the tunnel injector is its mass selectivity. The heavier the mass of the particle is the lower is its tunnelling probability. A tunnel injector was used to inject primarily light holes into a p type GaAs layer. For example, the selectivity of an AlGaAs tunnel barrier imbedded in GaAs, (10 nm thick and 0.2 eV high), for the light holes (with mass $0.082 \, m_e$) versus the heavy holes (with mass $0.2 \, m_e$) is greater than 10,000. As the barrier thins and the injected current density increases the selectivity decreases, however, sufficiently large current densities can be achieved with very thin barriers while still maintaining a large selectivity ratio.

9.4 Energy Spectroscopy

9.4.1 Spectroscopy Defined

The current density, $I(V)$, measured in a device for a particular applied voltage, V, can be expressed as $e\int n(E_\perp)v_\perp(E)dE_\perp$. Even though the energy distribution, $n(E_\perp)$, is very often highly nonuniform, (e.g. it peaks strongly at a particular energy), the $I(V)$ characteristic of a 'ballistic device' will usually be monotonic and featureless. Moreover, in sufficiently narrow regions (on the order of the Debye length), the uncertainties in determining the boundary conditions and the effects due to space charge make the extraction of the physics from the $I(V)$ very difficult. Electron energy spectroscopy, that determines the normal component $n(E_\perp)v_\perp(E)$, as proposed by *Hesto* et al. [9.4], for establishing the existence of ballistic transport is a much more valuable technique. This is usually done by measuring only a part of the distribution, and blocking the rest with an energy window, that can be moved controllably. An ideal spectrometer should (a) be transparent in the window of measurement and opaque outside it, (b) have a known dependence between its window movement and the external control, (e.g. barrier height changes versus an applied voltage change), and (c) be uniform spatially (in contrast with the potential fluctuations that can occur in the PDB diode previously described). Let's discuss two basic types of spectrometers.

9.4.2 Band Pass Spectrometer

The current density I, passing through a narrow normal energy window $\Delta E_\perp$, is $en(E_\perp)v_\perp(E)\Delta E_\perp$. If the energy window moves, I changes and its magnitude is proportional to $n(E_\perp)v_\perp(E)$. If the velocity is almost constant in the distribution width, than $I(E_\perp) \propto n(E_\perp)$, as seen in Fig. 9.13.

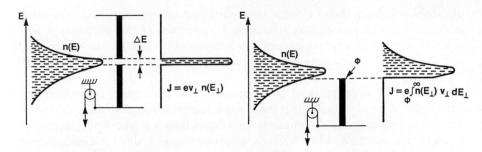

Fig. 9.13. Two types of spectrometers: 'band pass' (*on left*) and 'high pass' (*on right*) filters. In the first, the measured current is proportional to the carriers distribution, and in the second, the derivative $dJ/d\Phi$ is proportional to the carrier distribution. In both cases the velocity $v_\perp$ is assumed constant in the distribution width

Such a spectrometer was realized recently by *Capasso* et al. [9.57] using a resonant double barrier GaAs-AlGaAs structures. The resonant structure has a high transmission at a particular normal resonant energy. The width of this transmission window, δE, is determined – if scattering in the well is ignored – by the width of the two confining barriers and the tunnelling probability, which in turn determines the lifetime, τ, of the resonant state ($\delta E = \hbar/\tau$). Typical transmission windows are expected to be narrower than 1 meV and their transmissions peak sharply with values close to unity. However, the value at the peak is very sensitive to the exact shape of the barriers. As the external voltage across the resonant tunnel barrier varies, the position of the energy window relative to the bottom of the well changes (the Stark effect), and the transmission through the structure changes. These complications make this spectrometer more difficult to use quantitatively than the high pass type discussed below.

9.4.3 High Pass Spectrometer

When electrons with normal energies higher than some threshold value, Φ, pass and are collected, the resultant current density in the collector is $I = e \int_\Phi^\infty n(E_\perp) v_\perp(E) dE_\perp$. If Φ is changed to $\Phi + \Delta\Phi$, the change in the measured current density is $en(E_\perp) v_\perp(E) \Delta\Phi$. Thus, the distributions can be deduced from the derivatives $dj/d\Phi$, (rather than directly from $I(V)$), as shown in Fig. 9.13.

Any potential barrier with a variable and accurately controlled barrier height can serve as a high pass spectrometer. This type of spectroscopy was done in Si in the early sixties [9.5]. A *pn* junction, in close proximity to the semiconductor surface, was reversed biased. When minority carriers were generated by light absorption in the *p* layer, they drifted across the depletion region and heated up in the *n* layer adjacent to the surface. When the biasing voltage exceeded the Si work function, some of the electrons remained sufficiently hot, emitted into vacuum and subsequently were collected by a positive collector electrode. Here, rather than changing the height of a potential barrier (the work function of Si) to perform spectroscopy, the position of the conduction band in the p layer was varied relative to the vacuum level by the reverse bias voltage. Since the number of photoexcited electrons was independent of the biasing voltage, the hot distribution arriving at the surface reflected the photoexcited distribution.

Spectroscopy in GaAs was initiated recently by *Hayes* et al. in the PDBT [9.6] and by *Yokoyama* et al. in the THETA device [9.7]. The PDBT was designed so that the spectrometer barrier was higher than the injecting barrier, and its shorter triangular arm was near the base of the transistor. When a positive voltage V was applied between collector and base, the spectrometer barrier height was lowered (by some ratio to the applied voltage), the barrier tip scanned through the impinging electron distribution, and the collector current increased monotonically. The derivative of the collector current with respect to the applied voltage gave the current versus normal energy distribution with an energy axis scaled by a factor $dV/d\Phi$. The advantages of the PDBT as a spectrometer device are that electrons are analyzed near the end of the transport region (because of the very short arm of the triangular spectrometer barrier), and the possibility to analyze low energy electrons (since the top of the spectrometer barrier can be lowered substantially). On the other hand the PDB diode suffers from a few drawbacks: in practice, the barrier top is not well defined due to the finite width of the acceptor region. This nominal width is about 5 nm wide, but some unknown impurity segregation (Be dopants) most probably exists. In addition, electrons spill over from both confining n layers affecting the bottom edges of the triangular barrier [9.58]. These two effects make the dependence of Φ on V complicated to estimate and not necessarily constant over the entire biasing range (especially when Φ is very small). Another major drawback is the unaviodable fluctuations in the barrier height due to the random positions of the acceptor impurities (as was mentioned above and in [9.48]). Note that when the injector barrier is also of the PDB type, the situation is even worse since the injected distribution is smeared from the start. One could, at least in principle, eliminate almost entirely the fluctuations by building a triangular barrier from a linearly graded AlGaAs barrier. (Again, in practice, it is difficult to assure a linear grading, making thus $d\Phi/dV$ difficult to know.)

Another type of a spectrometer barrier is a simple, flat, square type barrier (this is the barrier that is imbedded in the THETA device), made from a uniform layer of AlGaAs, for example, with constant Al mole fraction (Fig. 9.14). This barrier can only be raised by applying a negative potential to the collector with respect to the base on its far side from the base edge. The main disadvantage this spectrometer has is that analysis is done after the electrons have traversed the total length of the barrier, increasing the chance of additional scattering and broadening of the electron distributions in the barrier.

The main cause of hot electron scattering in undoped AlGaAs, at low temperatures, is the alloy scattering. Measurements conducted by *Chandra* et al. [9.59] on high quality AlGaAs layers at low temperatures, led to an estimated alloy scattering dominated mobility of about 10^5 cm^2/Vs, and an approximate hot electron mfp of 0.5 μm, making high quality barriers of this type suitable for

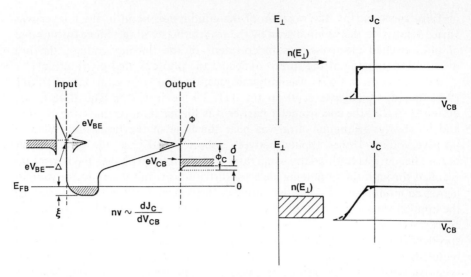

Fig. 9.14. The THETA device operating in the spectroscopy mode. The high pass filter is a square type AlGaAs barrier in front of the collector. Its height changes via the application of a negative V_{CB}, and $\Delta\Phi_C \neq \Delta V_{CB}$. Two examples of the expected $I_C(V_{CB})$ are shown for a delta function and a square type electron distributions

spectroscopy purposes. Additional advantages of this spectrometer barrier are the relation $dV/d\Phi \simeq 1$, and the uniform lateral barrier height free of doping related potential fluctuations. The same square type barrier, when used in a p type THETA device, was far from ideal with $dV/d\Phi > 1$, most probably due to unintentional charges in the barrier. The dependence $\Phi(V)$ had to be independently measured to deduce the hole energy distribuions.

9.4.4 Energy Resolution of the Square Type Barrier

Even in spectroscopic measurements employing a square AlGaAs barrier some modification of the electron distribution will be induced by the barrier itself. Apart from the quantum mechanical reflections, which we will discuss in Sects. 9.5 and 9.7, electrons can tunnel through the top 'tip' of the barrier. These electrons will be assigned a higher energy than they actually have. Therefore, we expect to measure both some smearing of the original distribution and a shift of the electron energy to higher values. However, for a typical barrier of the type employed in the THETA device, these effects are usually small.

In Fig. 9.15 we show the energy distribution which would be deduced from a 'high-pass' spectroscopy experiment. We assume a monoenergetic beam of carriers (delta function distribution) with excess energy of 50 meV above the top of a square type barrier with height $\Phi_B = 200$ meV, and thickness 50 nm. Using the WKB approximation to evaluate the tunnelling probability as a function of the bias applied across the barrier, and taking its derivative with respect to the

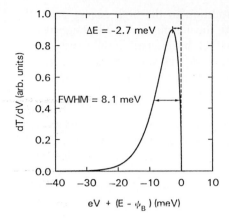

$eV + (E - \psi_B)$ (meV)

Fig. 9.15. Broadening and shift of a monoenergetic electron distribution incident on a square-barrier high-pass filter. The actual incident distribution is a delta function at the position indicated by the vertical dashed line, while the measured distribution (i.e. the derivative of the tunnelling probability with respect to the applied bias, V, solid line) is broadened and shifted at higher energies (more negative eV in the figure) because of electrons tunnelling through the top of the berrier. The WKB approximation has been employed to compute the tunnelling probability. The parameters employed are described in the text

applied bias, we obtain an apparent distribution some 8 meV wide, shifted by about 2 meV to the left (i.e. at higher energies) of the 'real' incoming energy. Obviously, the precise values of the broadening and shift of the monoenergetic distribution will depend on the various barrier parameters, and some additional broadening will result from quantum mechanical reflections of the beam with energy higher than the tip of the barrier, but in realistic cases they will be of the order of a few meV.

9.4.5 Observation of Quasi Ballistic and Ballistic Electron Transport in GaAs

Hayes et al. [9.6] and *Yokoyama* et al. [9.7] have published almost simultaneously spectroscopic results of electron transport conducted in GaAs. In both experiments, non equilibrium, quasi ballistic transport was verified. In *Yokoyama* et al.'s experiments with the THETA device, electrons were injected into a 100 nm wide base doped n-type to 5×10^{17} cm^{-3} and were analyzed by a 150 nm AlGaAs square type, undoped, collector barrier. Relatively narrow distributions, about 150 meV wide, were measured, with an average energy loss, (from the Fermi level at the emitter to the peak distribution at the collector), of about 250 meV. Note that in these experiments injection energies far in excess of the threshold for L-valleys transfer were used. In similar experiments done later, *Heiblum* et al. [9.8] have shown that when injection energies exceeded the Γ-L and Γ-X valleys energy splitting, all the electrons arrived at the end of 100 nm base devices almost completely thermalized.

Hayes et al. and *Levi* et al. [9.6, 9] had published a set of spectroscopy results done in PDBTs, having base widths from 170 nm down to 65 nm and doped n type to a level of 1×10^{18} cm^{-3}. In the thick-base devices the arriving electrons were completely thermalized, however, when the base became narrower than about 85 nm, a hot distribution was detected at the spectrometer. Unfortunately, because of the poor resolution of the PDB spectrometer [9.48], it was difficult to determine unequivocally the nature of the arriving distributions, namely the fractions of the ballistic and quasi ballistic electrons, and the possibility that small angle scattering events occur. In addition to the high energy peak, the authors reported a low energy peak near the Fermi level and assigned it to electrons that were excited from the Fermi level sharing part of the energy lost by the hot electrons. Note, however, that when Φ was very low a large leakage current, that has to be subtracted, dominated the transport, making the interpretation questionable. Also the linearity of the function $\Phi(V)$ is questionable.

Similar experiments were done by *Long* et al. [9.40], using a hybrid type device: a graded triangular AlGaAs emitter and a PDB spectrometer in the collector. In a 120 nm base devices they had found a weak high energy electron distribution peak, indicating some nonequilibrium transport.

Using a high quality AlGaAs square type barrier imbedded in a THETA device with a 30 nm wide base doped to 1×10^{18} cm^{-3} (Figs. 9.14, 16), *Heiblum* et al. have shown a very strong and narrow distribution peak [9.10]. The peak energy, detected at the collector side of the spectrometer barrier, was close to the injection energy and was most prominent when injection energies were lower or didn't exceed by much the L to Γ-valleys splitting. In Figs. 9.17 and 9.18 the output characteristics and the energy distributions are plotted. The observed distributions had 60 meV full width at half maximum and changed their peak position as the injection energy increased. To calculate energy loss, two corrections were taken into account: the band bending at the collector side of the spectrometer barrier, δ, (an accumulation region) and the small displacement of the normal distribution peak injected into the base down from the Fermi level in the emitter, $\varDelta$ (see Fig. 9.14). For the 'ballistic condition' to be fulfilled, the

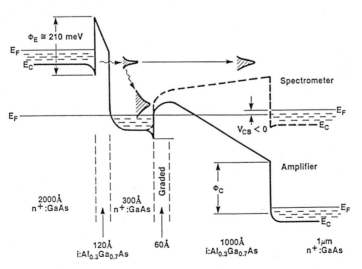

Fig. 9.16. The potential distribution in a THETA device with a 30 nm base and n doping of 1 $\times 10^{18}$ cm^{-3}. This was the first device to show ballistic transport (due in part to lower injection energies than in the device described in Fig. 9.7)

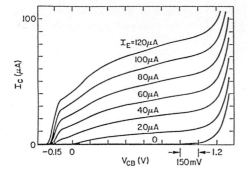

Fig. 9.17. The output characteristics of the device shown in Fig. 9.16. The parameter is the injection current, I_E

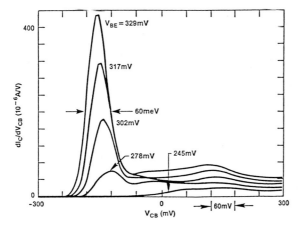

Fig. 9.18. The derivative of collector currents versus collector voltage when the injection voltage is the parameter. These derivatives are the momentum distributions of the ballistic electrons (nv, or the current distributions), which are similar to the 'number distribution', $n(E)$, assuming the electron velocity at the injector is almost constant over the 60 meV distribution spread

normal energy balance equation has to be satisfied:

$$eV_{BE} + \zeta - \Delta = \Phi_C + eV_{CB}(\text{at peak}) - \delta , \qquad (9.16)$$

where $\zeta = E_F - E_C$ is the energy separation between the Fermi level and the conduction band energies, V_{CB} (at peak) is the spectrometer negative applied voltage at the distribution peak, and V_{BE} is the injection voltage. Allowing an error of 4% in the nominal value of the Al mole fraction in the collector barrier and assuming the normally used uncertainties in knowing the barrier height, it was concluded that the peak of the collected distribution couldn't have shifted even by one phonon (36 meV) from that of the injected distribution [9.10].

A similar THETA device but with a base width of 72 nm (which was fabricated later) exhibited very similar peaked distributions (Fig. 9.19). The major difference between the distributions in these devices were in the 'ballistic fractions' of the collected currents, or the ballistic $\alpha(\alpha_B \simeq I_C(V_{CB} \simeq 0)/I_E)$. In the devices with the base widths of 30 nm and 72 nm, the α_B's were 0.3 and 0.15, respectively. The most interesting experimental fact we wish to stress is the preservation of the shape of the ballistic distribution. As the transport region

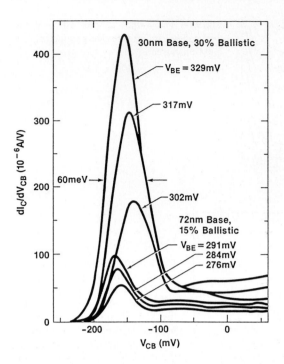

Fig. 9.19. Ballistic energy distributions detected in devices with base widths of 30 nm and 72 nm. Both distributions are similar in shape but the number of ballistic electrons in each is different. The difference in peak positions in the two devices is due to a slightly different Al mole fraction in the collector barriers

lengthened, more electrons were scattered and 'left' the ballistic distribution. If small angle scattering events did take place, one would have expected the distributions to broaden as the transit distance increased (due to a decrease in the normal energy). However, for base widths up to at least 72 nm no change in the distributions width was observed.

It is of course possible that electrons in the ballistic distribution can scatter via small angle scattering events without leaving the 'ballistic' distribution and thus never being separately detected. We can place an upper limit on the scattering angle for the most energetic electrons in the distribution, by solving $E_\perp \sin^2\theta_{max} = \Delta E$, where θ_{max} is the maximum scattering angle, and ΔE is some characteristic width of the distribution (no larger than $E_F - E_C$ at the interface of the emitter-tunnel barrier). Taking $E_\perp \simeq 250$ meV and $\Delta E \simeq 60$ meV for the most energetic electrons, we find $\theta_{max} \simeq 30°$ in 80 nm wide base. For most electrons (in the center of the distribution), $\Delta E \simeq 30$ meV and $\theta \simeq 20°$ in 80 nm wide base. Even though this is possible in principle, it is difficult to argue why the lower energy electrons do not scatter at these angles, and in particular when the base width was increased from 30 nm to 80 nm. From this and also from the experimental work with the PDBT [9.9, 40], it is reasonable to state that the dominant scattering mechanisms are highly inelastic, causing the electrons to thermalize. Small angle scattering events are thus highly unlikely. Since our spectroscopy measures only the normal energy distribution, the results could also be attributed to large angle elastic scattering events; those are less likely in heavily doped GaAs.

Based on their experimental results with the PDBT, *Hollis* et al. have suggested that the dominant scattering of hot electrons is due to the existence of coupled modes of plasmons and phonons in the heavily doped GaAs base regions of the devices [9.36]. This hypothesis was later on adopted by *Levi* et al. who calculated a mfp of about 30 nm for hot electrons that have excess kinetic energy of about 0.25 eV in GaAs layers doped to 1×10^{18} cm^{-3} [9.9, 60]. Note, however, that these calculations were done for hot electrons traversing bulk GaAs, while in reality the transport regions are thin. Unfortunately, the calculation of the scattering rates in a narrow base device is rendered nontrivial by the following considerations: We will see later that in actual devices, the number of occupied subbands formed in the narrow base varies between 2 and 5, depending on the bias conditions and the base width. This number is neither too large to justify a bulk, 3-dimensional approximation [9.60], nor too small to simplify the calculation of the relevant quantities as in the case of a single occupied subband [9.61, 62]. Except for very formal treatments of difficult numerical implementation [9.63, 64], the calculation of the dielectric constant (and thus of the scattering rates) for a multi-subband, two-dimensional electron gas must be worked out from first principles. In addition, there are the numerical difficulties – which will be discussed below – of obtaining the many matrix elements involving inter- and intra-subband excitations of the free electrons and of the coupled two-dimensional plasma-LO phonon modes starting from the correct electronic wavefunctions. As we shall see, these must be obtained from the self consistent solution of Poisson and Schrödinger equations giving the correct potential and charge density in the base. In any case, we should expect that, as the base gets thinner, the mean free paths should increase: The smaller two-dimensional density of the final states for the elementary excitations of the coupled optical-phonon/electron-gas system, and the weaker matrix elements between the incident hot electron state (with momentum mainly in the direction normal to the interfaces) and the excitations in the base (mostly with momentum parallel to the interfaces) should reduce the scattering rates.

Finally, we must also understand the role of the confining base-collector AlGaAs barrier, since in the 'spectroscopy mode' we require ballistic transport also through this region of the device (and in particular against a retarding electric field). Alloy scattering and poorly controlled properties of the AlGaAs layer can influence the transfer ratio of the devices and the deduced ballistic fractions.

An experimental determination of the mfp in a uniformly doped, thin, confined layer is not an easy task. In addition to the fundamental scattering events, the net transfer of ballistic electrons is also affected by quantum mechanical reflections from the base-collector barrier interface, alloy scattering in the AlGaAs collector barrier, and some transfer of electrons into the upper satellite *L*-valleys (theoretically possible even if injection energies are smaller than the Γ-L energy splitting [9.65]). Another effect that complicates matters is knowing the actual length of the doped base when electron injection takes place. As the injection voltage across the tunnel barrier increases, a substantial part of the base depletes, making thus the transport region highly non uniform. In calculations performed in Sect. 9.5 we show how to calculate the exact potential in the base.

9.4.6 Observation of Ballistic Hole Transport in GaAs

The p type THETA device is a complementary device to the n type device. Here, as discussed before in Sect. 9.3.3, the tunnel injector serves also as a separator between the majority of holes which are heavy (about 94% of the total hole population) and the light holes, injecting mostly the light ones. At energies close enough to the valence band the light hole mass is very similar to that of the electrons and their velocity is high. One might expect to observe a substantial fraction of ballistic light holes traversing a few tens of *nm* of heavily p doped GaAs. Because of the heavy hole band which is degenerate with the light hole band at $k = 0$, the final density of states available to the light holes to scatter to is very large, and the expected ballistic mfp is smaller than that of the ballistic electrons.

Spectroscopy performed with a p type THETA device at 4.2 K [9.77], with a 31 nm wide base doped to 2×10^{18} cm^{-3}, showed ballistic fractions of about 8%. Detected hole energy distributions were very narrow, about 35 meV FWHM, with a peak distribution following the injection energy. In the first few devices that had been tested, the AlGaAs quality was not good enough to support the transport of ballistic holes through out the full width of the collector barrier.

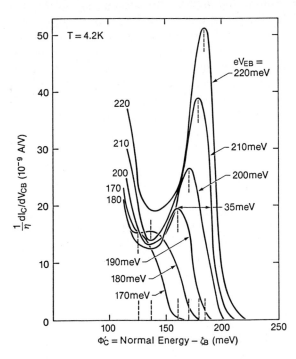

Fig. 9.20. Energy distributions of ballistic light holes after the traversal of 31 nm heavily p doped GaAs and some 20 nm of an undoped collector barrier. Note the lower energy tails of the distributions indicating hot, non ballistic holes, at lower energies

However, for negative collector voltage the potential peak of the spectrometer is near the base side of the barrier, and holes to be analyzed have to traverse only a short part of the collector barrier. Finding independently $\Phi_C(V_{CB})$ (via activation energy and threshold type measurements), the proportionality factor $dV_{CB}/d\Phi_C$ was evaluated, enabling thus to plot the collected hole distributions as shown in Fig. 9.20. Note the lower energy tails of the distributions. These tails belong to quasi ballistic holes or to holes that were excited from the Fermi distribution due to the relaxing hot holes. Here too, as in the case of ballistic electrons the narrow peaks that emerge from the lower energy distribution tails move in energy as the injection energy varies, proving the ballistic nature of the transport. It is too early at this point to speculate on the nature of the scattering mechanisms. In Sect. 9.5.5 a definite proof will be provided for the light nature of the ballistic holes.

9.5 Electron Coherent Effects in the THETA Device

9.5.1 Size Quantization Effects

As was mentioned briefly in the previous section, quantum size effects are expected to be important in thin and confined transport regions. If the length of these regions is of the same order of magnitude as the electron wavelength, then only a relatively small number of normal electron momenta, $p_\perp$, will be allowed in the regions. Consequently, the electronic charge and potential distributions there will deviate from the classical distributions, and the tunnelling probability of electrons tunnelling into these transport regions will strongly peak as a function of the injection energy, (assuming the transverse momentum is preserved in the tunnelling process). These quantization effects will affect the transport when the energy separation between the bottom of sequential quasi two dimensional subbands is comparable to the energy width of the normal injected distributions. Besides these described 'kinematic' effects, we expect the usual scattering events to be strongly modified as suggested before, but we won't elaborate on this issue here. In this section we will describe in some detail the 'kinematic' effects.

9.5.2 Classical and Self-Consistent Well Potential

In wide regions of the device, the potential distribution can be simply obtained by solving the Poisson equation, treating the electrons classically in the Thomas–Fermi approximation. However, in some regions of the device this approximation might fail badly: Typically, the charge density associated with the free electrons in quantized regions of the device (in accumulation layers and in the thin base of the THETA device) will differ significantly from the charge distribution we obtain in the 'classical' approximation. Figure 9.21 illustrates this situation: We have considered one of our structures with a base width of 29 nm. We have solved the Poisson equation, as described above, using the classical

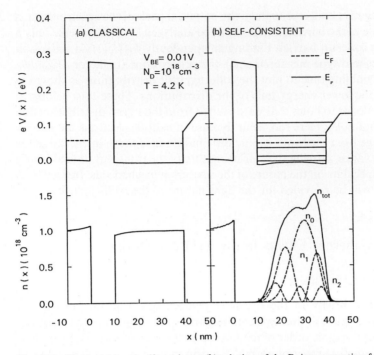

Fig. 9.21. Classical (**a**) and self consistent (**b**) solution of the Poisson equation for a THETA device. Notice the different shape of the self consistent potential in the base region and the shift of the Fermi energy at the AlGaAs-base interfaces. The charge distributions for the classical case and for the self consistent solution (having three subbands occupied) are also shown

electron charge shown in the lower half of Fig. 9.21a, obtaining the potential distribution shown in Fig. 9.21a. We have also solved the Poisson equation employing the charge density corresponding to the quantized electrons in the base regions, as illustrated in Fig. 9.21b. Of course, the Poisson and Schrödinger equations must be solved self consistently, as the electron wavefunctions $\zeta_\nu(x)$ (ν being the index of the subband of energy E_ν) depend on the potential distribution $V(x)$, which, in turn, depends on the charge density $e|\zeta_\nu|^2$. This problem is exactly the same problem tackled in the case of quantization in inversion [9.66] and accumulation [9.49] layers, but it is complicated by the more troublesome boundary conditions and by the absence of spatial symmetry of the structure.

In formulae, the form of the Poisson equation we solve is:

$$\frac{d}{dx}\left[\varepsilon(x)\frac{dV(x)}{dx}\right] = e\{\hat{F}_{1/2}[(E_F - E_C - eV(x))/k_BT] - N_D\} , \tag{9.17a}$$

$$\frac{d}{dx}\left[\varepsilon(x)\frac{dV(x)}{ds}\right] = e\left\{N_2\sum_\nu \hat{F}_\nu[(E_F - E_C)/k_BT]|\zeta_\nu(x)|^2 - N_D\right\} , \tag{9.17b}$$

where (9.17a) is valid in regions where electron quantization effects are neglected (i.e. the contact layers, including the troublesome accumulation layers which we treat classically), while (9.17b) is valid for the (quantized) free electron in the base region. In the equations above, N_D is the concentration of ionized donors, $\varepsilon(x)$ is the dielectric constant, E_C the bottom of the Γ-band, and the equivalent density-of-states factors N_C and N_2 are given by:

$$N_C = 2[(2\pi m_{C,0} k_B T)/(2\pi\hbar)^2]^{3/2} \tag{9.18}$$

for the bulk, three-dimensional electrons in the emitter and collector, and

$$N_2 = \frac{m_{C,0} k_B T}{\pi\hbar^2} \tag{9.19}$$

for the two-dimensional electron gas in the base. The two-dimensional Fermi integral is:

$$\hat{F}_v(\eta_F) = \int_0^\infty d\eta \, \frac{\theta(\eta - E_v/k_B T)(1 - 2\eta\beta)}{\exp(\eta - \eta_F) + 1}. \tag{9.20}$$

The nonparabolicity of the central valley has been accounted for by the usual parameter γ, or its counterpart in thermal units $\beta = \gamma k_B T$. The function $\theta(x)$ is the usual step-function.

The Schrödinger equation takes the form:

$$\frac{d}{dx} \left\{ \frac{1}{m_{en}[E - eV(x)]} \frac{d\zeta(x)}{dx} \right\} = \frac{2}{\hbar^2}[E - eV(x)]\zeta(x), \tag{9.21}$$

with the normalization condition $\int dx|\zeta(x)|^2 = 1$. In both cases of (9.17) and (9.21) we have accounted for the possibility of grading (as it occurs in our structures) and have imposed continuity of the electric displacement fields (the D-fields) and electron phase velocities at the heterojunctions. In addition we have assumed that the wavefunctions vanish at the emitter-AlGaAs and collector-AlGaAs interfaces, preventing in effect the electrons from 'leaking-out' of the base region. This might constitute a questionable assumption only for the highest-lying states. These, however, correspond to unoccupied subbands and do not contribute to the charge density in the base region. The wavefunctions corresponding to occupied subbands, on the contrary, have a negligible probability of tunnelling out at all applied biases of interest making our approximation justified.

The set the two coupled equations (9.17) can be solved by an almost standard iteration procedure. The classical Poisson equation is solved first with the desired boundary conditions (with the two biases V_{BE} and V_{BC} applied) in order to obtain a reasonable initial guess. (Typically, a 50 to 200 point mesh is used). The Schrödinger equation is then solved on a finer mesh (of 1000 or more points, because of the short electron wavelength at the higher energies). The charge density in the base can than be obtained from the resulting wavefunctions and inserted into (9.17b). The iteration proceeds until a maximum change of 10^{-6} eV is obtained for the potential at any position or for the normal energy levels when going from one iteration to the next. Several numerical 'tricks' are employed to accelerate the convergence (as described in [9.67]). Typically, 8 to 12 iterations are necessary to obtain convergence.

For the same configuration illustrated in Fig. 9.21, we show in Fig. 9.22 the overlay of the classical and self consistent solutions for the potential distributions and the wavefunctions corresponding to the occupied subbands. At higher biases, fewer subbands are occupied as the base becomes depleted of electrons. This is shown in Fig. 9.23 for a device having lower doping.

The major differences between the classical and self consistent solution are: 1) The potential distribution in the base shows a 'bump' at low biases in an attempt to 'flatten' the peaked electronic charge. 2) More importantly, the Fermi level is shifted upwards (with respect to the bottom of the conduction band at the interfaces). This will change in a significant way the relation between the total external voltage measured across the contacts of the device and the different components of voltage drop in different sections of the device.

9.5.3 Tunnelling into a Well

Somewhat interesting and surprising are the energy distributions obtained for the electrons tunnelling from the emitter into the base region. The presence of quantized energy levels in the narrow base changes dramatically the distribu-

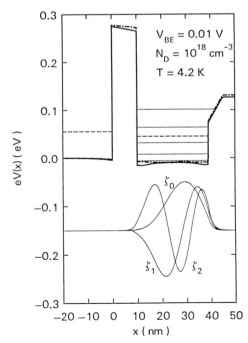

Fig. 9.22. The same potential distributions shown in Fig. 9.21 are plotted to stress the differences between classical (*dot-dashed line*) and self consistent solution. The electronic wavefunctions corresponding to the occupied subbands are also illustrated

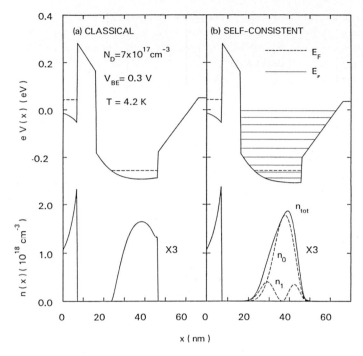

Fig. 9.23. A high bias situation in a 30 nm base THETA device is illustrated. Only two subbands are now occupied. Note the reduction in the carrier density on the left side of the base

tions that were illustrated in Figs, 9.11 and 9.12 by selecting particular 'resonant' normal energies and tunnelling angles. This is shown in Figs. 9.24 and 9.25. While the total energy distribution is still relatively wide (solid lines in Fig. 9.24, showing the steps corresponding to the eigenstates in the base), the normal energy distribution (dashed line) is rather narrow. Notice that we have not accounted for the broadening of the eigenstates in the base which will result from scattering processes and the finite life time of the states.

9.5.4 Nonparabolicity Effects, Real and Resonant States

The bound states in the base region of the THETA were observed experimentally with the appearence of resonances in the emitter or base currents, and a modulation in α of the device. Figures 9.26a and b show typical experimental results of these states. The numerical derivative of the emitter current with respect to the emitter-base bias, V_{BE}, is plotted in Fig. 9.26a, showing clear peaks associated with quantum levels in the base. Quantum reflections at the interfaces will occur also for electrons injected at energies above the confining base-collector barrier. These energies are associated with what we may call 'resonant', 'virtual', or 'unbound' states. Figure 9.26b shows the effect of the virtual states on

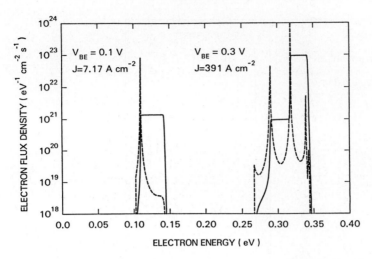

Fig. 9.24. The total (*solid line*) and normal (*dashed line*) energy distributions for electrons tunnelling into the base of the THETA device are plotted at two different base-emitter biases. Notice the spikes in at normal energies (and steps at total energies) corresponding to the energy eigenvalues in the quantized base region

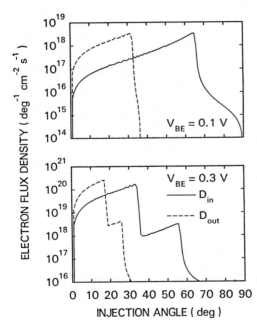

Fig. 9.25. Angular distributions of electrons tunnelling into the quantized base region of a THETA device. The solid line refers to electrons which 'begin to tunnel' at the emitter-barrier interface. The dashed line represents the angular distribution of electrons near the 'end' region of the base, close to the base-collector barrier interface. (Peaks are observed at angles such that the normal energy, $E_\perp$, matches the energy eigenvalues in the quantized base region)

α's of three different devices. Observation of these states is a very interesting result, as it follows, unambiguously, from the phase coherence maintained by the electrons as they cross the device, i.e. on the existence of ballistic transport.

Figure 9.27 illustrates schematically the difference we draw between real (bound) and virtual (unbound) states. The transition between the two regimes as

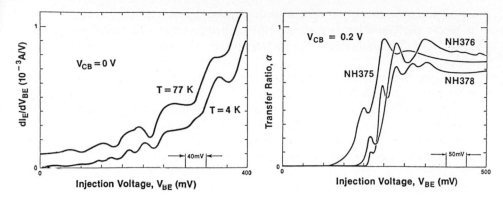

Fig. 9.26. (a) The derivative of the emitter current, I_E, with respect to the base-emitter bias voltage, V_{BE}, for a THETA device having a base 30 nm wide GaAs regions doped to a concentration of 1 $\times 10^{18}$ cm^{-3}, a confining collector-barrier height of about 260 meV. The oscillations correspond to bound ($V_{BE} < 220$ mV) and to 'virtual' ($V_{BE} > 220$ mV) states in the base region. (b) The 'virtual' states are also 'sensed' clearly by the α's of three different devices. The α's 'turn on' voltage indicate the collector barrier height above the Fermi level in the base, with $V_{CB} = 0.2$ V

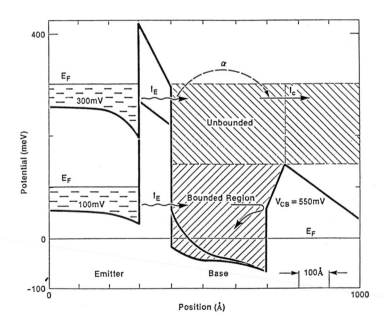

Fig. 9.27. Qualitative, schematic plot representing the potential distribution of a THETA device. Depending on the value of the applied base-emitter bias, V_{BE}, the emitter-base current will 'sense' the bound, real eigenstates in the quantized based region, or the virtual, unbound states. The virtual states will affect also the characteristic behavior of α

a function of base-emitter bias is also shown: As $V_{BE} + \xi$ (where $\xi = E_F - E_C$), is below the confining barrier, Φ_C, the emitter current will 'sense' the bound states. As V_{BE} is made larger, the emitter current or α will both 'sense' the virtual states.

Figure 9.28 shows a comparison between experimental derivative of the emitter current with respect to V_{BE} and the computed emitter-to-base transmission probability $T_{EB}(E_\perp, V)$ for an electron with normal energy $E_\perp$ tunnelling from the Fermi energy in the emitter. For the devices with base widths of 72 nm and 51.5 nm the agreement between experimental results and the simulation using the classical potentials is excellent. In the device with base width of 29 nm the agreement is rather poor. However, when the self consistent potential was used the agreement was much better, as evident in Fig. 9.28.

The emitter-to-base tunnelling probability $T_{EB}(E_\perp, V)$ is not easily defined in the present context. In the simple one dimensional picture we are using, there is no current flow in the base. Rather than defining the transmission probability from emitter-to-base as the ratio of the transmitted-to-incident current, we have considered instead the ratio between the average charge density in the base associated with the transmitted wave and the average charge density associated

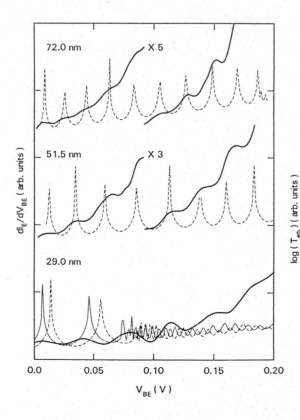

Fig. 9.28. Experimental dI_E/dV_{BE} curves (thick solid lines) for three THETA devices having three increasingly narrower base regions. The thin dashed lines represent the transmission probabilities for electrons tunnelling from the Fermi level in the emitter computed for a potential distribution obtained from the classical solution of the Poisson equation. Good agreement for the peak positions is obtained between experiment and simulation for the larger base devices. As the base width gets smaller than 30 nm, a self consistent solution of Poisson and Schrödinger equations is needed to compute the potential distributions and obtain a better agreement with experiment

with the incident wave. That is:

$$T_{E \to B}(E_\perp, V_{BE}) \simeq \frac{\int_{d_{EB}}^{d_{EB}+d_B} dx |\zeta(x)|^2}{\int_{-d_B}^{0} dx |\zeta_{inc}(x)|^2}, \qquad (9.22)$$

where d_{EB} and d_B are the thickness of the emitter-base barrier and of the base, respectively (the emitter-AlGaAs barrier interface being located at $x = 0$), and the incident wave, ζ_{inc}, is obtained by projecting the wavefunctions onto an incident plane wave:

$$\zeta_{inc}(x) \simeq \int_{-\infty}^{0} \frac{dx'}{\sqrt{2\pi}} e^{ik(x-x')} \zeta(x') . \qquad (9.23)$$

In our simulated results resonances are observed where bound states occur, which is our main interest here, but a quantitative agreement between experimental and simulated currents can not be expected (even if we could set aside experimental problems such as leakage currents, interface roughness, and alike).

The understanding of the resonances in the unbound regime requires additional work: The full integration over the distribution of the electrons in the emitter is necessary. This is due to unavoidable high frequency oscillations seen in the unbound regime, at high bias in Fig. 9.28 for the 29 nm base device. They are caused by additional reflections from the AlGaAs barrier-collector interface (on the far side from the base). These oscillations are not expected in a real device since they will be smeared out by the nonzero width of the energy distribution of the tunnelling electrons. To make the simulation more realistic, we have integrating the tunnelling probability over the Fermi distribution of the electrons in the emitter for each bias point. Then a numerical derivative (always a source of undesired numerical noise) with respect to the bias was taken. Noise reduction was obtained only by using the logarithm of the current and using 'a cubic spline' smoothing to extract the derivative. Figure 9.29 shows a comparison between experimental results and simulations in two narrow base devices. The resonances seem to appear at the 'right' biases, even in the unbound regime, up to very high energies.

We would like to stress strongly that after initial failures to fit the data with the simulation using the nominal 'growth' parameters and the usually used nonparabolicity parameters, particularly at the higher injection biases, several structural parameters were varied in an attempt to improve the agreement: doping concentration, barrier heights, barrier and base thickness, etc. This was not successful: For instance, varying the doping concentration shifted the Fermi level, and thus the entire curve, but did not change the wrong spacing between resonances. Varying the base width resulted in a poor overall agreement starting at the very first resonances. Only when the value of the nonparabolicity parameter given by *Blakemore* ((9.2) and [9.13]) was varied, have we obtained a

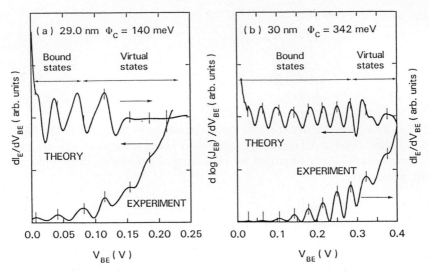

Fig. 9.29. Experimental dI_E/dV_{BE} curves and theoretical logarithmic derivatives of the tunnelling base current for two narrow-base THETA devices. Both the bound and unbound states regions are illustrated. A self consistent Poisson–Schrödinger solution for the potential and (9.12) have been employed in the simulation

marked improvement in the agreement. The value of the nonparabolicity parameter, γ, we have finally used was obtained from the empirical pseudopotential calculations that also gave us the band structure and the group velocities shown in Figs. 9.1 and 9.3, respectively. This value of $\gamma = -0.834\,\text{eV}^{-1}$ gave us excellent agreements seen for all the devices represented in Figs. 9.28 and 9.29, using the nominal 'growth' parameters. Our nonparabolicity parameter is plotted in Fig. 9.30 together with the commonly used values. Note also that the accuracy of our estimate for γ is better than a few percent: A larger error than this will easily drive the simulation 'off phase' after a few resonances.

This is a unique and powerful way to determine the effective mass up to very high energies (almost 0.4 eV in the device shown in Fig. 9.29). In this energy range, electrons are usually occupying upper satellite valleys and the direct valley mass is difficult to separate and measure. Since our resonances result only from the ballistic, interfering 'Γ-electrons', we accurately measure only their mass.

9.5.5 Interference Effects of Ballistic Holes

Similar quantum interference effects had been also observed in the p-type THETA device due to the ballistic holes traversing the base. These effects introduced resonances in the tunnelling current into the base (I_E), and strong peaks in the derivative of this current versus the injection voltage [9.77]. Figure 9.31 shows these peaks for different collector voltages. The number of resonances in the bounded regime and their energy positions agree well with

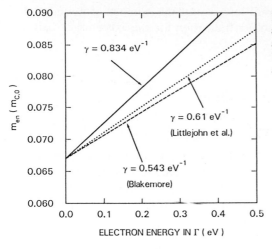

Fig. 9.30. The nonparabolicity parameter, γ, and the energy effective mass as a function of the electron energy in the Γ band. The usually used γ's [9.13, 17] are also shown for comparison

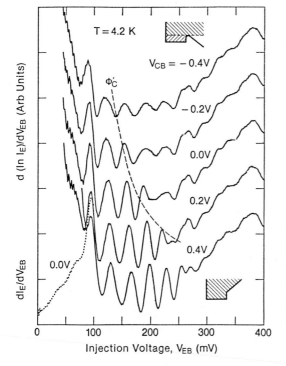

Fig. 9.31. Resonances (quantum interference effects) in the tunnelling currents into the confined base in a p-type THETA device, exhibiting bound and virtual states. The spacings indicate the transport of predominantly light holes. As the collector voltage changes the number of bound (and virtual) states changes

extremely simplified calculations for the energy positions of a light holes (with a constant mass, in a one dimensional square box). This unequivocally confirms that the ballistic holes are light. If the holes were heavy, one would expect at least sixteen sub-bands in the base. The bound states are distinguished from the virtual ones by the strength of the resonances. It is clearly seen that as the collector voltage changes from positive to negative, the confining potential barrier at the right side of the well lowers and the number of bound states decreases. The resonances are another indication for the existence of ballistic holes in the structure.

9.6 Transfer to the L Satellite Valleys

9.6.1 Spectroscopic Observations

Figure 9.32 shows the differential transfer ratios α's as a function of injection voltage, V_{BE}, of a few THETA devices. As observed, the α's tend to saturate or decrease above some threshold injection voltage V_{th}, and the modulation due to the quantum interference effects vanish. We attribute these effects to the scattering, of otherwise ballistic electrons, to the upper L satellite valleys in GaAs. There are eight of these subsidiary valleys, with minima located at the edge of the Brillouin zone in the $\langle 111 \rangle$ direction, and Γ to L-energy splitting of about 0.3 eV [9.68]. Electrons that scatter to the L-valleys require an added crystal momentum of π/a in the $\langle 111 \rangle$ direction, where a is the lattice constant in the $\langle 111 \rangle$ direction. This added momentum can be gained, most likely, by the absorption or emission of zone edge phonons and less likely by ionized impurity

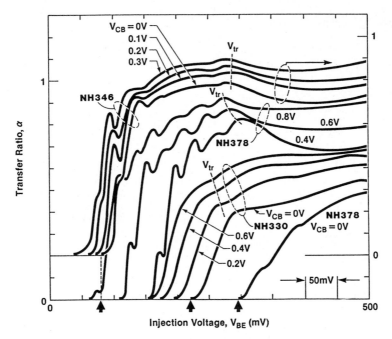

Fig. 9.32. The transfer ratio, α, as a function of the injection energy when the collector voltage is the parameter for three different devices. The threshold voltage, V_{th}, shows when transfer to the L-valleys occurs. Note the disappearance of the resonance peaks for $V_{BE} > V_{th}$

scattering (ionized impurity scattering is usually of a coluombic nature, thus being a long range order force that leads to a small momentum change of the scattered electrons).

Figure 9.33 depicts the values of the different band minima in the different layers of the THETA device. Electrons that transfer into the L-valleys and stay there while traversing the base encounter a potential barrier at the base-collector barrier interface. If that barrier potential is high relative to $k_B T$, most of these electrons will not be collected and eventually thermalize in the base, resulting thus with a base current and a decrease in α.

The density of states effective mass of the 'L electrons', m_L, and the available density of states in the L-band are some 5.6 and some 80 times greater than their equivalents at the bottom of the Γ-band, respectively. Assuming that intervalley

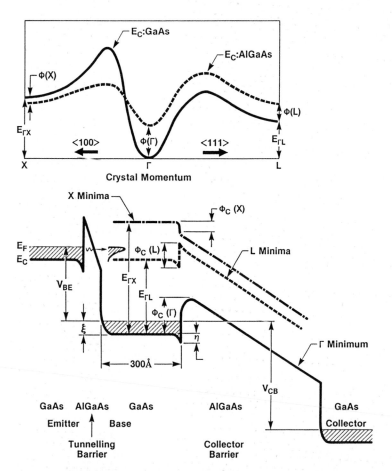

Fig. 9.33. The different bands in GaAs and AlGaAs in real and k space. The L-electrons have a barrier, $\Phi_C(L)$, to surmount before collection, however, the X-electrons have a negative barrier, $\Phi_C(X)$, at the same interface

scattering in GaAs is similar to that in Ge [9.69], the longitudinal acoustical and optical phonons will be responsible for the intervalley transfer, resulting in a scattering time from Γ to L, $\tau(\Gamma \rightarrow L)$, given by [9.70]

$$\tau(\Gamma \rightarrow L) = \frac{D_{\Gamma L}^2 m_L(E)^{3/2}}{2^{1/2}\pi\hbar^3 \rho_L(E)\omega_{\Gamma L}}(E - E_L - \hbar\omega_{\Gamma L})^{1/2}, \tag{9.24}$$

where $D_{\Gamma L} = 7 \times 10^8$ eV/cm is the deformation potential coupling coefficient [9.71], $\rho_L(E)$ is the density of states in the L-valleys, $\omega_{\Gamma L}$ is the zone-edge average phonon frequency, and E_L is the L-band edge energy. Since the $\langle 111 \rangle$ zone edge longitudinal acoustical and optical phonons have energy of 26 meV and 30 meV, respectively, we choose $\hbar\omega_{\Gamma L} = 28$ meV. For excess energy above the thresholdor transfer of 0.1 eV, we find $\tau(L \rightarrow \Gamma) \simeq 1$ pS (for the appropriate density of states in the Γ-band at about 0.3 eV above the bottom of the band). If the velocity of the ballistic electrons is taken as 1×10^8 cm/s, than about 10% of the ballistic electrons having kinetic energy of about 0.4 eV would be expected to transfer to the L-valleys in a 10 nm traversal distance. When electrons transfer to the L-valleys they lose their sense of original direction and move in a diffusive motion toward the collector barrier. Their diffusive velocity at low temperatures is very difficult to estimate since they, most probably, stay in a highly non-equilibrium state (a few might even continue in their original direction). If we assume a velocity of about 1×10^7 cm/s, then transferred electrons would tend to stay in the L-valleys as long as traversal distances do not exceed 100 nm. Upon arriving at the collector barrier, the L electrons will be reflected back from the barrier, $\Phi_L(C)$, and eventually scatter back into the Γ band and thermalize.

The results shown in Fig. 9.32 indicate a very weak dependence of the threshold voltage for L-valleys transfer, V_{th}, on the collector voltage V_{CB}. This is probably due to the induced band bending occurring in the base (the accumulation region near the collector barrier, η), or the reduction of the Fermi level, ξ. Both would lead to a transfer at smaller injection voltage, V_{BE}. The reduction observed in α, at some applied V_{CB}, depends on $\Phi_C(L)$, which depends on the grading length in the collector barrier, and the fraction of the total current carried by the ballistic electrons. Device NH330 carries only about 30% of the injected current ballistically, while the other two devices carry ballistic fractions in excess of 50% [9.72]. The reduction in α above the threshold for transfer is smaller in NH346 than in NH378 since the barrier heights $\Phi_C(L)$ are 25 meV and 110 meV at $V_{CB} = 0$, respectively, suggesting that some of the L-electrons can still arrive at the collector (via tunnelling through or thermionic emission above $\Phi_C(L)$). From the observed threshold voltage we can approximately determine the band splitting to be: $E_{\Gamma L} = V_{th} + \xi - (0.028 - 0.04)$ eV. Here, ξ is the relative position of the Fermi level to the conduction band in the base, 0.028 eV is the average zone edge phonon energy, and 0.04 eV is the approximate width of the 'total' energy distribution of the ballistic electrons. From here, we get $E_{\Gamma L} \simeq 0.29$ eV for all the devices tested, a value that is in close agreement with the published data [9.68]. Similar results were obtained later by *Hase* et al. [9.73].

The particular structures we studied so far were not appropriate for the determination of the exact fraction of the electrons that intervalley transfered. Since all the devices had graded collector-barrier–base interfaces, leading to a low $\Phi_C(L)$ at forward collector bias. However, from the reduction observed in α above threshold, a lower limit of 15% transfer can be estimated in a device with a 30 nm wide base ((9.24) predicts about 25% transfer). It is important to note also that when the injection energy into the base increased above the Γ-X energy splitting, where $E_{\Gamma X} \simeq 0.48$ eV, another decrease in α was not observed. This is most probably due to the absence of a potential barrier for the 'X electrons' at the collector barrier interface ($\Phi_C(X) < 0$ as seen in Fig. 9.33).

9.6.2 Verification of the Intervalley Transfer

To verify that the behavior described above is indeed due to intervalley transfer, we have applied hydrostatic pressure to the devices cooled to 77 K. Under pressure the conduction band edges (Γ, L, and X) move up in energy relative to the top of the valence band, but at different rates, resulting in $\Delta E_{\Gamma L} \simeq -5.5$ meV/kbar [9.74]. Figure 9.34 shows the change in α versus V_{BE} of device NH378 as the pressure was increased up to 10.8 kbar at a fixed V_{CB}. One can clearly see that V_{th} decreased with increased pressure, and that at the maximum applied pressure the onset for transfer had occurred some 60 mV earlier, as expected. Moreover, the fraction of electrons that had transferred is considerably greater than in the case of atmospheric pressure (for the same injection voltage). Note that the onset of α in V_{BE} is invariant, indicating that the barrier height $\Phi_C(\Gamma)$ is constant under an applied pressure. This suggests that the change in the

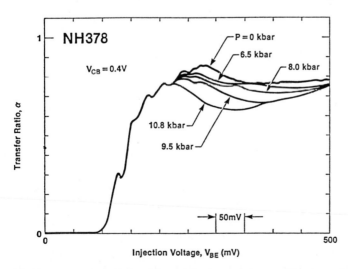

Fig. 9.34. The dependence of α on injection voltage at different applied hydrostatic pressures measured at 77 K. The onset of α and the resonances do not change, but V_{th} gets smaller by some 60 mV when the pressure increases from 0 to 10.8 kbar

conduction bands of GaAs and AlGaAs is similar, and ΔE_C stays constant as the pressure increases.

9.7 The THETA as a Practical Device

9.7.1 Gain Considerations

So far the THETA device has proven to be a useful tool in studying hot electron transport facilitating the demonstration of ballistic electron transport, the spectroscopic observation of intervalley transfer, the observation of electron interference effects that take place in the structures (detection of bound and resonant states), and the determination of the nonparabolicity parameter.

Operating the device as an amplifier, we have found in a great number of THETA devices an increase in the gain when the base doping was lower. This is certainly due to reduced electron–electron and electron–impurity scattering. Since the dominant scattering mechanisms in thin quantized regions are not yet understood, we can only speculate on the value of the maximum attainable gain. The maximum transfer ratio that had been measured in a common base configuration of a standard GaAs-AlGaAs THETA device is about 0.9 [9.11] (and about 0.93 in a InGaAs based device [9.42]). These results were obtained in devices with 30 nm (25 nm) base width and doping levels of $7 \times 10^{17} \, \text{cm}^{-3}$ $(1 \times 10^{18} \, \text{cm}^{-3})$. Recently, THETA devices with a strained InGaAs base exhibited current gains as high as 40 [9.76].

From device application view point, however, reducing the product nd_B where n is the number of free carriers in the base and d_B is the base resistance and the unwanted coupling between input and output. One way to partly solve this problem is to selectively dope the base. This can be done by introducing donors in the collector barrier [9.19] or by inducing electrons in the base with a positive collector voltage [9.44, 45]. By these methods, the impurities are removed from the base, its width can be reduced to about 10 nm without almost any degradation in the electron mobilities – which can be very high at 77 K – enabling thus a low base resistance (about 100 $\Omega/\square$). Indeed the induced base transistor was fabricated, and $\alpha_{max} = 0.96$ had been measured [9.43].

Another source of reduction of the transfer ratio is the quantum mechanical reflections from the base-collector barrier interface. Grading the interface (by gradually changing the Al mole fraction) or introducing another thin barrier in front of this interface (we will borrow the term 'antireflection coating' from optics), will reduce these reflections. Figure 9.35 shows a result of calculations of the transmission for monochromatic electrons passing above three types of barriers. Introducing a linear graded region or an 'antireflection coating' reduces the quantum mechanical reflections significantly. Thus, at least in principle, quantum mechanical reflections shouldn't be a major problem. Figure 9.36 shows experimental output curves measured in a CBC of two identical devices:

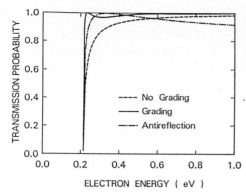

Fig. 9.35. The transmission probability of an electron with energy eV above an abrupt interface square barrier, a graded interface barrier, and a barrier with an 'antireflection' addition. The barrier heights is 0.215 eV; the graded region is 6 nm wide, linearly graded down to 90 meV; the antireflection added barrier has the same height as the square barrier (0.215 eV), it is 8 nm wide, and is separated from the collector barrier by an undoped GaAs well, 8 nm wide. One can see the improvement in the transmission in both cases relative to the simple 'step function' barrier

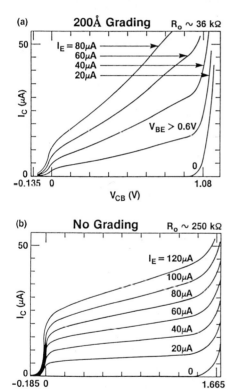

Fig. 9.36. The output characteristics of two similar THETA devices. The top has a graded collector barrier near the base over 20 nm region and the second has an abrupt barrier. One can see the dramatic difference in the output resistances (R_o) and in α's of both devices

one graded and one not. The larger gain in the graded device is obvious. Note, however, that a part of the higher gain may result from the added collection of quasi ballistic electrons, since in that device the collector barrier height is reduced significantly upon the application of a positive V_{CB}.

9.7.2 Speed Considerations

One might want to estimate the ultimate speed of the THETA device. Let's look at a device with a cross section shown in Fig. 9.37. The transit time through the device imposes a lower bound on the device speed. It is composed of three terms: the tunnelling time in the emitter (less than 10 fS [9.75]), the transit time through the base (30 fS in a 30 nm wide base), and the transit time through the collector barrier (250 fs through a 50 nm collector barrier, assuming group velocity of 2×10^7 cm/s). The total transit time is less than 0.3 pS (assuming transfer into upper valleys is avoided); thus it will not be the limiting factor in the device speed. The limit on the device speed is usually imposed by the parasitic capacitances that have to be charged and discharged and the dynamic charges that have to be moved in and out the base in every switching cycle. We can calculate the change of the stored charge in the base (is equal to that in the emitter and collector but with opposite sign).

$$\Delta Q_B = C_{EB}\Delta V_{EB} + C_{CB}\Delta V_{CB} + i_C\tau_B + i_C\tau_C + i_B\tau'_B . \tag{9.25}$$

The first and second terms are the charges across the emitter and collector barriers, the third and fourth terms are the dynamic charges in the base and collector barriers, and the last term is the charge that thermalizes in the base (since it is a function of position τ'_B rather than τ_B is used). This charge has to be supplied by the base current, thus $\Delta Q_B = i_B\Delta t$. If $\Delta V_{CB} = 2\Delta V_{EB} = \Delta V$ and the dynamic charges are neglected, then for a current source feeding the base the switching time is:

$$\Delta t \simeq \frac{\Delta V}{i_B}(C_{EB} + 2C_{CB}) \tag{9.26}$$

where i_B is the base charging current. However, if the base is fed by a voltage source, and we assume a base resistance R_B and $i_B R_B = \Delta V$, we get a switching time:

$$\Delta t \simeq C_{EB}R_B + 2C_{CB}R_B. \tag{9.27}$$

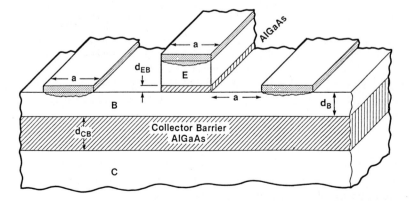

Fig. 9.37. A schematic cut through a THETA device showing the different dimensions

In an 'aggressive' device, the electrodes size and spacings a can be 0.25 μm, the tunnel barrier thickness $d_{EB} = 10$ nm, the base width $d_B = 30$ nm, and the collector barrier is $d_{CB} = 50$ nm (see Fig. 9.37). Then one gets a switching time of 1 pS for a voltage swing of $\Delta V = 0.1$ V, and a base current density of 2 $\times 10^5$ A/cm^2. For a voltage source driving the base with a base sheet resistivity of 500 $\Omega/\square$, we get a switching time of 0.6 pS in the same device. In both modes of operation, the times improve in a self-aligned configuration.

Let's examine the doping requirements in the base. The current density in the base layer is greater by a factor a/d_B than the current density flowing into the base electrode. For the above parameters and a uniformly doped base, if an electron velocity of 1.5×10^7 cm/s is assumed, a doping level of 7×10^{17} cm^{-3} is required to support the current density of 2×10^5 A/cm^2. In a selectively doped base structure, one might expect the electron velocity to be 2×10^7 cm/s. Then a sheet electron density of about 1.4×10^{12} cm^{-2} will be necessary to support the same current; a certainly achievable density in GaAs-AlGaAs heterojunctions. The main advantage, of course, in the selectively doped base structure is the low base resistance: If a 77 K mobility of 40×10^3 cm^2 Vs is assumed, a sheet base resistivity on the order of 100 $\Omega/\square$ can be achieved, leading to a much better $R_B C$ time constants than assumed before.

The p type THETA devices are potentially as fast as the n type devices due to the light nature of the ballistic holes. The disadvantage of these devices is the high base resistance which is governed by the heavy holes. This problem can be circumvented by selectively doping the base, thus increasing the holes' mobility.

9.7.3 Final Comments

Whether the 'ultimate speed' of the THETA device will be reached or not, some important results have already been obtained thanks to the class of hot electron and ballistic devices. As semiconductor devices are entering the submicron dimensions, there is no question that a deeper understanding of the fundamental properties of electron transport is needed. Paradoxically, we still miss clear experimental data on the high-energy transport properties of silicon, data on electron-phonon interaction for electron energies above a tenth of an electronvolt is not available. Hot electron devices, utilizing ballistic transport, are providing a powerful tool to fill this gap, at least in the case of GaAs. We have already seen how fundamental electronic properties (e.g. band structure and effective mass) and transport properties (e.g. transfer to the L-valleys) are clearly obtained from experiments with the THETA devices. Tests of the ideality of the structure (e.g. interface sharpness) can be made by comparing the quantum-mechanical idealization of the device to the measured $I-V$ characteristics. The most important contribution of the ballistic devices – constituted by the measured electron energy distributions – carries an even larger wealth of information; we will be able to learn about the interaction among 'hot' electrons, a gas of 'cold' degenerate two-dimensional electrons, and optical lattice modes. Ultimately, this understanding will benefit not only the ballistic devices themselves, but also the more conventional VLSI devices, and, more important, our understanding of the electronic properties of solids.

Acknowledgments. We wish to thank our collaborators E. Calleja, W. P. Dumke, D. J. Frank, C. M. Knoedler, M. I. Nathan, L. Osterling, and G. C. Wilson, and to C. J. Kircher and E. J. VanDerveer for their valuable comments on the manuscript. The work described in this chapter was partly supported by DARPA and administered by ONR, contract # N00014-87-C-0709.

References

9.1   M. S. Shur, L. F. Eastman: IEEE Trans. Electron Devices **26**, 1677 (1979)
9.2   J. J. Rosenberg, E. J. Yoffa, M. I. Nathan: IEEE Trans. Electron Devices **28**, 941 (1981)
9.3   L. F. Eastman, R. Stall, D. Woodard, N. Dandekar, C. E. C. Wood, M. S. Shur, K. Board: Electron. Lett. **16**, 525 (1980)
9.4   P. Hesto, J-F. Pone, R. Castagne: Appl. Phys. Lett. **40**, 405 (1982)
9.5   D. J. Barterlink, J. L. Moll, N. I. Meyer: Phys. Rev. **130**, 972 (1963)
9.6   J. R. Hayes, A. F. J. Levi, W. Wiegmann: Electron. Lett. **20**, 851 (1984); Phys. Rev. Lett. **54**, 1570 (1985)
9.7   N. Yokoyama, K. Imamura, T. Ohshima, N. Nishi, S. Muto, K. Kondo, S. Hiyammzu: IEEE Digest IEDM, 532 (1984)
9.8   M. Heiblum, D. C. Thomas, C. M. Knoedler, M. I. Nathan: Appl. Phys. Lett. **47**, 1105 (1985)
9.9   A. F. J. Levi, J. R. Hayes, P. M. Platzman, W. Wiegmann: Phys. Rev. Lett. **55**, 2071 (1985)
9.10 M. Heiblum, M. I. Nathan, D. C. Thomas, C. M. Knoedler: Phys. Rev. Lett. **55**, 2200 (1985)
9.11 M. Heiblum, I. M. Anderson, C. M. Knoedler: Appl. Phys. Lett. **49**, 207 (1986)
9.12 U. K. Reddy, J. Chen, C. K. Peng H. Morkoç: Appl. Phys. Lett. **48**, 1799 (1986)
9.13 J. S. Blakemore: J. Appl. Phys. **53**, R123 (1982)
9.14 Marvin L. Cohen, T. R. Bergstresser: Phys. Rev. **141**, 789 (1966). A slight modification was necessary: a pseudopotential parameter $V_s(G^2 = 11) = 0.055$ was used instead of 0.06, in order to obtain a more realistic Γ to L energy split of 0.32 eV
9.15 T. Hiroshima, R. Lang: Appl. Phys. Lett. **49**, 456 (1986)
9.16 J. H. Luttinger, W. Kohn: Phys. Rev. **97**, 869 (1954)
9.17 M. A. Littejohn, J. R. Houser, T. W. Gilson: J. Appl. Phys. **48**, 4587 (1977). Some of the reasons for the good empirical fits of the lower values of the commonly used nonparabolicity parameters to experimental data (such as the bulk plasma frequency vs. carrier concentration), are either the fact that second order corrections have been ignored even at high energies, or due to the incorrect use of the optical mass (Eq. (3b)). This mass includes an extra factor 2 in front of the parameter γ, thus implying an under estimation of the nonparabolicity parameter.
9.18 C. A. Mead: Proc. IRE **48**, 359 (1960)
9.19 M. Heiblum: Solid-St. Electron. **24**, 343 (1981)
9.20 C. A. Mead: J. Appl. Phys. **32**, 646 (1961)
9.21 J. P. Spratt, R. F. Schwarz, W. M. Kane: Phys. Rev. Lett. **6**, 341 (1961)
9.22 R. N. Hall: Solid-St. Electron. **3**, 320 (1961)
9.23 J. L. Moll: IEEE Trans. Electron Dev. **10**, 299 (1963)
9.24 M. M. Atalla, R. W. Soshea: Solid-St. Electron. **6**, 245 (1963)
9.25 M. Heiblum, S. Y. Wang, T. K. Gustafson J. R. Whinnery J: Quantum Electron. **14**, 159 (1978)
9.26 D. V. Geppert: Proc. IRE **48**, 1527 (1961)
9.27 D. Khang: Proc. IRE **50**, 1534 (1961)
9.28 J. M. Levine, A. A. Iannini: Solid-St. Electron. **5**, 109 (1962), and 273 (1962)
9.29 E. Rosencher, S. Delage, Y, Campidelli, F. A. D'Avitaya: Electron. Lett. **20**, 764 (1984)

9.30 J. C. Hensel, A. F. J. Levi, R. T. Tung, J. M. Gibson: Appl. Phys. Lett. **47**, 151 (1985)
9.31 C. O. Bozler, G. D. Alley, R. A. Murphy, D. C. Flanders, W. T. Lindley: IEEE Tech. Digest IEDM, 384 (1979)
9.32 J. M. Shannon: IEE J. Solid-St. Electron. Dev. **3**, 142 (1979)
9.33 M. Heiblum: IBM Tech. Disclosure Magaz. **24**, 4507 (1982)
9.34 J. M. Shannon A. Gill: Elect. Lett. **17**, 621 (1981)
9.35 R. J. Malik, K. Board, L. F. Eastman, D. J. Woodard, C. E. C. Wood, T. R. AuCoin: Proc. Conf. Active Microwave Dev., Cornell Univ. 1981 (unpublished)
9.36 M. A. Hollis, S. C. Palmateer, L. F. Eastman, N. V. Dandeker, P. M. Smith: Electron. Dev. Lett. **4**, 440 (1983)
9.37 J. M. Woodwock, J. J. Harris, J. M. Shannon: Physica **134B**, 111 (1986)
9.38 I. Hase, H. Kawai, S. Imanaga, K. Kaneko, N. Watanabe: Electron. Lett. **21**, 757 (1985)
9.39 N. Yokoyama, K. Imamura, S. Muto, S. Hiyamizu, H. Nishi, Jap: Appl. Phys. **24**, L853 (1985)
9.40 A. P. Long, P. H. Beton, M. J. Kelly: Semicon. Sci. Tech. **1**, 63 (1986)
9.41 U. K. Reddy, J. Chen, W. Kopp, C. K. Peng, D. Mui, H. Morin: IEEE Trans. Electron Device **33**, 1865 (1986)
9.42 K. Imamura, S. Muto, T. Fujii, N. Yokoyama, S. Hiyamizu, A. Shibatomi: Electron. Lett. **22**, 1148 (1986)
9.43 C. Y. Chang, Y. C. Liu, M. S. James, Y. H. Wang, S. Luryi, S. Sze: IEEE Electron. Dev. Lett. **7**, 497 (1986)
9.44 S. Luryi: IEEE Electron. Dev. Lett. **5**, 347 (1986)
9.45 P. M. Solomon: European Patent office Gazette, No. 92645, Filed 1983
9.46 K. Matsumoto, Y. Hayashi, N. Hashizumi, T. Yao, M. Kato, T. M. Ashita, N. Fukuhara, H. Hirashima, T. Kinosada: IEEE Electron Device Lett. **7**, 627 (1986)
9.47 R. J. Malik, T. R. AuCoin, R. L. Ross, K. Board, C. E. C. Wood, F. Eastman: Electron. Lett. **16**, 836 (1980)
9.48 D. Arnold, K. Hess: J. Appl. Phys. **61**, 5178 (1987)
9.49 E. Decastro, P. Olivo: Phys. Status Solidi **B132**, 153 (1985)
9.50 P. Price: Superlattices and Microstructure **2**, 213 (1986)
9.51 G. Krieger, R. Swanson: J. Appl. Phys. **52**, 5710 (1981)
9.52 Z. A. Weinberg: J. Appl. Phys. **53**, 5052 (1982)
9.53 Sadas Adachi: J. Appl. Phys. **46**, 3932 (1985)
9.54 G. Lewicky, J. Maserjian: J. Appl. Phys. **46**, 3032 (1975)
9.55 D. J. DiMaria, M. V. Fischetti, J. Batey, L. Dori, E. Tierney, J. Stasiak: Phys. Rev. Lett. **56**, 3213 (1986)
9.56 T. W. Hickmott: Appl. Phys. Lett. **44**, 90 (1984)
9.57 F. Capasso, S. Sen, A. Y. Cho, A. L. Hutchinson: Appl. Phys. Lett., **50**, 930 (1987)
9.58 M. Shur: Appl. Phys. Lett., **47**, 869 (1985)
9.59 A. Chandra, L. F. Eastman: J. Appl. Phys. **51**, 2669 (1980)
9.60 A. F. J. Levi, J. R. Hayes, P. M. Platzman, W. Weigman: Physica **B134**, 4801 (1985)
9.61 Frank Stern: Phys. Rev. Lett. **18**, 546 (1967)
9.62 Alexander L. Fetter: Annals of Physics **81**, 267 (1973); **88**, 1 (1974)
9.63 David A. Dahl, L. J. Sham: Phys. Rev. **B16**, 651 (1977)
9.64 Eric D. Siggia, P. C. Kwok: Phys. Rev. **B2**, 1024 (1970)
9.65 J. Lin, I. C. Chiu: Appl. Phys. Lett. **49**, 1802 (1986)
9.66 T. Ando, A. B. Fowler, Frank Stern: Rev. Mod. Phys. **54**, 427 (1982)
9.67 Frank Stern: J. Computational Phys. **6**, 56 (1970)
9.68 D. A. Aspnes: Phys. Rev. **B14**, 5331 (1976);
      H. J. Lee, L. Y. Juravel, J. C. Wooley: Phys. Rev. **B21**, 659 (1980)
9.69 T. P. McLean: *Progress in Physics*, (Wiley, New York, 1960), Vol. 5, p. 55
9.70 E. M. Conwell: *High Field Transport in Semiconductors*, Academic Press, New York (1967)
9.71 K. Kash, P. A. Wolf, Bonner: Appl. Phys. Lett. **42**, 173 (1983)
9.72 M. Heiblum, E. Calleja, I. M. Anderson, W. P. Dumke, C. M. Knoedler, L Osterling: Phys. Rev. Lett. **56**, 2854 (1986)

9.73 I. Hase, H. Kawai, S. Imanaga, K. Kaneko, W. Watanabe: International Workshop on Future Electron Devices: Superlattice Devices, (Japan, 1987), Conference Procedings, p. 63
9.74 M. Chandrasekhar, F. H. Pollack: Phys. Rev. **B15**, 2127 (1977);
     D. Olego, M. Cardona, and H. Müller, Phys. Rev. **B22**, 894 (1980)
9.75 M. Büttiker, R. Landauer: Phys. Rev. Lett. **49**, 1739 (1982)
9.76 K. Seo, M. Heiblum, C. M. Knoedler, W-P. Hong, P. B. Bhattacharya: to be published
9.77 M. Heiblum, K. Seo, H. P. Meier, T. W. Hickmott: Phys. Rev. Lett. **60**, 828 (1988)

10. Quantum Interference Devices

S. Datta

With 10 Figures

10.1 Background

Since 1985 experiments on submicron metallic and semiconducting structures have revealed three interrelated quantum effects: The Aharonov–Bohm effect, conductance fluctuations and non-local effects. The objective of this chapter is to explore theoretically the device implications of these exciting developments. The primary emphasis (Sect. 10.2) is on a new device concept based on the *Aharonov–Bohm effect*, where the current is modulated by controlling the quantum mechanical interference between alternative channels or paths connecting the source and the drain. The phase difference between the paths can be changed by π with a small potential difference (1 mV) so that a transistor based on this concept is expected to have high transconductance and low power dissipation. In Sect. 10.3 we discuss the possibility of quantum circuits relying on interference effects to implement individual resistors or resistor networks that can be programmed by a remote gate through *non-local quantum effects*. Though many hurdles remain to be overcome before these exotic devices become practical, the real power and utility of quantum devices may ultimately lie not in the implementation of conventional transistors having a source, a drain and a gate (where the low current capability is a major concern) but in the implementation of programmable multi-terminal quantum networks that could lead to radically new concepts for information processing with electronic devices.

It is well known that electrons possess wave-like properties and show interference much like electromagnetic waves. Why is it that in dealing with microwave networks or integrated optics we routinely worry about interference, and yet we ignore it completely in the analysis of conventional electronic devices? There are three distinct reasons. Firstly, the wave nature manifests itself only when the device size is comparable to a wavelength which is ~ 1 cm for microwaves, ~ 1 μm for light and ~ 100 Å for electrons in semiconductors. As we know, geometrical optics is usually adequate for describing ordinary optical systems using lenses and prisms while wave optics is necessary only when the medium varies on the scale of microns as in a diffraction grating or in integrated optics. Similarly, Newton's laws provide an adequate description of electronic motion in vacuum tubes or large semiconductor devices. But a wave description based on the Schrödinger equation can become necessary in describing electron transport in sub-micron structures. Secondly, inelastic processes due to phonons and other electrons within the device tend to destroy phase coherence and interference phenomena. Assuming an inelastic scattering time ~ 4 ps at $T \sim 1$ K and an average electron velocity $\sim 2.5 \times 10^7$ cm/s we obtain an inelastic mean free path ~ 1 μm.[1] Advances in microfabrication have now made it possible to build devices much smaller than a micron, so that there is hardly any scattering within the device. In fact, the approach commonly used to describe 'quantum devices' is based on the assumption that all inelastic scattering takes place in the contacts and not in the device.

Finally, it should be noted that while in electromagnetics monochromatic waves and single-moded waveguides are quite common, electron waves in solids commonly have a large spread in their energy (analogous to the frequency of classical waves) and electron waveguides are commonly multimoded (the 'modes' of an electron waveguide are commonly referred to as subbands). This gives rise to a large spread in the wavelengths of the electrons, which tends to wash out interference effects. It is for this reason that electron microscopists, who use the wave properties of electrons to determine crystal structures, try to obtain a monoenergetic and well-collimated beam of electrons. At low temperatures and low voltages, only electrons near the Fermi energy contribute to the conductance, so that the energy spread is small. The number of modes M is approximately equal to $n_s^{1/2} W$ where n_s is the areal density of electrons and W is the width of the device. A simple estimate shows that with $n_s = 3.6 \times 10^{11}$ cm^{-2}, a single-moded quantum wire needs to be $\lesssim 200$ Å. This may seem somewhat discouraging, but recent experiments have shown that semiconductor wires have a fairly wide depletion layer (3000–4000 Å) surrounding the actual conducting channel, much like the cladding layer in an optical fiber. This means that with adequate process control it may be possible to fabricate single-moded quantum wires whose geometrical width is ~ 0.4 μm which is well within the reach of present-day technology [10.1–3]. Recently, by using a gate to reduce gradually the width of a point contact, the number of transverse modes (and hence the conductance) was observed to decrease in discrete steps to one [10.4]. Such single-moded quantum wires raise the possibility of duplicating with electron waveguides many of the device concepts that are well-known in integrated optics.

There is another point that we would like to emphasize. Multimodedness is commonly viewed as an undesirable element that severely reduces interference effects. It is generally believed that if there are M different modes, then the magnitude of interference effects is $\sim 1/M$. However, this is only true if the different modes have completely random phases. Experiments on metallic wires and rings indicate that in many physical configurations the different modes are not totally uncorrelated, leading to quantum interference effects far in excess of the $1/M$ estimate. For example, conductance oscillations $\sim 0.1\%$ due to

---

[1] This number will be significantly smaller at higher temperatures and for hot electrons. We will concentrate on 'cold' electrons near the Fermi energy.

the Aharonov–Bohm (A–B) effect were observed in metallic rings with $M \sim 10^5 - 10^6$ [10.5]. Conductance fluctuations $\sim e^2/h$ have been observed in metallic and semiconductor samples with widely varying values of M [10.5–8]. This shows that multiple modes are often correlated despite the apparent randomness. More interestingly, with the present advances in microtechnology, it may be feasible to engineer structures where multiple modes are correlated in such a way as to produce large interference effects. For example, the device described in Sect. 10.2.2 is ideally expected to show nearly 100% interference effects even as $M \to \infty$. Of course, much experimental work remains to be done before we know the degree of correlation amongst the multiple modes that can actually be achieved with real semiconductor structures. This is an important consideration since a major concern about single-moded quantum devices is their low current capability.

10.2 Two-Port Quantum Devices

In this section we will describe a quantum device concept based on the Aharonov–Bohm effect. The two ports (source and drain) are connected by two alternative paths; their relative phases are controlled through the gate which changes the potential distribution along the paths.

10.2.1 Conductance Formula

The approach we will use to calculate the current-voltage characteristics of a quantum device is basically an extension of the approach widely used in the analysis of resonant tunnelling devices [10.9–13]. The device is assumed to be connected to two contacts by perfect leads that allow electron waves to propagate freely without any scattering. Inelastic scattering processes (and hence dissipation)[2] are assumed to take place only in the contacts and *not within the device*. Under these conditions we can describe the propagation of electrons with a fixed energy E from lead 'a' to lead 'b' using a scattering matrix (Fig. 10.1).

$$\begin{Bmatrix} a^- \\ b^- \end{Bmatrix} = \begin{pmatrix} r(E) & t'(E) \\ t(E) & r'(E) \end{pmatrix} \begin{Bmatrix} a^+ \\ b^+ \end{Bmatrix} \tag{10.1}$$

Here a^+, a^- (b^+, b^-) are the amplitudes of the incoming and outgoing waves respectively at lead 'a' ('b'). The lead is viewed as a waveguide having a discrete set of modes or subbands. The amplitudes a^+, a^- are both ($M_a \times 1$) column vectors where M_a is the number of modes in lead 'a'. Similarly r is an ($M_a \times M_a$)

---

[2] Strictly speaking we should use the word 'phase-breaking processes' which includes all scattering processes where the scatterer changes its state. A scattering process in which a magnetic impurity flips its spin is also phase-breaking though not necessarily inelastic.

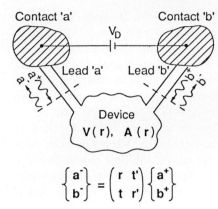

Contact 'a'   Contact 'b'

Lead 'a'   Lead 'b'

Device
$V(r)$, $A(r)$

$$\left\{\begin{matrix} a^- \\ b^- \end{matrix}\right\} = \begin{pmatrix} r & t' \\ t & r' \end{pmatrix} \left\{\begin{matrix} a^+ \\ b^+ \end{matrix}\right\}$$

Fig. 10.1. Schematic diagram of an arbitrary device connected to the contacts through two leads; all inelastic scattering and dissipation is assumed to occur only in the contacts and not within the device. In general, the problem is to calculate the scattering matrix $S = \begin{bmatrix} r & t' \\ t & r' \end{bmatrix}$ for the device, given the potentials $V(r)$, $A(r)$

matrix, t is an $(M_b \times M_a)$ matrix and so on. If we know the scattering matrix for a device, we can calculate the current I for a voltage V_D from the following expression:

$$I = \frac{2e}{h} \int dE \, [f(E) - f(E + eV_D)] \sum_{m=1}^{M_a} \sum_{n=1}^{M_b} |t_{nm}(E)|^2 \, . \tag{10.2}$$

Here $f(E)$ is the Fermi–Dirac factor.[3] For small voltages we can simplify (10.2) to

$$G = \frac{I}{V_D} = \frac{2e^2}{h} \int dE \left(-\frac{\partial f}{\partial E} \right) \sum_{m=1}^{M_a} \sum_{n=1}^{M_b} |t_{nm}(E)|^2 \, . \tag{10.3a}$$

At low temperatures $-\partial f / \partial E \simeq \delta(E - E_F)$, so that we can further simplify (10.3a):

$$G = \frac{2e^2}{h} \sum_{m=1}^{M_a} \sum_{n=1}^{M_b} |t_{nm}(E_F)|^2 \, . \tag{10.3b}$$

This formula is known as the two probe Landauer formula; it reduces the problem of calculating the conductance to a scattering problem not unlike those encountered in microwave circuits or integrated optics. We will not go into the details but the scattering matrix $S = \begin{bmatrix} r & t' \\ t & r' \end{bmatrix}$ can, in principle, be calculated from the Schrödinger equation if we are given the scalar and vector potentials $V(r)$, $A(r)$ in the device:

$$\left[\frac{(p - eA)^2}{2m^*} + eV \right] \Psi(r) = E \, \Psi(r) \, . \tag{10.4}$$

---

[3] Actually $|t_{nm}|^2$ in (10.2) should be replaced by $(|t_{nm}|^2 + |t_{mn}|^2)/2$. However, even though in a magnetic field $|t_{nm}|^2$ may not equal $|t_{mn}|^2$ the two terms are equal after summing over n and m [10.14].

p is the momentum operator defined by $p = - i\hbar \, V$. If there is no magnetic field present then the vector potential A can be taken to be zero and (10.4) simplifies to

$$V^2 \, \Psi = - \frac{2m^*}{\hbar^2} (E - eV) \, \Psi \; . \tag{10.5}$$

The scalar potential $eV(r)$ includes any discontinuities in the band-edge due to heterojunctions, band-bending due to space charge, as well as any microscopic scattering potential due to defects, impurities etc. It will be noted that (10.5) is very similar to Maxwell's equation used in integrated optics:

$$V^2 \mathscr{E} = \omega^2 \mu\varepsilon(r) \mathscr{E} \; . \tag{10.6}$$

Here $\mathscr{E}$ is the electric field, ω is the radian frequency, μ is the permeability and ε is the spatially varying dielectric constant; we have assumed $\mathscr{E} \cdot V\varepsilon = 0$ for simplicity. Comparing (10.5) to (10.6) it is evident that electron waves moving through a medium with a varying potential $V(r)$ is analogous to light moving through a medium with a varying dielectric constant (or refractive index). As we might expect, the quantum interference devices we will discuss have well-known optical or microwave analogs.

In Sect. 10.2.2 we will use the basic approach discussed above to describe the Aharonov–Bohm effect and a quantum device concept based on it. Before we proceed let us convince ourselves that (10.2) when applied to a resonant tunnelling diode [10.15], reduces to the familiar expression [10.10]. In a resonant tunnelling diode, neglecting any impurities or defects, the potential $V(r)$ varies only in the direction of propagation so that electrons are not scattered between different transverse modes:

$$t_{nm}(E) = T_m(E)\delta_{nm} \; . \tag{10.7}$$

Substituting (10.7) into (10.2)

$$I = \frac{e}{\pi\hbar} \int dE \, [f(E) - f(E + eV_D)] \sum_m |T_m(E)|^2 \; . \tag{10.8a}$$

Usually the cross-sectional area, A, is fairly large so that one can replace the sum over modes m by an integral over transverse wavevectors k_t to obtain the familiar expression

$$\frac{I}{A} = \frac{e}{\pi\hbar} \int dE \, [f(E) - f(E + eV_D)] \int \frac{dk_t}{4\pi^2} |T(E, k_t)|^2 \tag{10.8b}$$

10.2.2 Quantum Interference Transistor

Most of the work done on the Aharonov–Bohm effect in solids [10.5] has utilized lithographically defined ring structures of the form shown in Fig. 10.2a. This structure provides two alternative paths between the two leads and seems

(a)

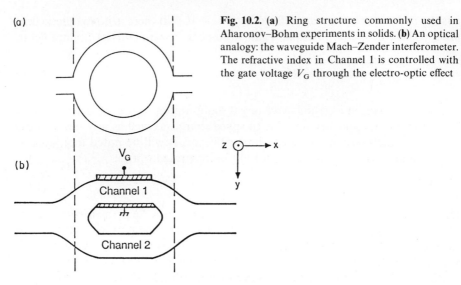

Fig. 10.2. (a) Ring structure commonly used in Aharonov–Bohm experiments in solids. **(b)** An optical analogy: the waveguide Mach–Zender interferometer. The refractive index in Channel 1 is controlled with the gate voltage V_G through the electro-optic effect

(b)

like an obvious structure for observing quantum interference. In fact an optical analog of this structure known as the Mach–Zender interferometer (Fig. 10.2b) is used as an optical modulator in integrated optics [10.16]. The transmission of light through the structure is modulated by changing the phase difference between the two arms through their refractive indices; this makes the wavelengths in the two channels different for the same frequency. In view of the similarity between (10.5) and (10.6) we might expect that for electron waves, the phase difference between the two arms can be changed by changing the potential V of one arm with respect to the other. This requires an electric field $\mathscr{E}$ *in the plane of the ring* and is known as the electrostatic Aharonov–Bohm effect which has not yet been clearly demonstrated in solids, though there is some preliminary experimental evidence [10.17]. What has been observed unequivocally in solids is the (magnetic) Aharonov–Bohm effect, where the vector potential A of one arm is changed with respect to the other by applying a magnetic field B *perpendicular to the plane of the ring.*

Neglecting multiple reflections, we can write

$$t_{nm} \simeq t_{nm}^{(1)} + t_{nm}^{(2)} \,. \tag{10.9a}$$

where the supercripts 1 and 2 represent the transmission amplitudes through the two arms of the ring in the absence of any external fields. Assuming that $t_{nm}^{(1)}$ and $t_{nm}^{(2)}$ have approximately the same magnitude but differ in phase by θ_{nm} we can write from (10.9a)

$$|t_{nm}|^2 \simeq 2|t_{nm}^{(1)}|^2(1 + \cos\theta_{nm}). \tag{10.9b}$$

A magnetic field changes the phase-shift θ_{nm} and thereby modulates the transmission probabilities $|t_{nm}|^2$. Assuming that the different transmission probabilities $|t_{nm}^{(1)}|^2$ are nearly equal and that $\theta_{nm}(B) = \theta_{nm}(0) + \alpha_{nm}B$ we can write from (10.9b) and (10.3b)

$$G \simeq G_0 \sum_{m,n} [1 + \cos(\theta_{nm}(0) + \alpha_{nm}B)]. \tag{10.9c}$$

If we assume that the coefficients α_{nm} are nearly equal, then it is apparent from (10.9c) that the conductance will oscillate as a function of the magnetic field B with a period equal to $2\pi/\alpha$. If the zero field phase $\theta_{nm}(0)$ corresponding to different t_{nm} are completely random, it can be shown that the percentage conductance modulation $\Delta G/G \sim 1/M$, M being the number of modes [10.12]. However, as we have mentioned earlier, experiments on metallic rings have shown conductance modulations far in excess of $1/M$ indicating that the zero field phases are partially correlated. Experiments have also revealed the importance of using rings whose thickness is small compared to the diameter. This can be understood as follows. It can be shown that the coefficients α_{nm} are approximately equal to $eA/\hbar$, where A is the area enclosed by the two arms of the ring (see Appendix). This means that there is a spread in the values of α_{nm} proportional to the difference in the areas enclosed by the inner and outer diameters. If this spread is large, there is no unique period to the Aharonov–Bohm oscillations and the conductance variation appears more like random fluctuations [10.5].

It seems that for device applications the electrostatic Aharonov–Bohm effect would be more suitable than the magnetic one. There is an important distinction between the magnetic and the electrostatic Aharonov–Bohm effects. It can be shown that for the electrostatic effect the phase-shift is proportional to the potential difference V_{12} between the two arms of the rings: $\theta_{nm}(V_{12}) = \theta_{nm}(0) + \alpha'_{nm}V_{12}$. The coefficients α'_{nm} are approximately equal to $e\tau_t/\hbar$, where τ_t is the transit time for an electron through the ring. This makes the electrostatic effect difficult to observe, since under the usual conditions of diffusive transport there is a large spread in the transit times [10.18]. The situation is analogous to the magnetic effect in rings with poor aspect ratios (= inner diameter/outer diameter). For this reason it seems that ballistic structures with minimal multiple reflections which minimize the spread in transit times are more suitable for observing the electrostatic effect. The structure that we have proposed as a possible design for a 'quantum interference transistor' (QUIT) is shown in Fig. 10.3a [10.18–23]. It is basically an ordinary field effect transistor (FET) with a barrier in the middle of the channel. The length L is small enough that electrons travel *ballistically* across it. The channels are narrow enough to be *single-moded* in the z-direction. One way to fabricate this structure may be to grow a barrier layer over the entire film, interrupt the growth to etch away the barrier where it is not needed, and then continue the growth process. The major challenge lies in ensuring the quality of the regrown interfaces. At this stage it is not clear whether this structure or the lithographically defined ring structure will eventually prove more suitable for device applications. An obvious concern about the structure in

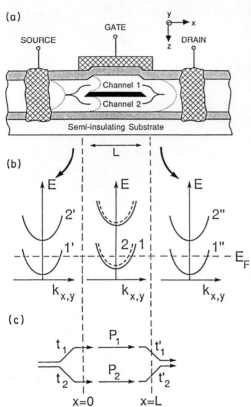

Fig. 10.3. (a) Proposed structure for a quantum interference transistor. The device is uniform along y with a width W_y. (b) Dispersion curves $E(k_x, k_y = 0)$ for different subbands in the three regions. In the middle region $(0 < x < L)$ the subbands corresponding to channels 1 and 2 are indicated by firm and dotted lines, respectively. The Fermi level E_F is shown assuming $V_D = 0$. (c) Two alternative paths from the input to the output, neglecting multiple reflections (after [10.22])

Fig. 10.3a is its poor aspect ratio. However, we believe that if the structure is single-moded in the z-direction, the aspect ratio is not very important. This is because every electron has a unique wavefunction in the z-direction (shown in Fig. 10.3a) and hence a unique phase-shift in an electric or magnetic field; hence there is, theoretically, no spread in θ.

Experiments on rings in high-mobility GaAs/Al GaAs heterostructures with $M < 10$ have shown conductance modulations $\sim 10\%$ in a magnetic field [10.2]. The obvious way to increase the percentage conductance modulation $(\Delta G/G)$ is to reduce the number of modes; however, this does not increase the absolute conductance modulation (ΔG). We will show in this section that if we could ensure perfect symmetry between the two channels in the structure shown in Fig. 10.3a then it is theoretically possible to attain a 100% modulation in the conductance even if the structure is very wide in the y-direction so that $M \to \infty$ [10.21, 22]. This is because the conditions of perfect symmetry, ballistic transport and single-modedness in the z-direction imply a perfect correlation among the different modes so that the zero field phases $\theta_{mn}(0)$ are all zero, leading to a $\Delta G/G$ far in excess of the $1/M$ estimate. To what extent this perfect correlation can be implemented in real semiconductor structures, only future experiments can tell.

We will base our discussions on the structure shown in Fig. 10.3a though the basic theoretical formulation presented here is quite general and could be applied to the ring structure in Fig. 10.2a as well. We assume that the structure is uniform in y having a width W_y. In each of the two end regions ($x < 0$ and $x > L$) and in the middle region ($0 < x < L$) we can calculate a set of transverse modes (or subbands) in the z-direction by solving the eigenvalue equation

$$\left[-\frac{\hbar^2}{2m^*}\frac{d^2}{dz^2} + E_c(z) \right]\psi_n(z) = \varepsilon_n\psi_n(z) . \tag{10.10}$$

The potential energy $E_c(z)$ includes the conduction band discontinuities as well as any band bending due to an applied electric field E_z or due to space charge effects. Since the function $E_c(z)$ is different in the three regions, the transverse modes obtained by solving (10.10) are also different. Each subband n has a parabolic dispersion given by

$$E(k_x, k_y) = \varepsilon_n + \frac{\hbar^2 k_x^2}{2m^*} + \frac{\hbar^2 k_y^2}{2m^*} . \tag{10.11}$$

The dispersion curves are sketched in Fig. 10.3b. It will be noted that there will be contact potentials between the different regions due to space charge, that will cause a vertical displacement of the dispersion curves in one region relative to the other regions. The relative positioning of the subbands in the three regions at equilibrium is fixed by the requirement of a constant Fermi level for the specified doping densities.

We now make three assumptions. First, we assume that the transport from $x = 0$ to $x = L$ is 'ballistic'; that is, there is no elastic or inelastic scattering and both E and k_y are conserved from the left to the right end. This is because the Hamiltonian is invariant in t and y. Second, we assume that the device (that is $E_c(z)$) is perfectly symmetric about $z = 0$ as any interferometer ideally should be. The effects of scattering and asymmetry are discussed at the end of this section. Third, we assume that only the lowest subband is occupied everywhere in the device. For a uniform potential well of width W along z, this requires that the electron density per unit area be less than the number of states in the lowest subband below the next higher subband.

$$n_s \lesssim (m^*/\pi\hbar^2)(3\hbar\pi^2/2m^* W^2) = 3\pi/2W^2 \tag{10.12}$$

For example, with $W = 250$ Å, $n_s \lesssim 7.6 \times 10^{11}$ cm^2.

Our objective now is to calculate the transmission coefficients t_{nm} in (10.3b). Since we have assumed only a single mode in the z-direction the subscripts n, m refer to modes in the y-direction. In a ballistic structure there is no scattering among these modes so that we can write

$$t_{nm}(E) = T_m(E)\delta_{nm} . \tag{10.13}$$

Using (10.13) in (10.2)

$$I = \frac{2e}{h} \int dE [f(E) - f(E + eV_D)] \sum_{m=1}^{M} |T_m(E)|^2 .$$ (10.14a)

Similarly from (10.3b) we have for the conductance at low voltages and at low temperatures

$$G = \frac{2e^2}{h} \sum_{m=1}^{M} |T_m(E_F)|^2 .$$ (10.14b)

If the width of the structure in the y-direction, W_y, is sufficiently large, we can convert the summation over modes in (10.14a, b) into an integral over k_y

$$I = \frac{2e}{h} \int dE [f(E) - f(E + eV_D)] \int \frac{W_y dk_y}{2\pi} |T(E, k_y)|^2$$ (10.15a)

$$G = \frac{2e^2}{h} \int \frac{W_y dk_y}{2\pi} |T(E_F, k_y)|^2 .$$ (10.15b)

To make further progress we need the transmission coefficients $T(E, k_y)$.

Simple Theory. Neglecting multiple reflections we can write

$$T(E, k_y) \simeq t_1' P_1 t_1 + t_2' P_2 t_2 ,$$ (10.16)

where t_1 and t_2 are the transmission coefficients from the left end region into channels 1 and 2 respectively, while t_1' and t_2' are the transmission coefficients out of the channels into the right end region (Fig. 10.3c). P_1 and P_2 are the phase-shifts in the two channels given by

$$P_1 = \exp(ik_{x1} L)$$ (10.17a)

$$P_2 = \exp(ik_{x2} L)$$ (10.17b)

where k_{x1} and k_{x2} are the x-components of the wave vectors in channels 1 and 2 respectively for a given E and k_y. Equation (10.16) is only approximately true because we have neglected multiple reflections at the two interfaces; these are discussed in Sect. 10.3.2.

In general, the coefficients t_1, t_1', t_2' have to be obtained by requiring that the wavefunction and its derivative be continuous across the two interfaces [10.24]. However, if we assume that $E_c(z)$ is symmetric about $z = 0$ then the wavefunctions $\psi_n(z)$ in the end regions obtained from (10.10) are either symmetric or antisymmetric about z^4. Since the two channels are symmetrically disposed

---

[4] This is strictly true only when the gate voltage and hence, the electric field E_z is zero. But for small electric fields we can assume that t_1, t_1', t_2 and t_2' are not perturbed significantly from their zero field values.

about $z = 0$, we expect that for symmetric wavefunctions $t_2 = t_1$ and $t'_2 = t'_1$ while for antisymmetric wavefunctions $t_2 = -t_1$ and $t'_2 = -t'_1$. We have assumed that only the lowest subband is occupied, which is symmetric; hence,

$$t_2 = t_1 \tag{10.18a}$$

$$t'_2 = t'_1 , \tag{10.18b}$$

From (10.16, 17a, b) and (10.18a, b),

$$|T(E, k_y)|^2 = 2|t'_1 t_1|^2 (1 + \cos\theta), \quad \text{where} \tag{10.19}$$

$$\theta = (k_{x2} - k_{x1})L \tag{10.20}$$

Substituting in (10.15a),

$$I = \frac{2e}{h} \int dE \, [f(E) - f(E + eV_D)] \int \frac{W_y dk_y}{2\pi} 2|t'_1 t_1|^2 (1 + \cos\theta) , \tag{10.21}$$

It will be noted that if multiple subbands are occupied in the end regions then we need to sum over pairs of subbands. The current is then proportional to (1 + cos θ) for pairs of subbands that have the same parity with respect to z, but it is proportional to (1 − cos θ) for pairs of subbands that have the opposite parity with respect to z. Since the current is modulated by varying cos θ with a gate voltage, the effect of multimodedness is to reduce the current modulation.

Now, let us consider how an applied gate voltage modulates cos θ. We have from (10.11)

$$E = \varepsilon_1 + \frac{\hbar^2 k_{x1}^2}{2m^*} + \frac{\hbar^2 k_y^2}{2m^*} = \varepsilon_2 + \frac{\hbar^2 k_{x2}^2}{2m^*} + \frac{\hbar^2 k_y^2}{2m^*} . \tag{10.22}$$

Here ε_1 and ε_2 are the energies at the bottom of the lowest subbands in channels 1 and 2, respectively. Since the Hamiltonian is invariant in t and y, E and k_y are good quantum numbers that are the same in both channels. Hence, from (10.22),

$$k_{x2} - k_{x1} = (\varepsilon_1 - \varepsilon_2)/\hbar v_x , \quad \text{where} \tag{10.23}$$

$$v_x = \hbar(k_{x2} + k_{x1})/2m^* . \tag{10.24}$$

The phase-shift θ is obtained from (10.23) and (10.20).

$$\theta = (L/v_x)(\varepsilon_1 - \varepsilon_2)/\hbar \tag{10.25a}$$

The physical origin of this phase-shift is quite simple. If $\varepsilon_1 > \varepsilon_2$ then the electrons have a higher kinetic energy in channel 2 than in channel 1 for the same total energy E. Hence the x-components of their wavevectors are different, giving rise to different phase-shits in the two channels. If ε_1 and ε_2 vary slowly with x, we should integrate over x:

$$\theta = \frac{1}{\hbar} \int \frac{dx}{v_x} (\varepsilon_1 - \varepsilon_2) . \tag{10.25b}$$

If the channel potentials are symmetric about $z = 0$ and the gate voltage is zero then $\varepsilon_1 = \varepsilon_2$ and $\theta = 0$. When we apply a gate voltage, the potential energy $E_c(z)$ in (10.10) is modified to

$$E_c(z) \to E_c(z) + eV(z) . \tag{10.26}$$

Consequently, the eigenfunctions $\psi_n(z)$ and the eigenvalues ε_n obtained from (10.10) are modified. For small electric fields we can assume that the wavefunctions $\psi_n(z)$ are unperturbed and use lowest order perturbation theory to calculate the change in ε_n

$$\varepsilon_1 = \varepsilon_0 + e\langle 1|V|1\rangle \tag{10.27a}$$

$$\varepsilon_2 = \varepsilon_0 + e\langle 2|V|2\rangle . \tag{10.27b}$$

Here ε_0 is the unperturbed energy and $|1\rangle$, $|2\rangle$ are the unperturbed eigenfunctions $\psi_1(z)$, $\psi_2(z)$ in the two channels. From (10.25a) and (10.27a, b),

$$\theta = (L/v_x)(eV_{12}/\hbar) , \quad \text{where} \tag{10.28a}$$

$$V_{12} = \langle 1|V|1\rangle - \langle 2|V|2\rangle . \tag{10.28b}$$

V_{12} is the difference between the *average* potentials in channels 1 and 2. This is analogous to neutron interference experiments in which the gravitational potential plays the role of the electrostatic potential [10.25]. The potential difference V_{12} needed to produce destructive interference is given by

$$eV_{12}(\theta = \pi) = h/2\tau_t , \tag{10.28c}$$

where $\tau_t \equiv L/v_x$ is the average transit time through the channels; with $\tau_t = 1$ ps, we have $V_{12}(\theta = \pi) = 2.1$ mV, showing that fairly low voltages can be used to turn off the transistor. This is the reason for the high transconductance mentioned earlier in the introduction. The actual gate voltage V_G will be somewhat larger than V_{12} because of (1) screening by the electrons in the quantum wells and (2) any potential drop between the gate electrode and channel 1 (Fig. 10.3a). To estimate the effect of screening accurately it is necessary to solve (10.10) self-consistently with the Poisson equation. However, since the channel widths are typically quite small $\sim 100 \, \text{Å}$, screening will probably not play a significant role.

The basic principle underlying the QUIT is thus very simple. The current I through the device in Fig. 10.3a for a drain voltage V_D depends on the phase-shift θ (10.21). The phase-shift θ can be modulated with a gate voltage (10.28) thus modulating the current. As we mentioned earlier, this is analogous to the waveguide Mach–Zender interferometer [10.16] used for optical modulators where the wavevectors in two paths for a given frequency are made slightly different by changing their refractive indices with an applied electric field (Fig. 10.2b). Usually in optical interference experiments monochromatic and collimated light beams are used, so that ω and k_y are limited to a very narrow range. By contrast, in solids we have an incoherent beam of electrons with a large spread in E and k_y. As we can see from (10.21) the current I depends on the 'average' value of $(1 + \cos\theta)$ over different E and k_y. If θ were independent of E and k_y we could achieve a 100% modulation of the current. However, it is evident from (10.28) that θ depends on v_x and hence on E and k_y, so that the maximum current modulation is less than 100%. If a magnetic field B_y were used instead of an electric field E_z then θ is indeed independent of E and k_y for small fields and 100% current modulation should be possible. A proper derivation of the phase-shift due to a magnetic field is somewhat complicated and is discussed in the Appendix. But we can get the right answer if we note that for a uniform electric field E_z

$$V_{12} = E_z(\langle z_1 \rangle - \langle z_2 \rangle) \tag{10.29a}$$

where $\langle z_1 \rangle = \langle 1|z|1 \rangle$ and $\langle z_2 \rangle = \langle 2|z|2 \rangle$ are the mean locations of the wavefunctions in channels 1 and 2, respectively. We now make the plausible replacement of E_z by $v_x B_y$ to get from (10.28a) and (10.29a),

$$\theta = eB_y L(\langle z_1 \rangle - \langle z_2 \rangle)/\hbar . \tag{10.29b}$$

Before concluding this section, it should be pointed out that the A-B effect was originally proposed as an experiment to demonstrate that observable effects could be produced by electromagnetic *potentials* even though there are no *fields* along the path of the electrons [10.26]. Actually, in all the experiments in solids the magnetic fields penetrate the paths of the electrons. In principle, however, if the magnetic field were shielded so as to be non-zero only in the central region between the two channels, the effect should still be present since the vector potential is different in the two channels. In the case of the electrostatic effect, the electrons are accelerated while entering one channel and retarded while entering the other channel. To keep the electrons from feeling the electric field, a time-dependent experiment is needed in which the gate voltage is turned on after the wavepacket is well within the channels. The steady state experiment discussed here does not demonstrate the reality of potentials as opposed to fields since the electrons do feel the electric field [10.27]. For this reason we have used the name quantum interference transistor rather than Aharonov–Bohm transistor.

Effect of Multiple Reflections. As we mentioned earlier, (10.16) is only approximately correct because it neglects multiple reflections. To take reflections into account we have to start from the scattering matrix for each junction. At the left junction $(x = 0)$ in Fig. 10.3a we can write a scattering matrix connecting the wave amplitudes for a given E and k_y (which are conserved from one end to the other) at $x = 0^-$ (A) to those at $x = 0^+$ (B):

$$
\begin{pmatrix} A^- \\ B_1^+ \\ B_2^+ \end{pmatrix} = \begin{pmatrix} \rho & \tau_1' & \tau_2' \\ t_1 & r_{11}' & r_{12}' \\ t_2 & r_{21}' & r_{22}' \end{pmatrix} \begin{pmatrix} A^+ \\ B_1^- \\ B_2^- \end{pmatrix}.
\tag{10.30}
$$

Here the superscripts ' $+$ ' and ' $-$ ' denote the amplitudes of waves travelling along positive and negative x, respectively, while the subscripts '1' and '2' denote channels 1 and 2, respectively. The amplitudes are defined as $\sqrt{k_x}$ times the wavefunction so that the currents are proportional to the squares of the amplitudes; with this definition the scattering matrix must be unitary since the current is conserved. We are assuming L is long enough that evanescent modes can be neglected. We can write (10.30) more compactly as

$$
\begin{bmatrix} A^- \\ B^+ \end{bmatrix} = \begin{bmatrix} \rho & \tau' \\ t & r' \end{bmatrix} \begin{bmatrix} A^+ \\ B^- \end{bmatrix},
\tag{10.31}
$$

where B^+ and B^- are (2×1) column vectors, t is a (2×1) column vector, τ is a (1×2) row vector and r' is a (2×2) matrix. Similarly at the right junction $(x = L)$ in Fig. 10.3a we can write a scattering matrix connecting the wave amplitudes at $x = L^-$ (D) to those at $x = L^+$ (D):

$$
\begin{bmatrix} C^- \\ D^+ \end{bmatrix} = \begin{bmatrix} r & \tau \\ t' & \rho' \end{bmatrix} \begin{bmatrix} C^+ \\ D^- \end{bmatrix},
\tag{10.32}
$$

The elements of the scattering matrices in (10.31) and (10.32) have to be calculated by requiring that the wavefunction and its derivative be continuous across the interfaces at $x = 0$ and $x = L$ [10.24]. Numerical results for a specific device are presented later in this section.

Since the two channels are isolated, the wave amplitudes at B and C are simply related as follows:

$$
\begin{bmatrix} B^- \\ C^+ \end{bmatrix} = \begin{bmatrix} 0 & P' \\ P & 0 \end{bmatrix} \begin{bmatrix} B^+ \\ C^- \end{bmatrix}.
\tag{10.33}
$$

P is a diagonal matrix whose diagonal elements describe the phase-shifts in the two channels:

$$
P = \begin{bmatrix} P_1 & 0 \\ 0 & P_2 \end{bmatrix}, \quad \text{where}
\tag{10.34}
$$

$$
P_1 = \exp(ik_{x1} L)
\tag{10.35a}
$$

$$
P_2 = \exp(ik_{x2} L).
\tag{10.35b}
$$

For a particular E and k_y, k_{x1} and k_{x2} are the wavenumbers in the x-direction in channels 1 and 2, respectively, given by (10.22). As long as there are no magnetic fields $P' = P$; but in the presence of a magnetic field B_y, the wavevectors k'_{x1} and k'_{x2} for propagation from $x = L$ to $x = 0$ are different from the wavevectors k_{x1} and k_{x2} for propagation from $x = 0$ to $x = L$ (see Appendix). P' is then given by

$$P' \equiv \begin{bmatrix} P'_1 & 0 \\ 0 & P'_2 \end{bmatrix}, \tag{10.36}$$

where

$$P'_1 = \exp(ik'_{x1} L) \tag{10.37a}$$

$$P'_2 = \exp(ik'_{x2} L), \tag{10.37b}$$

We now have scattering matrices (10.31–33) connecting A and B, B and C and C and D, respectively. Using straightforward algebra we can obtain the transmission coefficient T from A^+ to D^+. We can show that [10.28]

$$T = t'[I - Pr'P'r]^{-1} Pt . \tag{10.38}$$

This result can also be understood from Fig. 10.4. The total amplitude for transmission T is given by the sum of the amplitudes for all the multiply reflected paths:

$$T = t'[I + Pr'P'r + (Pr'P'r)^2 + \ldots] Pt . \tag{10.39}$$

The infinite geometric series within parenthesis is summed analytically to yield (10.38). Note that if we neglect the higher order reflections and retain just the first term we get back (10.16):

$$T \simeq t'Pt$$

$$= t'_1 P_1 t_1 + t'_2 P_2 t_2 .$$

(a)   (b)

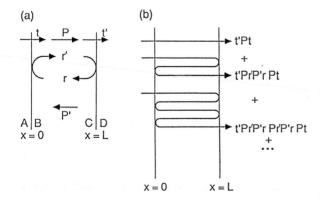

Fig. 10.4. (a) Definition of the transmission matrices $t(2 \times 1)$, $t'(1 \times 2)$, reflection matrices $r(2 \times 2)$, $r'(2 \times 2)$ and the propagation matrices $P(2 \times 2)$, $P'(2 \times 2)$. (b) Transmission amplitude T for the entire device is obtained by summing the amplitudes for all the Feynman paths involving multiple reflections

We could use (10.38) to calculate the transmission coefficient even if the device were multimoded; the matrices would just be larger. Since we have assumed the device to have a single occupied subband in the z-direction, P, r, P' and r' are only (2×2) matrices and we can perform the inversion analytically [10.22].

$$T = P_1 a + P_2 b , \quad \text{where} \tag{10.40}$$

$$a = (D t_1' t_1 + C t_2' t_1)/(AD - BC) \tag{10.41a}$$

$$b = (A t_2' t_2 + B t_1' t_2)/(AD - BC) \tag{10.41b}$$

$$A = 1 - P_1 P_1' r_{11} r_{11}' - P_1 P_2' r_{12}' r_{21} \tag{10.41c}$$

$$B = P_1 P_1' r_{11}' r_{12} + P_1 P_2' r_{12}' r_{22} \tag{10.41d}$$

$$C = P_2 P_2' r_{22}' r_{21} + P_2 P_1' r_{21}' r_{11} \tag{10.41e}$$

$$D = 1 - P_2 P_2' r_{22} r_{22}' - P_2 P_1' r_{21}' r_{12} . \tag{10.41f}$$

To evaluate the current I, we need $|T|^2$

$$|T|^2 = |a|^2 + |b|^2 + 2|a||b|\cos(\theta + \phi) , \quad \text{where} \tag{10.42}$$

$$\theta = (k_{x2} - k_{x1})L \tag{10.43a}$$

$$\phi = \text{phase of } a *b . \tag{10.43b}$$

Using (10.40–43) we can calculate the transmission coefficient T using θ from (10.28a) or (10.29b); inserting into (10.15a) we obtain the current.

A Numerical Example. Now that we have the basic theoretical framework for the discussion of Aharonov–Bohm devices, let us consider a numerical example. We assume the following parameters for the structure in Fig. 10.3a: $L = 2000$ Å, $n_s = 5 \times 10^{11}$ cm^{-2} in the end regions (of width 250 Å) and $n_s = 2 \times 10^{11}$ cm^{-2} in each of the channels (of width 100 Å each). The Fermi level E_F can be obtained from the carrier density n_s.

$$E_F = \varepsilon + n_s \pi \hbar^2 / m^* , \tag{10.44}$$

where ε is the energy at the bottom of the band. Assuming $m^* = .07 \, m_0$, we have: $E_F - \varepsilon = 6.9$ meV, corresponding to $k_F = 1.12 \times 10^8$/m. With the gate voltage V_G equal to zero, the energies ε_1 and ε_2 at the bottom of the subband in channels 1 and 2 are ideally equal. When a voltage is applied, the average potential in channels 1 and 2 differ by V_{12}. As we discussed earlier, for small voltages we can assume that the wavefunctions in the two channels are unperturbed, and write

$$\varepsilon_1 - \varepsilon_2 = eV_{12} . \tag{10.45}$$

It will be noted that although the electrostatic potential is different in channels 1 and 2, no current flows unless a voltage V_D is applied between the source and the drain; the chemical potential E_F is the same in both channels. If $\varepsilon_1 > \varepsilon_2$ then channel 2 has a higher carrier density than channel 1. For example, if $\varepsilon_1 - \varepsilon_2 = 1$ meV, then with the parameters listed above, $n_{s2} - n_{s1} = (\varepsilon_1 - \varepsilon_2)$ $(m^*/\pi\hbar^2) = 2.9 \times 10^{10}$ cm^{-2}; this is $\sim 14.5\%$ of the electron density in each channel with $V_G = 0$.

We first need to calculate the scattering matrix parameters to obtain $|T|^2$ from (10.40–43). Since we have assumed a small applied voltage, we can evaluate these parameters at $V_D = 0$ and neglect their change with V_D. Matching the wavefunction and its derivative across the interface we can calculate the elements of the scattering matrix in (10.30). At $k_y = 0$, we find [10.29]

$$\begin{pmatrix} A^- \\ B_1^+ \\ B_2^+ \end{pmatrix} = \begin{pmatrix} 0.69 \angle -140° & 0.51 \angle -41° & 0.51 \angle -41° \\ 0.51 \angle -41° & 0.84 \angle -117° & 0.17 \angle 87° \\ 0.51 \angle -41° & 0.17 \angle 87° & 0.84 \angle -117° \end{pmatrix} \begin{pmatrix} A^+ \\ B_1^- \\ B_2^- \end{pmatrix}.$$

Since the channels are symmetric, the scattering matrix is unchanged if we interchange the subscripts 1 and 2. At $V = 0$, the junctions at $x = 0$ and $x = L$ are identical, so that the wavefunction amplitudes at C and D are related by a similar matrix. These scattering matrix elements were calculated assuming an *abrupt* junction. Real devices will invariably have some grading and the parameters, t_1, r_{11} and r_{12} may change significantly depending on the design. Figure 10.5 shows the variation in t_1, r_{11} and r_{12} for electrons with different transverse wave vectors k_y. As we might expect, electrons with higher transverse momenta have a lower t and tend to reflect more. It will be noted that even at $k_y = 0$, $|r_{11}|^2 \sim 70\%$ while $|r_{12}|^2 \sim 3\%$ showing that an electron is reflected back into the same channel with a much higher probability than into the other channel. This is very different from the ring-like structures commonly used for A-B experiments (Fig. 10.2a). In such structures it appears intuitively that $|r_{12}| \gg |r_{11}|$; there is thus significant probability for electrons to go completely around the circle leading to the $h/2e$ oscillations discussed in [10.30].

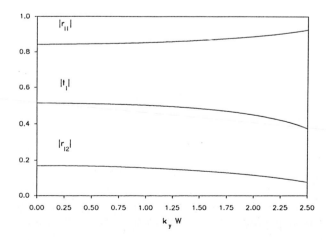

Fig. 10.5. Scattering matrix parameters $|t_1|$, $|r_{11}|$ and $|r_{12}|$ as a function of the transverse wave vector k_y ($W = 250$ Å)

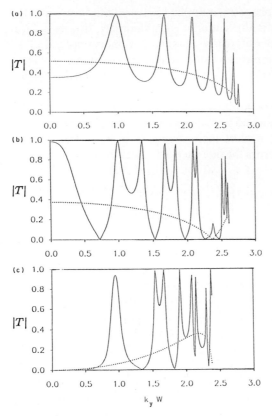

Fig. 10.6. Current transmission amplitude, $|T|$ versus transverse wavevector k_y $W(W = 250 \text{ Å})$ for **(a)** $V_{12} = 0$, **(b)** $V_{12} = 0.9 \text{ mV}$, **(c)** $V_{12} = 1.8 \text{ mV}$. The dotted line shows the transmission amplitudes calculated neglecting multiple reflections

Figure 10.6 shows a plot of $|T|$ as a function of the transverse wavevector k_y for different values of V_{12}; also shown for comparison is a plot of $|T|$ neglecting multiple reflections. It can be seen that multiple reflections give rise to peaks in the transmission coefficient due to 'Fabry–Pérot' resonances. In fact, if we neglect r_{12}, then this device could be viewed as two resonant tunnelling devices (with leaky barriers) in parallel. It has been pointed out [10.31] in the context of resonant tunnelling devices that in practice multiple reflections travelling back and forth many times will not add coherently due to scattering, even if L is shorter than the mean free path. For this reason we have neglected multiple reflections in computing the conductance G from (10.15b). It will be noted that $|T|$ cannot be reduced to zero for all k_y simultaneously since θ varies with k_y. For the magnetic A-B effect on the other hand, θ is independent of k_y and $|T|$ is reduced to zero for all k_y at certain values of the magnetic field (10.29b). The conductance is proportional to the integral of $|T|^2$ over k_y and can, in principle, be made zero in a magnetic field, but not with a gate voltage (Fig. 10.7). One way to increase the modulation is to reduce the width of the device in the y-direction so that only a few discrete values of k_y are allowed. If the width is reduced sufficiently that the device is single-moded in k_y, then 100% current modulation

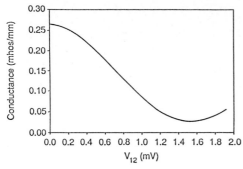

Fig. 10.7. Conductance G versus potential difference V_{12}, calculated from (10.15b) neglecting multiple reflections. The integration is carried out up to $k_y W = 2.38$ ($W = 250\,\text{Å}$)

should be possible, at least in principle. Reducing W_y, however, also lowers the conductance level.

In this discussion we have only considered the conductance for a small drain voltage V_D. The next question is what happens as the drain voltage is increased[5]. There are four factors to consider. First, as the drain voltage is increased the Fermi level at the drain end is lowered (Fig. 10.3b). At low temperatures the current is carried mainly by electrons with energies lying between the Fermi levels at the source and the drain. We thus expect the current to increase linearly with V_D at first; but it should saturate as the Fermi level in the drain falls below the bottom of the subband in the source. In the present example the current should saturate around $V_{DS} \sim E_F - \varepsilon = 6.9$ mV. Second, the effect of non-uniform potential profiles similar to those in ordinary FET's also needs to be considered. Third, if V_D is larger than the intersubband separation in the end regions, then the drain will no longer act as a single moded detector, thus degrading the transistor operation. In the present example, this factor limits the drain voltage to $\lesssim 26$ mV. Finally, if V_D is increased beyond the polar optical phonon energy (~ 36 mV) the electron scattering rate increases significantly.

An obvious question to ask is what advantages a transistor based on quantum interference offers over a conventional FET. We note that the device in Fig. 10.3a can be readily converted into an FET by removing the second channel and using the gate voltage to deplete the remaining channel. The threshold gate voltage V_{th} needed to deplete the channel at low temperatures is given by

$$eV_{th}|_{FET} = (E_F - \varepsilon)$$

$$= \hbar^2 k_F^2/2m^* .$$

(10.46a)

The main advantage of the QUIT is that the current is reduced to its minimum with a significantly smaller gate voltage since the change in the carrier densities in the channels is a small fraction of the total number. From (10.28c)

$$eV_{th}|_{QUIT} = \frac{\pi \hbar v_x}{L} \simeq \frac{\pi \hbar^2 k_F}{m^* L} .$$

(10.46b)

---

[5] In this discussion of an important factor is not mentioned. Increased bias causes electron heating, leading to a shorter inelastic scattering time due to electron–electron scattering.

From (10.46a, b) we have

$$V_{th}\bigg|_{QUIT} = \frac{2\pi}{k_F L} V_{th}\bigg|_{FET} . \tag{10.47}$$

The QUIT thus requires a gate voltage smaller than that required for an FET by a factor that is proportional to the length L in De Broglie wavelengths. This should lead to higher transconductance and smaller power dissipation. The length L is ultimately limited by the mean free path.

The intrinsic speed of the device is limited by the transit time τ_t through the channel region and should be comparable to a ballistic FET with a similar channel length. It should be noted that the critical dimension L is defined by the length of barrier; the gate as well as the source-drain spacing can be much larger. An interesting feature of this device is that it should be possible to obtain both negative and positive transconductances from the small device by a mere shift of bias.

Effect of Scattering and Asymmetry.   In all of our discussion so far we made two stringent assumptions, namely ballistic transport and symmetric $E_c(z)$. These assumptions ensure that the two channels are perfectly symmetric, as the two arms of a good interferometer must be. In practice, $E_c(z)$ will not be perfectly symmetric; moreover, there will be scattering potentials $V_s(r, t)$ due to impurities, defects and phonons. The question is whether devices can be fabricated by present-day technology that will show large and useful interference effects. Molecular beam epitaxy and modulation doping techniques have made it possible to fabricate extremely high mobility conductive channels isolated from the surface by epitaxial insulators. In GaAs with a mobility of 10^6 cm^2/Vs, the momentum relaxation time τ is as long as 40 ps. In the example considered earlier, $v_F = 1.86 \times 10^7$ cm/sec. and $L = 2000$ Å so that the transit time τ_t through the channel region is only 1.1 ps for electrons with $k_y = 0$. Electrons with a non-zero transverse wave-vector k_y have a smaller velocity in the x-direction and hence a longer transit time. However, it seems feasible to fabricate structures in which a significant fraction of the electrons travel ballistically through the channel region.

'Ballistic' transport does not necessarily ensure that interference effects can be observed. This is because the ballistic quality of transport is judged in terms of *momentum* relaxation while interference effects require a delicate balance of *phases*. An electron can lose very little momentum and travel ballistically; yet there can be a large difference in the phases between the channels. One example of this is electron–electron scattering which has little effect on the mobility since the total momentum of an ensemble of electrons is unchanged; but it can destroy phase coherence like other inelastic scattering processes. The inelastic scattering time due to electron–electron scattering is strongly temperature dependent and can be measured at low temperatures by 'weak localization' experiments [10.32]. At $T \sim 1$ K, inelastic scattering times ~ 40 ps have been reported in modulation-doped GaAs samples with carrier concentrations $\sim 6 \times 10^{11}$ cm^{-2}.

Now, let us consider the fluctuations in phase due to the fluctuating potentials in the channels. To estimate the degree of phase jitter between the channels let us use a WKB approximation to include the effect of potential fluctuations into (10.22)

$$E = \varepsilon_1 + \frac{\hbar^2 k_{x1}^2}{2m^*} + \frac{\hbar^2 k_y^2}{2m^*} + e\delta V_1$$

$$= \varepsilon_2 + \frac{\hbar^2 k_{x2}^2}{2m^*} + \frac{\hbar^2 k_y^2}{2m^*} + e\delta V_2.$$

(10.48)

Here δV_1 and δV_2 represent the fluctuating potentials in channels 1 and 2, respectively. The corresponding fluctuations in k_{x1} and k_{x2} can be written approximately as

$$\delta k_{x1} = e\delta V_1 / \hbar v_x$$

(10.49a)

$$\delta k_{x2} = e\delta V_2 / \hbar v_x$$

(10.49b)

where $v_x = \hbar k_x / m^*$ is the velocity, assuming $k_{x1} \simeq k_{x2} = k_x$. The phase-jitter $\delta\theta$ between the channels is given by

$$\delta\theta = \int_0^L (\delta k_{x1} - \delta k_{x2}) \, dx = \frac{\int_0^L (\delta V_1 - \delta V_2) \, dx}{\hbar v_x}.$$

(10.50)

We note that the phase-jitter $\delta\theta$ depends on the differential potential between the channels. Any scattering potential that affects both channels equally has no effect on the interference even if it is inelastic or time-dependent. Long wavelength acoustic phonons should thus have no effect on the interference. Physically, this is a consequence of the fact that the interference pattern is not affected if the entire interferometer is jiggled. It is thus important to have the two arms of the interferometer *physically as close as possible*. This factor should afford a significant advantage to semiconductor microstructures with the two channels separated by $\sim 100\,\text{Å}$ and in close mechanical and electrical contact (Fig. 10.3a) compared to rings with air gaps (Fig. 10.2a). It takes a large electric field δE_z to produce a differential potential $\delta V_1 - \delta V_2$ between two channels separated by a short distance W':

$$\delta E_z = \frac{\delta V_1 - \delta V_2}{e W'}.$$

(10.51)

Using (10.51) in (10.50) we have

$$\delta\theta = \langle \delta E_z \rangle e W' L / \hbar v_x$$

(10.52)

where $\langle \delta E_z \rangle$ is the average field over the length of the channels. Assuming $v_x = 1.86 \times 10^7$ cm/s, $L = 2000\,\text{Å}$, $W' = 50\,\text{Å}$ we have

$$\delta\theta = \langle \delta E_z \rangle / 1.2 \text{ kV/cm.} \tag{10.53}$$

It thus takes fairly large stray fields ~ 1 kV/cm. to produce a phase jitter of $\sim 45°$.

A very important source of potential fluctuations is fluctuations in the well width W leading to fluctuations in the subband energy ε. Assuming $\varepsilon = \hbar^2 \pi^2 / 2m^* W^2$,

$$\delta\varepsilon = (- \hbar^2 \pi^2 / m^* W^3) \delta W. \tag{10.54}$$

Since monolayer fluctuations in the well width are quite common it is advisable not to make the wells to narrow. If $W = 100$ Å and $\delta W = 3$ Å we have, $|\delta\varepsilon| = 3.3$ meV, which is equivalent to 3.3 kV/cm. Another source of asymmetry between the two wells is that the growth sequence affects the interface properties.

It should be noted that even if $\delta\theta$ were close to 2π or greater, the interference effect would not necessarily be washed out. If $\delta\theta$ were the same for all k_y then it would merely shift the G vs V_{12} curve in Fig. 10.7 horizontally. The same is true if the device were single-moded in the y-direction (no spread in k_y). It is the *variation in* $\delta\theta$ *over* k_y that washes out the interference pattern; at high temperatures, or at high drain voltages, the electrons have an energy spread about E_F and the variation in $\delta\theta$ over E is also important. Since $\delta\theta$ depends on v_x and gets larger with smaller v_x, we can expect that electrons travelling within a certain angle from the x-axis which have the largest v_x will exhibit interference effects while electrons outside this angle having large transverse wavevectors k_y (and hence a small v_x) will give rise to an incoherent background current. This angle will get smaller as $\delta V_1 - \delta V_2$ gets larger.

The basic point in a nutshell in this: Fig. 10.7 predicts a conductance modulation $\Delta G/G \sim 90\%$ even though $M \to \infty$. The reason $\Delta G/G$ is far in excess of $1/M$ (see discussion in Sect. 10.1) is that we have deliberately engineered it to ensure that the interference patterns of the different modes have near perfect correlation. The three assumptions we made in our analysis (ballistic transport over the length L, single subband occupancy in the z-direction and perfect symmetry of the two channels) ensure that the zero field phase $\theta_{nm}(0)$ (10.9) is equal to zero for all modes. Physically this means that with $V_{12} = 0$, every mode interferes constructively leading to a maximum in the conductance. Future experiments will show to what extent this perfect correlation amongst the modes can be implemented and how deleterious the inevitable asymmetries in real semiconductor structures will be. But a large percentage modulation $\Delta G/G$ in the conductance should be obtained despite the asymmetries if the number of modes is restricted by making the structure narrower in y; the absolute magnitude of the conductance modulation ΔG, however, would decrease.

From an applied point of view an important question is the temperature range over which the device can operate. Temperature affects the operation of the device in two distinct ways. Firstly, it increases the energy spread of the electrons so that the variation of $\delta\theta$ over E (as well as k_y) is important as we discussed earlier. Secondly, it increases the inelastic scattering in the device. It seems that even at 4 K, L can be made small enough that inelastic scattering should not be excessive. However, only future experiments can answer these questions conclusively.

10.3 Multiport Quantum Devices

In this section we will discuss the possibility of quantum circuits relying on interference effects to implement individual resistors or resistor networks that can be controlled by a remote gate through non-local quantum effects.

10.3.1 Conductance Formula

So far we have discussed structures having only two leads (Fig. 10.1). However, the same basic formalism can be extended to describe structures with multiple leads, such as the one shown in Fig. 10.8a [10.13]. Such multiport planar networks have found extensive use in millimeter-wave integrated circuits and integrated optics [10.33]. In general we could calculate a $(n \times n)$ scattering matrix describing an n-port network. For the 3-port shown in Fig. 10.8a, we have

$$\begin{pmatrix} a^- \\ b^- \\ c^- \end{pmatrix} = \begin{bmatrix} r_{aa} & t_{ab} & t_{ac} \\ t_{ba} & r_{bb} & r_{bc} \\ r_{ca} & r_{cb} & t_{cc} \end{bmatrix} \begin{pmatrix} a^+ \\ b^+ \\ c^+ \end{pmatrix} . \tag{10.55}$$

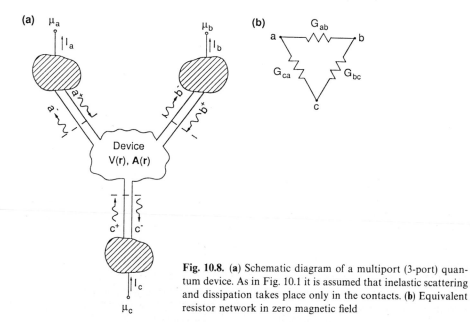

Fig. 10.8. (a) Schematic diagram of a multiport (3-port) quantum device. As in Fig. 10.1 it is assumed that inelastic scattering and dissipation takes place only in the contacts. (b) Equivalent resistor network in zero magnetic field

Each element of the scattering matrix is itself an $(M \times M)$ matrix if there are M modes in each lead. In the absence of any magnetic fields, the structure can be represented by a resistor network with 3 modes as shown in Fig. 10.8b. The conductance G_{ab} connecting nodes 'a' and 'b' is given by

$$G_{ab} = \frac{2e^2}{h} \sum_{m,n} |(t_{ab})_{m,n}|^2 . \tag{10.56a}$$

Similarly G_{ac} is given by

$$G_{ac} = \frac{2e^2}{h} \sum_{m,n} |(t_{ac})_{m,n}|^2 \tag{10.56b}$$

and so on. In general this concept can be extended to model any N-port structure as a network with N nodes connected pairwise through $N(N-1)/2$ resistors. It is assumed, of course, that there is no inelastic scattering within the device; all the dissipation occurs in the contacts. Recently we have shown that a structure with continuously distributed inelastic processes too can be viewed as a network of resistors, where the conductance connecting any two points r and r' is proportional to the probability that an electron inelastically scattered at r suffers its next inelastic scattering event at r' [10.34]. Thus in general we have a continuous network where every point is connected to every other point within a radius equal to the inelastic mean free path; the individual conductances are calculated from the Schrödinger equation. If we neglect inelastic scattering everywhere except in the contacts, then this continuous network reduces to a discrete network with one node for each contact as shown in Fig. 10.8b.

10.3.2 Quantum Reflection Transistor

Multiport structures of the type shown in Fig. 10.8a can be used to implement transistors of a somewhat different type than that discussed in Sect. 10.2 [10.35, 36]. Consider the 3-port network shown in Fig. 10.9a; ohmic contacts are made to two of the ports while a Schottky gate is used to change the phase of the reflection coefficient at the third port. As every microwave engineer knows, the transmission between two ports is influenced by the load conditions at the third port. Thus, if we change the phase of the reflection coefficient at port 3 by changing the gate potential, it should affect the current that flows between ports 1 and 2, labeled source and drain. The surprising feature of this device is that the gate is not positioned between the source and the drain as we are accustomed to expect in electronic devices; it can be located anywhere within an inelastic mean free path. However, this 'remote control' is well-known in microwave networks, and may find useful applications in quantum devices of the future. Non-local effects have been observed in experiments on conductance fluctuations in metallic and semiconducting wires and rings [10.2, 3, 7, 8, 37, 38].

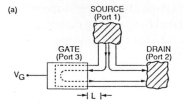

(a)

SOURCE
(Port 1)

GATE
(Port 3)

DRAIN
(Port 2)

V_G

→| L |←

Fig. 10.9. (a) A proposed quantum transistor with a remote gate. The gate potential changes the phase difference between the two primary paths between the source and the drain. **(b)** Normalized conductance as a function of the length L in wavelengths for a device with one propagating mode ($M = 1$). **(c)** Normalized conductance as a function of the length L in wavelengths (of the lowest mode having the shortest wavelength) for a device with eight propagating modes ($M = 8$)

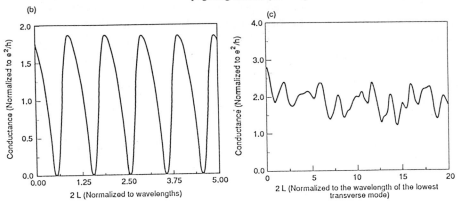

(b)

Conductance (Normalized to e^2/h)

2 L (Normalized to wavelengths)

(c)

Conductance (Normalized to e^2/h)

2 L (Normalized to the wavelength of the lowest transverse mode)

For a quantitative description of the operation of the device in Fig. 10.9a we need the scattering matrix describing the 3-way splitter:

$$\begin{pmatrix} S^- \\ D^- \\ G^- \end{pmatrix} = \begin{pmatrix} r_{SS} & t_{SD} & t_{SG} \\ t_{DS} & r_{DD} & t_{DG} \\ t_{GS} & t_{GD} & r_{GG} \end{pmatrix} \begin{pmatrix} S^+ \\ D^+ \\ G^+ \end{pmatrix}. \tag{10.57}$$

We have used $S^\pm$, $D^\pm$, $G^\pm$ to denote the incoming and outgoing wave amplitudes at the source, drain and gate respectively; if the leads are multimoded then the amplitudes are column vectors as we discussed earlier. If the wave amplitudes G^+ and G^- at the gate are related by the reflection matrix R

$$G^+ = R G^- \tag{10.58}$$

we can show from (10.57, 58) that

$$\begin{pmatrix} S^- \\ D^- \end{pmatrix} = \begin{pmatrix} r & t' \\ t & r' \end{pmatrix} \begin{pmatrix} S^+ \\ D^+ \end{pmatrix}, \quad \text{where} \tag{10.59}$$

$$r = r_{SS} + t_{SD}(I - R r_{GG})^{-1} R t_{DS} \tag{10.60a}$$

$$t' = t_{SD} + t_{SG}(I - R r_{GG})^{-1} R t_{GD} \tag{10.60b}$$

$$t = t_{DS} + t_{DG}(I - R r_{GG})^{-1} R t_{GS} \tag{10.60c}$$

$$r' = r_{DD} + t_{DG}(I - R r_{GG})^{-1} R t_{GD}. \tag{10.60d}$$

It is apparent from (10.60c) that the transmission t from the source to the drain (which determines the conductance) can be modulated by changing the reflection coefficient at the gate (R). We can get some physical insight by expanding (10.60c) in a geometric series as follows.

$$t = t_{DS} + t_{DG} R t_{GS} + t_{DG} R r_{GG} R t_{GS} + t_{DG}(R r_{GG})^2 R t_{GS} + \ldots \qquad (10.61)$$

The first term on the right in (10.61) is the amplitude for direct transmission from port 1 to port 2 while the succeeding terms are the amplitudes for transmission after one, two, three, ... reflections at port 3. If r_{GG} is small, then we can write approximately

$$t \simeq t_{DS} + t_{DG} R t_{GS} . \qquad (10.62)$$

With this approximation, we could view the device in Fig. 10.9a as providing two primary paths from the source to the drain with the gate controlling their interference, much like the Aharonov-Bohm device. Figures 10.9b and c show the calculated conductance for two specific devices having one mode and eight modes respectively. We assume that the reflection coefficient R is given by

$$R_{nm} = \delta_{nm} e^{i2k_m L} \qquad (10.63)$$

where k_m is the wavenumber of the mth mode at the Fermi level and L is the effective distance of the gate from the junction. Figure 10.9b shows that the conductance is modulated by 100% as the length L is changed. On the other hand for a device with eight modes (Fig. 10.9c), the variation in the conductance with L looks more like conductance fluctuations $\sim e^2/h$. It seems that devices of this type will only be useful if the number of modes is small. Using single-moded quantum wires at low temperatures we can conceive of a variety of devices analogous to well-known microwave and integrated optical devices. Even the polarization of electromagnetic waves has its analog in the spin of electrons. It may be possible to exploit this degree of freedom in narrow gap semiconductors having a large spin–orbit coupling that can be controlled with a gate potential [10.39].

10.3.3 Quantum Networks

The device in Fig. 10.9a utilized one port in a 3-port structure to modulate the conductance connecting the other two ports. We could go a step further and utilize *one port in an $(N + 1)$-port structure to control the network of $N(N - 1)/2$ resistors formed by the remaining N ports.* Consider for example the structure in Fig. 10.10a with four ports connected to the side branches of a main waveguide. The gate potential shifts the standing wave pattern in the main waveguide and thus alters the couplings between different ports. A strong coupling occurs when two ports are both located on the peaks of the standing wave pattern while a port located near a trough of the standing wave pattern is only weakly coupled to the

(a)

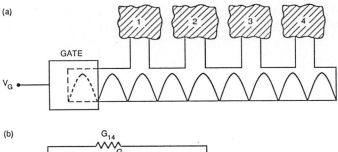

(b)

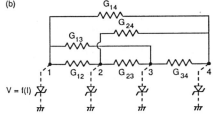

Fig. 10.10a, b. A programmable multiterminal quantum network. (a) Configuration. (b) Equivalent circuit. The dotted lines also show a non-linear conductance connected to each node

other ports. The coupling between two ports determines the magnitude of the conductance connecting the corresponding nodes in the equivalent resistor network (10.56a, b). We thus have a programmable resistor network (Fig. 10.10b) rather than a single resistor as in a conventional transistor. By connecting each node to a non-linear device such as a resonant tunnelling diode (this can be done vertically without external connections), we could implement a highly interconnected pattern of non-linear elements. If we model this device as a capacitance C in parallel with a non-linear conductance described by $V = f(I)$ then Kirchoff's law applied to the circuit in Fig. 10.10b yields

$$C\frac{dV_i}{dt} + I_i + V_i\sum_j G_{ij} = \sum_j G_{ij}V_j \tag{10.64}$$

where $V_j = f(I_j)$. (10.60) is very similar to the dynamical equations used to describe neural networks [10.40].

Many hurdles remain to be overcome before these exotic devices become practical. The device concepts discussed in this chapter are based on controlling quantum interference effects, which are expected to play a role even in the operation of conventional devices as they get smaller. However, new device concepts based on these effects can only be exploited if the technology is sufficiently advanced so as to allow adequate control over the phase of the wavefunction.

Acknowledgements. It is a pleasure to acknowledge my students and ex-students S. Bandyopadhyay (University of Notre Dame), M. Cahay (Scientific Research Associates), B. Das, R. Lake, Y. Lee and D. Miller for their contributions; in particular I would like to thank R. Frohne for Figs. 10.5–7 and 10.9 and M. McLennan for carefully reading the manuscript. I am greatly indebted to my collaborators who have helped make the experimental work possible: R. Reifenberger, P. K. Bhattacharya (University of Michigan), M. S. Lundstrom and M. R. Melloch. I also thank Prof. R. L. Gunshor for his encouragement. This work was supported by the National Science Foundation under Grant No. ECS-83-51-036, by the Semiconductor Research Corporation under Contract No. 87-SJ-089 and by the Office of Naval Research under Contract no. N00014-87-K-0693. Parts of this chapter have been excerpted from an earlier presentation by the author [10.35].

Appendix: Aharonov–Bohm Phase-shift in an Electric or Magnetic Field

In Sect. 10.2.2 the phase-shift between the two channels (Fig. 10.3a) due to an electric field was obtained using lowest order perturbation theory (10.28) while that due to a magnetic field was obtained using a plausible argument (10.29). In this appendix we present an exact solution for the phase-shift assuming a parabolic confining potential for each of the two channels [10.41]. This is possibly a fairly good approximation to the actual confining potential and should provide a useful guideline. We start from the Schrödinger equation (10.4) assuming $A = (Bz, 0, 0)$ and $V(r) = m^* \omega_0^2 (z - z_0) - e\mathcal{E}z$ where ω_0 is a parameter describing the parabolic confining potential, $\mathcal{E}$ is the electric field in the z-direction and B is the magnetic field in the y-direction. The center of the well is at z_0; later we will set $z_0 = z_1$ for channel 1 and $z_0 = z_2$ for channel 2

$$\left[\frac{(p_x - eBz)^2 + p_y^2 + p_z^2}{2m^*} + \frac{1}{2} m^* \omega_0^2 (z - z_0)^2 - e\mathcal{E}z \right] \Psi = E\Psi . \tag{A.1}$$

Assuming a solution of the form

$$\Psi(r) = \psi(z) e^{i(k_x x + k_y y)} \tag{A.2}$$

we obtain from (A.1),

$$\left[\frac{p_z^2}{2m^*} + \frac{(\hbar k_x - eBz)^2}{2m^*} + \frac{1}{2} m^* \omega_0^2 (z - z_0)^2 - e\mathcal{E}z \right] \psi = \left[E - \frac{\hbar^2 k_y^2}{2m^*} \right] \psi . \tag{A.3}$$

It is well-known that if $\mathcal{E} = 0$, $B = 0$ the eigenfunctions are given by the harmonic oscillator wavefunctions $f_n(z)$ centered at z_0

$$\psi_n = f_n(z - z_0) \tag{A.4a}$$

and the corresponding eigenvalues are

$$E_n = \varepsilon_n + \frac{\hbar^2 k_x^2}{2m^*} + \frac{\hbar^2 k_y^2}{2m^*} , \quad \text{where} \tag{A.4b}$$

$$\varepsilon_n = (n + \tfrac{1}{2}) \hbar \omega_0 . \tag{A.4c}$$

We will show that with $B = 0$, (A.4) is modified to

$$\psi_n = f_n\left(z - z_0 - \frac{e\mathscr{E}}{m^*\omega_0^2}\right) \tag{A.5a}$$

$$E_n = \varepsilon_n + \frac{\hbar^2 k_x^2}{2m^*} + \frac{\hbar^2 k_y^2}{2m^*} \tag{A.5b}$$

$$\varepsilon_n = \left(n + \frac{1}{2}\right)\hbar\omega_0 - e\mathscr{E}z_0 - \frac{e^2\mathscr{E}^2}{2m^*\omega_0^2}. \tag{A.5c}$$

Hence if we have two channels centered at $z_0 = z_1$ and $z_0 = z_2$ then the wavefunctions with the same E, k_y must have different values of k_x, say, k_{x1} and k_{x2}

$$\frac{\hbar k_{x1}^2}{2m^*} - e\mathscr{E}z_1 = \frac{\hbar^2 k_{x2}^2}{2m^*} - e\mathscr{E}z_2. \quad \text{Hence,} \tag{A.6}$$

$$k_{x1}^2 - k_{x2}^2 = \frac{2m^*e\mathscr{E}(z_1 - z_2)}{\hbar^2} \tag{A.7}$$

so that the phase-shift θ is given by

$$\theta = (k_{x1} - k_{x2})L = \frac{e\mathscr{E}(z_1 - z_2)L}{\hbar v_x}, \quad \text{where} \tag{A.8a}$$

$$v_x = \hbar(k_{x1} + k_{x2})/m^*. \tag{A.8b}$$

This is in agreement with the result obtained from perturbation theory (10.28). Again, with $\mathscr{E} = 0$, we will show that (A.4) is modified to

$$\psi_n = f_n\left[z - \frac{\omega_0^2 z_0}{\omega^2} - \frac{\hbar k_x \omega_c}{m^*\omega^2}\right] \tag{A.9a}$$

$$E_n = (n + \tfrac{1}{2})\hbar\omega + \frac{(\hbar k_x - m^*\omega_c z_0)^2\omega_0^2}{2m^*\omega^2} + \frac{\hbar^2 k_y^2}{2m^*}, \quad \text{where} \tag{A.9b}$$

$$\omega_c = eB/m^*, \quad \text{and} \tag{A.10}$$

$$\omega^2 = \omega_c^2 + \omega_0^2. \tag{A.11}$$

Hence with two channels centered at $z_0 = z_1$ and $z_0 = z_2$ for the same E, k_y we have

$$\hbar k_{x1} - m^*\omega_c z_1 = \hbar k_{x2} - m^*\omega_c z_2. \quad \text{Hence,} \tag{A.12}$$

$$\theta = (k_{x1} - k_{x2})L = \frac{eB(z_1 - z_2)L}{\hbar} \tag{A.13}$$

noting that $m^* \omega_c = eB$. This is in agreement with the result heuristically derived earlier (10.29b).

To prove (A.5): With $B = 0$, (A.3) can be simplified to

$$\left[\frac{p_z^2}{2m^*} + \frac{1}{2}m^* \omega_0^2 (z - z_0)^2 - e\mathscr{E}z \right]\psi = \varepsilon\psi , \quad \text{where} \tag{A.14a}$$

$$\varepsilon = E - \frac{\hbar^2 k_x^2}{2m^*} - \frac{\hbar^2 k_y^2}{2m^*} . \tag{A.14b}$$

(A.14a) can be rewritten as

$$\left[\frac{p_z^2}{2m^*} + \frac{1}{2}m^* \omega_0^2 \left(z - z_0 - \frac{e\mathscr{E}}{m^* \omega_0^2} \right)^2 \right]\psi = \left(\varepsilon + e\mathscr{E}z_0 + \frac{e^2 \mathscr{E}^2}{2m^* \omega_0^2} \right)\psi . \tag{A.15}$$

Clearly the eigenfunctions are given by

$$\psi_2 = f_n\left(z - z_0 - \frac{e\mathscr{E}}{2m^* \omega_0^2} \right) \tag{A.16a}$$

and the corresponding eigenvalues are

$$\varepsilon_n + e\mathscr{E}z_0 + \frac{e^2 \mathscr{E}^2}{2m^* \omega_0^2} = (n + \tfrac{1}{2})\hbar\omega_0 . \tag{A.16b}$$

Using (A.16b) and (A.14b) we obtain (A.5).

To prove (A.9): With $\mathscr{E} = 0$, (A.3) can be simplified to

$$\left[\frac{p_z^2}{2m^*} + \frac{1}{2}m^* \omega_0^2 (z - z_0)^2 + \frac{1}{2}m^* \omega_c^2 z^2 - \hbar k_x \omega_c z \right]\psi = \varepsilon\psi \tag{A.17}$$

with ε related to E through (A.14b). (A.17) can be rewritten as

$$\left[\frac{p_z^2}{2m^*} + \frac{1}{2}m^* \omega^2 (z - z_0)^2 - \alpha z \right]\psi = \left(\varepsilon + \frac{m^* \omega_c^2 z_0^2}{2} \right)\psi , \quad \text{where} \tag{A.18}$$

$$\alpha = \hbar k_x \omega_c - m^* \omega_c^2 z_0 . \tag{A.19}$$

ω^2 was defined earlier (A.11). Comparing with (A.15) it is evident that the eigenfunctions are given by

$$\psi_n = f_n\left(z - z_0 - \frac{\alpha}{m^* \omega^2} \right) \tag{A.20}$$

and the corresponding eigenvalues are

$$\varepsilon_n + \frac{1}{2}m^* \omega_c^2 z_0^2 = \left(n + \frac{1}{2} \right)\hbar\omega - \alpha z_0 - \frac{\alpha^2}{2m^* \omega^2} . \tag{A.21}$$

Using (A.19) to replace α in (A.21) we obtain

$$\varepsilon_n = \left(n + \frac{1}{2}\right)\hbar\omega + \frac{(\hbar k_x - m^*\omega_c z_0)^2 \omega_0^2}{2m^*\omega^2} - \frac{\hbar^2 k_x^2}{2m^*}. \tag{A.22}$$

From (A.22) and (A.14b) we obtain (A.9).

References

10.1   G. Timp, A. M. Chang, P. Mankiewich, R. Behringer, J. E. Cunningham, T. Y. Chang, R. E. Howard: Phys. Rev. Lett. **59**, 732 (1987)

10.2   C. J. B. Ford, T. J. Thornton, R. Newbury, M. Pepper, H. Ahmed, C. T. Foxon, J. J. Harris, C. Roberts: J. Phys. C: Solid State Phys. **21**, L325 (1988)

10.3   G. Timp, A. M. Chang, J. E. Cunningham, T. Y. Chang, P. Mankiewich, R. Behringer, R. E. Howard: Phys. Rev. Lett. **58**, 2814 (1987);
G. Timp, H. U. Baranger, P. deVegvar, J. E. Cunningham, R. E. Howard, R. Behringer, P. M. Mankiewich: Phys. Rev. Lett. **60**, 2081 (1988);
P. G. N. deVegvar, G. Timp, P. M. Mankiewich, J. E. Cunningham, R. Behringer, R. E Howard: Phys. Rev. **B38**, 4326 (1988)

10.4   B. J. van Wees, H. van Houten, C. W. J. Beenakker, J. G. Williamson, L. P. Kouwenhoven, D. van der Marel and C. T. Foxon: Phys. Rev. Lett. **60**, 848 (1988);
D. A. Wharam, T. J. Thornton, R. Newbury, M. Pepper, H. Ahmed, J. E. F. Frost, D. G. Hasko, D. C. Peacock, D. A. Ritchie, A. C Jones: J. Phys. C: Solid State Phys. **21**, L209 (1988)

10.5   The work on Aharonov–Bohm effect is reviewed in S. Washburn, R. A. Webb: Adv. Phys. **35**, 375 (1986)

10.6   S. Washburn, C. P. Umbach, R. B. Laibowitz, R. A. Webb, Phys. Rev. **B32**, 4789 (1985)

10.7   W. J. Skocpol, P. M. Mankiewich, R. E. Howard, L. D. Jackel, D. M. Tenant, A. D. Stone: Phys. Rev. Lett. **58**, 2347 (1987);
A. Benoit, C. P. Umbach, R. B. Laibowitz, R. A. Webb: Phys. Rev. Lett. **58**, 2343 (1987)

10.8   T. J. Thornton, M. Pepper, H. Ahmed, D. Andrews, G. J. Davies: Physical Review Letters, **56**, 1198 (1986)

10.9   R. Landauer: IBM J. Res. Dev. **1**, 223 (1957)

10.10 R. Tsu, L. Esaki: Appl. Phys. Lett. **22**, 562 (1973)

10.11 Y. Gefen, Y. Imry, M. Y. Azbel: Phys. Rev. Lett. **52**, 129 (1984)

10.12 M. Büttiker, Y. Imry, R. Landauer, S. Pinhas: Phys. Rev. **B31**, 6207 (1985)

10.13 M. Büttiker: Phys. Rev. Lett. **57**, 1761 (1986);
M. Büttiker: IBM J. Res. Dev. **32**, 63 (1988)

10.14 D. S. Fisher, P. A. Lee: Phys. Rev. **B23**, 6851 (1981)

10.15 E. R. Brown, T. C. L. G. Sollner, W. D. Goodhue, C. D. Parker: Appl. Phys. Lett. **50**, 83 (1987);
F. Capasso, S. Sen, A. C. Gossard, A. L. Hutchinson, J. H. English: IEEE Electron Device Letters **EDL-7**, 573 (1986)

10.16 W. E. Martin: Appl. Phys. Lett. **26**, 562 (1975);
F. J. Leonberger, C. E. Woodward, D. L. Spears: IEEE Trans. Circuits and Systems, **CAS-26**, 1125 (1979)

10.17 S. Washburn, H. Schmid, D. Kern, R. A. Webb: Phys. Rev. Lett. **59**, 1791 (1987)

10.18 S. Datta, M. Cahay, M. McLennan: Phys. Rev. **B36**, 5655 (1987)

10.19 S. Datta et. al.: Phys. Rev. Lett. **55**, 2344 (1985);
S. Datta et. al.: Second International Conference on Modulated Semiconductor Structures, Kyoto, Sept. 1985 (Surf. Sci. **174**, 439 (1986)).

10.20 A similar device using a lithographically defined ring structure is described in A. B. Fowler, US Patent No. 45503320 (1985)

10.21. S. Datta, M. R. Melloch, S. Bandyopadhyay, M. S. Lundstrom: Appl. Phys. Lett. **48**, 487 (1986)

10.22 S. Datta, S. Bandyopadhyay: Phys. Rev. Lett. **58**, 717 (1987)

10.23 S. Bandyopadhyay et. al.: Proceedings of the International Electron Devices Meeting, IEEE Catalog No. 86CH2381-2

10.24 A. M. Kriman, P. Ruden: Phys. Rev. **B32**, 8013 (1985); R. Frohne, S. Datta: J. Appl. Phys. **64**, 4086 (1988).

10.25 R. Colella, A. W. Overhauser, S. A. Werner: Phys. Rev. Lett. **34**, 1472 (1975)

10.26 Y. Aharonov, D. Bohm: Phys. Rev. **115**, 485 (1959)

10.27 G. Matteucci, G. Pozzi: Phys. Rev. Lett. **54**, 2469 (1985) and references therein

10.28 P. W. Anderson: Phys. Rev. **B23**, 4828 (1981)

10.29 R. Frohne: unpublished

10.30 B. L. Alt'shuler, A. G. Aronov, B. J. Spivak: Pis'ma Zh. Eksp. Teor. Fiz. **33**, 101 (1981) [JETP Lett. **33**, 94 (1981)]

10.31 S. Luryi: Appl. Phys. Lett. **47**, 490 (1985)

10.32 B. J. F. Lin, M. A. Paalanen, A. C. Gossard, D. C. Tsui: Phys. Rev. **B29**, 927 (1984)

10.33 T. Okoshi: *Planar Circuits for Microwaves and Lightwaves*, Springer Series in Electrophysics Vol. 18 (Springer, Berlin, Heidelberg 1985)

10.34 S. Datta, M. McLennan: Technical Report, TR-EE 89-12, Purdue University

10.35 S. Datta: Quantum Devices, International Conference on Superlattices, Microstructures and Microdevices, Trieste, Aug. 1988 Superlattices and Microstructures **6**, 83 (1989). Parts of this chapter have been excerpted from this reference

10.36 S. Datta: Proceedings of the International Conference on Solid State Devices and Materials, Tokyo, Aug. 1988

10.37 H. U. Baranger, A. D. Stone, D. P. DiVencenzo: Phys. Rev. **B37**, 6521 (1988)

10.38 C. P. Umbach, P. Santhanam, C. van Haesendonck, R. A. Webb: Appl. Phys. Lett. **50**, 1289 (1987)

10.39 Y. A. Bychkov, E. I. Rashba: J. Phys. **C17**, 6039 (1984)

10.40 H. Sompolinsky, A. Crisanti, H. J. Sommers: Phys. Rev. Lett. **61**, 259 (1988) and references therein; J. J. Hopfield, D. W. Tank: Science **233**, 625 (1986) and references therein

10.41 K. F. Berggren, G. Roos, H. van Houten: Phys. Rev. **B37**, 10118 (1988) and references therein

Additional References

J. R. Barker: In *Nanostructure Physics and Fabrication*, ed. by M. A. Reed, W. P. Kirk (Academic Orlando, FL 1989) p. 253

C. J. B. Ford, T. J. Thornton, R. Newbury, M. Pepper, H. Ahmed, D. C. Peacock, D. A. Ritchie, J. E. F. Frost, G. A. C. Jones: Appl. Phys. Lett. **54**, 21 (1989)

D. C. Miller, R. K. Lake, S. Datta, M. S. Lundstrom, M. R. Melloch and R. Reifenberger: In *Nanostructure Physics and Fabrication*, ed. by M. A. Reed, W. P. Kirk (Academic, Orlando, FL 1989) p. 165

F. Sols, M. Macucci, U. Ravaioli, K. Hess: Appl. Phys. Lett. **54**, 350 (1989)

F. Sols, M. Macucci, U. Ravaioli, K. Hess: In *Nanostructure Physics and Fabrication*, ed. by M. A. Reed, W. P. Kirk (Academic, Orlando, FL 1989) p. 157

P. G. N. de Vegvar, G. Timp, P. M. Mankiewich, R. Behringer, J. Cunningham: Phys. Rev. **B40**, 3491 (1989)

11. Carrier Confinement to One and Zero Degrees of Freedom.
Quantum Wires and Quantum Boxes in Gallium Arsenide: Optical and Structural Properties

P. M. Petroff

With 14 Figures

Since the early 1970s when the basic ideas on quantum wells [11.1, 2] were introduced, much progress has been realized in this field. The main catalysts for this development have been the advent of molecular beam epitaxy (MBE) which allows for the fabrication of ultra thin and highly perfect semiconductor epitaxial layers and the introduction of new devices based on the novel physical properties associated with carrier confinement. Carrier confinement in such structures, in the simplest way, is achieved by sandwiching the semiconductor layer with two wider band gap epitaxial semiconductor layers. If the narrower band gap material is in the form of a thin epitaxial layer, the carriers have 2 degrees of freedom within this layer (Fig. 11.1). The quantum properties appear in such structure for layer thicknesses smaller than ≈ 500 Å. The structure presenting this type of confinement are the well-known quantum wells (QW). Progress in reducing the carriers degrees of freedom i.e. increasing the degrees of confinement have been hampered by the complexity of the processing procedures. Indeed there is great interest from a technological point of view in realizing such structures since new device properties are expected [11.3]. For a smaller band gap region in the form of a thin wire (width smaller than ≈ 500 Å) surrounded by wider band gap material, carriers will have one degree of freedom for motion along the wire axis. If the region of smaller gap material is in the form of a box (again with dimensions ≤ 500 Å), the carrier motion is confined to zero degrees

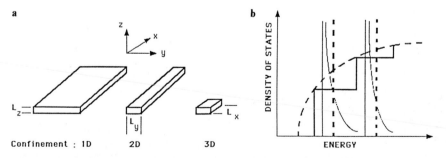

Fig. 11.1. (a) Schematic of the quantum structures with the corresponding degrees of confinement indicated. (b) Schematic of the density of states versus energy for the bulk semiconductor (*heavy dashed line*), the 1D confinement (*stair case function*), 2D confinement (*light continuous line*), and 3D confinement (*heaviest dashed line*)

of freedom (Fig. 11.1). When the wire and box exhibit dimensions which are smaller than the carrier deBroglie wavelength, their energy levels are quantized and these structures will be defined as quantum well wires (QWW) and quantum well boxes (QWB) respectively.

The structure dimensions L_x, L_y and L_z are indicated in Fig. 11.1 along with the respective density of states for the different structure dimensionality. The density of state changes with the structure dimensionality and is given by:

for the free electron case

$$\rho_3(E) = \left(\frac{2m_e/h^2}{2\pi^2}\right)^{3/2} \sqrt{E}$$

for electrons in a QW where $H(E)$ is the unit step function with $H(E \geq 0) = 1$ and $H(E < 0) = 0$

$$\rho_2(E) = \sum_{n=1}^{\infty} \frac{m_e}{\pi h^2 L_z} H\left(E - \frac{h^2 \pi^2 n^2}{2m_e L_z^2}\right)$$

for electrons in a QWW

$$\rho_1(E) = \sum_{n,\,1=1}^{\infty} \frac{(m_e/2h^2)^{1/2} \pi L_z L_y}{[E - E_y(l) - E_z(n)]^{1/2}}$$

and

$$\rho_0(E) = \sum_{n,\,1,\,k=1}^{\infty} \frac{1}{L_x L_y L_z} \delta\left[E - \frac{h^2 \pi^2}{2m_e}\left(\frac{n^2}{L_z^2} + \frac{l^2}{L_y^2} + \frac{k^2}{L_x^2}\right)\right]$$

for electrons in a QWB, where $\delta(E)$ is the delta function. E is the electron energy measured from the conduction band edge, m_e the free electron effective mass and h is Planck's constant. The quantized energy levels are defined as:

$$E_x = \frac{h^2 \pi^2 k^2}{2m_e L_x^2} \qquad E_y = \frac{h^2 \pi^2}{2m_e}\frac{l^2}{L_y^2} \qquad E_z = \frac{h^2 \pi}{2m_e}\frac{n^2}{L_z^2},$$

where n, l, k are the quantum numbers. In recent years, several schemes for fabricating such structures have been proposed. These may be divided into two classes. In the first category, a reduction in the system dimensionality is imposed by an external field (magnetic or electrostatic) applied to the free electron gas. In general, this approach requires the use of a quantum well structure if high magnetic fields are used [11.4]. Localized lithography with a structure containing a QW as well as additional sophisticated processing are required to achieve the additional confinement [11.3, 5] with the use of electrostatic fields. So far the only demonstration of one and zero degree confinement in GaAs-AlGaAs structures have been those of *Arakawa* et al. [11.4] who used high magnetic fields on GaAs lasers or QW to demonstrate the effect of 2 and 3 dimensional confinement on laser devices characteristics. The second category of structures attempt to achieve confinement effects using mesa type structures [11.6–8]. Because of the extremely small dimensions of the mesa structures, surface depletion layer effects due to deep traps become important and the characteristics of these structures are affected by these defects. Most of the important results using this approach have been obtained on silicon devices [11.8]. The results on GaAs structures [11.6] and InP [11.7] have been unclear and their interpretation remains difficult.

The alternative scheme for increasing the degrees of carrier confinement is to use a locally "built in" crystal potential within the structure. The first attempt used the anisotropic chemical etching of a GaAs QW superlattice and the regrowth of wider band gap GaAlAs by MBE [11.9]. The main difficulty with this approach resided in controlling the accuracy of the anisotropic etching and the quality of the regrown MBE layer. The main problems associated with achieving a uniform etching of the mesa structure and the regrowth of the AlGaAs cladding layer on the etched AlGaAs parts of the mesa structure were not completely solved. The type of structures achieved are shown schematically in Fig. 11.2a. A new spectral luminescence feature was observed on QWWs fabricated by this method and attributed to strain effects associated with the structure geometry. A different approach to building a localized crystal potential which did not involve any lithography was later proposed. With this method, fractional alternate monolayers of GaAlAs and GaAs are deposited by MBE on a vicinal (100) oriented GaAs substrate [11.10]. The structure obtained with this method is schematically shown in Fig. 11.2b. The period of the vertical superlattice is controlled by the misorientation angle while the superlattice perfection is function of the degree of ordering. The obtention of such structures requires that growth is taking place in a layer mode and that nucleation is initiated at step edges [11.10]. The presence of thermally induced kinks at the step edges had initially prevented the obtention of these vertical superlattices. However very recent reports indicate that such structures have been fabricated using atomic layer epitaxy by MOCVD [11.11, 12]; the degree of perfection. i.e. ordering in these vertical superlattices remains to be evaluated. In view of these recent success this may constitute a very promising approach to the processing of QWWs. The new growth methods which use a "growth interruption" [11.13]

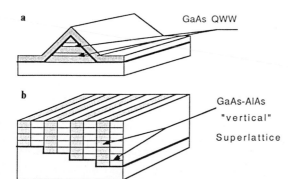

a   GaAs QWW

b   GaAs-AlAs "vertical" Superlattice

Fig. 11.2. Quantum well wire structures. Schematic of previously proposed structures for the processing of QWWs, (a): etched and regrown structure [11.9], (b): fractional alternate monolayers deposited by MBE on a vicinal (100) GaAs surface [11.10]

between the deposition of each fractional monolayer or the atomic layer epitaxy [11.14] method should minimize the density of thermal kinks and improve the perfection of such structures.

Recent progress in the manufacturing of 1D and 0D structures have been achieved using a new approach [11.15] which is presented in this paper. The optical properties measured on individual QWW and QWB are presented and compared to theoretically computed results for structures in which carrier motion is confined to 1 and 0 dimension.

11.1 Experimental Methods

The new approach in manufacturing 1D and 0D structures relies on intermixing locally the narrow and wider band gap material. Such intermixing produces regions of the material with a band gap intermediate with that of the two original materials [11.15, 16]. The schematic in Fig. 11.3 illustrates the principle of the

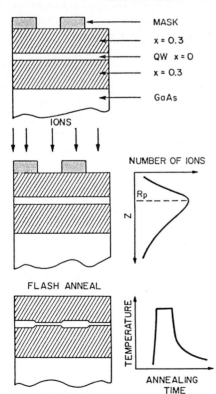

ION DAMAGE ENHANCED DIFFUSION IN $Ga As\text{-}Ga_{1-x}Al_xAs$
QUANTUM WELLS

MASK

x = 0.3

QW x = 0

x = 0.3

GaAs

IONS

NUMBER OF IONS

R_p

Z

FLASH ANNEAL

TEMPERATURE

ANNEALING TIME

Fig. 11.3. Schematic of the processing for achieving localized tuning of the band gap via implantation enhanced interdiffusion between AlGaAs and GaAs. The ion energy is adjusted to produce the maximum in the defect distribution in the QW interfaces region. Interdiffusion produces a narrower QW hence wider effective band gap material in these region

method. The localized intermixing is achieved in the case of GaAs-GaAlAs QW by interdiffusing selectively the Ga and Al across the interface. Ga$^+$ ions are used to introduce point defects in the unmasked parts of the QW and enhance the interdiffusion, in these regions. The ion energy is chosen to produce the maximum in the defect distribution in the region of the QW interfaces. We note that ion straggling underneath the masked area will introduce point defects. In the present case for a QW located 500 Å below the surface and a Ga$^+$ ion energy of 210 keV, the ion straggling underneath the mask is about 350 Å and consequently during interdiffusion the thickness and width of the undisturbed area underneath the mask are also reduced. Annealing of the ion induced damage was performed in a rapid thermal anneal furnace at temperatures ranging from 850°C to 950°C.

The enhancement in interdiffusion should be maximized to produce the largest band gap offset in the lateral confining potential along the y axis (see Fig. 11.3). It is fortuitous that the thermal interdiffusion coefficient, D_i, of Ga and Al is very small even at temperatures about 950°C. In Fig. 11.4 datas from several groups who have measured D_i over a wide temperature range and for $Ga_{1-x}Al_xAs$ layer composition ranging from $x = 0.25$ to 1. The thermally activated interdiffusion has an activation energy $E_t = 5.6 \pm 0.5$ eV and a preexponential term $D_0 = 10^7$ cm^2/sec [11.15] and both appear to be independent of the Al concentration.

The experimental measurement technique for measuring the implantation enhanced interdiffusion coefficient, D_i^*, is based on following the luminescence shift associated with changes in the QW thickness or composition profile after ion implantation and interdiffusion [11.15]. The luminescence originates from

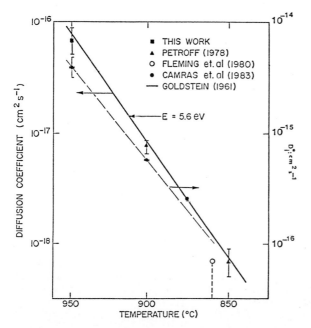

Fig. 11.4. Diffusion coefficient, D_i, for thermal interdiffusion and D_i^*, for the implantation enhanced interdiffusion (dashed line) between Al and Ga across the AlGaAs-GaAs interface as a function of annealing temperature

radiative recombination processes between the quantized energy levels for electrons and holes. The luminescence from the QW or QWW or QWB is stimulated by a highly focused (200 Å) electron beam (150 keV energy) on the structure. This cathodoluminescence (CL) technique [11.17] allows measurements on a single QWW or QWB at low temperature (< 12 K).

After interdiffusion, the QW interfaces are no longer compositionally abrupt and the Al concentration has an error function distribution which is given by:

$$X = X_0\left[1 + \frac{1}{2}\text{erfc}\left(\frac{Z - L_z/2}{2\Delta_i(Z)}\right) - \frac{1}{2}\text{erfc}\left(\frac{Z + L_z/2}{2\Delta_i(Z)}\right)\right],$$

where x_0 is the initial Al concentration and erfc( ) is the error function. D_i^* is the implantation enhanced interdiffusion coefficient and the corresponding interdiffusion distance is defined as $\Delta_i(z) = (D_i^* t)^{1/2}$ for an annealing time t. For an interdiffused QW, the band gap variation as a function of x, along the Z axis is:

$$E_g(z) = 1424 + 1247x(z) \text{ (in meV)} .$$

60% of this accounts for the variation of the conduction band edge. The computation of the energy levels for electrons and holes indicates a monotonic energy increase with $\Delta_i(z)$. The reduction in the QW width is followed by a filling of the well with Al. If we assume that the luminescence line accurately follows the energy levels (constant Stokes shift), the values of $\Delta_i(z)$ are easily obtained by solving Schrödinger's equation using (9) for the carrier confining potential.

Detailed measurements of $\Delta_i(z)$ as a function of annealing time indeed indicate large changes in the effective QW width. As shown in Fig. 11.5 a

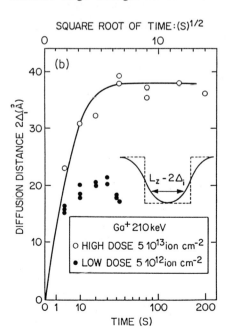

Fig. 11.5. Double interdiffusion distance, $2\Delta_i$, as a function of annealing time for 2 implantation doses and an annealing temperature $T = 950\,°C$

reduction of $\approx 40\,\text{Å}$ in the QW width is observed at $T = 950°\text{C}$ before a saturation effect is noticed. For the 50 Å QW used for these measurements, the energy shift introduced in the quantized electrons energy levels is ≈ 60 meV. A complete recovery in the QW luminescence efficiency is observed for annealing times ≥ 40 sec. for an annealing temperature $= 950°\text{C}$. This recovery in the material properties after processing is essential to this processing. As pointed out previously, [11.15, 18], success in manufacturing QWWS and QWBs by this method relies on the large difference in the interdiffusion between the ion implanted and the non implanted areas. The enhancement in the interdiffusion coefficient is ≈ 50 at $T = 950°\text{C}$ while at 900°C it is ≈ 500 (see Fig. 11.4).

CL measurements on QWW and QWB fabricated by this process show new luminescence lines with energies [11.18, 19] which are dependent on the dimensions on the structure tested. Figure 11.6 shows that for QWW with width decreasing from 3000 Å to 500 Å up to 5 new luminescence lines are observed. As shown in Fig. 11.7, all the lines shift to higher energies as the width of the QWW is reduced. As shown subsequently, this energy shift is accounted by both a filling in the QWW with Al and carrier confinement to one degree of freedom. The highest energy line observed correspond to carrier recombination at the edges of the QWWs. As L_y is reduced, the highest line energy shifts towards the emission energy of the large interdiffused area (Fig. 11.6).

Increasing the electron beam intensity by ≈ 100 times does not bring a saturation of the CL emission of the QWW: rather, the intensity of the highest energy line increases along with the line width. The CL intensity variations along a QWW imaged in the energy selected CL micrographs (Fig. 11.8) are in fact related to small variations in the emission wavelength along a wire and the

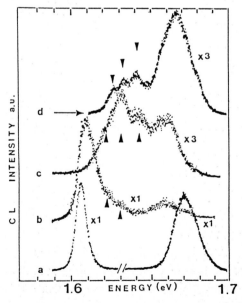

Fig. 11.6. CL spectra for a series of quantum wires with masks width 4500 Å b, 1700 Å c and 1400 Å d. Spectra in a correspond to the quantum well (*left line*) and the large interdiffused area (*right line*)

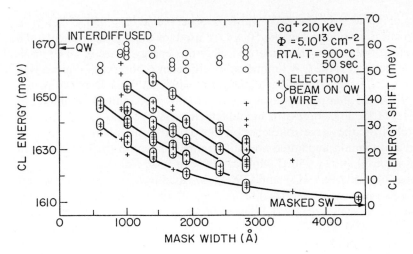

Fig. 11.7. Cathodoluminescence line energy versus mask width for Quantum wires. The arrows correspond to large masked areas or implanted annealed areas. A cluster of points around the same energy indicates measurements on several quantum wires with identical mask sizes

luminescence efficiency along a QWW wire is measured to be approximately constant. These variations in the spectrally resolved CL micrographs are, as will be discussed subsequently, related to small changes in the confinement energy along the wire.

A similar process has been used in the fabrication and processing of QWB's. CL spectra (Fig. 11.9) from an individual QWB also show a series of narrow luminescence lines which shift to higher energies as the dimensions of the mask are reduced. In Fig. 11.9, the non-uniformity in the QWB array is noticeable; however as in the case of QWW, an energy selected CL micrograph formed using photons with slightly different energies, shows some of the previously missing boxes in the array. This effect is attributed to variations in the confining potential from one box to another. The data in Fig. 11.10 again shows a large scatter in the CL line energies as a function of mask width. The linear regression lines show 2 sets of CL lines and the highest energy lines have been omitted from this plot because of the large scatter in the data points. For mask diameter smaller than 1000 Å the data are not accurate because the luminescence line energy is too close to that of the interdiffused area.

11.2 Discussion of Experimental Results

Interpretation of these results require a detailed understanding of the inter-diffusion process which defines the lateral carrier confining potential [11.20]. The schematic in Fig. 11.11 summarizes the main features of the interdiffusion

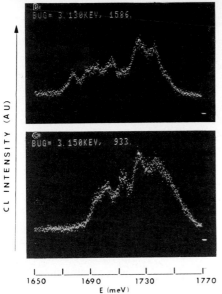

Fig. 11.8. (a) Spectrally resolved micrographs of a QWW structure for a photon energy $E = 1.705$ eV. **(b)** The 2 CL spectra correspond to 2 positions of the electron beam along the same QWW. $T = 12$ K. The mask width is $W = 1000$ Å

modeling. Point defects generated by the implanted Ga^+ ions are assumed to diffuse laterally underneath the mask. Their diffusion length, Λ, is function of y and t. The point defects diffusion constant is D. It is assumed, in this simple model, that an interdiffusion event takes place only at the end of the point defect diffusion path. The interdiffusion equation also takes into account the ion straggling which introduces point defects underneath the mask.

After the ion implantation, the point defect concentration $N(y, t)$ is given by:

$$N(y, 0) = N_0 \left[1 - \frac{1}{2}\mathrm{erfc}\left(\frac{L_y/2 - y}{\sigma}\right) - \frac{1}{2}\mathrm{erfc}\left(\frac{L_y/2 + y}{\sigma}\right) \right],$$

where σ is the lateral straggling tabulated in [11.14] (multiplied by $\sqrt{2}$).

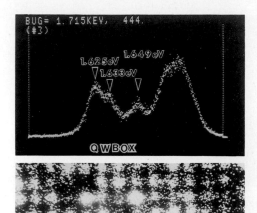

Fig. 11.9. (a) CL spectrum of a single QWB **(b)** Spectrally resolved CL micrograph of a quantum box array. Photon energy $E = 1.644$ eV. $T = 10$ K

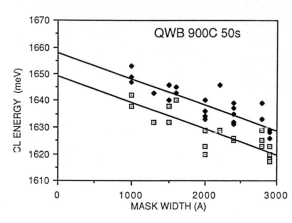

Fig. 11.10. CL energy emission versus size for quantum well box. Only the 2 lowest energy lines are shown

After an annealing time t, the defect distribution is given by:

$$N(y, t) = N_0 \left[1 - \frac{1}{2}\mathrm{erfc}\left(\frac{L_y/2 - y}{(\sigma^2 + 4Dt)^{1/2}} \right) - \frac{1}{2}\mathrm{erfc}\left(\frac{L_y/2 + y}{(\sigma^2 + 4Dt)^{1/2}} \right) \right].$$

The interdiffusion is controlled by the defect motion across the interface.
   The interdiffusion coefficient D_i^*, is proportional to the local defect density:

$$D_i^*(y, t) = KDN(y, t),$$

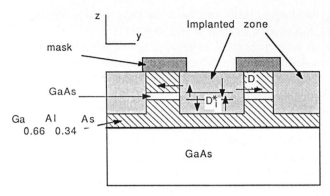

Fig. 11.11. Schematic of the interdiffusion modeling. D_i^* is the Al and Ga interdiffusion coefficient and D is the diffusion coefficient of point defects responsible for the interdiffusion

where K is a constant close to unity. The change in the Al concentration $c(y, t)$ is described by Fick's second law and gives

$$c(y, t) = c_0 \left[1 - \frac{1}{2} \text{erfc} \left(\frac{L_z/2 - z}{2 \Delta_i(y, t)} \right) - \frac{1}{2} \text{erfc} \left(\frac{L_z/2 + z}{2 \Delta_i(y, t)} \right) \right].$$

This expression assumes that interdiffusion at the center of the wire is due to defect diffusion parallel to the interface followed by interdiffusion across the interface. c_0 is the initial Al concentration in the cladding layer and $\Delta_i(y, t)$ is the interdiffusion length given by $\Delta_i^2(y, t) = KD \int N(y, \Omega) d\Omega$. For long annealing time, this expression has an exact analytical solution [11.20]. The computed Al profiles are shown in Fig. 11.12 for two values of Δ. Even for small values (5 Å) of Δ, the lateral concentration profile is no longer square if the mask width is ≤ 1000 Å. For smaller mask sizes, the width of the profile is not changed appreciably and only the Al concentration in the center of the wire changes. These effects are due to the ion straggling which introduces point defects underneath the mask and significantly reduce the effective mask width for the

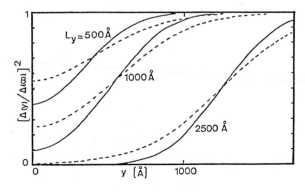

Fig. 11.12. Squared interdiffusion length (normalized to its values far away from the mask) versus position across the wire. The mask width considered are $L_y = 500$ Å, 1000 Å, 2500 Å. Two cases are plotted: the point defect diffusion length is small (5 Å) and large (250 Å, *dashed line*)

wire or the box. Only the large mask sizes ($w > 2000$ Å) yield a confining potential similar to that of a square well for $\varDelta = 250$ Å.

From measurements on large implanted areas (after annealing 50s at 900°C), it is found that using the calculated electronic levels, the interdiffusion far away from the mask is $\varDelta_i \approx 11$ Å; the corresponding amount of interdiffusion in the center of the masked areas is $\varDelta_i \approx 6$ Å for $\varDelta = 250$ Å and $w = 500$ Å. Thus for mask sizes smaller than 1000 Å a significant amount of interdiffusion is occurring during annealing in the center of the masked area. This Al interdiffusion in the center of the narrowest QWW accounts partially for the general shift of the electronic energy levels to higher energies as seen in Fig. 11.7.

A computation of the electronic energy levels was carried out for the QWW using a variational method. The lateral confining potential (in eV) is taken as $V(z, y) = 0.6 \times 1247\, c(z, y)$ for electrons and $V(z, y) = 0.5 c(z, y)$ for holes. Figure 11.13 shows the first two energy levels as a function the mask width. Comparing Fig. 11.7 and 11.13, we note a qualitative agreement for $w < 2000$ Å; the observed energy differences between the first two levels is 5 to 8 meV experimentally while the computed value is ≈ 4 meV. A similar computation could in principle be performed for QWBs, however the scatter in the experimental results is presently too large to make the comparison meaningful.

The relative luminescence efficiency of the QW, QWW and QWB are evaluated. In the simplest model, the photon flux, ϕ, collected from the quantum structure is given as:

$$\phi = n\rho V .$$

ρ is the efficiency for the radiative recombination process and n is the number of minority carriers per unit volume and time collected in a volume V; the volume V effectively contributing carriers to the radiative recombination process is dependent on the structure (see Fig. 11.14) and the minority carrier diffusion length L_0 (1 micron). The experimental measurements are carried out with a constant intensity electron beam positioned on the individual structures and the photon fluxes collected under identical conditions are obtained from the spectral

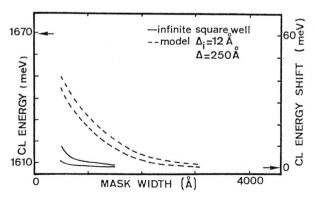

Fig. 11.13. Energy of the transition involving the first two levels of electrons and holes laterally confined in a QWW versus the mask width. The lateral confining potential is $V_0 = 60$ meV. A plot for the infinitely high square well is also shown in full lines

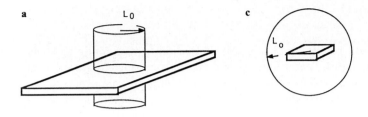

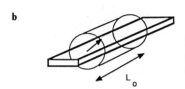

Fig. 11.14. Schematic of the volumes contributing to the CL signal for (a) the QW (b) the QWW and (c) the QWB structures

line intensities. For the QW, QWW and QWB these fluxes are respectively:

$$\phi_1 = \rho_1 n\pi L_0^2 L_z \tag{11.1}$$

$$\phi_2 = \rho_2 n L_0 L_z w \tag{11.2}$$

$$\phi_3 = \rho_3 n w^2 L_0 . \tag{11.3}$$

The ratios of the measured fluxes yield, the relative luminescence efficiencies using (11.1–3) and $L_0 \approx 10\ w$. The model assumes that the radiative life times are identical for all three structures. We observed that the CL efficiency of the QWW is about twice that of the QW and that of the QWB is about five to six times that of the QWW. The very high efficiency of the QWW and QWB may arise from the increased oscillator strength associated with the additional carrier confinement; recent theoretical calculations [11.22] which find the oscillator strength for the QWW case to be twice that of the QW seem to support this point of view.

The optical properties of these structures are presently not well understood. Indeed the multiplicity of high energy lines seem to indicate that intraband carrier thermalization is not dominant in QWWs and QWBs and that band filling could be important in these structures. Time resolved optical measurements and excitation luminescence experiments will be needed to better understand the effects of 1D and 0D carrier confinement. In addition we still need an improved processing of the interdiffused areas which still contains residual defects (yet exhibit good luminescence characteristics) in the form of dislocation loops (density = 10^8–10^9 cm^{-2}) which are affecting locally the interdiffusion process [11.23].

11.3 Conclusions

This review of recent results on ultra-small dimension carrier confining structures clearly points out the importance of the microprocessing science involved in their manufacturing. Novel optical features have already been observed and their interpretation is consistent with carrier quantum confinement effects to quantum wires and quantum box structures. The electronic properties of such structues should bring about novel devices in much the same way that occurred when quantum wells and quantum well superlattices were manufactured reliably. However, for QWW and QWB structures, the difficulty in manufacturing increases with the degrees of carrier confinement.

References

11.1   R. Tsu, L. Esaki: Appl. Phys. Lett. **22**, 562 (1973);
       L. Esaki, R. Tsu: IBM J. Res. Dev. **14**, 61 (1970)
11.2   R. Dingle, W. Wiegmann, C. K. Henry: Phys. Rev. Lett. **33**, 827 (1974)
11.3   H. Sakaki: Jpn. J. Appl. Phys. **19**, L735 (1980)
11.4   Y. Arakawa, K. Vahala, A. Yariv, K. Lau: Appl. Phys. Lett., **47**, 142 (1985)
11.5   S. Luryi, F. Capasso: Appl. Phys. Lett. **47**, 1348 (1985)
11.6   M. A. Reed, R. T. Bate, K. Bradshaw, W. M. Duncan, W. R. Frensley, J. W. Lee, H. D. Shi:
       J. Vac. Sci. Technol. **B4** (1), 358 (1986)
11.7   H. Temkins, G. J. Dolan, M. B. Panish, S. W. G. Chen: Appl. Phys. Lett. **50**, 415 (1987)
11.8   W. J. Skocpol, L. D. Jackel, E. L. Hei, R. E. Howard, C. A. Fetter: Phys. Rev. Lett., **49**, 951
       (1981)
11.9   P. M. Petroff, A. C. Gossard, R. A. Logan, W. Wiegmann: Appl. Phys. Lett. **41**, 635 (1982)
11.10 P. M. Petroff, A. C. Gossard, W. Wiegmann: Appl. Phys. Lett. **45**, 6, 620 (1984)
11.11 S. Yamada, T. Fukui, H. Saito: J. Vac. Sci. Tech., **50**, 329 (1987)
11.12 T. Fukui, H. Saito: Appl. Phys. Lett. **50**, 824 (1987)
11.13 C. W. Tu, R. C. Miller, B. A. Wilson, P. M. Petroff, T. D. Harris, R. F. Kopf, S. K. Sputz, M. G.
       Lamont: J. Cyrst Growth **81**, 159 (1987)
11.14 T. Fuki, H. Saito: Jpn. J. Appl. Phys., **23**, L521 (1984)
11.15 J. Cibert, P. M. Petroff, D. J. Werder, S. J. Pearton, A. C. Gossard, J. H. English: Appl. Phys.
       Lett., **49**, 223 (1986)
11.16 Y. Hirayama, Y. Suzuki, H. Okamoto: Jpn. Appl. Phys., **24**, 1498 (1985)
11.17 P. M. Petroff, D. V. Lang, J. L. Strudel, R. A. Logan: "Scanning Electron Microscopy" Vol. 1,
       SEM Inc. AMF O'Hare, III. 60666 (USA) 325 (1978)
11.18 J. Cibert, P. M. Petroff, G. J. Dolan, S. J. Pearton, A. C. Gossard, J. H. English: Appl. Phys.
       Lett., **49**, 1275 (1986)
11.19 J. Cibert, P. M. Petroff, G. J. Dolan, S. J. Pearton, A. C. Gossard, J. H. English: Second
       International Conference on Superlattices, Gotteborg, Sweden (1986)
11.20 J. Cibert, P. M. Petroff: Phys. Rev. B **36**, 6, 3243 (1987)
11.21 J. F. Gibbons, W. H. Johnson, S. K. Milroie: *Range Statistics in Semiconductors* (Academic,
       New York 1975)
11.22 K. B. Wong, M. Jaros, J. S. Hagon: J. Vac. Sci. Techn. (1987) to be published
11.23 D. J. Werder, S. J. Pearton: J. Appl. Phys. to be published

12. Quantum Effects in Quasi-One-Dimensional MOSFETs

W. J. Skocpol

With 18 Figures

This chapter reviews quantum transport phenomena in narrow MOSFET inversion-layer devices at low temperatures. At low electron densities, transport is by tunnelling and hopping through strongly localized electron states. At higher electron densities, the transport is by diffusion that preserves quantum phase information for typical distances L_ϕ much greater than the mean free path. In large systems, weak-localization and interaction effects can be used to characterize the fundamental length scales L_ϕ and L_T. In small systems, random quantum interference leads to conductance variations from device to device and as a function of magnetic field and gate voltage that have a predictable rms amplitude of e^2/h at scale L_ϕ. The dependence of these universal conductance fluctuations on spacing between measuring probes reveals a crossover at L_ϕ to nonlocal quantum behavior characteristic of scale L_ϕ. Small MOSFETs also reveal the trapping of single electrons at individual interface traps. This can be used to study the effect of a single scatterer on the quantum interference phenomena.

12.1 Background

At a Workshop on Submicron Technology in October 1985, participants were discussing ways to promote public awareness of the field. A prominent proponent of GaAs devices suggested featuring the just-announced Nobel Prize in Physics – awarded to Klaus von Klitzing for his discovery of the Quantum Hall Effect "in a MODFET device". A sizeable fraction of the audience replied, almost in unison, "No, L___, it was a MOSFET!" This chapter is intended to serve, where appropriate, as a similar reminder.

The metal-oxide-semiconductor field-effect transistor (MOSFET) was first developed in the early 1960's [12.1]. Its evolution into the dominant commercial integrated-circuit technology has been influenced by many disciplines, ranging from materials science and physics to electrical engineering and economics. By 1966, experiments by *Fowler* et al. [12.2] showed that the silicon MOSFET was a quantum-mechanically two-dimensional device at liquid-helium temperatures – i.e., inversion-layer electrons were bound by the gate in a potential well so thin that the transverse motion perpendicular to the oxide-silicon interface remained in the lowest quantum state. This fact may not be essential to commercial practice, but it is certain that two decades of interesting physics have followed from this observation [12.3].

The silicon MOSFET continues to be a useful tool for learning new things about quantum transport. The gate voltage controls the electron density of the conducting channel, providing a way to tune the conduction from strong localization and quantum-hopping transport to essentially metallic electron densities and quantum-coherent transport. This chapter will review recent developments, with primary emphasis on laterally restricted, narrow, "quasi-one-dimensional" devices, which accentuate many quantum effects. In the course of this discussion we will emphasize the special nature of "one-dimensional" transport, the resulting unique opportunities to study the behavior of electrons in single quantum states, and the more general lessons to be learned about "mesoscopic systems" – in which the detailed quantum behavior of devices is not predictable from the average properties that are under the fabricator's control.

12.2 MOSFET Length Scales

To understand what kinds of quantum physics are relevant to MOSFET devices it is necessary to consider the hierarchy of relevant length scales [12.4].

By changing the gate voltage V_G above threshold V_T, the electron density in a MOSFET conducting channel

$$N_s = (\varepsilon\varepsilon_0/ed_{ox})(V_G - V_T) \; [\,= 1.1 \times 10^{16} \text{ electrons/m}^2 \text{ V for 20 nm SiO}_2\,]$$
$$(12.1)$$

can be varied from essentially zero to a maximum of approximately 2×10^{17} electrons/m^2 limited only by the 1 V/nm dielectric breakdown strength of SiO$_2$. At such fields, the electrons are bound so strongly to the interface that the quantum-mechanically self-consistent average layer thickness z_{av} is approximately 2 nm (20 Å) [12.5]. At low temperatures for (100) silicon z_{av} increases to perhaps 7 nm at low, less-tightly-bound densities. It increases by at most another factor of three at room temperature due to the occupation of higher subbands [12.5]. At all densities, the average lateral distance between electrons ($N_s^{-1/2}$) is at least as large as the thickness.

Moreover, at low temperatures and most accessible densities, the motion is strictly (quantum-mechanically) two-dimensional. The energy $E_k = \hbar^2 k^2/2m^*$ corresponds to an electron wavelength $\lambda = 2\pi/k$, where $k^2 = k_x^2 + k_y^2$. For a (100) silicon orientation, with effective mass $m^* = 0.19\,m_e$ and twofold spin and valley degeneracies, the 2D density of states is

$$N_{2D} = 2m^*/\pi\hbar^2 = 1.6 \times 10^{18}/\text{eV}m^2 = 10^{37}/\text{J}m^2 \; ,$$
$$(12.2)$$

so that the Fermi energy and wavevector are

$$E_F = \pi\hbar^2 N_s/2m^*; \quad k_F = m^*v_F/\hbar = (\pi N_s)^{1/2} \; .$$
$$(12.3)$$

The Fermi energy for 10^{17} electrons/m^2 in one subband is 63 meV, corresponding to a wavelength of 11 nm. Even under this high-density condition, the second 2D subband is barely occupied [12.5].

A fixed charge located at or near the Si-SiO$_2$ interface is strongly screened by the electron gas. The 2D screening constant $K_{2D} = e^2 N_{2D}/2\varepsilon$ corresponds to a characteristic screening length K_{2D}^{-1} of about 0.5 nm (assuming a dielectric constant ε intermediate between those of Si and SiO$_2$) [12.6]. This means that the scattering potential is localized on the scale of the electron wavelength and the scatterer has an effective cross-section of width λ_F [12.7]. This implies a mean free path

$$l = v_F \tau = k_F/N_i \, , \tag{12.4}$$

where τ^{-1} is the elastic scattering rate, and N_i is the number of fixed scatterers per unit area. The corresponding 2D conductivity $G_\square$ (inverse of sheet resistance $R_\square = RW/L$) is

$$G_\square = N_s e^2 \tau/m^* = (e^2/h)(2k_F l) \, . \tag{12.5}$$

Thus the metal theorist's small expansion parameter $1/k_F l = N_i/\pi N_s$ is just $r_\square$, the sheet resistance in units of $h/e^2 = 25.8$ kΩ. Even our relatively low-mobility devices (0.3 m^2/V sec maximum) typically have a minimum sheet resistance of 500 $\Omega/\square$ ($k_F l = 25$) at high densities, corresponding to $N_i \le 10^{16}$ m^{-2}, and mean free paths as large as 50 nm. From this we conclude that MOSFET devices can be an excellent realization of a two-dimensional *metal*.

Like disordered metal films, MOSFET devices show quantum corrections to the conductivity at low temperatures due to localization phenomena [12.8–12]. These interference effects are cut short by both inelastic scattering and magnetic fields. Thus magnetoresistance measurements can be used to determine inelastic scattering rates in MOSFETs [12.13–20]. The dominant *inelastic* scattering mechanism in liquid-helium-temperature MOSFETs is electron–electron scattering. Below ~ 4.2 K, the scattering rate in MOSFETs of various mobility can be summarized as approximately

$$\tau_{in}^{-1} = 3 \times 10^7 R_\square T \text{ [MKS]} \, . \tag{12.6}$$

Above 4 K, a T^2 rate becomes increasingly significant. For our devices τ_{in} can be as large as 80 psec at temperature $T = 1$ K and at helium temperatures is always much longer than typical elastic scattering times of 0.1 psec.

Thus the fundamental nature of low-temperature quantum transport in MOSFETs is *diffusive*, with multiple scattering leading to various quantum interference phenomena. The quantum diffusion persists for a phase-preserving diffusion length L_ϕ, approximately equal to the inelastic diffusion length

$$L_{in}^{2D} = (D\tau_{in})^{1/2} \, , \tag{12.7}$$

Table 12.1. Characteristic MOSFET Length Scales [nm]

Inverse screening constant	$K_{2D}^{-1} = 0.5$
Inversion layer thickness	$z_{av} = 7\, n_s^{-1/2}$
Mean free path	$l = 2.8\, g_\square\, n_s^{-1/2}$
Fermi wavelength	$\lambda_F = 35\, n_s^{-1/2}$
Inelastic diffusion length	$L_{in} = 14\, g_\square\, t^{-1/2}$
Coherence length	$L_T = 107\, g_\square^{1/2}\, t^{-1/2}$

where the diffusion constant

$$D = v_F^2 \tau / 2 = G_\square / e^2 N_{2D} = 3.9 G_\square \ [\text{MKS}]. \tag{12.8}$$

In our MOSFETs, L_ϕ can be of order 1 μm at 0.4 K.

A final length scale to consider in characterizing the quantum transport in MOSFETs is the coherence length

$$L_T = \pi (D\hbar / k_B T)^{1/2} \tag{12.9}$$

This is the average distance that electrons at different energies within several $k_B T$ of the Fermi surface diffuse before getting "out of step". In our MOSFETs, $L_T \geq L_\phi$, and thus plays little role.

The interplay of these fundamental length scales for MOSFETs with the practically realizable dimensions of actual devices determines the precise nature of the quantum phenomena that are observable. Table 12.1 summarizes the magnitude of the characteristic quantum lengths expressed in terms of $n_s = N_s/(10^{16}/\text{m}^2)$, $g_\square = G_\square/(e^2/h)$, and $t = T/1\ K$.

12.3 Special MOSFET Geometries

Given the widespread interest in the 2D nature of conduction in MOSFETs, it was perhaps inevitable that the progress of fabrication technology would be applied to scientific studies of narrow, increasingly "1D" systems. In Chapter 11, Pierre Petroff has reviewed a wide variety of schemes for one-dimensional confinement. The three basic types that have been implemented in MOSFETs are: A) simple electrostatic confinement under a narrow gate [12.21–28]; B) electrostatic confinement by nearby doped regions under a wider gate [12.29–38]; and C) physical confinement by etching away material adjacent to the narrow channel [12.20, 39–52]. Fabrication details are most easily found in [12.22, 24, 27–29, 33, 41, and 48].

The effective width of the narrow devices depends on the confinement method. The two electrostatic confinement schemes lead to considerable uncertainty about the actual width of the channel, which may be a function of gate voltage. The etched confinement that we use here at Holmdel at least sets an upper bound to the width. In practice, our electron-beam lithography and reactive-ion-etching can be used to define structures as small as 10–20 nm. At our current 20 nm oxide thickness, however, it becomes exceedingly difficult to turn on channels of less than about 40 nm width at accessible gate voltages [12.49]. In the range from 100 nm to 40 nm in width, the mobility of channels decreases, consistent with a mean free path limited by diffuse scattering at the sidewalls. [12.49].

One advantage of studying transport in devices with long, narrow sections is that the narrow sections have the highest resistance per unit length, so that even two-terminal measurements between wide inversion layers at either end can have their largest contributions from the narrow section. To go beyond the limitations of such two-terminal measurements, however, we have recently worked with a new generation of MOSFET devices [12.45–52] in which up to eight different external n^+ contacts can be connected by a single patterned inversion layer under a patterned gate. Thus a narrow channel with sidebranches used as voltage probes can be used to make four-terminal measurements of channel segments as narrow as 40 nm at various length scales down to 150 nm. Figure 12.1 shows our favorite picture of such a device.

Comparison of these practical size scales with Table 12.1 shows that the widths can be comparable to the mean free path and the Fermi wavelength, and much less than the inelastic diffusion length. This allows us to explore a variety of "one-dimensional" phenomena. Our accessible channel length or voltage probe spacing cannot probe inside the mean-free-path length scale, but can attempt to probe inside systems that have phase-preserving diffusion throughout. First, however, I will review the work of others in the "strongly localized" regime.

12.4 Strictly 1D Transport

A popular oversimplification is that one-dimensional electron systems are localized, and therefore do not conduct at low temperatures. Careful qualification of this assertion is necessary.

Fig. 12.1. Top and perspective views of narrow MOSFET gate structures etched to confine a narrow conducting channel. Sidebranches are used as voltage probes

We start with the theorist's ideal of a truly one-dimensional system in which the motion of the electrons has only one degree of freedom. As early as 1961, *Mott* and *Twose* [12.53] observed that the electron states of such a system with a disordered potential energy are likely to be localized, and fall off exponentially with distance. By 1970, *Landauer* [12.54] had established a clear physical picture in which the conductance of such a system at a given energy E_F at $T = 0$ could be related to the quantum mechanical transmission coefficient $T(E_F)$ for electrons (of both spins) at that energy:

$$G(E_F) = (e^2/h)[2T(E_F)]/[1 - T(E_F)] = (e^2/h)g . \tag{12.10}$$

When applied to the addition of quantum-mechanical resistances (without phase-randomization between segments), it indicated that the average resistance would grow exponentially with length! A vast theoretical literature has since developed, from which the following picture emerges.

12.4.1 Localization and Resonant Tunnelling

The calculated transmission at zero temperature as a function of electron energy E_F for each specific 1D conductor of finite length L and specific choice of disorder is typically exponentially small, but exhibits sharply peaked resonances at specific energies, analogous to the resonant tunnelling discussed in Chaps. 5–7 [12.55, for example]. As a result, the average resistance and conductance are not statistically well behaved, being dominated by extremely rare but exponentially large resonances. The exponent itself is the statistically well-behaved quantity, in the sense that the inverse localization length $\alpha = -(1/2L)\ln g$ has an increasingly well-defined average L_0^{-1} as the system length is increased [12.56–59]. The localization length depends, of course, both on the degree of disorder and the electron energy [12.57, 59].

At nonzero temperature, inelastic scattering broadens the resonant peaks by cutting short the lifetime, and the transmission over a several $k_B T$ range of energies must be considered [12.60]. According to *Stone* and *Lee* [12.61], the resonant tunnelling peaks are not only broadened but also decreased in amplitude by inelastic scattering, so that their integrated transmission remains constant. *Fowler* et al. [12.62] have recently measured isolated, temperature-independent conductance peaks below about 50 mK in Si MOSFETs approximately 1–2 µm wide and 0.5 µm long. The low-and-intermediate-temperature behaviour is consistent with the Stone and Lee model. Figure 12.2 shows typical conductance data as a function of gate voltage. When $k_B T$ exceeds the intrinsic resonance width, the temperature dependence of the side slope (inset) implies an electron density of states (for converting V_G to E_F) in this band-tail region of about 10% of (12.2). At still higher temperatures, the temperature dependence of the nonresonant background is consistent with 2D variable-range hopping with a localization length of 30–40 nm. For such parameters, it is very probable that each low-temperature conductance peak corresponds to tunnelling through a

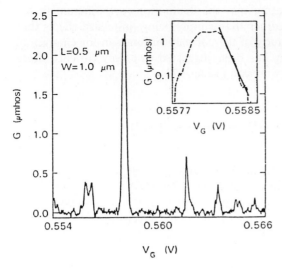

Fig. 12.2. Conductance peaks due to resonant tunneling through single quantum states in short, strongly localized MOSFETs. (from *Fowler* et al. [12.62], with permission)

single resonant quantum state. In this sense, the conduction is quantum-mechanically one-dimensional. From the device point of view, this behaviour is similar to the negative transconductance device proposed by *Luryi* and *Capasso* [12.63]. Since the source-drain voltage was limited to about 5 µV to prevent electron heating, the demonstrated transconductance of this very delicate device is of order 0.01 mS/mm!

12.4.2 Hopping Transport

Devices longer and narrower than the one that showed resonant tunnelling have been the subject of extensive studies of one-dimensional variable-range hopping for a number of years. In such devices, one-step tunnelling through a particular localized state for the entire length is exceedingly improbable, and inelastic processes that involve a series of hops to states nearby in energy and position are very likely to predominate. A crossover from "2D" to "1D" hopping occurs when the typical hopping distance substantially exceeds the width of the conducting channel. Because the various hops are thermally activated, and depend exponentially on both the energy distance from the Fermi level and the degree of spatial wavefunction overlap, a theoretical model in which the resistance is set by one or more critical hops is quite plausible [12.64]. Conductance peaks result from the crossover from one critical hop to another. Subtle shifts and asymmetries of the low temperature conductance peaks observed in such devices by *Webb* et al. [12.36] are consistent with this model, and may allow study of individual quantum-mechanical "bottlenecks" to the conduction process. Evidence for the spatially localized nature of these bottlenecks has been presented by *Kwasnick* et al. [12.24]. In very long devices, the fractional fluctuations of the logarithm of the variable-range-hopping resistance as a function of Fermi energy are calculated to fall only logarithmically with the length of the sample, demonstrating that the fluctuations are inherent in the variable-range-hopping model, rather than simply being finite size effects that average away [12.65]. Careful study of the correlation function for changes of magnetic field and Fermi energy has been suggested as a way to learn more about spin-dependent hopping processes [12.66, 67].

12.5 Multichannel Transport (Particle in a Box?)

Strictly speaking, if electrons have more than one possible state of transverse motion, the situation is not one dimensional. The preceding chapter has already discussed the quantized states of transverse motion in ideal confining potentials. In a perfect wire (no disorder, no interactions) the electrons at E_F occupy longitudinal free-electron states in each of the 1D subbands (index m) that have transverse quantization energies

$$E_m = E_0 + \frac{\hbar^2}{2m^*}\left[\frac{m\pi}{W}\right]^2$$

that are less than E_F. Electrons of the same energy therefore have different longitudinal velocities in the different subbands. At the bottoms of subbands, just where the longitudinal velocity goes to zero, there are compensating peaks in the density of states. Therefore, whether the subbands are detectable by conductance measurements as a function of E_F (gate voltage) in narrow MOSFETs is of considerable interest [12.23, 28, 42, 49].

Wheeler et al. [12.23] have argued that the subbands will be evident by a second-order effect in which the density of states affects the inelastic scattering rate, which in turn affects the magnitude of weak localization effects. Whether the subband structure survives the disorder required to produce weak localization is not clear, however. In this view, the density of states correspond to resistance minima. On the other hand, *Buttiker* et al. [12.68] have derived a multichannel generalization of (12.10) in which the *conductance* decreases at the density-of-states peaks, in a way that is "delicately dependent on the exact details" of their model. The derivation of even the 1D version of the Landauer conductance formula (12.10) depends subtly on definitional aspects of the ideal measurement [12.69–71], and is affected by electron-electron interactions [12.72]. Alternative multichannel generalizations have been proposed. [12.73, 74] Explicit calculations of the effect of transverse quantization on conductance and magnetoconductance have also been carried out in other theoretical frameworks. [12.75, 76]

In actual devices with minimal disorder, the subband energies would depend on the confining potential. The classic "particle in a box" potential is of course easily solved, and may be appropriate for our etched confinement scheme. For electrostatic confinement, *Laux* and *Stern* [12.77] have calculated the subband energies based on self-consistent numerical solutions of the Poisson and

Schroedinger equations for realistic narrow-gate and narrow-slit MOSFET geometries. Both *Kaplan* and *Warren* [12.78] and *Berggren* et al. [12.79] have calculated the subband energies for the exactly soluable case of a parabolic confining potential in a magnetic field.

The existing experimental evidence, although tantalyzing, is not really strong enough, in my opinion, to settle the fundamental question of the observability of subbands. *Wheeler* et al. [12.23] saw rather regularly spaced structure that could be accounted for by two different widths in their long electrostatically confined high-mobility MOSFETs. (Inspection revealed considerable width variation.) However, the high index of the subbands involved (23–32) would seem to require a much higher degree of geometrical perfection to be seen at all. Our own group [12.42, 49] also saw structure as a function of gate voltage. Figure 12.3 shows the two-terminal conductance of a set of our MOSFET devices each 1 μm long but varying in width by a factor of two. The numbers indicate where density-of-states peaks might be expected (for the measured $d_{ox} = 65$ nm, and allowing a different V_T for each curve because of fringing effects in the capacitor). Unfortunately, the structure is quasi-random and does not vary convincingly with width. Dean and Pepper [12.30] and *Licini* et al. [12.25] noted similar quasi-random structure in

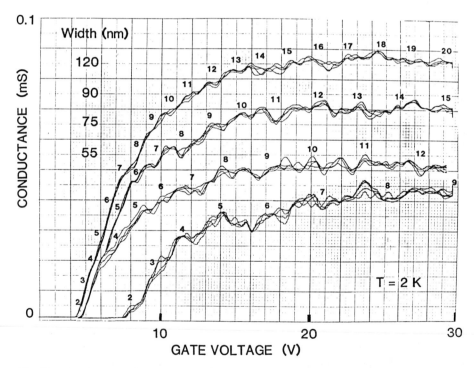

Fig. 12.3. Conductance of 1 μm-long MOSFET channels of various widths as a function of gate voltage. The numbers indicate expected positions of possible structure due to 1D subbands. The actual structure, although tantalyzing, is probably due to the random fluctuations observed in small devices (Sect. 12.7)

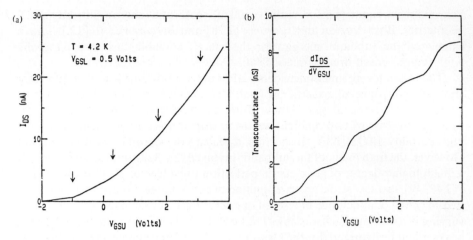

Fig. 12.4. Current and transconductance of a MOSFET consisting of many long, narrow channels in parallel, showing possible evidence of 1D subbands. (from *Warren* et al. [12.28], with permission)

larger devices. We now understand that all these devices are greatly affected by random-quantum-interference phenomena referred to as "universal conductance fluctuations" (see below). Whether this was superimposed on top of additional subband structure is not clear.

By measuring the conductance of parallel arrays of long narrow MOSFET channels, Warren et al. [12.28] averaged away much of the random fluctuations, and observed small, regular structure with a spacing roughly that expected from modeling of the electrostatic confinement. Figure 12.4 shows the current versus gate voltage and the transconductance (derivative of the conductance with respect to gate voltage) versus gate voltage for the device in which they saw an effect. Wide channels showed no structure. Only one set of data was presented, however, and reproducibility and systematic width dependence remains undemonstrated. More recent experiments by *Berggren* et al. [12.79] looked at the shift of Landau level structure in a GaAs heterostructure device of electrically controllable width. The data were consistent with their calculations, but again were very sparse.

12.6 Averaged Quantum Diffusion

As stated in Sect. 12.2, the fundamental nature of low-temperature quantum transport in typical MOSFETs is phase-preserving diffusion. Weak localization and electron-electron interactions change the average properties of this diffusion, particularly in 2D and quasi-1D ($W < L_\phi, L_T$) systems [12.8–12]. This average behavior can be observed in systems large enough to *self-average* over many quantum-interference domains of size L_ϕ. As a result of these effects, the conductivity depends on temperature and magnetic field instead of simply being characterized by a residual resistivity due to impurity scattering. In this section I will emphasize the quasi-1D case.

Figure 12.5 shows the magnetic field dependence at two temperatures of the conductance of 40 nm-wide MOSFET channels with $V_G = 7$ V. Our device actually consisted of 40 channels in parallel, each 14.3 µm long. The conductance per channel has been multiplied by the channel length and normalized to e^2/h, for reasons that will become apparent below. The main point to be noted is that in these MOSFET channels, both field and temperature cause large fractional changes in the conductivity. (There is no surpressed zero in the figure.)

12.6.1 Weak Localization

The physics of weak localization has been extensively reviewed [12.8–12]. It is difficult to draw pictures of typical diffusing waves, but fortunately it is legitimate to think of the motion of electrons as random walk trajectories. Standard techniques for computing the behaviour of waves include integrating over all possible trajectories, keeping track of phase relations. Typical random-walk paths are very complicated and frequently self-intersect. Electrons traversing a closed path can do so in either direction, with identical path length. In zero magnetic field, [neglecting spin-orbit and spin-flip effects, as is appropriate in MOSFETs], these electron waves return and interfere constructively, giving an enhanced probability of return to the origin. In quasi-1D devices, this "weak localization" decreases the conductance of each phase-preserving region (L_ϕ long and W wide) by an amount $2e^2/h$ (on average). This is usually interpreted by saying that only a fraction $2L_\phi/L_0$ of complete localization is observed, where L_0 is the length of a channel with conductance e^2/h. L_0 is thus the scale at which the localization corrections are comparable to the conductance itself, and a cross-over to strong localization occurs. Thus L_0 is closely related to the localization length α^{-1} discussed in Sect. 12.4.

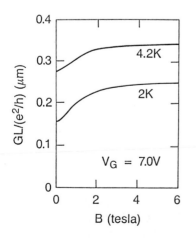

Fig. 12.5. Large fractional conductance changes due to weak localization and interaction effects in 40 nm-wide MOSFET conducting channels a few volts above threshold. Changes of the normalized conductance give L_ϕ (weak localization change from low to high fields) and $c\Delta L_T$ (interaction change with temperature at high fields). The half-width of the magnetoconductance can be used to determine $L_\phi W$

In nonzero fields, the otherwise constructive interference for each closed path is phase-shifted by an amount $4\pi\Phi/\Phi_0$, where Φ is the enclosed magnetic flux, and Φ_0 is the single-electron flux quantum h/e. [See Chap. 10]. This first affects the paths with largest area, which begin to randomly cancel each other's effect. Because contributing paths are already limited by L_ϕ and the boundaries of the quasi-1D sample, significant reduction of the weak localization effect first occurs at $B = \Phi_0/WL_\phi$. Both the zero-field magnitude and magnetic-field-halfwidth of the weak localization effect in quasi-1D conductors can be used to determine L_ϕ. Specifically [12.80–82].

$$\Delta GL = -(2e^2/h)[L_\phi^{-2} + L_{H1D}^{-2}]^{-1/2}, \tag{12.11}$$

where $L_{H1D} = \sqrt{3}\Phi_0/2\pi HW$. The self-consistency of all aspects of this expression have been quantitatively confirmed by *Licini* et al. [12.83] and *Bishop* and *Dolan* [12.84] in experiments on parallel arrays of quench-condensed Li wires. In the latter experiment, an additional known length scale was introduced by doping the wires with a high density of magnetic impurities at submicron intervals. For the 2 K data in Fig. 12.5, both the half-width and total conductance change are consistent with an L_ϕ of approximately 50 nm, just barely 1 D. Because narrow channels have high thresholds (approximately 5 V in this case), this data corresponds to relatively low electron densities. At higher V_G, the electron density, conductivity, diffusion constant, and, hence L_ϕ are all correspondingly larger. L_ϕ also increases with decrease of temperature.

The value of L_ϕ obtained from a 1D conductor need not be the same as the corresponding 2 D material. The dimensionality d of electron-electron scattering in disordered systems is governed by the coherence length $L_T = \pi(D\hbar/k_B T)^{1/2}$, and the rate varies as $(T/D)^{d/2}$. According to *Wheeler* et al. [12.22], the 1D rate is enhanced by a factor of $(4\sqrt{2}/\pi)L_T/W$. Moreover, the accumulation of phase randomization from quasi-elastic 1D ("Nyquist") scattering provides another distinct mechanism with a rate proportional to $T^{2/3}$. Under appropriate circumstances in Al wires, *Wind* et al. [12.85] found precise quantitative agreement with the rate predicted by *Al'tshuler* et al [12.86, 87].

Although there have been a number of studies of quasi-1D localization in narrow MOSFETs [12.20, 22, 29–32, 39–41, 51], detailed quantitative analyses of the magnetoconductance remain sparse [12.20, 22]. The measured inelastic scattering rates for typical conditions studied so far are such that the quasi-elastic mechanism is not a major correction. Such data as exists is generally in factor-of-two agreement with the empirical formula

$$L_\phi = 14 g_\square T^{-1/2} \text{ [nm]}. \tag{12.12}$$

12.6.2 Electron-Electron Interactions

The strong temperature dependence of the conductivity at high fields in Fig. 12.5 (where weak localization is already quenched) is due to interaction effects.

Electron-electron interactions not only cut short the interference that leads to weak localization, but also cause many-body renormalizations of the electron energies near the Fermi surface, thereby altering the diffusion coefficient at low temperatures. These effects are largest in systems of reduced dimensionality, where the diffusion is most constrained. For the quasi-1D case ($W < L_T$), the correction is

$$\Delta GL = - c(e^2/h)L_T \,, \tag{12.13}$$

where the coefficient c depends on the Fermi liquid interaction parameter F [12.88]; in silicon MOSFETs ($F \sim 1$), c is approximately 0.5. Interaction effects have been shown to make important contributions to the temperature dependence of narrow metal wires [12.89] and narrow MOSFET channels [12.39–41]. Because the temperature dependence is similar to that of the zero-field weak localization effects, definitive confirmation of the dependences in (12.13) by *Licini* et al. [12.90] could be undertaken only after complete analysis of the weak-localization magnetoconductance in the same quench-condensed Li wires [12.83].

The field dependence of the interaction effects is relatively small. It is complicated by the fact that various contributing diagrams are affected in different ways by a magnetic field (orbital, Zeeman, or not at all) [12.91] In AlGaAs/GaAs heterostructures, the weak localization effects cut off at such low fields that a parabolic positive magnetoconductance associated with interaction effects can be identified [12.92]. Narrow channels of this material have been used to investigate the crossover from 2 D to 1 D interaction effects [12.93].

12.7 Mesoscopic Quantum Diffusion
(Universal Conductance Fluctuations)

Constructing devices with many long channels in parallel consisting of a large number of quantum subunits of size L_ϕ is an excellent way to obtain sufficient self-averaging so that the average weak localization behavior is not masked by mesoscopic effects. "Mesoscopic" devices are ones comparable to the intermediate scale L_ϕ—small enough that their properties depend in detail on the microscopic arrangement of scatterers, yet large enough that the resulting behaviour can be quite complex.

Figure 12.6 shows the conductance of such a "mesoscopic" device as a function of gate voltage and magnetic field. The conductance meanders with gate voltage, and changing the magnetic field leads to new random patterns, representing large fractional changes. Viewed in this way, the effect looks of practical importance, but very messy. In fact, the statistical properties of these "universal conductance fluctuations" are quite predictable, and very funda-

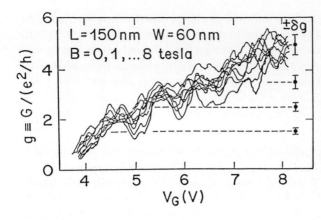

Fig. 12.6. Conductance versus gate voltage for a short, narrow MOSFET channel segment at various values of magnetic field. At each gate voltage, the conductance has a predictable range of reproducible but random values at different fields, caused by changes of the quantum interference inside the device

mental, corresponding to conductance changes of approximately e^2/h when measured at scale L_ϕ.

As noted above, we first encountered frustratingly random perturbations in conjunction with our search for particle-in-a-box subbands. (Fig. 12.3). Subsequently, *Umbach* et al. [12.94] described aperiodic magnetoresistance variations in small metal wires that obscured their search for quantum interference (Aharanov-Bohm) oscillations with flux periodicity h/e in small metal rings. By the time that they succeeded in clearly isolating the h/e periodicity [12.95], their colleague *Stone* [12.96] had demonstrated by numerical simulations that the aperiodic component of the magnetoresistance was associated with random quantum interference effects *within the wire*.

12.7.1 Universal Conductance Fluctuations at Scale L_ϕ

The relative insensitivity of Stone's results to the size of the system lead *Lee* and *Stone* [12.97] to formulate an analytic theory of random quantum interference. They used diagrammatic techniques to calculate the $T = 0$ correlation function

$$F(\Delta E, \Delta B) = \langle g(E_F, B)g(E_F + \Delta E, B + \Delta B)\rangle - \langle g(E_F, B)\rangle^2, \qquad (12.14)$$

where the angular brackets represent an average over different microscopic arrangements of impurities. Here g is the conductance in units of e^2/h. $F(0, 0) = (\delta g)^2$ is the variance of the ensemble of conductances corresponding to the different impurity configurations. For 1D channels ($W < L$), 2D squares, and 3D cubes *Lee* and *Stone* found $\delta g \sim 1$, *independent of the degree of disorder*. This means that similarly prepared conductors (that differ only in the microscopic arrangement of scatterers) will tend in practice to differ from each other in conductance by typically e^2/h, regardless of whether the average conductance in units of e^2/h is large (metals) or small (MOSFETs). This result, dubbed "universal conductance fluctuations", was also independently found by *Al'tshuler* [12.98].

As a statement about nominally similar conductors, the universal conductance fluctuations would be difficult to test. The experimentalist would have to make many devices, measure them all, and then convince the skeptical referee that the devices grouped into each ensemble actually belonged together.

Fortunately, the theory suggests a useful *ergodic hypothesis* about the behavior of a single device. The correlation half widths $F(E_c, 0) = -F(0, B_c) = 1/2$ set the characteristic energy and field scales $E_c = \pi^2 D\hbar/L^2$ and $B_c = \sqrt{3}\Phi_0/LW$ over which the conductance of a member of the ensemble typically remains correlated. E_c is the energy uncertainty associated with the time to diffuse across the device, and B_c is the field required to substantially perturb the phase difference between typical trajectories. The latter demonstrates that the effect is associated with random quantum interference throughout the conductor. Because F was found not to depend on the absolute magnitude of E_F and B, *Lee* and *Stone* pointed out that the correlation function that they calculated should be equivalent to the experimental correlation function constructed for a single device from data obtained by varying E_F (electron wavelength) and B (electron phase accumulation along trajectories) over a wide range. This ergodic hypothesis assumes that even for one specific arrangement of scatterers, changing E_F and B leads to new interference patterns that eventually explore a representative subset of the possibilities.

Even so, there are practical limits to the amount of data that can be collected from a single device. In a metal wire, only B can be varied, up to some maximum available field $B_{\max}$. (The theory itself assumes $\omega_c\tau < 1$.) Thus each wire gives at most $B_{\max}/B_c$ independent examples of the conductance variation. With a MOSFET, one also can get new patterns by changing E_F (gate voltage). Of course this may also change the average conductivity, so that the average of *each* magnetic field trace should be used to compute its deviations. Moreover, if the average conductivity changes too much, the device will belong in a different ensemble.

There also is the practical question of how the measurements are made. The theory was constructed for a perfect conductor of width W containing a disordered region of length L. Electrons diffuse back and forth through the disordered region, but once they exit to the perfect leads, they do not return. Implicit in the definition of the conductance is the existence of phase-randomizing measuring reservoirs at the ends of the perfect leads. Thus, the phase-preserving-diffusion length L_ϕ in the $T = 0$ two-terminal theory is by definition equal to the length L of the disordered region. More complete theories including electron-electron interactions at nonzero temperatures by *Al'tshuler* and *Khmel'nitskii* [12.99] and *Lee* et al. [12.100] suggest that the conductivity of larger systems can be interpreted as combining fluctuations of magnitude e^2/h across multiple regions of scale L_ϕ. (Sect. 12.7.2). From this it is plausible to believe that four-terminal measurements with voltage leads spaced L_ϕ apart should measure conductance fluctuations of approximate magnitude e^2/h. (The role of voltage probes will be investigated more closely in Sect. 12.7.3.)

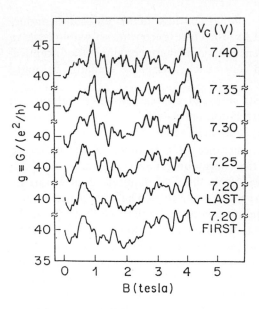

Fig. 12.7. Conductance versus magnetic field at closely spaced gate voltages for a MOSFET device with $L \simeq W = L_\phi$. The reproducible nature of the universal conductance fluctuations is clear

Figure 12.7 shows the conductance variations of a MOSFET channel 0.25 μm wide as measured between voltage probes 0.3 μm apart, at 2 K where L_ϕ in this gate voltage range is about 0.3 μm. The conductance varies rapidly with magnetic field and evolves progressively as the gate voltage is changed by small increments. The bottom two traces, taken at the beginning and the end of this data set, illustrate that the behaviour is highly reproducible, not simply random fluctuations with time. A data set consisting of about a dozen independent traces can be used to construct the experimental correlation function

$$F(\Delta V_G, \Delta B) = \sum_{V_G, B} [g(V_G + \Delta V_G, B + \Delta B) - \bar{g}(V_G + \Delta V_G)]$$
$$\times [g(V_G(V_G, B) - \bar{g}(V_G)], \tag{12.15}$$

where $\bar{g}$ is the tracewise average. From this, the rms amplitude δg, and the halfwidths B_c and V_c can be extracted.

Figure 12.8 shows the correlation function for a more complete data set ($T = 4.2$ K, $B = 2$–8 tesla, $V_G = 5.0$–5.55 V, same device as Fig. 12.7). Each curve shows how F depends on ΔB, for a particular value of ΔN_G. Information relevant to the random fluctuations is contained in the peaks at small ΔB. Analyzing this range, we obtain $\delta G = 1.1\, e^2/h$, $B_c = 0.18$ tesla, and $V_c = 0.14$ V. The halfwidths correspond to 2.5 flux quanta in an area of $L_\phi W [(0.25\ \mu m)^2]$ and a Fermi energy change of about $3\, k_B T$.

Particularly in these wide devices, there are strong correlations in the data for larger ΔB, some of which are sensitive to changes of gate voltage. Landau levels and subbands could lead to systematic variations of the "background" average conductance, but no clear picture has yet emerged. *Main and Eaves* [12.101]

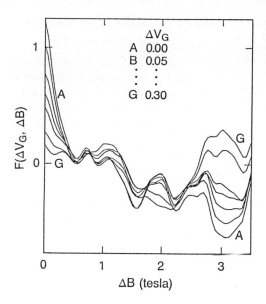

Fig. 12.8. Autocorrelation function for a typical set of conductance-versus-magnetic-field traces for closely spaced gate voltage changes. The amplitude and half-widths at small ΔB charactersize the universal conductance fluctuations. Additional structure for larger ΔB is not understood

have suggested that this range contains data about simple, small closed orbits constructed from a few scattering events, but I find it hard to believe that these would be sufficiently uniform to add coherently. *Timp* et al. [12.102] have emphasized the role of dimensional resonances in AlGaAs/GaAs heterostructure devices with particularly long mean free path. For now this aspect of our data remains unexplained.

The "background" effects in correlations functions such as Fig. 12.8 are typically large enough to introduce considerable uncertainty into the amplitude and halfwidths of the portion of the data identified with the random fluctuations. In addition, there are factor-of-two uncertainties in our ability to accurately estimate L_ϕ from (12.12). Nevertheless, we can make a reasonable test of the universal conductance fluctuations theory at scale L_ϕ. Of the approximately 50 data sets that we have analyzed, seven corresponded to situations in which the probe spacing L fell within 25% of the independently estimated value of L_ϕ. These seven different devices had widely different parameters: $L = 0.15-0.5$ μm, $W = 0.06-0.25$ μm, $G = 4.7-36\ e^2/h$, and $T = 0.4-4.2$ K. Nevertheless, the measured δg's all fell in the range 0.5–1.8, averaging 1.2.

This demonstrates the universality of δG_ϕ, the rms amplitude of the conductance fluctuations at scale L_ϕ. If expressed in terms of resistance $R_\phi = 1/G_\phi$, the fluctuation amplitude $\delta R_\phi = \delta G_\phi/G_\phi^2$ is *not* universal, varying here by as much as a factor of 30. Conductance fluctuations of size e^2/h have also been observed in appropriate metal wires and rings, where they are a much smaller fractional effect, because the conductance of metals is so much larger [12.103–105].

12.7.2 Self-Averaging of Conductance Fluctuations at Larger Probe Spacings

In large devices, the fluctuations tend to self-average away. For MOSFETs, L_ϕ is typically less than L_T. In this case, the theory [12.99, 100] can be interpreted simply by dividing the system into units of size L_ϕ, each with conductance fluctuations of typical size $\delta G_\phi = e^2/h$ that are uncorrelated from one unit to the next. These are to be combined "classically" like resistors in series and parallel. [12.50, 104, 106] If the device is $N = L/L_\phi$ units long and $M = W/L_\phi$ units wide, the fractional fluctuation $\delta G/G = \delta R/R$ of the whole system is a factor of $(NM)^{1/2}$ smaller than that of each unit. Thus for larger systems, or at higher temperatures (shorter L_ϕ), the fractional effects become smaller. At truly macroscopic scales, the effect becomes negligible.

Combining the $(NM)^{-1/2}$ dependence of the fractional fluctuations with the $W/L = M/N$ dependence of the average conductance, it is clear that the actual conductance fluctuations increase weakly with width, like $(W/L_\phi)^{1/2}$, and decrease strongly with length, like $(L/L_\phi)^{-3/2}$. For resistance fluctuations this is reversed, varing as $(W/L_\phi)^{-3/2}$ and $(L/L_\phi)^{1/2}$. The latter dependence is simply the $N^{1/2}$ accumulation of the uncorrelated fluctuating voltage drops across each quantum unit.

The size of the quantum units that are being incoherently combined can be approximately determined from the half-width B_c of the correlation function. Several flux quanta in an area of $L_\phi W$ are required to perturb the interference enough to significantly change the conductance. The precise coefficient is uncertain, with analytic estimates of 1.7, 1.2, and 2.1 being given in [12.97, 100 and 107] respectively, and simulation results of 1.6 and 2.4 being found in [12.100] for larger and smaller systems, respectively. To test the general idea, we have measured B_c of a number of data sets from MOSFET devices with various widths, lengths, and values of L_ϕ (estimated from the temperature and the average conductance per square, using (12.12) [12.50]). Figure 12.9 shows the agreement between experimental values and the prediction $2.4\,\Phi_0/WL_\phi$. Factor-of-two agreement is achieved within comparable scatter, leaving the question of precise coefficients unresolved.

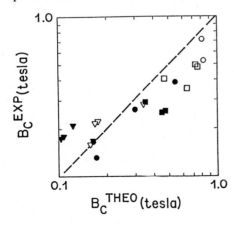

Fig. 12.9. Characteristic field scale of universal fluctuations in small MOSFETs of various dimensions, compared with the theoretical prediction 2.4 flux quanta h/e in an area of $L_\phi W$

A comparable test of the amplitude dependence is deferred to Sect. 12.7.4. For the moment, I merely refer back to Fig. 12.6. The vertical lines at the right indicate the magnitude $\pm \delta g$ expected for different values of L/L_ϕ corresponding to the indicated conductance level. The structure at low conductances is relatively insensitive to field and too large to be fully accounted for by the random conductance fluctuations. Still, it is important to realize that in this range B_c can be so large that available fields are not expected to produce significant phase shifts.

12.7.3 Nonlocal Response of Conductance Fluctuations at Shorter Probe Spacings

In the $T = 0$ theory, the conductance fluctuations are e^2/h independent of width for $W < L$, but by definition L is just L_ϕ. In the $T > 0$ theory [12.99, 100], L_ϕ is the scale below which the conductance fluctuations are independent of width; the corresponding resistance fluctuations then vary with width like $(W/L_\phi)^{-2}$. The existing two-terminal theories cannot predict what would be measured in a multiterminal experiment with probe-spacing $L < L_\phi$. Somewhat to our surprise, we found experimentally that, in this range, the *resistance* fluctuations are independent of L, and characteristic of scale L_ϕ. As a result, the apparent conductance fluctuations grow larger than e^2/h like $(L/L_\phi)^{-2}$! Explaining this goes to the heart of the nonlocal nature of quantum devices and measurements.

Multiterminal quantum models [12.108–10] emphasize that each potential probe connects the current carrying channel to a macroscopic measurement reservoir associated with phase randomization. For slow changes of external parameters, the electrochemical potential of each reservoir adjusts to cancel net current flow through the probes. For sufficiently high-impedance voltmeters, the potential differences between these macroscopic reservoirs can be logged without significantly perturbing the system, and can therefore be added and subtracted to infer additional combinations. That simultaneous measurements with fixed probes are additive does not imply that the measurements would be unaffected by physically connecting or disconnecting a probe, since electrons can diffuse into and out of the probes without necessarily losing their phase information. As we will see in Sect. 12.8.2, changing even a single scatterer is expected to substantially change the interference patterns.

Just because simultaneous measurements can be added does not imply that the statistical properties of sets of those measurements are additive. Figure 12.10 shows a set of additively related resistance traces for various combinations of four closely spaced probes (labels 1–4). The traces on the left show that the average voltage drop between probes accumulates linearly as measurements between adjacent pairs of probes are added. But the amplitude of the fluctuation does not grow, because of significant cancellations. For example, the prominant feature below the label "31" is associated primarily with probe 3, (i.e., does not appear in "41" and "21"). Because probe three subtracts from "43" and adds to "32", this feature contributes to each with opposite sign, and cancels out when

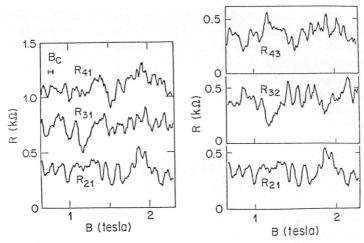

Fig. 12.10. Resistance fluctuations measured with various combinations of closely spaced potential probes. The amplitudes and correlations show that each potential probe fluctuates independently of its neighbors

they are combined. If each measuring reservoir fluctuates independently of its neighbours, the amplitude of the resistance fluctuations will be independent of spacing between probes. In contrast, for longer length scales, the fluctuating voltage drop along the channel accumulates with only partial cancellation ($N^{1/2}$) and soon exceeds the contribution by the probes.

Figure 12.11 shows the amplitude of the resistance fluctuations measured for 0.25 μm-wide channels at 0.4 K where L_ϕ is roughly 0.6 μm. For 5–15 μm probe spacings, with many quantum units between each pair of probes, the amplitude is proportional to $L^{1/2}$, as described above. But for 0.15–0.45 μm spacings, with many probes simultaneously inside a single quantum domain, the amplitude is constant, and approximately equal to that for probes separated by L_ϕ. Additional data obtained for probes on *opposite* sides of the same channel (not shown), also show approximately 50 Ω fluctuations, superimposed on top of the average voltage drop proportional to magnetic field associated with the ordinary Hall effect.

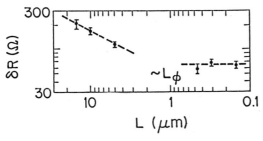

Fig. 12.11. Amplitude of resistance fluctuations measured for various probe spacings. For closely spaced probes, all measurements are characteristic of scale L_ϕ

Our understanding of this behavior of closely spaced probes is somewhat heuristic, representing an experimental discovery, yet to be fully explained by a comprehensive theory. Roughly speaking, we have found that the voltage fluctuations between two probes separated by L_ϕ are determined by the condition $\delta G_\phi = e^2/h$, and that the voltage fluctuations between any two more closely spaced probes are comparable. We attribute this to the fact that the quantum interference involves electrons diffusing *throughout* a device of complicated shape, bounded by L_ϕ, and find that the fluctuating response to a net current through any part of the region can be measured equally well by disordered probes with no net current flow that are connected anywhere in the interior. Thus the average conductivity and the fluctuations are determined on different characteristic spatial scales (l and L_ϕ, respectively).

The independent behavior of closely spaced probes is confirmed by analysis of the statistical correlations within sets of traces like Fig. 12.10.2 [12.52, 111]. For widely spaced probes, the statistical correlations are consistent with independent contributions from the many quantum units in the channel between the probes, so that two adjacent segments defined by three probes show uncorrelated traces, for example. For closely spaced probes, the correlations are very different. Two adjacent "segments" defined by three probes show approximately − 50% correlations between the traces, because the independent behavior of the shared probe contributes to the definition of each trace, but with opposite sign.

It is probably incorrect to think of additive contributions to the variance from the probes and the channel, since at least on short length scales, each configuration of channel and probes represents a single quantum-mechanical system. One can think of measuring two widely separated groups of closely spaced probes, where any of the closely-spaced probes should be as good as any other for determining the long-length-scale behavior, up to some accuracy. In the absence of a comprehensive theoretical treatment, and given the factor-of-two uncertainties inherent in the experiments, precise interpretations of the crossover region are not yet available.

The B_c for our recent device with closely spaced probes is up to a factor of two smaller than for the device with widely spaced probes. This may reflect the fact that the diffusion spreads into the probes, which occupy considerable area. With this correction to the effective width, and again using the coefficient 2.4 Φ_0, L_ϕ in both cases is estimated to be about 0.5 µm. In any case, the characteristic field scale for the fluctuations confirms that each closely spaced probe is responding to flux over an area of size L_ϕ much larger than the distance between their attachment points.

A particularly graphic demonstration of this nonlocality has recently been presented by *Umbach* et al. [12.112], who measured the magnetoresistance of a metal wire that had a metal ring dangling as a sidebranch (outside the classical current path). The structure showed a combination of aperiodic magnetoresistance associated with the area of the wire and h/e oscillations associated with the much larger area of the ring, even though the ring carries no *net* current through it! This *nonlocality* of the interference is a fundamental feature of phase-preserving diffusion.

12.7.4 Comprehensive Comparison Between Theory and Experiment

Table 12.2 summarizes the predicted dependences of the amplitude of conductance and resistance fluctuations on the normalized width $w = W/L_\phi$ of a conducting channel and normalized spacing $l = L/L_\phi$ between measuring probes, in comparison with the phase-preserving diffusion length L_ϕ. Conductances and resistances are in units of e^2/h and h/e^2, respectively. The predictions for short devices are somewhat speculative, based on our empirical independent-probes model.

All these interrelations are based on the assumption that the fractional fluctuations are small, as will certainly be the case in sufficiently large devices. In some small devices, however, the fractional fluctuations may be large. In extremely short devices with closely spaced voltage probes, the voltage fluctuations between two closely spaced probes can exceed the average voltage drop between them, leading to zero or negative "resistance". In this case, the very definition of an experimental conductance $G_{ij} = I/V_{ij}$ is problematic. Alternatively, in extremely narrow devices the fractional fluctuations can be exponentially large if the conductance is small compared to e^2/h, i.e. in the strong localization regime. Except for such cases, the relations in Table 12.2 should apply.

Overall, several features of Table 12.2 are worth reiterating. The magnitude of resistance fluctuations δr depends explicitly on the $r_\Box$ (degree of disorder), unlike the conductance fluctuations. Once that is accounted for, the geometrical dependence of conductance and resistance fluctuations are the dual of each other, with the roles of length and width interchanged. The conductance fluctuations of narrow channels are independent of width and degree of disorder, yet depend strongly on distance between probes, and therefore provide a good way of testing the theory using data from many devices.

Figure 12.12 shows the rms amplitude of the conductance fluctuations of all our quasi-1D devices as a function of L/L_ϕ, with L_ϕ estimated from (12.12). The solid circles each represent the rms amplitude of an entire set of traces for a

Table 12.2. Fluctuation amplitudes at different normalized length and width

	δg		$\delta r/r_\Box^2$	
	Long	Short	Long	Short
Wide	$w^{1/2} l^{-3/2}$	$w^{1/2} l^{-2}$	$w^{-3/2} l^{1/2}$	$w^{-3/2}$
Narrow	$l^{-3/2}$	l^{-2}	$w^{-2} l^{1/2}$	w^{-2}

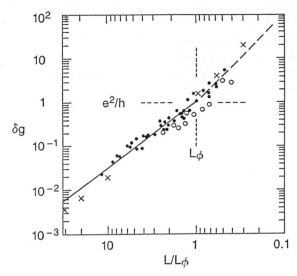

Fig. 12.12. Amplitude of conductance fluctuations in units of e^2/h, versus normalized probe spacing L/L_ϕ for a variety of data sets from our quasi-1D MOSFETs. This confirms the universality of the conductance fluctuations. The solid line is the UCF theory ignoring coefficients of order unity, and the dashed line is our empirical extension of the theory to shorter probe spacings

particular length, width and value of L_ϕ. The various points correspond to length of 150, 300, 400 nm, widths of 60, 100, and 250 nm, and values of L_ϕ ranging from 60 to 300 nm, corresponding to temperatures of 2 K and 4.2 K and various gate voltages. The device widths are typically less than L_ϕ, so that a significant width dependence is not expected. The open circles are earlier less complete data sets taken during the exploratory phase before the nature of the random fluctuations had been identified. They may underestimate the variance observed in a larger data set. The X's are our most recent data, corresponding to Fig. 12.11. These are particularly helpful in identifying the change of slope in the vicinity of L_ϕ. The solid line is the $T > 0$ universal conductance fluctuation theory, assuming $\delta G_\phi = e^2/h$ (i.e., neglecting coefficients of order one). The dashed line is our empirical result described above. Within the factor-of-two scatter, these dependences give a good account of the data over several orders of magnitude of variation. The universality of the conductance fluctuations is confirmed in the sense that devices of various widths and conductivities all fall near the same "universal" curve, which has an identifiable change of slope near the normalizing non-universal length scale L_ϕ.

Other presentations of the dependences in Table 12.2 are of course possible. For a single width and conductivity, plots of rms resistance fluctuation such as Fig. 12.11 are better for conveying the idea that at short length scales the response is characteristic of L_ϕ. To compare many devices, however, it would be necessary to normalize δR to R_ϕ^2, to demonstrate universality. As a pedagogical matter this would obscure the actual measured quantities, and magnify the effects of uncertainty in L_ϕ. In conclusion, I note that systematic tests of the width dependence beyond the scale L_ϕ have not been carried out, although such data as exists does not contradict the expected dependence.

12.7.5 Internal Asymmetries of Mesoscopic Devices

Theoretical work by *Buttiker* [12.109] and experiments by *Benoit* et al. [12.111] have investigated the question of whether the aperiodic fluctuations should be symmetric between B and $-B$. For two-terminal measurements, this is required by the Onsager relations (fundamental thermodynamics). For multi-terminal measurements symmetric and anti-symmetric combinations can be constructed by linear combinations of data for various configurations of current and voltage leads. Symmetries in the raw data required by Onsager for simultaneous exchange of current leads and field direction were observed. *Ma* and *Lee* [12.113] have explicitly investigated the symmetry properties of the conductance fluctuations in an ideal Hall geometry, and conclude that the transverse fluctuations have comparable magnitudes for their symmetric and antisymmetric parts (i.e., symmetry is unimportant). Figure 12.13 shows more data from our 0.25 μ-wide channels at 0.4 K, for probes geometrically across from each other, as a function of gate voltage for fixed magnetic fields. Voltage fluctuations occur as the gate voltage (electron wavelength) is changed. Even in zero magnetic field, probes on opposite sides of the channel fluctuate with respect to each other. For fields greater than 1 tesla, we subtracted off a smooth gate-voltage dependence and found resistance fluctuations in the range 46–68 ohms (5 traces). For the two available zero-field traces, the rms resistance fluctuations were approximately 100 and 130 ohms. Part of the difference may be that the particle-particle diagrams [12.100] are not suppressed in low fields.

In Fig. 12.13, the zero-field trace has a slight positive bias, while the other available trace tended to be negative. This could be accounted for by slight geometrical offsets. To set the scale, we have included the smooth curve corresponding to 1/50th of the average longitudinal resistance for segments 5 μm long. This therefore corresponds to the average voltage drop of 0.1 μm of current-carrying channel. If the fluctuations are interpreted as displacements of the "effective electrical centers of the probes", extreme displacements frequently exceed the 50 nm probe width. Because of the nonlocal nature of the response,

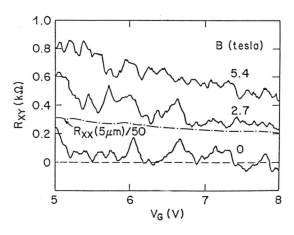

Fig. 12.13. Resistance between a pair of probes on opposite side of a 0.25 μm-wide MOSFET channel, as a function of gate voltage. Random potential fluctuations are superimposed on top of the average Hall voltage, even at zero field

this crude way of thinking is probably only helpful in reminding us that the internal electrical symmetry of a mesoscopic device may have little or nothing to do with its nominal geometrical symmetry.

12.8 Effect of One Scatterer

An interesting additional theme of our research on small MOSFET devices has been our discovery that it is possible to observe, and to some extent control, the trapping of single electrons at a particular interface trap [12.43]. This provides an excellent opportunity to probe the effect of a single scatterer on quantum transport, as well as to learn about interface traps.

Figure 12.14 shows the resistance of a two-terminal device 1 μm long and 0.15 μm wide as a function of time in a particular range of gate voltages at 28 K. The resistance switches between two states at random times but with controllable average duty cycle. These easily identifiable switching sequences are caused by individual electrons being captured and emitted at a particular interface defect. This changes the charge state of the defect, and creates or destroys one scatterer that affects the other electrons passing through the narrow channel. By classical reasoning, the 0.25% effect corresponds to one scatterer out of 400, or a density of 3×10^{11} scatterers in the device. This is a very plausible density.

Our group [12.43, 45, 46] and others [12.114, 115] have studied this phenomenon in MOSFETs in some detail. Related behavior in which electron trapping in an oxide affects the barrier height in a tunnel junction has also been extensively studied [12.116–119]. Effects of this type in GaAs diodes have also been seen.

12.8.1 Interface Traps

The crystalline silicon in the channel region of a MOSFET makes a poorly understood transition to the amorphous SiO_2 gate insulator. (See Chapter 2.)

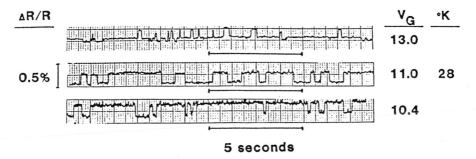

Fig. 12.14. Resistance switching caused by a single-electron trapping at a particular interface defect. The duty cycle is a function of gate voltage

Localized defects associated with dangling bonds or misplaced atoms in the oxide can function as electron traps. The electron occupancy determines the net charge of the defect. The following discussion of the trapping process is based on my analysis [12.120] of a quite general configuration-coordinate defect model similar to that presented by *Baraff* et al. [12.121].

The various defects occur in a broad range of environments and therefore have a wide variety of total energies (lattice distortions plus electron energies). The equilibrium energy difference between the occupancy states of a given defect governs the fraction of the time that each state is occupied. The energy difference between the different occupancy states is influenced by an electric field (gate voltage) that changes the potential energies of the electrons. For determining the occupancy fractions (but not the actual transition rates), a simple trap energy level may be incorporated in the usual one-electron energy-band diagram. Figure 12.15 shows a band diagram with such an energy level indicated for a defect located a definite distance into the oxide. The deeper the trap is located in the oxide, the more sensitive its energy is to gate voltage. Under most conditions the level is almost always empty or almost always full. However, in the particular gate voltage range that adjusts the electron energy level to lie within several $k_B T$ of the Fermi level, both states are occupied a controllable fraction of the time. Because $k_B T$ is a known energy, the sensitivity of the switching "duty cycle" to gate voltage can be used to determine the position of each trap [12.52]. Our results for a number of traps show that the ones that we are sensitive to are all located within roughly 1 nm of the interface.

The transition rates themselves depend on additional considerations. The equilibrium position of atoms near a defect depends on the electron occupancy. If an additional electron is present, but the lattice has not yet relaxed to the

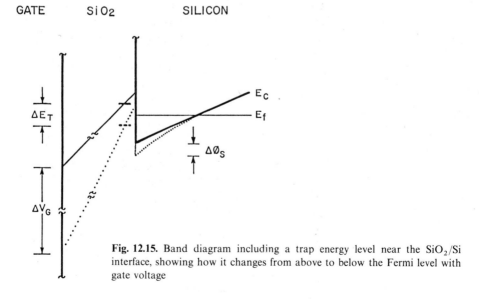

GATE   SiO₂   SILICON

Fig. 12.15. Band diagram including a trap energy level near the SiO_2/Si interface, showing how it changes from above to below the Fermi level with gate voltage

appropriate configuration, the total energy is much higher. For each electron energy in the inversion layer, some intermediate configuration of defect atoms represents the situation where the total system energy is the same whether the electron is in the trap or in the inversion layer. Thermal activation of the lattice to this bridging configuration allows capture or emission of the electron. Electron capture or emission requires either thermal activation over this energy barrier or quantum-mechanical "configurational tunnelling" through it [12.116]. If the barrier is large, and the tail of the electron wavefunction in the oxide is small, the rates will be exponentially slow, and can perhaps be adjusted into the observable range. We observe that the transition rate decreases as the temperature is lowered, so that a substantial degree of the thermal activation is required. In [12.45], we have further shown that the emission rate from the trap is independent of the electron temperature in the inversion layer, and depends only on the temperature of the lattice. This is direct evidence of the importance of lattice relaxation in the trapping process.

Figure 12.16 shows the domain of active switching for a particular interface trap located in spatial segment B of a multiterminal device (see inset). Each curve is a slow sweep of gate voltage that lowers the trap level past the Fermi level. At lower temperatures $k_B T$ is smaller and the transition from mostly empty to mostly full occurs over a narrower range of gate voltage. The transition rate also slows down at lower temperatures. At the lowest temperature, the trap fills only once.

Each particular interface trap will have its own range of gate voltage and temperature in which it is actively switching, as shown in Fig. 12.17. In a small device with few traps, it is necessary to hunt around in temperature and gate voltage in order to find an active trap. In larger devices, there are more traps, each with smaller fractional effect, and many traps are active at once. Thus the

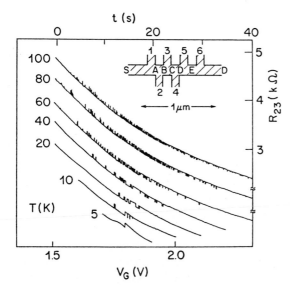

Fig. 12.16. Domain of active switching for a single interface trap. Each trace corresponds to a slow time sweep of gate voltage, at a particular temperature. This trap had its largest effect in segment B of the device (inset)

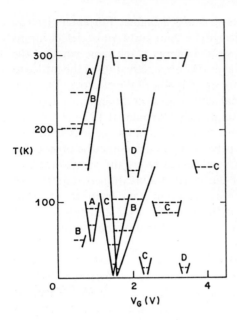

Fig. 12.17. Survey of domains of active switching for device of Fig. 12.16. The letters indicate the apparent spatial location of each trap

Lorentzian power spectra of individual traps with different characteristic frequencies are superimposed. For an appropriate distribution of trapping times, $1/f$ noise can be the result. This sort of behavior was neatly demonstrated by *Uren* et al. [12.114].

12.8.2 Quantum Effect of One Scatterer

The ability to control the switching of a single scatterer at low temperatures in small devices provides a means of identifying its individual contribution to the quantum interference. Diffusion has the special property that both the number of scatterers and the probability of returning to a particular scatterer scale equally with the size of the system in 2D. As a result, the effect of a given scatterer on the random quantum interference (universal conductance fluctuations) is independent of the number of scatterers in each quantum domain of size L_ϕ [12.122, 123]. According to *Feng* et al [12.123], moving one scatterer typically changes the δg of one quantum unit by $(k_F l)^{-1/2}$ in 2D. For small $k_F l$, the change can be comparable to the $\delta g = 1$ bound for changing *all* the scatterers! In narrow channels comparable to the mean free path l, unavoidable multiple scattering from a single scatterer is predicted to further enhance the effect by a factor L_ϕ/l, up to the rms bound of $\delta g = 1$ for the particular quantum unit.

We have not yet carried out a systematic study of the magnitude of the switching effects within the Feng-Lee-Stone picture. MOSFETs are clearly a good choice, because comparable switching phenomena have not yet been observed in narrow channels made from III–V heterostructures, and the 3D metals studied thus far should have the switching effects reduced by a very large

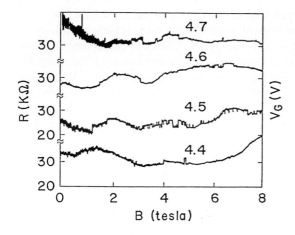

Fig. 12.18. Switching effects in a device consisting of several quantum subunits with several active traps. The data suggests that changing one scatter has a significant effect on the random quantum interference (universal conductance fluctuations)

factor $(k_F l)$. Preliminary results from studies of the semimetal Bi also look promising [12.124]. Figure 12.18 shows resistance-switching data from a low $k_F l$ device consisting of about four quantum domains. This particular device had been repeatedly subjected to examination in a scanning electron microscope, and had lower conductivities and much more switching than devices with less exposure. Several different traps appear to be switching, but even over limited ranges the magnitude of the effect of a single trap seems field-dependent. At several points in Fig. 12.18, the trend of the magnetoresistance trace suddenly changes with a single switching event, as if a new configuration of scatterers corresponds to a substantially different interference pattern. The magnetic field, in turn, also seems to affect the switching rates, as if the trap is sensitive to fluctuating local potentials.

If this device consisted of a single quantum domain with one trap switching, we would expect to be able to trace and retrace a given field range, defining two different magnetoresistance traces that for small $k_F l$ would be substantially uncorrelated. To the extent that the magnetic field affects the switching rate, it might be necessary to hunt in gate voltage to maintain the condition for active switching over wider ranges of field. Experiments to search for such an ideal example are underway.

12.9 Conclusion

In this chapter, I have tried to show the current state of our understanding of low temperature quantum transport in small silicon MOSFETs. A fairly complete picture emerges.

At low electron densities, transport is by tunnelling and hopping, allowing detailed investigation of individual localized electron states. At high electron densities, the transport is *diffusive*, with quantum interference phenomena persisting to length scales L_ϕ much larger than the mean free path. The crossover between the strong localization and the weak localization regime occurs when the conductance at scale L_ϕ is of order e^2/h. The well-understood weak-localization effects can be used to determine L_ϕ for a given system, if the system is large enough to allow considerable self-averaging of the conductance. Because of the disorder, 1D sub-bands in the weak localization regime have not been clearly demonstrated.

In small devices, random quantum interference leads to conductance variations from device to device and as a function of magnetic field and gate voltage that have a predictable rms amplitude of e^2/h at scale L_ϕ. Unlike the weak-localization and interaction effects, which survive self-averaging, these universal conductance fluctuations decrease predictably in large systems, because of partial cancellation of the individual resistance fluctuations of quantum subunits of size L_ϕ. Because of the nonlocal scale L_ϕ of the random interference, attempts to use closely spaced voltage probes to probe *inside* the quantum regions of size L_ϕ actually measure the same amplitude of voltage fluctuations characteristic of probes separated by L_ϕ.

Individual scatterers formed by the trapping of single electrons at particular interface defects can be controlled by adjusting the energy level of the trap with respect to the Fermi level. The universal conductance fluctuations also prove a framework for understanding the magnitude of the quantum effect of a such single scatterer.

References

12.1   E. H. Nicollian, J. R. Brews: MOS (Metal Oxide Semiconductor) Physics and Technology Wiley, New York 1982) Chap. 1

12.2   A. B. Fowler, F. F. Fang, W. E. Howard, P. J. Stiles: Phys. Rev. Lett. **16**, 901 (1966)

12.3   Consider, for example, the series of biennial International Conferences on Electronic Properties of Two-Dimensional Systems, 1975-present: Surface Science **58, 73, 98, 113, 142, 170**

12.4   T. Ando, A. B. Fowler, F. Stern: Rev. Mod. Phys. **54**, 437 (1982)

12.5   Frank Stern: Phys. Rev. **B5**, 4891 (1972)

12.6   Frank Stern, W. E. Howard: Phys. Rev. **163**, 816 (1967)

12.7   Shechao Feng, P. A. Lee, A. D. Stone: Phys. Rev. Lett. **56**, 2772 (1986); ibid. **59**, 1062 (1987)

12.8   R. C. Dynes: Physica **109/110B**, 1857 (1982)

12.9   G. Bergmann: Phys. Reports, **107**, 1 (1984)

12.10   Patrick A. Lee, T. V. Ramakrishnan: Rev. Mod. Phys. **57**, 287 (1985)

12.11   B. L. Altshuler, A. G. Aronov: In *Electron-Electron Interactions in Disordered Systems*, ed. by A. L. Efros and M. Pollak (Elsevier, Amsterdam 1985) p. 1

12.12   B. Kramer, G. Bergmann, Y. Bruynseraede (eds): *Localization, Interaction, and Transport Phenomena* (Springer, Berlin Heidelberg 1985)

12.13   Y. Kawaguchi, S. Kawaji: J. Phys. Soc. Japan **48**, 699 (1980)

12.14   R. G. Wheeler: Phys. Rev. **B24**, 4645 (1981)

12.15   M. J. Uren, R. A. Davies, M. Kaveh, M. Pepper: J. Phys. **C14**, L395 (1981)

12.16   D. J. Bishop, D. C. Tsui, R. C. Dynes: Phys. Rev **B26**, 773 (1982) gives a factor of three larger rate than (12.6)

12.17   R. A. Davies, M. Pepper: J. Phys. **C16**, L353 (1983)

12.18   K. K. Choi: Phys. Rev. **B28**, 5774 (1983)

12.19   D. J. Bishop, R. C. Dynes, B. J. Lin, D. C. Tsui: Phys. Rev. **B30**, 3539 (1984)

12.20   W. J. Skocpol: In *The Physics and Fabrication of Microstructures and Microdevices*, ed. by M. J. Kelly and C. Weissbuch (Springer, Berlin Heidelberg, 1986) p. 255

12.21   V. A. Petrov: Sov. Tech. Phys. Lett. **4**, 285 (1978)

12.22   R. G. Wheeler, K. K. Choi, A. Goel, R. Wisnieff, D. E. Prober: Phys. Rev. Lett. **49**, 1674 (1982)

12.23   R. G. Wheeler, K. K. Choi, R. Wisnieff: Surface Sci. **142**, 19 (1984)

12.24   R. F. Kwasnick, M. A. Kastner, J. Melngailis, P. A. Lee: Phys. Rev. Lett. **52**, 224 (1984)

12.25   J. C. Licini, D. J. Bishop, M. A. Kastner, J. Melngailis: Phys. Rev. Lett. **55**, 2987 (1985)

12.26   P. H. Woerlee, G. A. M. Hurkx: In Proc. Int. Conf. on Localization, Interaction, and Transport Phenomena in Impure Metals, Supplement (PTB, Braunschweig 1984) p. 34

12.27   P. H. Woerlee, G. A. M. Hurkx, W. J. M. J. Josquin, J. F. C. M. Verhoeven: Appl. Phys. Lett. **47**, 700 (1985)

12.28   A. C. Warren, D. A. Antoniadis, Henry I. Smith: Phys. Rev. Lett. **56**, 1858 (1986)

12.29   C. C. Dean, M. Pepper: J. Phys. **C15**, L1287 (1982)

12.30   C. C. Dean, M. Pepper: J. Phys. **C17**, 5663 (1984)

12.31   C. C. Dean, M. Pepper: In Proc. 17th Int. Conf. Phys. Semicond., San Francisco, 1984, ed. by J. D. Chadi, W. A. Harrison (Springer, New York, 1985) p. 425

12.32   C. C. Dean, M. Pepper: In [12.12], p. 169

12.33   A. B. Fowler, A. Hartsein, R. A. Webb: Phys. Rev. Lett. **48**, 196 (1982)

12.34   A. B. Fowler, A. Hartstein, R. A. Webb: Physica **117/118B**, 661 (1983)

12.35   A. Hartstein, R. A. Webb, A. B. Fowler, J. J. Wainer: Surf. Sci. **142**, 1 (1984)

12.36   R. A. Webb, A. Hartstein, J. J. Wainer, A. B. Fowler: Phys. Rev. Lett. **54**, 1577 (1985)

12.37   S. B. Kaplan, A. Hartstein: Phys. Rev. Lett. **56**, 2403 (1986)

12.38   A. Hartstein: In [12.12], p. 266

12.39   W. J. Skocpol, A. M. Voshchenkov, R. E. Howard, E. L. Hu, L. D. Jackel, R. E. Epworth, L. A. Fetter, P. Grabbe, D. M. Tennant: Physica **109/110B**, 2105 (1982)

12.40   W. J. Skocpol, L. D. Jackel, E. L. Hu, R. E. Howard, L. A. Fetter: Phys. Rev. Lett. **49**, 951 (1982)

12.41   W. J. Skocpol, L. D. Jackel, R. E Howard, E. L. Hu, L. A. Fetter: Physica **117/118B**, 667 (1983)

12.42   W. J. Skocpol, L. D. Jackel, R. E Howard, H. G. Craighead, L. A. Fetter, P. M. Mankiewich, P. Grabbe, D. M. Tennant: Surf. Sci. **142**, 14 (1984)

12.43   K. S. Ralls, W. J. Skocpol, L. D. Jackel, R. E. Howard, L. A. Fetter, R. W. Epworth, D. M. Tennant: Phys. Rev. Lett. **52**, 228 (1984)

12.44   W. J. Skocpol, L. D. Jackel, R. E Howard, P. M. Mankiewich, R. E. Behringer, L. A. Fetter, D. M. Tennant: In [12.18], p. 7

12.45   L. D. Jackel, W. J. Skocpol, R. E. Howard, L. A. Fetter, R. W. Epworth, D. M. Tennant: In Ref. **23**, p. 221

12.46   R. E. Howard, W. J. Skocpol, L. D. Jackel, P. M. Mankiewich, L. A. Fetter, D. M. Tennant, R. W. Epworth, and K. S. Ralls: IEEE Trans. Electron Dev. ED-32, 1669 (1985)

12.47   R. E. Howard, L. D. Jackel, P. M. Mankiewich, W. J. Skocpol: Science **231**, 346 (1986)

12.48   P. M. Mankiewich, R. E. Howard, L. D. Jackel, W. J. Skocpol, D. M. Tennant: J. Vac. Sci. Technol. **B4**, 380 (1986)

12.49   W. J. Skocpol, L. D. Jackel, R. E. Howard, P. M. Mankiewich, D. M. Tennant, Alice E. White, R. C. Dynes: Surf. Sci. **170**, 1 (1986)

12.50   W. J. Skocpol, P. M. Mankiewich, R. E. Howard, L. D. Jackel, D. M. Tennant, A. Douglas Stone: Phys. Rev. Lett. **56**, 2865 (1986)

12.51   W. J. Skocpol: In Proc. 18th Int. Conf. on Phys. of Semiconductors, Stockholm, Aug. 1986, ed. by O. Engstrom (World Scientific, Singapore 1987) p. 1491

12.52   W. J. Skocpol, P. M. Mankiewich, R. E. Howard, L. D. Jackel, D. M. Tennant, A. Douglas Stone: Phys. Rev. Lett. **58**, 2347 (1987)

12.53   N. F. Mott, W. D. Twose: Adv. Phys. **10**, 107 (1961)

12.54   Rolf Landauer: Phil. Mag. **21**, 863 (1970)
12.55   M. Ya. Azbel: Solid State Commun. **45**, 527 (1983)
12.56   P. W. Anderson, D. J. Thouless, E. Abrahams, D. S. Fisher: Phys. Rev. **B22**, 3519 (1980)
12.57   Barbara S. Andereck, Elihu Abrahams: J. Phys. **C13**, 383 (1980)
12.58   A. Douglas Stone, J. D. Joannopoulos: Phys. Rev. **B24**, 3592 (1981)
12.59   M. Ya. Azbel, Paul Soven: Phys. Rev. Lett. **49**, 751 (1982)
12.60   M. Ya. Azbel, D. P. DiVincenzo: Phys. Rev. **B30**, 6877 (1984) and references therein.
12.61   A. Douglas Stone, P. A. Lee: Phys. Rev. Lett. **54**, 1196 (1985)
12.62   A. B. Fowler, G. L. Timp, J. J. Wainer, R. A. Webb: Phys. Rev. Lett. **57**, 138 (1986)
12.63   Serge Luryi, Federico Capasso: Appl. Phys. Lett. **47**, 1347 (1985)
12.64   Patrick A. Lee: Phys. Rev. Lett. **53**, 2042 (1984)
12.65   R. A. Serota, R. K. Kalia, P. A. Lee: Phys. Rev. **B33**, 8441 (1986)
12.66   V. L. Nguen, B. Z. Spivak, B. I. Shklovskii: Pis'ma Zh. Eksp. Teor. Fiz. **43**, 35 (1986) [English
        transl.: JETP Lett. **43**, 44 (1986)]
12.67   Rajiv K. Kalia, Weige Xue, Patrick A. Lee: Phys. Rev. Lett. **57**, 1615 (1986)
12.68   M. Buttiker, Y. Imry. R. Landauer, S. Pinhas: Phys. Rev. **B31**, 6207 (1985)
12.69   R. Landauer: Phys. Lett. **85A**, 91 (1981) and references therein
12.70   R. Landauer: In *Localization, Interaction, and Transport Phenomena*, ed. by B. Kramer, G.
        Bergmann, and Y. Bruynseraede (Springer, Berlin, Heidelberg 1985) p. 38
12.71   Y. Imry: In *Directions in Condensed Matter Physics Vol 1*, ed. by G. Grinstein and G.
        Mazenko (World Scientific, Singapore 1986) p. 101
12.72   W. Apel: J. Phys. **C16**, 2907 (1983)
12.73   D. S. Fisher, P. A. Lee: Phys. Rev. **B23**, 6851 (1981)
12.74   D. C. Langreth, E. Abrahams: Phys. Rev. **B24**, 2978 (1981)
12.75   D. G. Cantrell, P. N. Butcher: J. Phys. **C18**, 5111 (1985)
12.76   L. Smrcka, H. Havlova, Akira Ishihara: J. Phys. **C19**, L475 (1986)
12.77   S. E. Laux, F. Stern: Appl. Phys. Lett. **49**, 91 (1986)
12.78   S. B. Kaplan, A. C. Warren: Phys. Rev. **34**, 1346 (1986)
12.79   K.-F. Berggren, T. J. Thornton, D. J. Newson, M. Pepper: Phys. Rev. Lett. **57**, 1769 (1986)
12.80   B. L. Al'tshuler, A. G. Aronov: Pis'ma Zh. Eksp. Teor. Fiz. **33**, 515 (1981) [English transl.:
        JETP Lett. **33**, 499 (1981)]
12.81   B. L. Al'tshuler, A. G. Aronov: A. Yu. Zyuzin: Zh. Eksp. Teor. Fiz. **86**, 709 (1984) [English
        transl.: Sov. Phys. JETP **59**, 415 (1984)]
12.82   P. Santhanam, S. Wind, D. E. Prober: In Proc. 17th Int. Conf. on Low Temp. Phys.,
        Karlsruhe, West Germany, August 1984, ed. by U. Eckern, A. Schmid, W. Weber, H. Wuhl
        (Elsevier, Amsterdam 1984) p. 495
12.83   J. C. Licini, G. J. Dolan, D. J. Bishop: Phys. Rev. Lett. **54**, 1585 (1985)
12.84   D. J. Bishop and G. J. Dolan: Phys. Rev. Lett. **55**, 2911 (1985)
12.85   S. Wind, M. J. Rooks, V. Chandrasekhar, D. E. Prober: Phys. Rev. Lett. **57**, 633 (1986)
12.86   B. L. Al'tshuler, A. G. Aronov, D. E. Khmel'niksii, J. Phys. **C15**, 7367 (1982)
12.87   [Ref. 12.11, Sect. 4.2]
12.88   B. L. Al'tshuler, A. G. Aronov: Solid State Commun., **46**, 429 (1983)
12.89   Alice E. White, M. Tinkham, W. J. Skocpol, D. C. Flanders: Phys. Rev. Lett. **48**, 1752 (1982)
12.90   G. J. Dolan, D. J. Bishop, J. C. Licini: private communication
12.91   H. Fukuyama: In [12.11], p. 191
12.92   M. A. Paalanen, D. C. Tsui, J. C. M. Hwang: Phys. Rev. Lett. **51**, 2226 (1983)
12.93   K. K. Choi, D. C. Tsui, S. C. Palmateer: Phys. Rev. **B33**, 8216 (1986)
12.94   C. P. Umbach, S. Washburn, R. B. Laibowitz, R. A. Webb: Phys. Rev. **B30**, 4048 (1984)
12.95   R. A. Webb, S. Washburn, C. P. Umbach, R. B. Laibowitz: Phys. Rev. Lett. **54**, 2696 (1985)
12.96   A. Douglas Stone: Phys. Rev. Lett. **54**, 2692 (1985)
12.97   P. A. Lee, A. Douglas Stone: Phys. Rev. Lett. **55**, 1622 (1985)
12.98   B. L. Al'tshuler: Pis'ma Zh. Eksp. Teor. Fiz. **41**, 530 (1985) [English transl.: JETP Lett. **41**,
        648 (1985)]

12.99   B. L. Al'tshuler, D. E. Khmel'nitskii: Pis'ma Zh. Eksp. Teor. Fiz. **42**, 291 (1985) [English transl.: JETP Lett. **42**, 291 (1985)]

12.100 P. A. Lee, A. Douglas Stone, H. Fukuyama: Phys. Rev. **B35**, 1039 (1987)

12.101 R. P. Taylor, M. L. Leadbeater, G. P. Whittington, P. C. Main, L. Eaves, S. P. Beaumont, I. McIntyre, S. Thoms, C. D. W. Wilkinson: Surf. Sci. **196**, 52 (1988)

12.102 G. Timp, A. M. Chang, P. M. Mankiewich, R. E. Behringer, J. E. Cunningham, T. Y. Chang, R. E. Howard: Phys. Rev. Letters **59**, 732 (1987)

12.103 S. Washburn, C. P. Umbach, R. B. Laibowitz, R. A. Webb: Phys. Rev. **B32**, 4789 (1985)

12.104 C. P. Umbach, C. Van Haesendonck, R. B. Laibowitz, S. Washburn, R. A. Webb: Phys. Rev. Lett. **56**, 386 (1986)

12.105 A. D. Benoit, S. Washburn, C. P. Umbach, R. B. Laibowitz, R. A. Webb: Phys. Rev. Lett. **57**, 1765 (1986)

12.106 Y. Imry: Europhys. Lett. **1**, 249 (1986)

12.107 M. Buttiker, R. Landauer: private commun.

12.108 H. -L. Enquist, P. W. Anderson: Phys. Rev. **B24**, 1151 (1981)

12.109 M. Buttiker: Phys. Rev. Lett. **57**, 1761 (1986) and unpublished

12.110 S. Maekawa, Y. Isawa, and H. Ebisawa, J. Phys. Soc. Japan **56**, 25 (1987)

12.111 A. D. Benoit, C. P. Umbach, R. B. Laibowitz, R. A. Wcbb: Phys. Rev. Lett. **58**, 2343 (1987)

12.112 C. P. Umbach, P. Santhanam, C. van Haesendonck, R. A. Webb: Appl. Phys. Lett. **50**, 1289 (1987)

12.113 M. Ma, P. -A. Lee: Phys. Rev. **B35**, 1448 (1987)

12.114 M. J. Uren, D. J. Day, M. J. Kirton: Appl. Phys. Lett. **47**, 1195 (1985)

12.115 M. J. Kirton, M. J. Uren: Appl. Phys. Lett. **48**, 1270 (1986)

12.116 C. T. Rogers, R. A. Buhrman: Phys. Rev. Lett. **53**, 1272 (1984); Phys. Rev. Lett. **55**, 859 (1985)

12.117 R. H. Koch, A. Hartstein: Phys. Rev. Lett. **54**, 1848 (1985)

12.118 M. E. Welland, R. H. Koch: Appl. Phys. Lett. **48**, 724 (1986)

12.119 R. T. Wakai, D. J. Van Harlingen: Phys. Rev. Lett. **58**, 1687 (1987)

12.120 W. J. Skocpol: *In Science and Technology of Microfabrication*, ed. by R. E. Howard, E. L. Hu, S. Pang, S. Namba, Mater. Res. Soc. Sym. Proc. Vol. 76 (MRS, Pittsburgh, PA 1987) p. 3

12.121 G. A. Baraff, E. O. Kane, M. Schulter: Phys. Rev. **B21**, 3563 (1980)

12.122 B. L. A'ltshuler, B. Z. Spivak: Pis'ma Zh. Eksp. Teor. Fiz. 42, 294 (1985) [English transl: JETP Lett. **42**, 363 (1985)]

12.123 Shechao Feng, Patrick A. Lee, A. Douglas Stone: Phys. Rev. Lett. **56**, 1960 (1986); erratum, Ref. 12.7

12.124 D. E. Beutler, T. L. Meisenheimer, N. Giordano: Phys. Rev. Lett. **58**, 1240 (1987)

Subject Index